Three

Population
Resources, and
The Environment

**The Commission on
Population Growth and
the American Future
Research Reports**

Edited by
Ronald G. Ridker

U.S., Commission on Population Growth and
the American Future. *Population, Resources,
and the Environment*, Ronald G. Ridker, Editor.
Vol. III of Commission research reports.
Washington, D.C.: Government Printing Office, 1972.

Library of Congress Catalog Card No. 72-600125

For sale by the Superintendent of Documents
U.S. Government Printing Office
Washington, D.C. 20402 Price $4.25
Stock Number 5258–00003

☆ U. S. GOVERNMENT PRINTING OFFICE : 1972 O - 479- 888

The Commission

Chairman
John D. Rockefeller 3rd

Vice Chairman
Grace Olivarez
Executive Director
Food for All, Inc.

Vice Chairman
Christian N. Ramsey, Jr., M.D.
President
The Institute for the Study
of Health and Society

Joseph D. Beasley, M.D.
The Edward Wisner Professor of
Public Health
Tulane University Medical Center

David E. Bell
Executive Vice President
The Ford Foundation

Bernard Berelson
President
The Population Council

Arnita Young Boswell
Associate Field Work Professor
School of Social Service
Administration
University of Chicago

Margaret Bright
Professor
Dept. of Behavioral Sciences and
Dept. of Epidemiology
School of Hygiene and Public
Health
The Johns Hopkins University

Marilyn Brant Chandler
Housewife, Volunteer, Student

Paul B. Cornely, M.D.
Professor
Dept. of Community Health
Practice, College of Medicine
Howard University
Assistant to the Executive Medical
Officer
Welfare and Retirement Fund
United Mine Workers of America

Alan Cranston
United States Senator
California

Lawrence A. Davis
President
Arkansas Agricultural, Mechanical
& Normal College

Otis Dudley Duncan
Professor of Sociology
University of Michigan

John N. Erlenborn
United States Representative
14th C. District of Illinois

Joan F. Flint
Housewife, Volunteer

R. V. Hansberger
Chairman and President
Boise Cascade Corporation

D. Gale Johnson
Chairman
Department of Economics
University of Chicago

John R. Meyer
President
National Bureau of Economic
Research
Professor of Economics
Yale University

Bob Packwood
United States Senator
Oregon

James S. Rummonds
Student
Stanford School of Law

Stephen L. Salyer
Student
Davidson College

Howard D. Samuel
Vice President
Amalgamated Clothing Workers
of America

James H. Scheuer
United States Representative
22nd C. District of New York

George D. Woods
Director and Consultant
The First Boston Corporation

Commission Staff

Executive Director
Charles F. Westoff

Deputy Director
Robert Parke, Jr.

Directors of Research
Sara Mills Mazie
Elliott R. Morss
A. E. Keir Nash
Ritchie H. Reed*
Dianne Miller Wolman

Director of Policy Coordination
Carol Tucker Foreman

Assistant to the Chairman
David K. Lelewer

Director of Public Information
Gerald Lipson

General Counsel
Ben C. Fisher

Administrative Officer
Lois A. Brooks

Editorial Coordinator
Carol F. Donnelly

Press Officer
Rochelle Kutcher Green

Composition
Lloyd Boucree

Production Coordination
W. S. Pickens

Professional Staff
Gail K. Auslander
Phyllis Coghlan
Florence F. Einhorn
Duane S. Elgin
Dorothy Mann
Susan McIntosh
Steve W. Rawlings

Special Consultants
Daniel Callahan
Lenora T. Cartright
Robert F. Drury
Edgar M. Hoover
Frederick S. Jaffe
Peter A. Morrison
Ronald G. Ridker
Norman B. Ryder
Irene B. Taeuber

Support Staff
Marilyn L. Cleek
Mary Ann Ferguson
Mildred G. Herald
Kathryn E. Herron
Mac Arthur C. Jones
Kituria D. Littlejohn
Betty Marshall
Pearl R. Phillips
Diane O. Sergeant
Judith M. Stock
Mary C. Wilcher

Production Staff
Bea Garcia
Eugenia Harrison
Bea Rodgers
James Sumiel
Margell Yep

Foreword

These research reports are reports to the Commission by independent scholars and research organizations; they are not reports by the Commission itself. Publication of any of the reports should not be taken to imply endorsement of their contents by the Commission, or by any member of the Commission's staff. Both the credit and the responsibility for the reports lie solely in each case with the authors. Unpublished materials are on file at the National Archives.

Population Projections – Much of the Commission's research was a comparison of the consequences of different rates of population growth in the United States. For this purpose, two basic projections of the population, prepared by the U.S. Bureau of the Census, were used: Series B (corresponding closely to the growth expected if each family were to average three children over a lifetime) and Series E (corresponding to a two-child average). The projections use by the Commission's researchers were published in: U.S. Bureau of the Census, Current Population Reports, Series P-25, No. 448, August 1970. Subsequent revisions of the projections were published by the Census Bureau in Series P-25, No. 470, November 1971, after our research was completed. The revised figures were used in the Commission's Final Report, *Population and the American Future*. This gives rise to relatively small differences, inconsequential for the analysis, between the projections shown in the final report and those used in the research papers.

Economic Projections – Because the impact of population change is mediated in part by its effects on the economy, the Commission requested the Bureau of Economic Analysis (formerly Office of Business Economics), Department of Commerce, to prepare aggregate projections of the state of the economy associated with population growth Series B and E. These projections are published in Volume II of the Commission's research reports. They served as a point of departure for a number of the Commission's studies. In addition, they served as part of the basis for unpublished projections of the distribution of families by family income, prepared by the Population Division of the Bureau of the Census, which were used in certain of the Commission's studies.

Table of Contents

CONTENTS OF OTHER VOLUMES

Robert Lamson: Staff Associate, Plans and Analysis Office, National Science Foundation, Washington, D.C.

LOS ANGELES, CALIFORNIA, MAY 3-4, 1971

S.I. Hayakawa: President, San Francisco State College, accompanied by *John Westfall:* Chairman, Geography Department

The Hon. Jerome Waldie: U.S. House of Representatives, 14th C. District, California

Mrs. Tee Bertha Springs: Member, Board of Directors, Los Angeles Regional Planning Council

Henry Gibson: Television Entertainer, Malibu

Kingsley Davis: Professor of Sociology, International Population and Urban Research and Dept. of Sociology, University of California, Berkeley; *Frederic G. Styles:* Executive Director, Science and Technology Advisory Council, California State Assembly; and *Eduardo Arriaga:* University of California, Berkeley

Manuel Aragon, Jr.: General Manager, City of Commerce Investment Company; former Executive Director, Economic and Youth Opportunity Agency, Los Angeles County

Kenneth M. Mitzner: President, Mobilization for the Un-named, Los Angeles

Joe C. Ortega: Associate Counsel, Mexican-American Legal Defense and Education Fund, Inc.

Walter R. Trinkaus: President, Right to Life League of Southern California; Professor of Law, Loyola University of Los Angeles

Judith Ayala: Registered Nurse, Los Angeles

Johnson C. Montgomery: Attorney, Representing Zero Population Growth, Palo Alto

Stuart W. Knight: Attorney, Anaheim

The Hon. Tom Bradley: Los Angeles City Council

Addie Klotz, M.D.: Director of Student Council Services, San Fernando Valley State College, and three students

David S. Hall: Senior Public Health Educator, Los Angeles County Public Health Department

Laura Anderson: Coordinator, Comprehensive Family Planning Program, Berkeley

Calvin S. Hamilton: Director of Planning, City of Los Angeles

Clarence R. Allen: Professor of Geology and Geophysics, Seismological Laboratory, California Institute of Technology, Los Angeles

Walt Thompson: Chairman, Journalism Department, Laney College, Oakland

Alfred Heller: Director, California Tomorrow, San Francisco

Ernest Loebbeke: Past President, California State Chamber of Commerce, Los Angeles

Robert Sassone: President, League for Infants, Fetuses and the Elderly, Santa Ana

James Edinger: Associate Professor of Meteorology, University of California, Los Angeles

LITTLE ROCK, ARKANSAS, JUNE 7-8, 1971

The Hon. John L. McClellan: U.S. Senate, Arkansas

The Hon. David Pryor: U.S. House of Representatives, 4th C. District, Arkansas

Eddie White: Seasonal Farm Worker, Altheimer

Colin Clark: International Economist; Fellow of Monasch University, Melbourne, Australia

William (Sonny) Walker: Director, Equal Opportunity Division, U.S. Department of Housing and Urban Development, Little Rock

Gordon D. Morgan: Professor of Sociology, University of Arkansas, Fayetteville

The Hon. Winthrop Rockefeller: Former Governor of Arkansas, Little Rock

Calvin L. Beale: Economic Research Service, U.S. Department of Agriculture, Washington, D.C.

Mariah Gilmore: Trainee in Operation Mainstream, a Project Funded by Opportunities Industrialization Center, Little Rock, accompanied by *Mrs. Mitchell:* Counselor, Opportunities Industrialization Center, Little Rock

Barton A. Westerlund: Director, Industrial Research and Extension Center, College of Business Administration, University of Arkansas, Fayetteville

Jason Rouby: Executive Director, Metroplan, Little Rock

John H. Opitz: Executive Director, The Ozarks Regional Commission, Washington, D.C.

William W. Blunt, Jr.: Chief Counsel, Economic Development Administration, U.S. Department of Commerce, Washington, D.C.

William C. Nolan, Jr.: Vice President, El Dorado Chamber of Commerce

Paul Stabler: Field Representative for the Oklahoma Indian Affairs Commission, Tulsa, Oklahoma

Russell Thomas: Director of Industrial Relations, Wolverine Toy Company, Booneville

David L. Barclay, M.D.: Professor and Chairman of the Department of Obstetrics and Gynecology, University of Arkansas Medical Center, accompanied by *Rex Ramsey, M.D.:* Director of Maternal and Child Health Division, Arkansas State Health Department

Trusten H. Holder: Private Consultant in the Areas of Ecological Studies, Outdoor Recreation, Environmental Planning, Little Rock

Pratt Remmel, Jr.: Director, Arkansas Ecology Center, Little Rock

The Hon. Dale Bumpers: Governor of Arkansas

CHICAGO, ILLINOIS, JUNE 21-22, 1971

Philip M. Hauser: Professor of Sociology, University of Chicago

The Hon. Alderman Marilou Hedlund: Member Chicago City Council

Jeffrey R. Short, Jr.: President, J. R. Short Milling Company, Chicago

Richard Babcock: Attorney, Past President, American Society of Planning Officials, Chicago

Lawrence B. Christmas: Technical Director, Northeastern Illinois Planning Commission, Chicago

Norman Lazarus: President, N. Lazarus Company, Chicago

John Yolton: Administrative Assistant to Olga Madar, Vice President of the United Auto Workers, Detroit, Michigan

Conrad E. Terrien: Chemical Engineer, Villa Park

Rev. Don C. Shaw: Executive Director, Midwest Population Center, Chicago

Ellen Peck: Author, Baltimore, Maryland

Rev. Jesse Jackson: National Director, Operation Breadbasket, Chicago

Anthony Downs: Senior Vice President, Real Estate Research Corporation, Chicago

Jean Phillips and *John E. Lester:* Students, Northeastern Illinois State College, Chicago

Frances Frech: Housewife, Kansas City, Missouri

The Hon. William Cousins: Member, Chicago City Council

Ione Du Val: Director of Immigrant Services, The Travelers Aid Society of Metropolitan Chicago

NEW YORK, NEW YORK, SEPTEMBER 27-28, 1971

The Hon. Percy Sutton: President, Borough of Manhattan

Gordon Chase: Health Services Administrator, City of New York, and Chairman, Health and Hospital Corporation

Timothy Costello: Deputy Mayor, City of New York

George Trombetta, M.D.: Chief of Obstetrics and Gynecology, Highland Hospital, Rochester

Alyce Friend: Family Planning Counselor, Rochester

Sylvester Charleston: Student, Bernard Baruch College, New York, N.Y.

Harriet Surovell: High School Women's Coalition, New York, N.Y.

Frank Febus: Student, New York Institute of Photography

Bill Baird: Lecturer on Abortion and Birth Control; Director of the Parents' Aid Society, Hempstead, Long Island

Robert M. Byrn: Professor of Law, Fordham University School of Law

Bernard Pisani, M.D.: Director, Department of Obstetrics and Gynecology, St. Vincent's Hospital, New York, N.Y.

Alvin F. Moran: Executive Vice President, Planned Parenthood of New York, N.Y.

Donald Hohl: Assistant Director of Migration and Refugee Services, U.S. Catholic Conference, Washington, D.C.

Edward J. Logue: President, New York State Urban Development Corporation

Mr. Magee: New York, N.Y.

Paul Ylvisaker: Professor of Public Affairs and Urban Planning, Princeton University

Betty Rollin: Author, New York, N.Y.

Patricia Cooper: Director, Pennsport Civic Association, Philadelphia, accompanied by *Mrs. Fizur:* Community Worker, Philadelphia

Joseph Monserrat: New York City Board of Education, Former Director of Migration Services, Department of Labor, Puerto Rico

Robert O. Anderson: Chairman of the Board, Chief Executive Officer, Atlantic-Richfield Company, New York, N.Y.

Irving Stern: Director of Local 342, Amalgamated Meat Cutters and Retail Food Store Employees Union; International Vice President, Amalgamated Meat Cutters and Butchers Union; Vice President, New York City Central Labor Council

STATEMENTS SUBMITTED BUT NOT DELIVERED

The Hon. Robert H. Finch: Counsellor to President Richard M. Nixon

Rits Tadema: Westminster, California

Student D: San Fernando Valley State College, California

Student E: San Fernanco Valley State College, California

E.L. Bud Stewart, Jr.: Federal Co-Chairman, the Ozarks Regional Commission, Washington, D.C.

Mrs. J. De Friend: The Illinois Area Motorede Committees, Chicago, Illinois

Fred Domville: Oak Park, Illinois

Lee Gilbert: Illinois Citizens Concerned for Life, Chicago, Illinois

Bart T. Heffernan, M.D.: President, Illinois Right to Life Committee, Chicago, Illinois

Eugene S. Callender: President, New York Urban Coalition, New York, New York

Richard B. Rogers: Executive Director, Planned Parenthood League of Massachusetts, Boston, Massachusetts

Introduction

In the fall of 1970, the Commission on Population Growth and the American Future requested that Resources for the Future undertake a project to identify the principal resource and environmental consequences of future population growth in the United States. Part I of this volume is the result of that request. It attempts to assess these consequences under a variety of alternative assumptions about population growth, economic growth, changes in policy, changes in technology, and so on, wherever possible quantitatively as well as qualitatively.

At the same time, the Commission invited statements from scientists on related topics. Part II presents two of these statements; while their approach and views differ from each other and from ours in important ways, they are provocative and should be of considerable interest to the reader.

To complete our work on this project within the year available, choices had to be made about which resources and environmental consequences to emphasize, how deeply to go into the literature on each subject, and how much new ground to attempt to break. The result is a compromise that leans a bit more in the direction of emphasizing a few important topics than of providing a broad, balanced coverage. In part, this emphasis arises from the fact that a comprehensive, sober, and readable overview—Sterling Brubaker's *To Live on Earth*—has recently been published for RFF by Johns Hopkins Press. Much of the present volume can be considered an extension of portions of that book into areas associated with population growth and the United States. Nevertheless, in Chapters 1 and 10, we do attempt a more integrated perspective.

Another compromise results from our desire to avoid tediousness and excessive length, on the one hand, and our attempt, on the other, to make our methods and assumptions explicit, so the interested reader, rather than having to take our word for many things, can make his own assessment of the conclusions. The result is a summary chapter placed at the beginning, two methodological chapters placed at the end, and a style of writing in between that, hopefully, is not too general for the specialist or too specialized for the generalist.

To as great an extent as possible, all chapters were keyed to the same set of assumptions, the broader macro assumptions being placed in Chapter 2, micro assumptions common to most studies placed in Chapter 11 and 12, and the remainder being discussed at the point needed. The reader will find that our economic projections differ from those used in other Commission research volumes. This occurs because our procedure involved the use of a complex econometric model which incorporates somewhat different definitions and assumptions than does that implicitly used by other studies. Growth rates, however, are much less different than levels of major aggregates.

While some corraling of interests and enthusiasms was at times necessary to keep everyone on the same topic, each author bears sole responsibility for his chapter. Actually, our views have tended to converge as we have worked together, but some differences, particularly in tone and emphasis, remain and should be noted.

We are grateful to Clopper Almon and his associates at the University of Maryland for permitting us to use the Maryland Interindustry Forecasting Model, a labor-saving device which made possible a considerable amount of what we accomplished in this short time. Others whose help in providing large masses of data or programs should be acknowledged are Dr. Sidney Goldstein of Brown University; the Regional Analysis Division of the Office of Business Economics, Department of Commerce; Leon Hyatt and James MacFarland, formerly with the Water Commission; Jerome P. Pickard; and the staff of the Commission. David Gilmartin, formerly of the University of Maryland, and Margaret Buckler of the University of Maryland helped in the early stages of this project to understand the workings of the Maryland Model. A sizable number of RFF colleagues were pulled into the act to provide suggestions, and review manuscripts. Especially important were the contributions of Blair Bower, Sterling Brubaker, Marion Clawson, Joseph Fisher, and Allen Kneese, who, along with Hans Landsberg, served as an informal steering committee for this project. In addition, Michael Brewer, Edwin Haefele, Orris Herfindahl, Robert Kelly, John Krutilla, and Fred Smith read and offered important suggestions on one or more of the individual chapters. To all these the authors of this volume owe a collective debt of gratitude.

Finally, I am personally grateful to Henry Herzog, Jr., who, in effect, postponed working on his dissertation for a year to work—very hard—with me on this project, to Michael Harrell whose dedication to detail and deftness at skirting around gaps and inconsistencies in data made his assistance invaluable, and to Diantha Stevenson who rode herd on all stages of the manuscript. Above all I must thank my fellow authors not only for their contributions but for their patience with me and each other during the course of this hectic project.

Ronald G. Ridker

PART I

Resource and
Environmental
Consequences
of Population
Growth in the
United States

Chapter 1

Resource and Environmental Consequences of Population Growth in the United States.. A Summary

by
Ronald G. Ridker
Resources for the Future Inc.

COMMISSION ON POPULATION GROWTH AND
THE AMERICAN FUTURE, *RESEARCH
REPORTS, VOLUME III, POPULATION
RESOURCES AND THE ENVIRONMENT,*
EDITED BY RONALD G. RIDKER

CONTENTS

FIGURES

Resource and Environmental Consequences of Population Growth in the United States: A Summary

What are the resource and environmental implications of population growth in the United States during the next 30 to 50 years? How important is population growth relative to other causes of the problems we find? In particular, what difference would a change in population growth make within this time frame?

In an effort to provide answers to these questions within the year allotted for this project, Resources for the Future brought together experts in a variety of fields, provided them with a common set of questions, assumptions and suggested approaches, and set them to work. The result is the set of studies presented in this volume. In this opening chapter, we present a brief summary of our principal findings, plus some interpretations and overall conclusions that do not automatically emerge from the diversity of detailed considerations presented in the individual studies.

The central issue emerging from this study is one of choice. While population growth and perhaps economic growth ultimately must come to a halt on this finite planet, there is still considerable room to choose when, where, and how.

If because of personal preferences, we choose to have more rather than less children per family—on the average, say, three rather than two—we commit ourselves to a particular package of problems: more rapid depletion of domestic and international resources, greater pressures on the environment, more dependence on continued rapid technological development to solve these problems, fewer social options and perhaps the continued postponement of the resolution of other social problems, including those resulting from past growth. So long as population growth continues, these problems will grow, slowly but irreversibly forcing changes in our current way of life.

If we choose to have fewer children per family, leading to a stable population within the next 50 to 75 years, we purchase time, resources, and additional options: time to overcome our ignorance and to redress the mistakes of past growth, resources to implement solutions, and additional freedom of choice in deciding how we want to live in the future.

Similar consequences could emerge from the choice open to us with respect to alternative rates of economic growth. Indeed, the numerical analysis of Chapter 2 indicates that a reduction in economic growth would reduce resource consumption and pollution emissions by more than would a comparable reduction in population growth. But growth in the economy can be utilized for different ends than it is put to now. While it adds to problems that need solution, it also adds to capacity to solve problems. It is difficult to find similar offsetting advantages from additional population growth at this stage in United States history.

Such consequences of today's choices will not become evident for some time. But as we project farther and farther out into the future, the two societies they give rise to would become increasingly distinct. Assuming technological options available to both societies would be the same, the one with continuing population growth would be forced to live with far greater risks and fewer options with which to solve problems in a manner compatible with our current way of life.

While a reduction in population growth would be a blessing in these respects, it would hardly be a panacea, at least not within the next half century. During that time period, more direct attacks on problems of resource and environmental depletion will be needed in any case; and as our studies show, they can generally accomplish far more.

Moreover, while we believe the United States can find ways to cope with a continuation of population growth if it has to, we have no similar faith for the less developed two-thirds of the world, unless aided in this task by substantial transfers of resources and appropriate knowhow from richer countries. Struggles amongst the haves and the have-nots will increasingly plague us and make the resolution of our domestic problems more difficult.

But these conclusions are far too encapsulated. To understand them, to see what they mean in specific instances, we must review each of the areas covered by this study, starting with a few comments on general method and approach.

THE APPROACH

In some very long-run, ultimate sense, population growth may well be the single most important factor determining resource adequacy and environmental quality. But this study is limited to the next 30 to 50 years, during which time changes in technology, tastes, institutions, policies, and international relations will all play important roles. Not only may some of these factors be more important in certain contexts, but all of them will significantly influence the nature of the relationship between population variables and resource and environmental variables. Within the confines of this project, it would have been impossible to provide a best single forecast for all these nondemographic variables. Instead, we chose assumptions for them, hopefully useful ones, but assumptions nevertheless. Accordingly, our conclusions should not be viewed as absolute forecasts, but rather as conditional predictions the significance of which depends upon the specific assumptions made about all the other factors that can influence the relationships of principal interest.[1] Sometimes we slip into the terminology of forecasting, but only for convenience in exposition.

Assumptions about these nondemographic variables have been chosen with an eye towards policy relevance. So far as environmental policy is concerned, we have attempted to compare the effects of population growth assuming little or no public interference in the environmental field—more or less the situation that existed in the late 1960's—with a situation in which rather stringent environmental quality standards are imposed. So far as technology is concerned, we have made the conservative assumption that current trends toward more efficient use of labor and resources plus some substitutions of cheaper for more expensive materials continue, but that no dramatic breakthroughs such as cheap electricity from fusion, mining of the seabed, synthesis of high valued materials from common elements, or desalinization occur during the next half century. The possibilities of such breakthroughs are discussed, but they never enter into the quantitative analysis. Consumer preferences are handled in a similar way: Except for a few cases where saturation levels appear to be reached, they are assumed to change with income, demographic factors, and time in much the way they have in the past. The net effect is a continuation of the slow change in the composition of consumption away from durables towards services, but no sudden, significant shift, for example, away from a desire for material goods in general. In addition, international demand for resources is assumed to grow more or less in line with trends since World War II, that is, relatively

rapidly compared to earlier portions of this century. Such assumptions are conservative in the sense that they tend to produce pictures of the future with slightly more difficult problems than in fact may occur.

The only explicitly introduced assumption that may violate this criterion pertains to United States military expenditures, which, as explained in Chapter 2, are assumed to level off for a few years and then begin rising again but at a much slower rate than the rate of growth in GNP.

The results of this study are influenced not only by the time horizon and the assumptions made about nondemographic variables, but also by its focus primarily on the United States, a limited set of resources and pollutants, and on two particular population projections, Census Series B, more or less equivalent to a continuation of the three-child norm, and Census Series E, which introduces the two-child norm and brings population growth to a halt, except for immigration, in about the year 2040. As time and materials permitted, we did attempt to move beyond these initial bounds; but such extensions have been undertaken mainly with an eye to checking out and if necessary qualifying our conclusions, rather than as carefully articulated studies in their own right.

The impact of population growth, as well as that of other variables, can be viewed from two perspectives. First, one can compare how things are today with how they are likely to be in some future year. Second, one can compare two possible situations that may arise in the future. From the first perspective, differences in reasonable population projections appear relatively small. Between now and the year 2000, population will increase by somewhere between 30 percent and 57 percent. From this vantage point, the important question is how to cope with an increase within this general range. On the other hand, if we imagine we are sitting in the year 2000, the difference between the two population estimates—E being 17 percent less than B—is likely to appear much more significant. Wherever possible, we have tried to look at the situation from both perspectives, generally by first asking what the situation would be like in the year 2000 (or 2020) if path B in Figure 1 were to prevail and then asking what difference it would make in that year if the population size were to be smaller, the level that would be reached under the E projection.

THE ECONOMY

Population growth affects resource needs and the environment largely through the economy. Our starting point, then, is the development of a picture on a sector by sector basis of what the economy might look like in

FIGURE 1-1
U.S. POPULATION WITH PROJECTIONS, 1950-2020

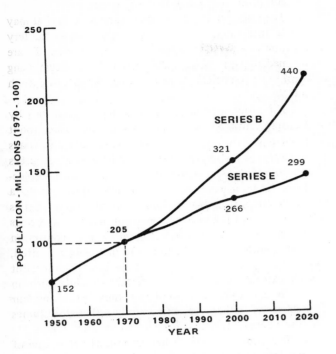

Nevertheless, by comparing the B-High with the E-Low or the B-Low with the E-High scenarios, at least limited consideration of some alternative assumptions is possible.

While independent of the above factors, population and associated demographic changes are assumed to affect aggregate demand, consumption patterns, and the size of the labor force. Figures 2 and 3 portray the quantitative effect of these, plus more detailed assumptions on GNP and GNP per capita.

Whether or not these projections actually occur will depend in large part on whether the United States can solve the resource and environmental problems that this growth would entail, an assessment to be made in the course of this study. But assuming for the moment that they can occur, three main conclusions emerge from these materials.

First, under any scenario considered, the American economy, which is already large by world standards, will become gargantuan. Even if there is a substantial shift in preferences towards leisure and a significant slowdown in population growth rates, this economy is likely to be twice its current size in the year 2000 and more than three and one-half times its current size in 2020. With a more rapid growth in population and a less rapid shift in preferences toward leisure (or a more rapid growth in

the next 30 to 50 years. Since we are interested in determining the effects of a change in economic growth rates as well as in population growth rates, four basic scenarios were developed: high population and economic growth (B-High), low population and economic growth (E-Low), and the two intermediate cases (B-Low and E-High). We have already discussed the alternative assumptions used for the population projections. For alternative economic assumptions, we chose to compare a "high" growth case in which man-hour productivity grows at 2.5 percent per year and annual work hours decline by 0.25 percent per year—more or less on trend—with a "low" growth case in which work hours decline by 1.0 percent per year (growth in man-hour productivity remaining the same). The shift towards leisure implied by the low growth case is fairly dramatic: While weekly work hours are now close to 40 and would decline over a 30-year period to 37 in the high growth case, they would fall to 29 in the low growth scenario.[2]

Common to all these scenarios is the assumption that changes in productivity, work hours, aggregate savings rates, and the ability of the government to maintain full employment are independent of changes in the population. While there are some arguments to the contrary, within the range of the population estimates and over the time period being considered, we do not believe any other assumption is more defensible.[3]

FIGURE 1-2
U.S. GROSS NATIONAL PRODUCT WITH PROJECTIONS, 1950-2020

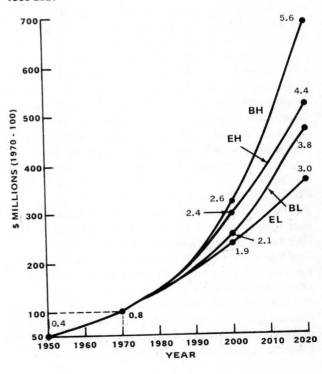

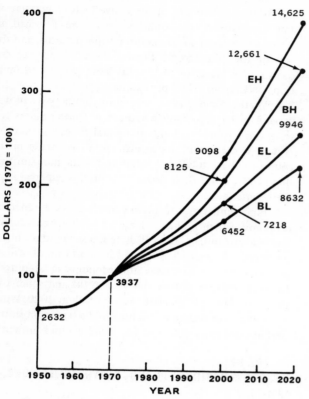

FIGURE 1-3

U.S. GROSS NATIONAL PRODUCT PER CAPITA WITH PROJECTIONS, 1950-2020

man-hour productivity) the economy would be seven times its current size by the latter date. This would occur not because of any implicit assumption of large annual growth rates—the highest of which is no more than four percent per annum—but merely because these rates are sustained for such a long period. Second, because GNP per capita increases more rapidly under the Series E than under the Series B population projections, total GNP is not lower in proportion to the extent that population is lower; but even so, this difference between total GNP in the two cases grows dramatically over time. In 2000, the difference in projected GNP resulting solely from alternative population assumptions amounts to more than half the total size of GNP today; by 2020, it amounts to more than the total size of today's GNP. And third, sector breakdowns of the economy indicate a gradual shift in output towards services, a shift that proceeds a bit faster under the Series E than under the Series B population assumptions.

The result is a strong prima facie case in favor of the two-child family on two important welfare grounds. Per capita GNP can be taken as a measure of material welfare, conventionally defined; and since resource use

and pollution levels are associated more with total than with per capita output levels, total GNP might be taken as a crude indicator of environmental degradation. In these terms, the E projections, with their higher levels of per capita and lower levels of total GNP—as well as with an environmentally more favorable composition of output—are clearly superior.

Two qualifications must be kept in mind, however. First, parents may prefer larger families than are compatible with the lower population growth rate; if they do, this preference must be balanced against the social benefits of the smaller population. Second, the savings in resources and environmental depletion resulting from a slowdown in population growth rates may not be as great as intuition might lead one to believe based on these projections of total GNP. This could arise as a result of changes in other important factors linking resources and the environment to population and GNP. As we shall see, in several important instances this qualification turns out in fact to be important.

MINERALS AND FUELS ADEQUACY

We have studied some 19 minerals plus major sources of energy to determine what United States demand would be under alternative population and economic projections, what difference an increased emphasis on recycling would make, and whether United States plus world reserves are likely to be adequate within the time horizon of this study.

The question of adequacy cannot be answered without a careful definition of the word in mind. Here, adequate means sufficient supplies to meet demand assuming current prices, currently known reserves, and possibilities to substitute one for another material in production. If an item proves to be inadequate in this sense, one must ask about the extent of the price increase necessary to eliminate the gap between demand and supply and the possibilities for adjusting to this increase in order to assess the seriousness of the situation. With this in mind, the following broad generalizations emerge from the analysis.

Minerals

On a worldwide basis and out to the year 2020, there appear to be sufficient reserves of at least nine non-fuel minerals: chromium, iron, nickel, vanadium, magnesium, phosphorous, potassium, cobalt, and nitrogen. Of these, domestic reserves may not be sufficient to meet needs for chromium, vanadium, cobalt, and nickel. Access to foreign supplies is currently quite reliable; but if it became questionable, modest efforts at research and development, recycling, stockpiling, and substitution could overcome this difficulty.

22

Worldwide reserves as now estimated are inadequate through the year 2020 for 10 of the minerals studied: manganese, molybdenum, tungsten, aluminum, copper, lead, zinc, tin, titanium, and sulfur. However, there are significant differences in the outlook. Modest price increases, for example, in sulfur, would bring in supplies from potential reserves, probably beyond what requirements call for. The same is true for aluminum, for which poorer—and thus initially at least more costly—sources of ore are abundant. At the other end of the scale is tungsten, for which it is difficult to establish a reserve picture that promises adequacy. Here main reliance might have to be placed on gradual phasing out of the metal in applications that can get along, though perhaps at higher cost and reduced efficiency, with substitute materials or substitute processes. In between these extremes lie materials like copper, where a combination of resort to even poorer ores, increased substitution, greater recycling of what is now a very large above-ground stock of copper, and increased exploration seems indicated if requirements as here projected are to be met.

A change in population growth appears to have a smaller impact than a change in economic growth, at least over the range considered in this study. Substitution of the lower for the higher population growth assumption generally results in a reduction of cumulative United States demand by only one to eight percent by the year 2000, and no more than 14 percent by 2020. Most of these modest savings would occur late in the period. In contrast, different assumptions as to economic growth would affect mineral consumption more significantly. Through the year 2000, the low productivity assumption would generally yield savings in cumulative demand of 10 to 14 percent, rising to 18 to 26 percent for demand through the year 2020. These begin to look more interesting. In combination with low population growth, savings would generally rise to 14 and 19 percent through 2000, and 27 to 35 percent through 2020.

An alternative way to compare the impact of population and economic growth on consumption of resources is to ask what the effect would be in a given year, say 2000, of a one-percentage-point reduction in the population size compared to a one-percentage-point reduction in per capita GNP. The conclusion emerging is similar to the above: A one-percent reduction in population would reduce consumption of resources in the year 2000 by 0.2 to 0.7 percent, whereas the equivalent percentage reduction in per capita GNP would reduce consumption in that year 0.6 to 3.5 percent.

The most important reason for this result has to do with the fact that a reduction in population induces some offsetting increase in per capita GNP and hence in demands for resources, whereas a decline in per capita GNP can take place independently of a change in population. While it is unlikely that a change in population would occur without any change in GNP per capita, a trial run of the model in which per capita GNP was held constant when alternative population assumptions were introduced makes the savings from a reduction in population size roughly equal to that of a reduction in GNP per capita.

Increased recycling as a means of stretching reserves was tested for five principal minerals: iron, copper, lead, zinc, and aluminum. Defined as an "active recycling policy," the increased effort directed at recapturing a larger percentage of used material would reduce demand for primary materials significantly for aluminum and zinc, modestly for copper, and barely at all for iron and lead. The differences, which are quite dramatic, result from differences in the extent to which recycling is now taking place: high for iron and lead, moderate for copper, and very low for aluminum and zinc. Savings in terms of reserves would be substantial, especially for zinc and copper (40 and 15 percent respectively of world reserves if projected for 50 years). Extension of "active recycling" to a world scale can be assumed to increase these savings. While these are magnitudes not to be dismissed lightly, costs in terms of additional resources required to achieve such recycling, as well as the additional pollutants arising from the recycling, need careful analysis to ascertain net savings and benefits.

Energy

Historically, energy consumption in the United States has closely paralleled the growth in real GNP. While there are many factors that could alter this relationship—increased needs for energy per unit of output because of recycling and the mining of lower grade ores, and decreased needs because of shifts in composition of output towards services and improvements in efficiency, to mention just a few—it is probably safest to assume that the historical association will continue during our time horizon. Population growth, then, will play the same role in determining energy growth as it does in determining overall growth in GNP.

Increasingly, energy will be used in the form of electricity, although standard projections of the extent to which such a substitution will occur are probably exaggerated. Moreover, more and more electricity in the United States will be produced with nuclear fuel, perhaps as much as half by the year 2000.

World supply projections depend very heavily on the technological changes assumed to occur during the next quarter to half century. Even without assuming any breakthroughs, however, world fossil fuel reserves (including potential as well as proved) appear adequate for at least the next half century. This reckoning appears to be true even leaving out oil reserves in shale and tar sands, and uranium and thorium. Beyond these possibilities, if man learns to harness nuclear fusion—a reasonable possibility within the next 50 to 100 years—the limits of worldwide industrial expansion will be set by factors other than availability of energy.

Relative to other countries, the United States is in good shape, provided we have sufficient lead time to develop domestic alternatives to foreign sources should the need arise. Although proved reserves of gas and oil as a ratio to production have declined somewhat since World War II—more for gas than for oil—estimates of commercially recoverable reserves when added to proved reserves provide adequate coverage for well into the next century. This judgment does not take account of shale oil reserves of the United States and the tar sands of Canada. Coal reserves and nuclear fuels, assuming the development of breeders, are adequate for at least another century. While United States imports as a share of consumption may rise due to the availability of cheaper fuels abroad, given these domestic possibilities, this rise should not necessarily be taken as a sign of increasing long run vulnerability.

Qualifications

All these points suggest that there is no serious reason to believe that projected standards of living cannot be met because of minerals or fuels shortages. Adjustments will be necessary, but none of them are likely to entail a significant loss in material welfare during the next half century. This is not to say that there will be no problems so far as minerals and fuels are concerned. Three in particular need emphasis.

First, environmental concerns could interfere with this prognosis. Virtually every stage of energy use—from mining to transport and conversion—has significant environmental consequences. If public concern over siting of conventional and nuclear electric plants, strip mining, oil spills, and pipelines slows down development of new capacity, a greater price rise will be necessary to close the gap between supply and demand. Even if development is not slowed down in this way, demands for pollution control will have some effect on costs (the extent of which is considered below).

Second, there is a tendency to assume that adjustments will be made smoothly, that prices will correctly reflect scarcity sufficiently far in advance that appropriate remedial action can be taken before the problem becomes severe. But resource markets are not free from monopolistic interferences and governmental interventions; and business decision makers often behave myopically. If too short a time horizon is taken or if markets are dominated by buyers, key prices might remain constant at too low a level until a serious shortage is upon us, only then to rise dramatically as near exhaustion occurred. Alternatively, since major new discoveries and technological changes are difficult to predict, prices may be set too high in some circumstances as well as too low. The only solution may be continuous monitoring to detect growing shortages sufficiently far in advance that appropriate remedial action can be instituted.

Third, far more serious than the threat of overall physical shortages, however, are growing worldwide imbalances. Between 1925 and 1967, energy imports as a fraction of total consumption for Western Europe increased from two percent to 61 percent, and that for Japan from zero to 80 percent. Eastern Europe, which exported over 15 percent of its energy production, now imports five percent. (In contrast, the United States figures are less dramatic, shifting from a three percent net exporter to a seven percent net importer of energy.) Corresponding to these figures are dramatically increased exports from a handful of countries, principally in North Africa, the Middle East, and the Caribbean. Trends for some other minerals are similar. Geographic imbalances are severe today and may well become more severe in the future. While the United States will remain amongst the haves, relatively speaking, these disparities are likely to affect international power balances involving this country in serious ways, whether or not the United States becomes more directly dependent on world supplies.

POLLUTION

We have divided pollutants into two rough classes. The first class includes major combustion products—carbon monoxide, carbon dioxide, oxides of nitrogen, oxides of sulfur, hydrocarbons, and particulates—and several measures of water pollution—including biological demand for oxygen and suspended and dissolved solids. The primary characteristics of this group are first, that they all have relatively short half-lives—sufficiently short that cumulative effects are not a problem—and second, that sufficient information exists about them to permit linking them to economic sectors or population. In addition, this group contains the more massive and commonly discussed pollutants. The second set of pollutants is a miscellaneous group including those with longer half-lives—radiation, pesticides, and heavy metals—plus a wide variety of ever-changing chemicals emitted by our high technology industries, most of which are emitted in small, though often highly toxic, amounts. For many of these pollutants, future developments depend more heavily on changes in technology than on changes in population and economic growth; in any case, they are very difficult to link to population and economic growth in a simple and quantitative fashion. Accordingly our emphasis here is on the first class of pollutants, although a number of others are discussed in Chapters 7 and 10.

Our principal conclusions regarding this first set are most easily discussed in relation to Figure 4. While this figure relates only to hydrocarbons, the general conclusions are similar for other pollutants, as Table 8 of Chapter 2 indicates. Bar A for 1970 represents the level of hydrocarbons generated by the production and use of economic goods and services. If no changes in technology associated with the production of this pollutant were to occur, the amount of hydrocarbons generated

FIGURE 1-4
HYDROCARBONS GENERATED AND EMITTED UNDER ALTERNATIVE ASSUMPTIONS

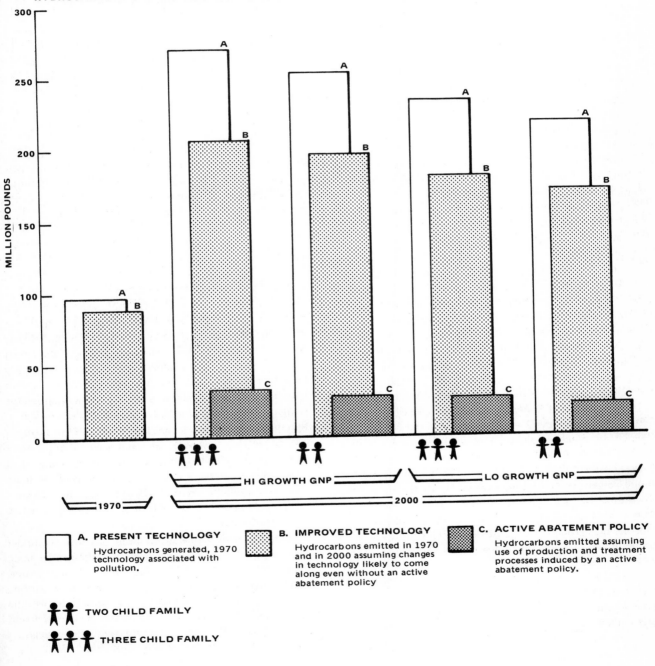

A. PRESENT TECHNOLOGY
Hydrocarbons generated, 1970 technology associated with pollution.

B. IMPROVED TECHNOLOGY
Hydrocarbons emitted in 1970 and in 2000 assuming changes in technology likely to come along even without an active abatement policy

C. ACTIVE ABATEMENT POLICY
Hydrocarbons emitted assuming use of production and treatment processes induced by an active abatement policy.

TWO CHILD FAMILY

THREE CHILD FAMILY

Resources and Environmental Consequences of Population
Growth in the United States: A Summary

would be at the levels indicated by one of the other bars labeled A in the year 2000, the difference between them depending on population and economic assumptions.

For 1970, the bar labeled B indicates the amount of hydrocarbons emitted into the atmosphere, the difference between A and B accounted for by treatment. For 2000, B indicates projected emission levels taking into account the changes in technology likely to come along anyway, without public pressures to restrict emission of harmful residuals. In principle, these changes could result in either a higher or a lower level of emissions. In fact, however, most of the technological changes we have studied tend on net to reduce residuals. This is because even without pressures to clean up the environment, entrepreneurs have an interest in conserving on raw materials. For example, we anticipate that more and more sawdust and timber trimmings will be used in making paper and pulp rather than being dumped into streams. As a consequence of such technological changes, as well as because the shift towards services makes the year 2000 composition of output slightly less polluting than the 1970 composition, we find the pollutants studied are likely to grow over time less rapidly than the growth in GNP.

The heart of this story involves the bars labeled C, which indicate the levels of emissions that could prevail if an active abatement policy were in force. These estimates are conservative in the sense that no technological breakthroughs (such as the adoption of the Rankine cycle engine which could occur within this time frame) were assumed.[4] As Figure 4 indicates—and comparable data for the other pollutants studied confirm—the choice to be made is between no policy change with higher levels of emissions than exist today, and an active abatement policy with lower than current levels of emissions, whatever the rates of population and economic growth within the range investigated. As of 1972, the United States appears to be choosing in favor of the active policy.

How much would such an active abatement policy cost? In 1970, annualized costs of pollution abatement were estimated to be $8.45 billion (1967 dollars), about one percent of GNP. Under the active abatement policy, we estimate that these same categories of costs would mount to over $47 billion for the high population-high economic growth case and $34 billion for the low population-high economic growth case in the year 2000. While these are very large figures, they amount to less than two percent of GNP in the year 2000. In terms of growth, these figures signify that we would have to give up less than one-tenth of a percentage point in annual growth of GNP to purchase this active abatement policy.

At least within the time frame and for the set of pollutants under investigation, then, a direct attack on pollution clearly dominates over a reduction in population or economic growth as a strategy for obtaining a cleaner environment. A brief investigation of other pollution control strategies—for example, a selective reduction in the consumption of commodities which are heavy users of the environment, restrictions on the use of the automobile, and zoning—supports this general conclusion. Considering how little we have done in the past to control pollution, this result should not be all that surprising.

Such direct attacks on pollution will not be easy to implement; and once implemented at whatever levels prove feasible, further reductions in emissions will become very difficult and costly. It is at this point—and especially as we look beyond 2000 when such policies may prove inadequate—that reductions in population and economic growth come into their own as important means of containing pollution.

But even within the next 30 years, special regions of the country will face difficult problems despite improvements in overall emission rates. Data on 47 urbanized areas and three air pollutants were used to illustrate this point, assuming that the land area of these places increases with population in such a way that population density remains constant. In 1970, two cities—Chicago and Philadelphia—had sulfate (SO_2) concentration levels that were above the Environmental Protection Agency's primary standard of 80 micrograms per cubic meter of air. If no change in abatement policy (after 1967-70) occurred, only these two would remain in violation in the year 2000, although may other cities would closely approach the standard. If there were an active abatement policy as defined above, all cities would fall significantly below the standard in 2000. A similar situation exists for particulates except that 36 areas are initially above the standard and some improvement would occur even in the absence of an active abatement policy. For nitrogen oxides, however, where 36 metropolitan areas were above the 100 micrograms per cubic meter standard in 1970, and 41 areas would be above in 2000 with no change in policy, two—Los Angeles and San Diego—would remain above the standard even with an active abatement policy.

The nitrogen oxide situation in Los Angeles, under the assumptions made, is particularly striking. Compared to a 1970 level of 275 micrograms per cubic meter, under any of the four alternative scenarios regarding national population and economic growth rates, the 2000 level will be near 500 with no change in policy and around 150—still some 50 percent above the standard—

with an active policy in that year. This assumes that land area increases in proportion to population. But during the past decade, population density has been increasing. If this trend continues, nitrogen oxide levels in 2000 under the active abatement policy would be around 170; and if land area were to cease expanding, all the increased population being absorbed within this region's current boundaries, the active abatement policy could not hold nitrogen oxide levels below 570. Clearly, in this region of the country, something must give: rates of inmigration, the use of the internal combustion engine especially for personal transport, or the standard itself.

Pollution concentrations are not only distributed unequally amongst urbanized regions. Variations within such regions and even from one hour to the next can be extremely large. Indeed, carbon monoxide levels along downtown streets during rush hours can be more than 10 times those along suburban streets at the same time of day. Such problems will require special treatment whatever national abatement policy is adopted.

CONGESTION AND OUTDOOR RECREATION

Congestion is a difficult concept to define, measure, and project. Clearly, it depends on many more factors than sheer numbers. Geographic distribution of population, transportation facilities, income levels, homogeneity of tastes, type of facilities, and the way they are managed all play important roles. Yosemite, for example, is more crowded today than it was 20 years ago not just because the United States population is larger but also because of westward migration, better transportation facilites, especially highways, increased incomes and leisure time, and increased preferences for organized outdoor experiences. In this situation, what can be said about the amount of congestion that the United States will experience in the future under the two population assumptions?

At a general level, perhaps the most important point to make is that with a slower rate of growth, we close off fewer options. If all the land in the United States were divided equally amongst its citizens, each American would have 11 acres at his disposal (nine acres excluding Alaska and Hawaii). Of this amount, approximately two are used to grow crops; six are used (or are available) for pasture and range, forest and recreation; and one-half an acre is occupied, for example, by buildings and roads, or is held out of use by special institutions (the remaining two and one-half acres being a residual, largely unusable category). With the higher population growth rate, each American would have seven acres at his disposal in

2000 and five in 2020. By European standards, the United States would still be considered a land-rich country. But a style of life based on such an abundance of land would be slowly but progressively eliminated, with no possibility of turning back. The same is true with the two-child population with the important difference that the rate of deterioration would be much slower, reaching 7.5 acres per person in 2020, and would all but cease at around 7.1 acres per person in 2040. (See Chapter 8 for a more detailed discussion of future trends in land use.)

Beyond such general comments, little can be said about the differential degree of congestion implied by alternative population projections without detailed studies of specific facilities. Within the confines of this project, we have undertaken one such study of a particularly important amenity associated with the American way of life, outdoor recreation. This study uses an econometric model to project participation rates for some 24 different outdoor recreation activities on the basis of information about the supply and location of recreational facilities and the extent to which congestion affects use, as well as important demographic and economic characteristics of the population. Together with other trends, it points to another significant difference between the two population projections.

Between 1970 and 2000, an individual's income and hours of leisure will rise, and recreational facilities will improve, so that he will have more time, money, and opportunities to "recreate" if he wishes. To do so under the high population projection, however, he will have to adopt a different style of life. There will be fewer opportunities for spontaneous communion with raw nature. More and more such contacts will be controlled, regulated, and contrived. On the other hand, his income and the increase in man-made recreational facilities will permit him to substitute organized sports, sightseeing and foreign travel, plus artistic and cultural activities, if he so desires. For a small but important segment of our population, these alternatives are unlikely to provide an adequate compensation; for many others, however, they will.

On the other hand, under the E population in the year 2000, the typical individual will be significantly older and therefore less interested in participating in some kinds of outdoor recreation activities. This fact, plus the smaller population size, will substantially reduce congestion, so that whatever he does participate in is likely to give him more pleasure. Once again, the style of life will change, shifting from more active to more sedentary recreational pursuits; but in this case, it would be voluntary, determined by the needs and preferences of an older population rather than being imposed by the desire to avoid overcrowding.

WATER

On a national basis, the United States has more than enough water to meet all of its needs far beyond the year 2020. But to take advantage of it, substantial outlays for treatment facilities and storage will be needed. Such costs will increase at a rate slightly less than that for GNP.

In contrast to our findings with respect to minerals and pollution, population has a dominant role to play in determining these costs. If we substitute the two-child for the three-child population in the year 2000, savings would be 23 percent; by 2020, these savings would mount to 32 percent. In contrast, savings due to a slower growth in income are 11 percent in 2000 and 17 percent in 2020.

But there are great regional disparities in the demand and supply of water. When regions are defined as being deficient in water if, after high levels of treatment are applied, the maximum regulated supply is insufficient to meet requirements for water of given qualities, several regions in the southwest are already in deficit. As the maps in Chapter 8 show, these deficit regions will slowly spread across the country, faster with the high than with the low population growth rate.

These results are significant not only because deficits are defined in a stringent way, but also because the analytical model used to obtain them does not take account of biological wastes from the non-sewered population, problems of nutrient runoff into ground-water supplies or adequately treat costs of managing slack water areas such as estuaries or of separating storm from sanitary sewers. Moreover, the scope for redistributing water, people, and economic activities between regions is more limited and difficult than might appear at first glance.

On the other hand, there are considerable possibilities for using water more prudently. Most water is used either free of cost or on a flat fee basis that provides no incentive for conservation. Yet in the largest areas of use—for irrigation and cooling—substantial possibilities are present to reduce withdrawals without serious welfare losses. Finding equitable means to increase prices or otherwise ration major users would not be easy, but certainly could be done if the need arises.

AGRICULTURE

The agriculture study is based on the same set of scenarios used for other sectors except that several were added to investigate the impact of a policy which entails a restriction on the use of agricultural chemicals particularly fertilizers and pesticides, and the possibility of urban sprawl encroaching on high quality agricultural land. In the case where restrictions on chemical inputs are assumed, the use of fertilizer is projected to be half the level it would have been without restrictions and that of pesticides to be 80 percent below levels otherwise projected. These levels were chosen on the basis of the judgment that they are the largest fore-seeable reductions that could be made between now and the year 2000 without dramatic increases in costs, but yet sufficient to make significant improvements in environmental quality.

Between now and the year 2000, under the conditions assumed, the United States will have no serious problem in producing sufficient food for its own population even if government-assisted exports continue to be the same proportion of total output as they are today. With the high population and high economic growth rate assumptions, and assuming no restrictions on the use of fertilizer and pesticides, most idle, high quality, cropland would have to be put back into production. But because of its availability, as well as because of expected increases in yields, farm prices relative to other prices would be only marginally higher than they are today. Fertilizer and pesticide use would increase significantly, but for a number of reasons probably not in proportion to the increase in food output. These reasons have to do with (1) the expected continuation of efforts started in the early 1960's to regulate pesticide applications and find less persistent formulations; (2) increases in the price of fertilizer—which can be expected to induce better timing and placement of application, better distribution over different crops, and use of formulations such as controlled release preparations that improve efficiency and reduce leaching; and (3) the easing of acreage restrictions which in the past two decades have induced excessively rapid rates of increase in fertilizer and pesticide consumption to compensate by increasing yields.

Moreover, urban sprawl is unlikely to have any significant effect on the ability of the United States to meet projected food and fiber requirements. While urban areas are spreading out, rural-to-urban migration is continuing as well, the net effect being a more unequal distribution of people on the land. Such a population implosion, which is expected to continue in the future albeit at a diminishing rate, partly offsets the effect of increases in the population. Of course, local agricultur-alists are likely to face increasing challenges in regions where inmigration of people and other economic activities is especially rapid; but, once their activities are relocated, total output should not be adversely affected to any appreciable extent.

If, in the interest of environmental quality, restrictions on the use of fertilizer and pesticides were put in force, an additional 50 million acres of land would have to be brought into production. Since most high quality land would already be in use, considerable investment would have to be made to bring these additional acres into production. The result would be something like a 15-percent increase in the farm price of food over what it would otherwise have been in the year 2000. By that time, such a price rise would probably not be very detrimental from a welfare point of view. On the other hand, with the low population growth assumption, restrictions on the use of fertilizer and pesticides could be accomplished without any increase in price. Indeed, if economic growth were to be lower as well, farm prices might fall marginally.

While no formal assessment beyond the year 2000 was made, these differences between the high and the low population growth rates are likely to magnify substantially. By 2020, only the low population growth case might be compatible with a policy of restricting inputs in the interest of environmental quality, since the price increase under the high growth case with restrictions would be considered intolerable, perhaps even as high as 40 to 50 percent. Of course, such a price rise would occur only if we tried to maintain current patterns of consumptions; in fact, they would be dampened by shifts away from consumption of animal livestock towards vegetables and synthetic meats which would reduce acreage requirements. Moreover, technological breakthroughs that significantly reduce acreage requirements could also invalidate this assessment. But, in any case, it is clear that much of the fat in our agricultural system would have been trimmed away.

A number of open questions on the environmental consequences of these developments remain. Will any of these different levels of fertilizer use result in nitrate poisoning of groundwater on a significant scale? Without heavy costs, is it possible to shift agriculture from one part of the country to another to the extent implied by this and the water analysis? And how can we stay ahead of the adaptability of pests to our means of control without harming man or other animals in the process? Such questions cannot be answered without substantially more information than is now available. Perhaps in the end a new closed system of agriculture will be necessary, as suggested in Chapter 10. Given these unknowns, an additional advantage of the slower over the more rapid population growth path is that it provides us with more time to find answers to these questions.

URBAN ENVIRONMENTAL PROBLEMS

There is mounting evidence that environmental quality is lower in metropolitan areas that are larger and in regions that are more densely populated. Certainly this is the case with air pollution, noise, traffic congestion, and time spent on journey to work. Other factors are less clear. Sewerage and water treatment costs per capita decline as city size increases to about 100,000; thereafter, engineering data suggest that costs should be more or less constant for conventional facilities, although actual costs appear to rise. Certainly if large cities are forced to use tertiary treatment or separate storm and sanitary sewers—which may be necessary to maintain adequate standards in some cases—per capita costs will be much higher. Similarly, solid waste disposal costs are also either U-shaped or increasing with city size and density over the relevant range. There is evidence that increasing urban scale affects local hydrology and climate; but not all these effects are bad. While raw data indicate a strong correlation between urban scale and crime rates, the effect is greatly attenuated once the effects of race and income are removed.

But it does not necessarily follow from this evidence that a policy of redistributing people and economic activities so as to reduce city size and density would be beneficial as a general proposition. First, there are many tradeoffs for the individual living in the larger city: In general, deflated money incomes for the same jobs are higher; and there are more occupational and social opportunities, and a larger variety of goods and services. To mention one important example, medical services, especially those involving highly trained specialists, are clearly superior in larger urban centers. Given free movement of people between urban areas—a condition which is probably met fairly well despite income and housing discrimination that inhibits movement within urban areas—these tradeoffs are in the nature of compensation payments for poorer environmental quality, payments which everything considered may leave the urban dweller no worse (or better) off than his counterpart in smaller towns.[5] Second, there is some evidence that the large city may be a major generator of national economic growth. Communication and transport costs are lower; greater specialization and division of labor is possible; and growth industries, information industries, and universities tend to locate there. Third, conscious efforts in this and other countries to influence locational decisions, in particular to stop the growth of large cities, have been largely unsuccessful in the past; there is no reason to believe the future will be different on this score.

Finally, the underlying causes of poorer environmental quality in larger urban centers may often not be scale, but factors associated with or exacerbated by scale: urban forms and transportation systems more appropriate to an earlier era; old, unintegrated service facilities; inappropriate pricing of public facilities and common property resources such as roads and waste disposal media; multiple political jurisdictions; and the factors leading to inadequate financing and a predominance of minority groups and poor in many central cities. Many such problems will remain to be solved whatever population distribution policy is adopted. As a consequence, the historical evidence relating environmental quality to urban scale may not be applicable to the building of new cities and the "retrofitting" of older ones.

For these reasons, we are skeptical about the value of proposals to reduce urban size and density across the board. As a general proposition, it is better to work on underlying causes rather than effects, and to attack problems where they exist, permitting people to adjust by moving out or in as they judge best for themselves. Some new town developments are certainly called for, not so much as a way of reducing average urban size and density—hopefully, some of these developments would try out solutions with more rather than less density, and others might usefully occur within existing urban areas—but as an experimental means of gaining information on the best way to solve our real urban problems.

SOME BROADER CONSIDERATIONS

While the studies included in this volume cover a vast range of topics in a fair amount of detail, they obviously do not exhaust the subjects of relevance to the questions posed at the outset of this chapter. Conclusions based solely on what has been covered could provide a misleading overall impression. Before drawing final conclusions, therefore, we wish to emphasize the importance of at least four additional considerations.

Other Environmental Concerns

We must now return to the second set of pollutants mentioned but set aside in the above discussion. These include pollutants with long half-lives and an ever-changing group of potential threats to the environment generated at what seems like an increasing rate by our high technology industries. But what can be said about them? The principal problem here is ignorance.

The case of radioactive wastes from nuclear power plants is instructive. We know there are likely to be more nuclear power plants if rapid population and economic growth occurs; but all dimensions of nuclear management and technology are changing so rapidly that there

is no stable launching pad from which to project the amounts of radioactive wastes likely to escape to the environment. Once in the environment, we know they can travel long distances through space and food chains before coming to rest, and we know the kinds of damages they can cause; but we do not know where they will come to rest, the extent of the damages, or when in the future these dangers will occur.

In truth, the situation is similar for all pollutants. It is difficult to link emissions to concentration levels in specific places and, with a few exceptions, close to impossible to make quantitative statements with reasonable confidence about the consequences—the damages—resulting from these concentrations. The crude method we were forced to use to relate emissions to air quality, discussed in Chapter 11, and in the review of what is known about damage and cost functions for urban pollutants in Chapter 9, illustrate these points all too well. Nevertheless, often because of longer "half-lives," greater toxicity in smaller doses, rapid changes in types of pollutants, and time lags between emissions and the appearance of damages, the situation is more disturbing for the second group of pollutants. More serious yet, these very characteristics insure that we shall not quickly improve our knowledge in this area.

Apart from adopting a more positive and encouraging posture than now exists towards basic research in many of these areas, perhaps the only way to cope with this ignorance is to proceed cautiously and prudently, playing it safe with nature. Given our affluence and the fact that many pollutants result from attempts to satisfy relatively trivial preferences—for unblemished fruits, labor saving detergents, faster accelerating cars, brightly colored paper products—much could be done within our time frame without significant adverse effects on welfare or growth rates. But a slowdown in population and economic growth would clearly help; and in a longer time frame could possibly be a necessity.

We have also said precious little about global pollutants—rising levels of carbon dioxide and heat in the earth's atmosphere, for example—and the more fundamental concerns of some ecologists about man's threat to the basic life support system of the earth. Here again ignorance dominates. But an up-to-date, careful review of this whole range of problems suggests that while lead times may be long, most such threats are not imminent, at least not the way non-ecologists reckon time.[6]

Institutional and Social Concerns

Our investigation of the resource and pollution problems inherent in attempting to achieve alternative growth rates suggests that all these rates are feasible during the next 30 to 50 years: Problems will arise— more rapidly under the high than under the low growth rate assumptions—but the United States has the physical and technological capability to resolve them without serious losses in material welfare. This country is amazingly rich. If we cannot mine a resource, we can import, design around it, find a substitute, or just reduce our consumption by a small bit. If water deficits threaten a particular part of the country, we can choose between higher charges to reduce its consumption, transfers of population and economic activities to other regions, and longer and larger canals. If pollution emissions cannot be tolerated, we can change production processes, improve treatment, separate polluters and their victims, treat the symptoms, or simply produce less of the commodity causing the pollution. Congestion during commuter hours can be handled by restricting the use of private cars, mass transit and, if necessary, staggered work hours. Congestion at recreation sites can be handled by building additional facilities, better management, encouraging substitutes (for example, foreign travel) and, if necessary, staggering vacation periods. Even land shortages for agriculture can be handled, given sufficient lead time, through farming the sea, changes in diet, synthetic foods, and shifts in the direction of hydroponic production. None of these adjustments raises specters of dramatic downfall and collapse.

But physicial, technological, and even managerial capabilities of this sort are not enough. Beyond the economic costs of adjusting to growing resource and environmental problems, there are social and institutional prices to pay. Indeed, in a discussion of these difficulties, we come to the real nature of our problem with population growth. Such non-resource costs are of four types.

First, population growth forces upon us a slow but irreversible change in life style. Imbedded in the folklore of what constitutes the American way of life is freedom from public regulation: freedom to hunt, fish, swim, and camp where and when we will; free use of water and access to uncongested, unregulated roadways; freedom to do as we please with what we own; and freedom from permits, licenses, fees, red tape, and bureaucrats. Obviously, we do not live this way now. Maybe we never did. But everything is relative. Americans of 2020 may look back with envy on what from their vantage point appears to be our relatively unfettered way of life, much as some today look back with nostalgia on the Wild West.

Conservation of our water resources, preservation of wilderness areas, protection of animal life threatened by man, restrictions on pollutant emissions, and limitations on fertilizer and pesticide use all require public regulation. Rules must be set and enforced, complaints heard and adjudicated. True enough, the more we can find means of relying on the price system, the easier will be the bureaucratic task. But even if effluent charges and user fees became universal, they would have to be set administratively, emissions and use metered, and fees collected. It appears inevitable that a larger portion of our lives will be devoted to filling out forms, arguing with the computer or its representatives, appealing decisions, waiting for our case to be handled, finding ways to evade or move ahead in the queue. In many small ways, everyday life will become more contrived.

Many such changes will have to occur no matter which population projection occurs, merely to correct for the external costs of past growth. But the difference, of small degree at first, would grow with time until, by the year 2020, the two societies may appear qualitatively different.

A second social cost involved in continued population growth is the further postponement of solutions to social problems. While such growth continues, top priority must be given to finding the necessary resources, controlling pollutants, correcting the damages they have done, and building ever larger reservoirs, highways, mass transit systems. A large and perhaps growing fraction of our physical and intellectual capital is directly or indirectly devoted to these tasks, to finding ways to cope with the problems that continuing growth throws up. From past experience, we can predict with a fair degree of confidence that equally impressive efforts will not be devoted to resolving fundamental social problems.

For similar reasons, we are forced to introduce solutions to problems before their side effects are known. It might, for example, be far better environmentally to postpone the introduction of nuclear power plants until the inherently cleaner fusion reactors are developed. When one pesticide or food additive is found to be dangerous to man, it is replaced with another about which we know less. Programs involving the expenditure of billions on water treatment are set in motion without knowing whether the benefits outweigh the costs of other opportunities foregone. Once again, lower population growth will not automatically change this situation, but at least a bit of the urgency, the "crash program" character to much that we do would be eliminated.

Finally, continued population growth closes off options. In the case of the larger population, there is less land per person, less choice, less room for diversity, less room for error. Technology must advance; life styles must change. Many may like this emerging world; but for those who do not, there will be fewer alternatives.

To emphasize the point, it is tempting to exaggerate the importance of population as opposed to economic growth in causing these social costs, and to overemphasize the difference that a slowdown in population would make. But, in such an emphasis, perhaps we come closer to the heart of the problem of population growth in this country. For a rich, technologically sophisticated and flexible country like the United States, adequacy of resources and control of pollutants are not seriously in doubt during the next half century; we can conquer these problems if we wish. The real question is whether we will like the society that conquering these problems entails.

International Relations

For the poorer two-thirds of the world, at least, this formulation of the problem is the height of luxury. Not only are social options exceedingly narrow in contrast to those of the United States, but in many of these countries, even concerns about toxic pollutants must be given low priority compared to problems of food and resource adequacy. Short of dramatic technological breakthroughs, rapid declines in birthrates, or massive transfers of resources from richer countries, their relative position, if not their absolute position as well, is likely to deteriorate further during the next 30 to 50 years. The turmoil caused by this poverty and inequality in the distribution of the world's wealth can only grow worse with time. One can be sanguine about America's long-term future only by ignoring this problem.

A reduction in United States consumption of resources will not automatically help these countries. It will do so only if sale of these raw materials is not a particularly important fraction of their exports—but for many it is—and if some means can be found to transfer to them in usable form the resources we release by consuming less. Permitting these resources to remain idle does not help poorer countries.

Because of more rapid population and economic growth rates in the rest of the world, the United States share in world consumption of resources can be expected to fall in coming decades. At the same time, because of rapid increases in domestic consumption, United States dependence on the rest of the world will probably increase. While technological developments could alter this picture, these trends seem highly likely no matter which population and economic growth assumptions come to pass, within the range investigated. Sooner or later, we will also have to face the environmental problems generated by this growth on a worldwide scale.

Realignments of relative power positions and potentially grave issues of clashing national and regional interests will arise from these trends. As such worldwide problems become larger and increasingly interlocked, it becomes more and more an act of self interest and less one of altruism on our part to help in evolving a sensible international economic order capable of dealing with the joint problems of economic development, international trade, resources, and the environment.

Beyond 2020

The most significant aspect of what lies beyond 2020 is the continued divergence in the population projections for the United States. If the high growth rate continues, all the problems discussed above would magnify, increasingly taxing our ingenuity to solve them. Life will continue to become more regulated and contrived. If by 2030-2040 population growth ceased, at least some aspects of this progressive deterioration would all but end; and resources would be released to deal with the others.

Increasingly, therefore, the essential difference between the high and the low projections would become one between necessity and choice. In the first case, dramatic technological breakthroughs must be achieved; in the second, we could get along if they did not. In the first case, life styles must change; in the second, beyond a certain point they need not.

Apart from these few comments, however, we cannot usefully speculate further. Our methods of analysis and imagination are not up to it. It is of course possible to continue projections of demand farther and farther out until our conservative assumptions about technological progress are overwhelmed. But there is no justification for this. Why continue with an assumption that productivity is going to double every 25 to 50 years; why not a slowdown or a technological breakthrough such as fusion that could make a 500 to 1000 fold difference? And why assume that birthrates and demand will continue rising exponentially? Beyond a certain point, there is no basis whatsoever for making any assumptions. Indeed, the year 2020 is probably far beyond this point!

All we can say is that if population growth continues, the long-term future will be dominated by a race between growth in technological knowledge and growth in population. Unless the two rates are positively linked to each other we will always be better off with a smaller population growth rate. But we have no way to know which rate will win, or for how long.

REFERENCES

1. Of course, all studies of the future are conditional in this sense. But since there has been a tendency to impute absolute forecasting power to some recent long-term projection exercises, it cannot hurt to emphasize this point.

2. As explained in Chapter 2, an equivalent low-growth case could also be generated by assuming that growth in man-hour productivity slows down to 1.5 percent per year, the decline in work hours remaining the same, or by assuming some intermediate combinations which in fact may be more realistic.

3. For example, it is sometimes argued that innovation is more rapid with a higher rate of turnover of the labor force, that the need to care for and educate children induces parents to work harder and save more than they would with fewer children, and that it is easier to maintain full employment when aggregate demand is buoyed up by increases in population growth. But empirical evidence to support these arguments is weak; some counterarguments can be advanced; and in any case, it is difficult to believe that, within our time frame, whatever negative effects there might be could be so large that they could not easily be offset by appropriate government action. A number of such arguments and related empirical evidence are discussed elsewhere in research reports prepared for the Commission on Population Growth and the American Future. A summary and evaluation of these arguments is included in Ronald G. Ridker, "The American Economy During the Next Half Century" (paper presented to Annual Meeting of the American Association for the Advancement of Science, Symposium on Technology and Growth in a Resource-Limited World, December 1971).

4. They were obtained by applying emissions standards recommended by the Environmental Protection Agency for introduction in 1973 (for water) and 1975 (for air), after ascertaining that abatement strategies to meet these standards exist at least on a pilot, if not yet on a commercial, basis. In cases where a strategy is not yet in commercial use, cost estimates were taken from feasibility studies. A fuller discussion is included in Chapter 2. On the Rankine cycle engine, see R. U. Ayres and Richard V. McKenna, *Alternatives to the Internal Combustion Engine* (Baltimore: Johns Hopkins Press for Resources for the Future, 1972).

5. This is not to suggest that this arrangement is optimal in an economic sense. It still fails to appropriately "internalize" the externalities.

6. Sterling Brubaker, *To Live on Earth* (Baltimore: Johns Hopkins Press, 1972).

Chapter 2

The Economy, Resource Requirements, and Pollution Levels

by
Ronald G. Ridker
Resources for the Future, Inc.

COMMISSION ON POPULATION GROWTH AND
THE AMERICAN FUTURE, *RESEARCH
REPORTS, VOLUME III, POPULATION
RESOURCES AND THE ENVIRONMENT,*
EDITED BY RONALD G. RIDKER

CONTENTS

The Economy, Resource Requirments, and Pollution Levels

As indicated in Chapter 1, the impact of population on resources and the environment depends on a host of intervening variables, some of which may prove to be more important than population growth, and all of which could change considerably in the next 30 to 50 years. To answer the questions posed we must become very specific, quantitative, and empirical; there are too many trends operating in different directions to say much on a general level.

In this situation, aggregate analysis is of little help; indeed, it may give highly misleading results. Each sector of the economy has different resource requirements and emits different types and quantities of wastes. The effect of wastes on the environment depends on the form in which they are emitted. Moreover, the kinds of treatment possible, as well as their costs, vary between sectors and types of pollutants. Despite the fact that we are interested in an overall assessment, disaggregation is an absolute necessity.

On top of these complexities we must reckon with a vast number of interdependencies. All activities involve wastes. If these wastes are not emitted into the air, they will show up in liquid or solid forms. If restrictions are placed on the use of the automobile, some other form of transport with its own array of resource requirements and pollutants must be substituted. It is not enough, for example, to say that sulfur oxide emissions from railroads will fall over time due to electrification; we must also say something about the additional resources and pollutants arising from greater use of electricity in the transport sector. But these are examples of interdependencies in the small. Far more important for judging resource adequacy and pollution levels in the future will be changes in our ability to substitute one resource for another; changes in attitudes towards work, leisure, and migration; and a host of international contingencies, all of which have multiple effects. In truth, to say much about the impact of population growth, we really should write a history of the human race during the next quarter to half century.

We have attempted to cope with these difficulties in two ways: first, through the development and application of a mathematical-economic model of the American economy, its resource requirements and pollution loadings; and second, through a number of special studies of items not handled particularly well by the model. This chapter reports on the principal results of the modelling effort.

GENERAL PROCEDURE AND ASSUMPTIONS

As Figure 1 indicates, we begin with assumptions about population and overall levels of economic activity. These were used to develop estimates of required production levels by sector, and year by year into the future. From these levels, plus estimates on the extent of recycling and treatment of wastes that might occur in different years, pollution loads on the environment were estimated. At the same time, the model indicates resource requirements to meet these output levels. Once obtained, these were compared (outside the model) with resource availabilities in the United States and abroad to determine levels of imports and possible international problems.

The linkages between population and the model are three-fold. First, the age structure of the population, plus attitudes towards work, have a substantial bearing on assumptions about the labor force, hours of work per year, and (to a lesser extent) labor productivity, all of which enter the model through our specification of macroeconomic assumptions. Second, a number of demographic characteristics—principally, the number of family units, their size and age structure—along with economic assumptions about prices and the level and distribution of personal income, determine consumption levels and therefore what is required from the economy. These factors also influence many categories of government spending (for example, expenditures on school construction, roads and sewers) although not all (for example, military expenditures). And third, the actual use of these consumption goods—heating a home, driving a car, opening and discarding tin cans—sooner or later creates a waste load that must be absorbed by the environment or recycled back into the economy.

The central core of the model is a dynamic input-output model of some 185 economic sectors developed at the University of Maryland by Clopper

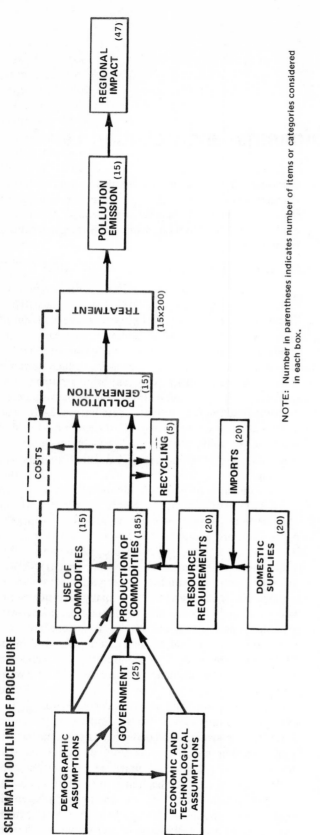

**FIGURE 2-1
SCHEMATIC OUTLINE OF PROCEDURE**

NOTE: Number in parentheses indicates number of items or categories considered in each box.

Almon and his associates.[1] To it we have added a new set of consumption functions which depend upon demographic as well as economic characteristics of spending units, government expenditure equations that are influenced by demographic characteristics as well as per capita income, a set of resource coefficients covering some 20 commodities, and sets of pollution, treatment, and treatment cost coefficients covering some 15 pollutants. In addition, the attempt has been made to allow for the possibilities of more recycling and substitutions of one resource for another over time. Chapters 11 and 12 provide more detailed descriptions of the model and data sources.

The model was run year by year into the future against sets of assumptions chosen in such a way as to highlight the effect of variables of principal interest. Common to all runs is a set of assumptions that can best be described as a picture of the future that is surprise free: no apocalypse, no messiahs, no dramatic changes in life style or international relations, just a modestly bumpy road towards a future that the more adventurous among us might characterize as hardly worth the journey. This, of course, is assumed as only a first step in the analysis, so that we can see whether such a path is feasible given mounting pressures on resources. In the end, we return to question such a picture of the future and ask what if anything must or can be substituted for it.

But as a starting point, such an assumption is very convenient. It provides us with a basis to compare the future with the present, something which is familiar and at least partially understandable. It focuses attention on what we believe to be the central issue, whether we can go on as we have or must make adaptations that in the aggregate add up to a significant change in our way of life. And finally, this approach obviates much (not all) of the necessity of entering fields as diverse as biology, astrophysics, social psychology and international relations to conjure up pictures of likely tomorrows.

This does not mean that we assume no changes in technological knowledge, or the composition of demand and output. To have done so would be very surprising indeed. The most surprise-free assumption we can make about such changes is that current trends continue. Thus, we assume that man-hour productivity for the whole economy continues to grow (we will be more specific about this in a moment), that many of the identifiable substitutions of one material for another— aluminum for steel, plastics for metals and paper, computers for semi-skilled manpower, electricity for human and other forms of energy, air transport for land and water transport, etc.—continue to work themselves out, that production processes used by newer plants spread throughout the economy, and that many of the trends on consumer spending habits continue for a reasonable period into the future.

So far as military expenditures are concerned, we assume that they will mark time for a while—the pull-out from Viet Nam being offset to a large extent by increased pay and expenditures on projects postponed by Viet Nam—and then begin rising again but at a much slower rate. This pattern, plus some changes in the composition of these expenditures, is in keeping with a relatively surprise-free future: In effect, we are assuming that remaining United States manpower will be pulled out of Viet Nam within the next year or so, that the United States will not commit troops to similar conflicts in the future, but that we will continue offering military assistance to others in such situations. Other elements of government spending are assumed to grow more or less as one would expect: Construction expenditures on such items as highways and education (the two biggest construction items) will grow less rapidly than in the past; public expenditures for safety, sanitation, health, residential housing, urban renewal, etc., will grow more rapidly; and all such rates will be influenced by the rates of growth in population, in per capita income, and in the need to maintain close to full employment.

All such assumptions are held constant for all runs of the model (at least for those reported on herein). This permits us to focus on the differential impact of a small set of variables of principal interest: population growth rates (and associated demographic variables such as age, labor force, and size of household), economic growth rates (insofar as they are independent of population growth rates), and a variety of policy changes with reference to conservation and environmental quality.

As indicated in Chapter 1, the alternative population assumptions center around Census Series B and E, the former involving an average of 3.1 and the latter 2.1 children per woman.[2] Both series assume that net immigration continues at 400,000 per year. Table 1 indicates the size of these two populations plus associated labor force estimates, at various points in time.

The alternative economic growth assumptions are entered into the model through changes in labor productivity, or output per worker. Since output per worker equals output per man-hour times the number of hours worked per man, we can specify a change in labor productivity by altering man-hour productivity or work hours. For convenience, we have assumed that total output per man-hour continues to grow at 2.5 percent per year and made two assumptions about changes in work hours: first, that work hours continue to decline as they have in the past, by about 0.25 percent per year;

and second, that this rate of decline increases to one percent per year. In the first case, this would mean a decline in the work week from approximately 40 hours to 37 hours by 2000; in the second case, the 2000 figure would fall to 29 hours per week. While this second case represents a very significant and perhaps unrealistically rapid increase in leisure time, it is still far from assuming an end to economic growth.

We could, however, just as well have held work hours constant and varied man-hour productivity. For present purposes, the difference between these two ways of generating a "high" and a "low" rate of economic growth is unimportant. Accordingly, we shall talk about our high and low assumptions in terms of labor productivity, or economic growth, rather than in terms of man-hour productivity or work hours. We do assume, however, that the rates of growth in labor productivity are unaffected by a change in population growth rates, at least within the range of rates considered in this study. Other more detailed assumptions and variations are discussed as the need arises.

These alternative population and economic growth assumptions lead to four basic scenarios: a high population and high economic growth case (labeled B-High, or simply B-H in most tables), a low population and economic growth case (E-Low or alternatively E-L), and the two intermediate cases (B-Low and E-High). We begin by discussing the characteristics of the four "economies" that these cases lead to and then move on to consider the resource requirements and pollution emissions likely to be associated with each.

In discussing the resource and pollution implications, two policy versions are considered. First, we assume that policy trends with respect to the environment continue as one would have expected as of 1967 (the base period for most of our data): no pressure to search for and introduce dramatically cleaner technologies, no increased pressures to recycle, no taxes on the consumption of commodities that are heavy users of common property resources, and so on. The acceptance of this scenario does not mean that resource needs and pollutant emissions per unit of output will not change over time, but merely that such changes will arise as a consequence of the businessman's general interest in substituting cheaper for more expensive resources and reducing overall resource requirements in order to minimize his costs. Second, this policy regime is changed, the model being asked to tell us what the implications of alternative rates of population and economic growth would be given more active policies aimed at inducing an improvement in environmental quality: more recycling, more process change to reduce pollution generated per unit of output, more treatment

Table 1.—Demographic and Economic Indicators for Scenario B-High with no Change in Policy

Indicator	Absolute figures					2000 compared to 1970		Percent of total				
	1967	1970	1980	2000	2020	Ratio	Annual growth rate	1967	1970	1980	2000	2020
Population (millions)	199	205	237	321	440	1.57	1.5	100.0	100.0	100.0	100.0	100.0
Labor force (millions)	81	85	101	136	186	1.60	1.6	40.7	41.5	42.6	42.4	42.3
Households (millions)	59	62	77	106	145	1.71	1.8	29.6	30.2	32.5	33.0	33.0
GNP per capita ('67$)	3809	3937	5198	8125	12661	2.06	2.4	n.a.	n.a.	n.a.	n.a.	n.a.
Disposable income per capita ('58$)	2398	2595	3461	5399	8650	2.08	2.5	n.a.	n.a.	n.a.	n.a.	n.a.
GNP (bil. '67$)	758	807	1232	2608	5571	3.23	4.0	100.0	100.0	100.0	100.0	100.0
Consumption (bil. '67$)	474	524	806	1704	3747	3.25	4.0	62.4	65.0	65.4	65.3	67.3
Investment (bil. '67$)	113	99	165	341	688	3.44	4.2	14.9	12.3	13.4	13.1	12.3
Government (bil. '67$)	174	186	268	579	1170	3.11	3.9	23.0	23.1	21.8	22.2	21.0
Defense (bil. '67$)	68	62	66	97	149	1.56	1.5	(9.0)	(7.7)	(5.4)	(3.7)	(2.7)
Non-defense (bil. '67$) . . .	106	124	202	482	1021	3.89	4.6	(14.0)	(15.4)	(16.4)	(18.5)	(18.3)
Net exports (bil. '67$)	−3	−3	−8	−17	−33	6.22	6.3	0.4	0.3	0.6	0.6	0.6
Total output (bil. '67$)	1239	1326	2021	4174	8900	3.15	3.9	100.0	100.0	100.0	100.0	100.0
Primary (bil. '67$)	75	84	116	207	406	2.46	3.1	6.1	6.3	5.7	5.0	4.6
Mining (bil. '67$)	21	22	32	59	119	2.68	3.4	1.7	1.6	1.6	1.4	1.3
Construction (bil. '67$) . . .	53	57	90	181	382	3.17	3.9	4.3	4.3	4.5	4.4	4.3
Manufacturing (bil. '67$) . .	567	585	880	1776	3689	3.04	3.8	45.8	44.1	43.5	42.6	41.4
Food (bil. '67$)	85	93	127	214	405	2.30	2.8	6.9	7.0	6.3	5.1	4.6
Paper (bil. '67$)	20	22	34	73	155	3.32	4.0	1.6	1.7	1.7	1.7	1.7
Petroleum (bil. '67$) . .	23	26	36	60	115	2.31	2.9	1.9	1.9	1.8	1.4	1.3
Chemicals (bil. '67$) . .	41	45	70	152	321	3.38	4.1	3.3	3.4	3.5	3.6	3.6
Primary metals (bil. '67$) .	48	44	66	122	251	2.77	3.5	3.9	3.3	3.2	2.9	2.8
Rubber and plastics (bil. '67$)	13	14	24	54	117	3.86	4.7	1.0	1.0	1.2	1.3	1.3
Stone and clay (bil. '67$)	14	14	22	48	101	3.43	4.2	1.1	1.1	1.1	1.2	1.1
Textiles (bil. '67$) . . .	21	24	37	69	140	2.88	3.5	1.7	1.8	1.8	1.6	1.6
Lumber and wood (bil. '67$)	12	12	20	43	92	3.58	4.3	1.0	1.0	1.0	1.0	1.0
Leather (bil. '67$) . . .	5	4	6	14	31	3.50	4.2	0.4	0.3	0.3	0.3	0.3
Services (bil. '67$)	544	600	935	2009	4424	3.35	4.1	43.9	45.2	46.3	48.1	49.7
Electricity (bil. '67$) . .	17	19	32	72	163	3.79	4.5	1.4	1.4	1.6	1.7	1.8
Consumption purchases (bil. '67$).	474	524	806	1704	3747	3.25	4.0	100.0	100.0	100.0	100.0	100.0
Durables (bil. '67$)	48	52	89	207	478	3.98	4.7	10.1	9.9	11.0	12.1	12.8
Nondurables (bil. '67$) . . .	118	128	181	333	667	2.60	3.2	24.9	24.4	22.5	19.6	17.8
Services (bil. '67$)	208	344	536	1164	2602	3.38	4.1	65.0	65.7	66.5	68.3	69.4

to reduce emissions per unit of pollution generated, changes in the composition of demand and output, and so on. Obviously, there are many such "active abatement policies" that would be interesting to consider. In this chapter, we present the results—sometimes rather tentative given the state of knowledge in this area—for only a few possibilities, but a sufficient number to permit a comparison of the differential impact that such policies would make compared to a slowdown in growth of population and the economy.

THE ECONOMY

Tables 1 and 2 portray the main economic implications of the four basic scenarios. Principal interest

Table 2.—Demographic and Economic Indicators for Alternative Population and Economic Assumptions, No Policy Change

Indicator	1970	Absolute figures 2000 B-H	E-H	B-L	E-L	Absolute figures 2020 B-H	E-H	B-L	E-L	% reduction from B-H in 2000 E-H	B-L	E-L	% reduction from B-H in 2020 E-H	B-L	E-L
Population (millions)	205	321	266	321	266	440	299	440	299	17.1	0	17.1	32.0	0	32.0
Labor force (millions)	85	136	127	136	127	186	146	186	146	6.6	0	6.6	21.5	0	21.5
Households (millions)	62	106	101	106	101	145	113	145	113	4.7	0	4.7	22.1	0	22.1
GNP per capita ('67$)	3937	8125	9098	6452	7218	12661	14625	8632	9946	(12.0)[a]	20.6	11.2	(15.5)[a]	31.8	21.4
Disposable income per capita ('58$)	2595	5399	6018	4241	4721	8650	9848	5804	6558	(11.5)[a]	21.4	12.6	(13.8)[a]	32.9	24.2
GNP (bil. '67$)	807	2608	2420	2071	1920	5571	4373	3798	2974	7.2	20.6	26.4	21.5	31.8	46.6
Consumption (bil. '67$)	524	1704	1577	1339	1237	3747	2899	2514	1930	7.5	21.4	27.4	22.6	32.9	48.5
Investment (bil. '67$)	99	341	309	278	252	688	551	492	400	9.4	18.5	26.1	19.9	28.5	41.9
Government (bil. '67$)	186	579	548	468	442	1170	948	813	659	5.4	19.2	23.7	19.0	30.5	43.7
Defense (bil. '67$)	62	97	102	88	92	149	158	128	133	(5.2)[a]	9.3	5.2	(6.0)[a]	14.1	10.7
Non-defense (bil. '67$) . .	124	482	446	380	350	1021	790	685	526	7.5	21.2	27.4	22.6	32.9	48.5
Net exports (bil. '67$)	−3	−17	−15	−13	−11	−33	−25	−22	−16	(11.8)[a]	(23.5)[a]	(35.3)[a]	(24.2)[a]	(33.3)[a]	(51.5)[a]
Total output (bil. '67$)	1326	4174	3843	3334	3064	8900	6933	6124	4747	7.9	20.1	26.6	22.1	31.2	46.7
Primary (bil. '67$)	84	207	192	174	161	406	318	297	231	7.2	15.9	22.2	21.7	26.8	43.1
Mining (bil. '67$)	22	59	57	49	47	119	100	87	72	3.4	16.9	20.3	16.0	26.9	39.5
Construction (bil. '67$) . .	57	181	164	148	133	382	296	274	209	9.4	18.2	26.5	22.5	28.3	45.3
Manufacturing (bil. '67$) . .	585	1776	1628	1437	1316	3689	2877	2587	2012	8.3	19.1	25.9	22.0	29.9	45.4
Food (bil. '67$)	93	214	198	184	170	405	312	306	234	7.5	14.0	20.6	23.0	24.4	42.2
Paper (bil. '67$)	22	73	66	58	53	155	119	107	82	9.6	20.5	27.4	23.2	31.0	47.1
Petroleum (bil. '67$) . .	26	60	62	51	52	115	105	87	76	(3.3)[a]	15.0	13.3	8.7	24.3	33.9
Chemicals (bil. '67$) . .	45	152	142	120	112	321	254	218	173	6.6	21.1	26.3	20.9	32.1	46.1
Primary metals (bil. '67$)	44	122	111	100	90	251	197	180	140	9.0	18.0	26.2	21.5	28.3	44.0
Rubber and plastics (bil. '67$)	14	54	48	43	38	117	88	80	60	11.1	20.4	29.6	24.8	31.6	48.7
Stone and clay (bil. '67$)	14	48	43	39	35	101	79	74	56	10.4	18.7	27.1	21.8	26.7	44.6
Textiles (bil. '67)	25	69	60	52	46	140	102	89	65	13.0	24.6	33.3	27.1	36.4	53.6
Lumber and wood (bil. '67$)	12	43	39	34	31	92	71	63	49	9.3	20.9	27.9	22.8	31.5	46.7
Leather (bil. '67$) . . .	4	14	10	11	7	31	20	20	12	28.6	21.4	50.0	35.5	35.5	61.3
Services (bil. '67$)	600	2009	1858	1575	1454	4424	3442	2966	2295	7.5	21.6	27.6	22.2	32.9	48.1
Electricity (bil. '67$) . .	19	72	66	58	53	163	127	114	88	8.3	19.4	26.4	22.1	30.1	46.0
Consumption purchases (bil. '67$)	524	1704	1577	1339	1237	3747	2899	2514	1930	7.5	21.4	27.4	22.6	32.9	48.5
Durables (bil. '67$)	52	207	188	159	144	478	362	314	236	9.2	23.2	30.4	24.3	34.3	50.6
Nondurables (bil. '67$) . .	128	333	313	278	261	667	525	482	377	6.0	16.5	21.6	21.3	27.7	43.5
Services (bil. '67$)	344	1164	1076	902	832	2602	2012	1718	1317	7.6	22.5	28.5	22.7	34.0	49.4

[a]% Increase from B-H.

should focus on changes in GNP and other aggregates over time and between runs at the same point in time, not their absolute values. This is because the definitions used in the model are somewhat different from those used in official United States national accounts. For example, exports and imports include only merchandise and margin items, and consumption excludes these import items plus a category called "services rendered without payment by financial intermediaries." As a consequence, GNP as determined by the model in 1967 and 1970 is respectively 4.6 percent and 4.7 percent less than officially defined GNP in those years. We have no

reason to believe that this relationship will change significantly in the future.

The dominant effect of shifting from a three- to a two-child population projection—from Series B to Series E—is an increase in the fraction of the population in the labor force. This increase occurs for two reasons: first, because the number of persons in the labor force ages increases as a fraction of the population—indeed, assuming no change in entrance or retirement age, this fraction remains higher under Series E all the way out to 2040: and second, because more women can be expected to enter the labor force when they have fewer children to take care of at home.[3] The principal consequence is a higher per capita GNP and, except for the first 10 to 15 years (when because of greater female participation the labor force might actually be larger), a lower GNP under the Series E than under the Series B projections.

Per capita GNP (more accurately, per capita disposable income) can be taken as a measure of material welfare, conventionally defined. Since resource use and pollution levels are associated more with total than with per capita output levels, total GNP might be taken as a crude indicator of environmental degradation. In these terms, it is best to have a high per capita GNP but a low total GNP. This is just what we find. Compare, for example, the B-High and the E-High scenarios for the year 2000 in Table 2. While population size under Series E is 17 percent lower than under Series B, the labor force is only 6.6 percent less. As a consequence, GNP is 7.2 percent less and per capita GNP is 12 percent more. This pattern continues at least until the year 2020, by which time the differences between these runs become much sharper than they are in 2000. Table 2 also indicates the difference arising from the change in assumptions about labor productivity (compare B-High with B-Low or E-High with E-Low).

In terms of its principal national accounting aggregates, the composition of GNP changes only marginally over time and between runs. The tables, however, provide a somewhat misleading picture of this situation in that they assume constant prices from 1967 on. If the same calculations had been undertaken in current dollars, we would probably observe that government spending becomes an increasing percentage of GNP, while consumption and investment as percents of GNP fall over time. This is because service and labor prices are likely to rise more rapidly than the average price level; indeed this may happen to a greater extent when we assume a slower growth rate in the labor force.

The composition of both output and consumption will shift somewhat in the direction of services and away from commodities. This trend is more marked under the high productivity assumption than under the low, and under the Series E than under the Series B population assumptions.

Future output estimates are more or less as expected except perhaps those for the electricity, which are below recently past trends and Federal Power Commission (FPC) projections. While the model's projections may be a bit on the low side for this sector, other evidence suggests that past trends and FPC projections could be far too high;[4] in any event, since the model assumes a slower shift towards nuclear production than is likely to occur, its projections of conventional fuels and residuals per unit of electricity generated are probably on the high side.

RESOURCE REQUIREMENTS

Estimates on resource requirements for these four basic economic scenarios are presented in the relevant chapters as needed for comparison with estimates for available supplies. Here, we present statistics derived from these materials for a selected group of minerals and fuels in order to characterize the role played by population and economic growth during the next half century. Table 3 presents these materials for primary mineral requirements, that is, total requirements less the amount met by scrap or recycled materials. Here, the assumption is made that the rate of use of these secondary materials is no greater than it was in the base period.

From this table, one can see that resource requirements generally grow at rates more closely associated with the rate of growth of GNP than with that of its components, population or per capita GNP. With the exception of energy, the growth rates implied by these data were derived from the model, differences between them for a given scenario being explained by changes in the composition of output and technical change. For reasons explained in Chapter 5, the growth rate of total energy requirements, although not its components, was assumed to be equal to that of GNP, as it has been over long periods in the past.

To assess resource adequacy, we must compare requirements not only with the amount of a mineral that can be mined in a given year but also with the stock of a mineral remaining to be mined, assuming some estimate of this stock can be made. For this purpose, we need an indication of cumulative as well as annual requirements. These were obtained by aggregating annual requirement figures (actually, to shorten the process, by assuming constant growth rates between checkpoint years).

While annual requirements grow at rates not too different from those of GNP, it is interesting to note that cumulative requirements rise much less rapidly. The consequence is that the percent savings in cumulative requirements between now and the year 2000—or even 2020—due to a slower population growth rate, a slower economic growth rate, and both combined, appears to be relatively small. This results from the fact that the differences in resource requirements are small in early years and only begin to mount after some time passes. The farther out in time such projections are made the more impressive are the savings.

Table 3 also suggests that greater savings in resources can be obtained from a slowdown in economic

Table 3.—Comparison of Resource Requirements for Alternative Population and Economic Assumptions

A. Ratios

Item	1970	Annual requirements							
		2000/1970				2020/1970			
		B-H	E-H	B-L	E-L	B-H	E-H	B-L	E-L
Population (mil.)	205	1.6	1.3	1.6	1.3	2.1	1.4	2.1	1.4
GNP (bil. '67$)	807	3.2	3.0	2.6	2.4	6.9	5.4	4.7	3.7
GNP per capita ('67$)	3937	2.1	2.3	1.6	1.8	3.2	3.7	2.2	2.5
Primary minerals (tons)									
Iron (mil.)	95.0	2.3	2.1	1.9	1.7	4.6	3.6	3.3	2.6
Aluminum (mil.)	3.7	4.7	4.3	3.9	3.5	10.4	8.2	7.5	5.9
Copper (mil.)	1.6	2.5	2.2	2.0	1.8	5.1	3.9	3.6	2.8
Lead (mil.)	0.8	3.0	2.8	2.5	2.1	6.0	4.8	4.2	3.4
Zinc (mil.)	1.3	3.4	3.0	2.7	2.4	7.2	5.5	4.9	3.8
Manganese (mil.)	1.6	1.8	1.6	1.5	1.3	2.8	2.2	1.9	1.7
Chromium (mil.)	0.5	2.2	2.0	1.8	1.6	4.0	3.4	2.8	2.4
Nickel (mil.)	0.15	3.4	2.7	2.4	2.1	5.9	5.0	4.3	3.5
Tungsten (thous.)	7.5	5.5	4.9	4.5	4.0	16.7	14.4	12.5	10.1
Molybdenum (thous.)	22.0	5.4	4.9	4.4	3.9	16.4	13.6	11.8	9.7
Vanadium (thous.)	10.0	4.6	4.1	3.8	3.4	12.6	10.4	9.3	7.8
Cobalt (thous.)	6.6	2.7	2.4	1.6	1.5	5.3	4.4	2.3	2.0
Tin (thous.)	60.0	1.6	1.6	1.4	1.3	2.2	2.1	1.7	1.6
Magnesium (mil.)	1.2a	2.5	2.2	1.2	1.1	4.4	3.8	1.4	1.2
Titanium (mil.)	0.5a	4.8	4.4	2.0	1.8	12.8	11.0	3.0	2.6
Sulfur (mil.)	10.2a	4.1	3.7	2.5	2.3	9.8	8.2	4.5	3.8
Phosphorus (mil.)	3.6	3.9	3.6	3.2	2.9	9.9	8.6	6.9	5.9
Potassium (mil.)	3.9	4.7	4.3	3.8	3.4	12.9	11.2	9.1	7.9
Nitrogen (mil.)	10.3	5.6	5.1	4.5	4.1	17.6	15.2	12.3	10.6
Energy (trillion Btu)	68810	3.2	3.0	2.6	2.4	6.9	5.4	4.7	3.7
Coal	13792	2.2	2.0	1.8	1.6	n.a.	n.a.	n.a.	n.a.
Natural gas	22546	2.5	2.3	2.0	1.8	n.a.	n.a.	n.a.	n.a.
Petroleum	29617	2.4	2.2	1.9	1.7	n.a.	n.a.	n.a.	n.a.
Hydro	2647	2.5	2.3	2.0	1.8	n.a.	n.a.	n.a.	n.a.
Nuclear	208	302.5	277.0	240.0	220.0	n.a.	n.a.	n.a.	n.a.

B. Percent Savings Over B-H

Item	Annual						Cumulative (1968-)					
	2000			2020			2000			2020		
	E-H	B-L	E-L	E-H	B-L	E-L	E-H	B-L	E-L	E-H	B-L	E-L
Primary metals:												
Iron	10.0	17.8	26.5	22.0	27.3	43.7	4.1	10.0	14.1	11.8	17.4	27.2
Aluminum	8.6	18.3	25.1	21.4	28.7	43.9	3.3	11.3	14.2	12.0	19.7	28.8
Copper	10.0	20.0	27.5	22.2	28.4	44.4	3.4	12.6	13.8	11.7	19.4	28.2
Lead	8.3	16.7	19.2	20.8	29.2	43.5	2.1	10.6	14.8	10.2	18.8	27.4
Zinc	11.4	20.5	29.5	23.7	31.2	47.3	5.9	11.8	17.6	14.1	20.9	32.3
Manganese	10.3	17.2	27.6	18.1	29.5	38.6	6.0	10.1	14.7	10.6	17.6	24.5

The Economy, Resource Requirements, and Pollution Levels

Table 3.—Continued

B. Percent Savings Over B-H

Item	Annual						Cumulative (1968-)					
	2000			2020			2000			2020		
	E-H	B-L	E-L	E-H	B-L	E-L	E-H	B-L	E-L	E-H	B-L	E-L
Chromium	9.1	18.2	27.3	15.0	30.0	40.0	5.5	9.7	14.8	9.9	17.8	26.
Nickel	9.1	18.2	27.3	15.8	27.0	40.4	5.7	10.2	15.9	10.6	17.9	27.
Tungsten	9.8	17.1	26.8	13.6	24.8	39.2	6.5	11.3	17.7	10.2	19.0	29.
Molybdenum	10.8	18.3	27.5	17.2	28.3	41.0	7.0	12.3	18.2	12.3	20.8	30.
Vanadium	10.9	17.4	10.9	17.3	26.2	38.1	7.9	11.8	18.4	12.6	19.3	28.
Cobalt	11.2	38.8	44.4	17.3	57.1	62.8	5.6	22.2	25.0	11.4	38.6	43.
Tin	4.1	14.4	18.6	6.7	23.7	29.6	2.4	7.9	9.9	3.9	13.4	16.
Magnesium	10.0	50.0	56.7	15.1	67.9	73.6	4.6	32.3	36.7	8.8	48.3	53.
Titanium	8.3	58.3	62.5	14.1	76.6	79.7	5.0	40.0	42.5	8.9	60.2	63.
Sulfur	9.9	37.7	44.0	16.5	25.6	61.1	7.3	26.5	29.5	11.6	40.1	45.
Phosphorus	8.5	19.0	26.1	13.4	30.8	40.1	5.6	14.1	18.7	11.4	26.3	34.
Potassium	8.4	19.2	26.4	13.1	29.8	39.1	5.6	14.3	19.0	11.3	26.4	34.
Nitrogen	8.3	19.3	26.1	13.3	30.0	39.5	6.8	12.8	18.8	11.4	25.5	34.
Energy:[b]	8.3	20.7	27.3	22.1	31.9	47.1	6.4	15.8	20.9	13.3	23.5	33.
Coal	8.4	20.8	27.4	n.a.	n.a.	n.a.	5.8	14.3	18.8	n.a.	n.a.	n.a
Natural gas	8.5	20.8	27.4	n.a.	n.a.	n.a.	6.0	14.8	19.5	n.a.	n.a.	n.a
Petroleum	8.4	20.7	27.4	n.a.	n.a.	n.a.	5.9	14.5	19.2	n.a.	n.a.	n.a
Hydro	9.2	21.5	27.7	n.a.	n.a.	n.a.	6.6	15.4	19.8	n.a.	n.a.	n.a
Nuclear	8.4	20.7	27.3	n.a.	n.a.	n.a.	8.4	20.6	27.2	n.a.	n.a.	n.a

[a] Base year is 1968, not 1970.
[b] The cumulative totals for energy begin in 1970.

n.a. = Not available.

Source: Table 1, Chapter 4 and relevant tables in Chapter 5.

growth than from a slowdown in population. Now, this finding could result from the particular choice of assumptions about population and economic growth that were made: Perhaps the difference between the high and the low population assumptions is smaller in some sense than is the difference between the high and low economic assumptions. To investigate this possibility, we compared the effect on resource requirements of a one-percentage point reduction in population with that of a one-percentage point reduction in per capita GNP, all changes assumed to occur in the year 2000.[5] The results, presented in Table 4, confirm the impression derived from Table 3: The elasticities for population are about two-thirds those for per capita GNP.

Among the factors that explain this result, the most important derives from the fact that we have permitted the change in GNP per capita that occurs because of the change in population to influence the elasticity calculation. A decline in GNP per capita can occur independently of a change in population size, but it is difficult to imagine a change in population size that would not be accompanied by some change in per capita GNP, so long as we assume no change in the rate of employment and

the level of labor productivity. Since a fall in population size is associated with an increase in GNP per capita, the effect of the decreased numbers is partially offset by the greater income. As an experiment, we tried a special run of the model which factored out the population-induced change in GNP per capita, and found that the elasticities for population in this special case are about the same as those for GNP per capita.

The resource requirement estimates provided in Table 3 assume no change from the base period in waste material recovery and reuse practices, what we shall loosely call recycling practices for the purposes of this chapter. What would be the impact on resource requirements if an active recycling policy were introduced? Recycling practices and policies are discussed in detail in Chapter 3; here we are concerned only with a rough quantitative estimate of the impact that such policies might have.

Of course, depending on how much we are willing to spend, we could have practically any level of recycling we wanted; but after a point, costs rise very steeply. Moreover, these costs will be much greater if we insist on the implementation of an active recycling policy in the

Table 4.—Resource Elasticities with Respect to Population and GNP per Capita in 2000[a]

Resources	Elasticities	
	Population	GNP per capita
Iron	0.56%	0.85%
Aluminum	0.48	0.88
Copper	0.56	0.97
Lead	0.46	0.79
Zinc	0.64	0.99
Manganese	0.58	0.82
Chromium	0.51	0.87
Nickel	0.51	0.87
Tungsten	0.55	0.81
Molybdenum	0.61	0.88
Vanadium	0.61	0.83
Cobalt	0.64	1.40
Tin	0.22	0.68
Magnesium	0.56	2.90
Titanium	0.46	3.59
Sulfur	0.56	1.76
Phosphorus	0.74	0.92
Potassium	0.46	0.92
Nitrogen	0.46	0.93

[a]Percent change in resource requirements associated with a one percent change in population (comparing B-High with E-High) or a one percent change in GNP per capita (comparing B-High with B-Low). Results comparing B-Low with E-Low and E-High with E-Low are similar.

immediate future rather than permitting the development of new institutions and technologies to accommodate such a policy over, say, a 10-year period. The question we would like to answer, therefore, is something like the following: Given sufficient time for adjustments and without very exorbitant increases in costs—say, no more than 10 to 15 percent—how much recycling might occur and what difference in the demand for the primary product might it make?

It has proved to be very difficult to satisfactorily answer this question. Too little is known about current practices, let alone costs and the kinds of technologies and institutions that might come into being in the future. Table 5 provides rough estimates for five minerals based on the judgmental methods described in Chapter 4. From it one can conclude that at least for some minerals the savings are greater than those for the reduction in the population growth rate being considered. But as the more detailed discussion of Chapter 3 makes clear, recycling industries often use great quantities of energy, generate their own pollutants and may not be economical without the introduction of certain institutional and economic changes. While far more

research needs to be undertaken before we can know for sure, it is likely that an active recycling policy will prove on net to be beneficial for some but certainly not for all important resources.

POLLUTION LEVELS

Some additional explanation of the procedure utilized to estimate pollution levels is useful at this stage before presenting results. First, an estimate was made of the amount of individual pollutants generated by different production and consumption activities by 10-year intervals out to the year 2000. (Because the basis upon which to project generation and emission coefficients is so flimsy, no attempt was made to go beyond 2000.) Even when we assume no change in environmental policy (from the 1967-70 base period), the coefficients utilized to estimate these levels still change over time. This is because of changes in production processes, end-product specifications, and input mixes that would be coming along anyway. A few examples will help explain this point as well as illustrate the type of judgments that had to be made to determine the likely time path of these coefficients.

In the pulp and paper industry, there has been a gradual changeover from the sulfite to the sulfate (kraft) production process. This has resulted in a reduction of waste generation coefficients for suspended solids, dissolved solids, and biochemical oxygen demand in waste water by some 30 percent per unit of economic activity (although other problems such as odors are increased). It is reasonable to assume that this trend will continue in the future because the kraft process results in reduced production costs (as well as because of pressures for cleaner water). At the same time, however, trends in end-product specifications are operating in the opposite direction. The principal development is the production of brighter paper products which require additional bleaching of the pulp and result in sizeable increases in waste generation. For example, using the kraft process, dissolved inorganic solids and dissolved organic solids from the production of household tissue would be, respectively, about 90 percent and 85 percent less if no bleaching were required.[6]

Similarly, while the most advanced technology employed in the production of primary ferrous metals generate a minimum of 30 percent less wastes than does the prevailing technology, the increasing variety of end-products, which require additional finishing operations, will result in increased waste generation. In addition, the need to utilize marginal ores as better quality deposits become exhausted also increases waste generation in the production of primary ferrous metals. On the other hand, the conversion of space heating

Table 5.—Cumulative Requirements for Selected Minerals, 1968-2020

Alternative Assumptions About Recycling (million tons)

Mineral	B-High			E-High		
	Constant recycling	Active recycling	% Savings	Constant recycling	Active recycling	% Savings
Iron	11293	10931	3.2	9956	9669	2.9
Aluminum	853	576	32.5	751	513	31.7
Copper	206	166	19.4	182	148	18.7
Lead	117	111	5.1	105	98	6.7
Zinc	220	171	22.3	189	147	22.2

Source: Tables 1 and 3 in Chapter 4.

Table 6.—Pollution Emissions Under Various Scenarios, No Change in Policy

	1970	Amount (billion pounds) 2000				Ratio 2000/1970				Percent reduction from B-H in 2000		
		B-H	E-H	B-L	E-L	B-H	E-H	B-L	E-L	E-H	B-L	E-L
Air												
Particulates	41	49	45	41	38	1.20	1.10	1.00	.93	8.2	16.3	22.4
Hydrocarbons	89	207	196	181	171	2.33	2.20	2.03	1.92	5.3	12.6	17.4
Oxides of sulfur	85	132	122	108	100	1.55	1.44	1.27	1.18	7.6	18.2	24.2
Carbon monoxide	231	493	470	489	466	2.13	2.03	2.12	2.02	4.7	0.8	5.5
Oxides of nitrogen	30	58	55	54	51	1.93	1.83	1.80	1.70	5.2	6.9	12.1
Water												
Waste water[a]	188	323	307	296	283	1.72	1.63	1.57	1.51	4.9	8.4	12.4
COD[b]	202	462	416	398	359	2.29	2.06	1.97	1.78	10.0	13.8	22.3
BOD[c]	68	134	121	115	103	1.97	1.78	1.69	1.51	9.7	14.2	23.1
Refractory organics[d]	6	10	8	10	8	1.67	1.33	1.67	1.33	20.0	0.0	20.0
Suspended solids	804	1,591	1,441	1,352	1,229	1.98	1.79	1.68	1.53	9.4	15.0	22.8
Dissolved solids	137	294	265	251	225	2.15	1.93	1.83	1.64	9.9	14.6	23.5
Nitrogen	23	43	38	37	33	1.87	1.65	1.61	1.43	11.6	13.9	23.3
Phosphorus	8	16	15	14	12	2.00	1.88	1.75	1.50	6.2	12.5	25.0
Solid												
Solid waste[e]	321	863	718	860	715	2.69	2.24	2.68	2.23	16.8	3.5	17.1

[a]Trillion gallons.
[b]COD = Chemical Oxygen Demand.
[c]BOD = Biochemical Oxygen Demand (5 day).
[d]The results for refractory organics are an artifact of the method of calculation: There are no data on this pollutant except for the household sector.
[e]Trillion pounds.

The Economy, Resource Requirements, and Pollution Levels

cilities from coal to oil and gas, from oil to gas, and
om all three to electricity, will substantially reduce
llutants from this source.[7]

For other sectors, where there was found to be a
ajor discrepancy between generation coefficients for
e most efficient plants and for the average of the
dustry, it was assumed that today's most efficient
ant would become the norm by the year 2000. But
anges in technology beyond today's "best practice"
re not introduced.

Second, these gross emission levels were reduced by
rtain percentages to reflect improvements in treatment
ficiency (again generally assuming today's best practice
comes the norm) which are expected to come along
dependently of policy changes. The pollution levels
ported in Table 6 are, then, net of treatment, that is,
at is actually emitted into the environment. The
ocedure followed to obtain emissions under an active
atement policy is presented in the relevant sections
low.[8]

There is, of course, a difference between pollution
ission levels and pollution concentration levels, the
fference depending on the speed with which the
vironment cleanses itself. However, all the pollutants
ted in Table 6 have "half-lives" of less than six
onths, so that we can assume that their concentration
vels in a particular year are proportional to their
ission levels: If the emission of sulfur oxides doubles
tween 1970 and 2000, we can assume that its
ncentration level also doubles. Such an assumption is
t valid for long-lasting pollutants such as pesticides
d radiation, treated in other chapters of this study.

ational Emissions

o Change in Policy

Table 6 presents pollution emissions for the nation
a whole for 1970 and projections for 2000, assuming
change in abatement policy. Table 7 presents
llutant elasticities comparable to those for resources
esented in Table 4. Three principal conclusions
erge. First, if the intensity of treatment is not stepped
, even a substantial slowdown in the growth rates of
th population and economic activities from the rates
evailing in recent years will not be enough to keep the
vels of pollution in the year 2000 below current levels.

But second, future rates of growth in these pollu-
nts will be lower than they appear to have been in
cent years.[9] They are lower than assumed rates of
owth in GNP; and for some pollutants, they are even
wer than growth rates for GNP per capita and for
pulation. These results arise principally from two
ctors. First, the year 2000 composition of output
ppens to be slightly less polluting than the 1970

Table 7.—Pollution Elasticities with Respect to Population and GNP per Capita in 2000[a]

Pollutant	Elasticity	
	Population	GNP per capita
Particulates	0.46%	0.78%
Hydrocarbons	0.29	0.59
Sulfur oxides	0.42	0.87
Carbon monoxide	0.26	0.04
Nitrogen oxides	0.29	0.31
Biological oxygen demand . .	0.55	0.67
Suspended solids	0.53	0.71
Dissolved solids	0.56	0.69

[a]Percentage change in a particular item associated with a one
percent change in the column heading, as in Table 4.

composition, mainly (but not entirely) because of the
small but definite shift away from goods towards
services, noted earlier. Second, while a few individual
waste generation and emission coefficients are expected
to increase over time (for the kinds of reasons noted in
the above illustrations) more are expected to decrease as
best practice replaces inefficient plants.

While we feel fairly confident about these results for
the pollutants listed in Table 6, a potentially important
qualification must be entered for pollutants not listed in
this table. It may be that more advanced industries will
generate new kinds of pollutants in the future at a rate
that invalidates these results. Unfortunately, from our
analysis we have no way of knowing.

Third, as in the case of the resource commodities
discussed above, pollution emissions seem to be related
somewhat more to growth in the economy than to
growth in the population, although there are marked
differences amongst pollutants. Solid wastes and carbon
monoxide, for example, appear more related to population, whereas sulfur oxides, suspended solids and
phosphorus are more closely associated with the level of
economic activity. The principal explanation is the
same: namely, that a slowdown in population growth
induces some offsetting increase in economic growth
whereas an independent slowdown in economic growth
involves no comparable offset.

Active Abatement Policy

By an active abatement policy we mean a policy
that induces reductions in pollution generation or
emission coefficients. This can be done in a number of
ways, the most commonly discussed being the use of
effluent charges and the imposition of emission

standards. While effluent charges are preferable on economic efficiency grounds, the use of standards is more common and, for the purposes of this demonstration, easier to work with. Accordingly, in this section, we shall imagine that emissions are limited to certain specified levels and observe the effect that this has on aggregate pollution levels and costs of production.

The standards used for this demonstration are the 1973 water and the 1975 air emission standards recommended by the Environmental Protection Agency (EPA).[10] These standards were accepted for this exercise only after it was ascertained that it is technologi-cally feasible to meet them without assuming an dramatic technical breakthroughs. For a number c sectors and pollutants, methods of reducing generatio and emission coefficients to meet the standards are already used on a sufficiently large scale that we ca have confidence in our cost estimates. An important cas in point is waste water treatment where the EPA standards call for "secondary treatment," well-established procedure (at least for municipal trea ment plants) that removes 90 to 95 percent of th biological oxygen demand (BOD) from waste water. I other cases—for example, nitrogen oxide abatement an

Table 8.—Pollution Generated and Emitted under Alternative Assumptions, A (Generated under 197 Technology), B (Emitted, 2000 Technology, Passive Abatement Policy), C (Emitted, 2000 Technology Active Abatement Policy), (billions of lbs.)[a]

	1970	2000			
		B-H	E-H	B-L	E-L
Particulates					
A	54.2	175.2	160.0	153.8	133.7
B	41.4	49.0	45.3	41.4	38.3
C		5.6	5.2	4.7	4.4
Hydrocarbons					
A	96.5	270.1	254.0	233.2	218.8
B	89.4	207.4	196.2	180.9	170.9
C		31.4	29.4	27.4	25.6
Oxides of nitrogen					
A	29.9	80.5	76.0	72.7	68.5
B	29.9	57.6	55.0	54.0	51.3
C		17.8	16.6	16.7	15.8
Biological oxygen demand					
A	71.9	186.3	167.2	160.3	143.8
B	67.6	134.4	120.8	114.8	103.1
C		16.9	15.2	14.4	12.6
Suspended solids					
A	846.3	1998.4	1808.5	1698.2	1534.8
B	804.0	1591.2	1440.6	1352.3	1229.2
C		98.9	89.5	84.0	76.4
Dissolved solids					
A	137.2	363.1	328.9	305.2	275.6
B	137.2	294.5	264.8	250.9	224.7
C		284.7	256.1	242.5	217.3

[a]A = Pollution generated assuming 1970 technology associ-ated with pollution, that is, no changes in pollution generation coefficients (technological changes resulting in substitutions amongst inputs—e.g., plastics for metals—are included, however). B = Pollution emitted in 1970 and in 2000 assuming changes in pollution generation coefficients and efficiency of treatment likely to come along even without an active abatement policy. C = Emissions in 2000 assuming use of production and treatment processes induced by an active abatement policy. Figures for B-L and E-L in row C are approximations, interpolated from the B-H and E-H estimates calculated in detail.

Population, Resources, and the Environment

Table 9.—Annualized Cost of An Active Pollution Abatement Policy under Two Population Assumptions

Pollutant medium	Expenditures (billions of 1967 $)					2000 compared to 1970				Percent savings from B-H
	1970[a]	1980		2000		Ratio		Annual growth rates		
		B-H	E-H	B-H	E-H	B-H	E-H	B-H	E-H	
Air	0.45	11.68	11.67	14.87	14.05	32.00	31.20	12.3	12.1	5.52
Water	2.82	8.11	8.04	13.82	12.67	4.90	4.49	5.4	5.1	8.32
Solid	5.18	10.61	10.50	18.77	16.85	3.62	3.25	4.4	4.0	10.23
Total	8.45	30.40	30.21	47.46	33.57	5.62	5.16	5.9	5.6	8.20
Percent of GNP	1.05	2.47	2.41	1.82	1.80					

[a]U.S. Council on Environmental Quality, *Environmental Quality—The Second Annual Report of the Council on Environ-mental Quality,* August 1971, Table 2, p. 111. Deflated to 1967 dollars.

sulfur removed from fuel—where abatement strategies that would meet the standards are not used commercially at the present time, we made sure that at least one strategy was available, accepted the most feasible one, and developed cost estimates accordingly.[11]

These standards are being recommended for introduction by 1975; we are applying them to the year 2000. By that time, it is likely that additional, more efficient methods of production and treatment will be available that will reduce costs. For example, by 2000 it is possible that a competitive external combustion engine, with much lower generation coefficients than are possible with the internal combustion engine, will be in commercial use. Similarly, energy production from use of fuel cells would reduce sulfur and other emissions, and the use of matted plastics for paper would reduce residuals from pulp production. But we have assumed no such technical breakthroughs in making our estimates.

Table 8 presents the results of this exercise for a representative set of pollutants. The rows labeled A, provided for background, are the levels of pollution that would be generated using 1970 technology so far as waste generation coefficients are concerned. The rows labeled B indicate actual emissions for 1970, and expected emissions for the year 2000, assuming no change in abatement policy from the base period. A comparison of rows A and B indicate the extent to which changes in generation and emission coefficients that are likely to come along anyway will improve the situation. For a sample of pollutants, rows C indicate the level of emissions likely in 2000, assuming the active abatement policy outlined above. It can be seen that such a policy would bring all pollution levels down significantly below current levels (except for dissolved

solids where standards are not very stringent, partly because available treatment technologies are very expensive).[12]

Table 9 indicates the annualized costs of such an active abatement policy. While it does not include a number of cost items that a broad clean environment policy might entail—for example, additional water storage facilities, separation of storm and sanitary sewers in those cities where this might prove necessary, and correction of damages caused by strip mining—it does contain those items conventionally included in official cost estimates. In 1970, such costs amounted to $8.45 billion (1967 dollars): By 2000, these figures could mount to more than $47 billion, growing at a faster rate than GNP.

The most rapid period of rise would be the next decade. Thereafter, because we would have caught up with past neglect and because sufficient time would have elapsed to find cheaper ways to reduce emissions—substitutes for heavily polluting materials and processes—the increase in costs would be much less rapid. The same need to catch up in order to achieve the assumed standards suggests that in 1980 the savings involved if the lower rather than the higher population projections were to occur would be negligible. By the year 2000, however, these savings would amount to over eight percent.

Despite these very large figures, the growth of GNP during this time period would keep the burden of meeting them within quite modest dimensions. In 1970, these costs accounted for one percent of GNP; by 1980, they would be close to 2.5 percent; but, by 2000, they would be no more than two percent of that year's GNP. In terms of growth, these figures signify that we would have to give up less than one-tenth of one percentage point in annual growth of GNP to purchase this active abatement policy.

Quite clearly, then, a direct attack on pollution dominates over a reduction in population or a reduction in economic growth as a strategy for obtaining a clean environment, at least insofar as the particular set of pollutants we have looked at are concerned. In retrospect, since we have done so little about pollution in the past, this should not be considered a very surprising result. But it should also be made clear—although this is the wrong place to go into detail—that such a policy will not be easy to implement and enforce. Table 8 also makes clear that if such a policy were not implemented we could be faced with considerably higher levels of pollution than we have today.

Other Pollution Control Strategies

Reductions in population growth, reductions in economic growth, and direct abatement policies are certainly not the only ways to deal with pollution problems. Taxes can be used to change the composition of consumption and production in order to reduce the use and production of commodities that are directly or indirectly heavy users of the environment. Zoning regulations can be applied to separate polluting activities and those who may be inadvertently hurt by the resulting pollutants. The emission of pollutants can be regulated through time so that maximum use is made of the absorptive capacities of the environment. Recycling can be used to reduce the emissions of some pollutants. While we cannot discuss their relative importance in detailed quantitative terms, a few examples related to the first two of these additional methods are useful to indicate that they can be very effective.

Reductions in population and economic growth are very general in their impact on pollution levels (and on resource requirements). What would be the impact of a more selective approach, perhaps using a tax on certain commodities the production or consumption and use of which involved heavy use of the environment? Two illustrations are sufficient to indicate that it is likely to be considerable. In 1970, our data indicate that one single item of consumption was responsible for 12 percent of hydrocarbon emissions, 60 percent of carbon monoxide emissions, and 25 percent of nitrogen oxide emissions from all man-made sources, stationary as well as mobile. This item, of course, is the private passenger car. Since most of these emissions are concentrated in time and space (commuting hours in urbanized areas) a reduction in commuter passenger car miles would reduce concentration levels in these areas by considerably more

than these figures suggest. Of course, mass transit produces its own effluents, but these are generally much less than for passenger cars. Hydrocarbon emissions per passenger mile from a diesel bus average 1/20 that of a car; the comparable figures for carbon monoxide, oxides of nitrogen, and oxides of sulfur are 1/218, 1/3 and 5/6, respectively.[13]

Another illustration can be provided by imagining that a reduction is imposed on the output of those production sectors that directly or indirectly contribute the most to emissions of a given pollutant, say sulfur oxides. Table 7 indicates that a one-percentage-point reduction in GNP per capita would reduce emissions of this pollutant by 0.87 percent. If the output of the five sectors with the highest emission coefficients were reduced by 2.5 percent, that same 0.87 percent reduction could be achieved with about one-third of a percentage point reduction in GNP per capita.[14]

A final example involves the use of another technique, zoning. For many sources of pollution—those associated with consumption and use of commodities—separation of people and sources of pollution emissions cannot be accomplished easily. But many production activities involving pollution can be separated from residences to a greater extent than is currently the case. In one application of the regional model discussed in the next section, we investigated the effect that a shift in the location of economic activities might have on pollution concentration levels, assuming the relocation in nonurban areas of activities that would otherwise have added 10 percent to the value added in urbanized areas in 2000. Such a change would reduce the number of urbanized areas not meeting sulfate standards (out of the 47 areas studied) from two to one and the number not meeting particulate standards from 27 to 17, with those not meeting nitrate standards remaining the same.

Such a move would involve increased emissions from the greater number of commuter miles that would have to be traveled. But the diluting power of the greater volume of air that the dispersed pattern makes possible more than compensates for the greater emissions so that overall concentration levels would go down.[15]

Some of these strategies may prove too costly on economic grounds. For example, moving a significant amount of economic activity out of urbanized areas may be more expensive than mass transit and restrictions on the use of the private passenger car from some cities. But they deserve a thorough investigation before being rejected in favor of more general approaches. They do provide additional illustrations of the central point, that there are important alternatives to reduction in population and economic growth to be considered.

Regional Impact of Air Pollution

So far we have been talking about the total tons of various pollutants emitted in the United States. If we stop at this point, inferences about environmental quality must be based on the assumption that the geographic distribution of emissions does not change during the next 30 years or that the relationship between emissions and ambient concentration levels is the same for all places. Neither assumption, of course, is true. If the density of population and economic activities decreases—for example, because of continued migration to the suburbs or from more to less densely populated metropolitan areas in general—air quality could improve despite increased emissions. On the other hand, if net migration of population or economic activities is towards regions where meteorological conditions are less favorable for breaking up and dissipating pollutants, air quality could worsen even with no increase in emissions. Similar statements could be made about the impact of changes in the geographic distribution of population and economic activities on water pollution.

For three major air pollutants and 47 urbanized areas, we have found it possible to employ a general air diffusion model to go beyond this assumption.[16] Accordingly, utilizing our modelling results, plus projections of shares of population and economic activities relevant for the economic regions within which these urban areas fall, and assumptions about the proportion of these regional activities lying within the urban area, pollutant emissions were estimated for each of the 47 urban areas. The diffusion model, which takes into account such factors as the ventilation potential of different regions and the area and density of each urban area, was then applied to estimate air quality under alternative assumptions about the future. Chapter 11 provides a more detailed description of methods and sources.

Tables 10, 11, and 12 present results for a special case in which it is assumed that the land area of each city expands in proportion to its population increase, thereby maintaining 1970 density. At the bottom of each table, the percentage of cities not meeting specified standards is presented. As can be seen, a number of urban areas are already in violation of these standards. Moreover, even if land area increases with population, the number of cities violating these standards would grow over time. But if the active abatement policy (specified earlier in this section) were implemented, none of the 47 cities would have pollution levels above the standards, except Los Angeles and San Diego, so far as nitrates are concerned. As can be seen, these two areas

are already significantly above the nitrate standard and would become dramatically so if the active abatement policy were not initiated. Even with such a policy, some restrictions on the use of internal combustion engines or the influx of population and economic activities during the next 30 years would appear necessary if standards are to be met.

An interesting feature emerging from these tables—one that appears illogical at first glance—is the fact that the smaller population assumption in the year 2000 always leads to higher pollution levels. The explanation lies in the fact that urban land area is not independent of the population assumption, and the way that this fact enters the air diffusion model being used. If fewer people (and economic activities) were to be located in a given area, air quality would improve, as expected. But if area changes in proportion to the changes in the population, other factors must be considered. Unit emissions—emissions per unit area—times atmospheric concentration per unit emissions equals air quality. Because income levels are higher with the smaller population, emissions do not fall in proportion to the fall in population. Accordingly, if the area falls in proportion to the fall in population, unit emissions increase. Atmospheric concentrations per unit emissions are a function, among other things, of the diameter of the urban area; assuming the area is circular, it falls less rapidly than does the area. The product of these two changes leads to the observed effect. This result could have significance for urban land planning.[17]

The final feature of note is the wide variation in levels of pollution experienced by urban areas in 1970 and the diversity of the projections into the future. For sulfates in 1970, the highest average concentration level for any city is six times the lowest; and even under the constant abatement policy, some areas appear likely to improve while others worsen. Moreover, the trend is not the same for the three pollutants: Particulate levels are likely to improve in many cities even without an active abatement policy, while nitrate concentrations will worsen in a few cities even with an active abatement policy. When we assume a continuation of the trend in land density established during the past decade—a variation not reported on here—the diversity of experience in different cities, as a consequence of the change in national emission levels, grows even greater.

CONCLUDING COMMENTS

To this point, the basic message of this chapter is that while there are savings in resource and environmental depletion to be gained from a slowdown in population and economic growth, some policies that

Table 10.—Urbanized Area Mean-Air Quality Projections for SO_2 (Micrograms per Cubic Meter) under Two Abatement Policies, Cities Maintain 1970 Population Density

Urban areas	1970[a]	Continuation of present abatement policy 2000				Active abatement policy 2000			
		B-H	E-H	B-L	E-L	B-H	E-H	B-L	E-L
New Haven, Conn.	39	33	35	27	29	5	5	4	4
Rochester, N.Y.	32	30	32	25	27	4	5	4	4
New York, N.Y.	74	73	78	60	63	11	12	9	9
Philadelphia, Pa.	84	86	93	70	76	13	14	10	11
Baltimore, Md.	54	66	71	54	58	10	11	8	9
Richmond, Va.	24	29	31	24	25	4	5	4	4
Norfolk—Portsmouth, Va.	26	36	39	30	32	5	6	4	5
Greensboro, N.C.	12	11	12	9	9	2	2	1	1
Miami, Fla.	5	6	6	5	5	1	1	1	1
Tampa, Fla.	16	21	23	18	19	3	3	3	3
St. Petersburg, Fla.	17	24	26	20	21	4	4	3	3
Montgomery, Ala.	6	8	8	6	6	1	1	1	1
Columbus, Ga.	7	8	8	6	6	1	1	1	1
Atlanta, Ga.	19	20	21	16	17	3	3	2	3
Memphis, Tenn.	16	22	23	18	19	3	3	3	3
Ft. Worth, Texas	7	8	9	7	7	1	1	1	1
Chattanooga, Tenn.	17	18	19	14	15	3	3	2	2
Nashville, Tenn.	15	18	19	15	16	3	3	2	2
Charlestown, W. Va.	27	38	42	31	34	6	6	5	5
Evansville, Ind.	25	31	35	26	28	5	5	4	4
Indianapolis, Ind.	33	41	44	34	36	6	7	5	5
Dayton, Ohio	24	25	27	21	22	4	4	3	3
Columbus, Ohio	21	25	27	20	22	4	4	3	3
Pittsburgh, Pa.	57	77	82	63	67	12	12	9	10
Cleveland, Ohio	64	79	85	65	69	12	13	10	10
Toledo, Ohio	13	17	19	14	15	3	3	2	2
Detroit, Mich.	37	37	40	31	33	6	6	5	5
Saginaw, Mich.	17	24	26	19	21	4	4	3	3
Grand Rapids, Mich.	13	16	18	14	15	2	3	2	2
South Bend, Ind.	10	14	15	12	12	2	2	2	2
Chicago, Ill.	119	154	164	127	135	23	25	19	20
Milwaukee, Wisc.	15	17	18	14	15	3	3	2	2
Tacoma, Wash.	9	11	12	9	10	2	2	1	2
Minneapolis-St. Paul, Minn.	38	43	46	36	38	6	7	5	6
Des Moines, Iowa	11	12	13	10	11	2	2	1	2
Wichita, Kansas	5	6	7	5	6	1	1	1	1
Oklahoma City, Oklahoma	6	8	8	6	7	1	1	1	1
Dallas, Texas	6	7	8	6	6	1	1	1	1
New Orleans, La.	6	7	8	6	7	1	1	1	1
Houston, Texas	9	10	11	9	9	1	2	1	1
San Antonio, Texas	6	9	10	7	8	1	1	1	1
El Paso, Texas	23	23	25	19	21	3	4	3	3
San Francisco-Oakland, Calif.	7	8	9	7	7	1	1	1	1
Denver, Colorado	12	13	14	11	12	2	2	2	2
Salt Lake City, Utah	8	10	11	8	9	1	2	1	1

Table 10.—Continued

Urban areas	1970[a]	Continuation of present abatement policy 2000				Active abatement policy 2000			
		B-H	E-H	B-L	E-L	B-H	E-H	B-L	E-L
Los Angeles-Long Beach, Calif.	34	45	47	37	39	7	7	6	6
San Diego, Calif.	9	11	12	10	11	2	2	1	2
Percent of these urban areas that do not meet the primary ambient air quality standard (annual arithmetic mean of 80 micrograms per cubic meter)	4	4	6	2	2	0	0	0	0
Percent of these urban areas that do not meet the secondary ambient air quality standard (annual arithmetic mean of 60 micrograms per cubic meter)	9	13	13	9	11	0	0	0	0

[a]U.S. Environmental Protection Agency, Division of Air Quality and Emission, Air Quality Control Office, unpublished data.

Table 11.—Urbanized Area Mean-Air Quality Projections for NO$_2$ (Micrograms per Cubic Meter) under Two Abatement Policies, Cities Maintain 1970 Population Density

Urban areas	1970[a]	Continuation of present abatement policy 2000				Active abatement policy 2000			
		B-H	E-H	B-L	E-L	B-H	E-H	B-L	E-L
New Haven, Conn.	158	213	239	201	225	66	74	62	70
Rochester, N.Y.	153	201	223	186	206	62	69	58	64
New York, N.Y.	149	208	228	194	213	64	71	60	66
Philadelphia, Pa.	228	312	344	288	317	97	107	89	98
Baltimore, Md.	180	245	273	228	253	76	85	71	78
Richmond, Va.	134	196	218	182	202	61	68	56	63
Norfolk-Portsmouth, Va.	150	253	282	244	272	78	87	76	84
Greensboro, N.C.	144	229	255	218	242	71	79	68	75
Miami, Fla.	132	217	241	207	230	67	75	64	71
Tampa, Fla.	132	214	238	199	221	66	74	62	69
St. Petersburg, Fla.	47	79	88	74	83	24	27	23	26
Montgomery, Ala.	43	69	77	66	74	21	24	20	23
Columbus, Ga.	77	126	140	120	133	39	43	37	41
Atlanta, Ga.	165	281	305	265	288	87	95	82	89
Memphis, Tenn.	141	231	255	219	242	72	79	68	75
Ft. Worth, Texas	56	87	96	82	91	27	30	25	28
Chattanooga, Tenn.	116	188	207	174	193	58	64	54	60
Nashville, Tenn.	164	276	302	263	288	86	94	82	89
Charlestown, W. Va.	142	174	194	156	174	54	60	48	54
Evansville, Ind.	84	115	129	106	118	36	40	33	37

Table 11.—Continued

Urban areas	1970[a]	Continuation of present abatement policy 2000				Active abatement policy 2000			
		B-H	E-H	B-L	E-L	B-H	E-H	B-L	E-L
Indianapolis, Ind.	119	184	201	172	188	57	62	53	58
Dayton, Ohio	125	182	201	171	189	56	62	53	59
Columbus, Ohio	131	194	214	180	199	60	66	56	62
Pittsburgh, Pa.	213	262	287	241	264	81	89	75	82
Cleveland, Ohio	183	254	281	237	262	79	87	73	81
Toledo, Ohio	151	212	237	197	221	66	73	61	69
Detroit, Mich.	169	222	247	208	232	69	77	64	72
Saginaw, Mich.	66	91	102	82	92	28	32	25	29
Grand Rapids, Mich.	155	220	244	205	228	68	76	64	71
South Bend, Ind.	45	66	74	62	69	20	23	19	21
Chicago, Ill.	102	146	158	135	147	45	49	42	46
Milwaukee, Wisc.	121	168	184	157	172	52	57	49	53
Tacoma, Wash.	60	97	109	94	105	30	34	29	33
Minneapolis-St. Paul, Minn.	142	210	228	195	212	65	71	60	66
Des Moines, Iowa	79	117	130	110	122	36	40	34	38
Wichita, Kansas	104	148	166	140	157	46	51	43	49
Oklahoma City, Oklahoma	105	162	179	152	168	50	55	47	52
Dallas, Texas	84	133	146	125	138	41	45	39	43
New Orleans, La.	120	178	200	167	186	55	62	52	58
Houston, Texas	179	268	293	246	268	83	91	76	83
San Antonio, Texas	133	224	251	216	242	69	78	67	75
El Paso, Texas	116	154	171	142	158	48	53	44	49
San Francisco-Oakland, Calif.	153	232	251	218	235	72	78	68	73
Denver, Colorado	68	109	119	104	113	34	37	32	35
Salt Lake City, Utah	131	201	220	189	208	62	68	59	64
Los Angeles-Long Beach, Calif.	275	491	525	465	497	152	163	144	154
San Diego, Calif.	172	364	396	363	394	113	123	113	122
Percent of these urban areas that do not meet the primary and secondary ambient air quality standard (annual arithmetic mean of 100 micrograms per cubic meter)	77	87	91	8 7	89	4	6	4	4

[a]U.S. Environmental Protection Agency, Division of Air Quality and Emission, Air Quality Control Office, unpublished data.

Table 12.—Urbanized Area Mean-Air Quality Projections for Particulates (Micrograms per Cubic Meter) under Two Abatement Policies, Cities Maintain 1970 Population Density

Urban areas	1970[a]	Continuation of present abatement policy 2000				Active abatement policy 2000			
		B-H	E-H	B-L	E-L	B-H	E-H	B-L	E-L
New Haven, Conn.	93	64	69	54	58	7	8	6	6
Rochester, N.Y.	116	92	98	76	81	10	11	8	9
New York, N.Y.	123	93	99	78	83	10	11	9	9
Philadelphia, Pa.	135	104	113	88	94	11	12	10	10
Baltimore, Md.	113	95	102	80	86	10	11	9	9
Richmond, Va.	83	68	73	57	61	7	8	6	7
Norfolk-Portsmouth, Va.	78	80	87	70	76	9	10	8	8
Greensboro, N.C.	94	80	86	68	73	9	9	7	8
Miami, Fla.	69	69	75	60	65	8	8	7	7
Tampa, Fla.	87	82	90	70	77	9	10	8	8
St. Petersburg, Fla.	43	43	47	37	40	5	5	4	4
Montgomery, Ala.	80	80	87	70	75	9	10	8	8
Columbus, Ga.	56	47	50	41	43	5	6	5	5
Atlanta, Ga.	82	81	86	70	73	9	9	8	8
Memphis, Tenn.	78	77	82	65	69	8	9	7	8
Ft. Worth, Texas	78	70	76	61	65	8	8	7	7
Chattanooga, Tenn.	113	96	103	80	86	11	11	9	9
Nashville, Tenn.	90	93	97	79	83	10	11	9	9
Charlestown, W. Va.	156	142	155	118	128	16	17	13	14
Evansville, Ind.	82	75	82	63	68	8	9	7	7
Indianapolis, Ind.	106	84	90	72	76	9	10	8	8
Dayton, Ohio	92	71	76	61	65	8	8	7	7
Columbus, Ohio	90	78	83	65	70	9	9	7	8
Pittsburgh, Pa.	127	116	123	96	102	13	14	11	11
Cleveland, Ohio	116	96	103	80	86	11	11	9	9
Toledo, Ohio	77	68	75	57	63	7	8	6	7
Detroit, Mich.	113	81	88	69	75	9	10	8	8
Saginaw, Mich.	77	63	69	52	57	7	8	6	6
Grand Rapids, Mich.	75	65	69	54	58	7	8	6	6
South Bend, Ind.	89	80	86	67	72	9	9	7	8
Chicago, Ill.	112	100	106	84	88	11	12	9	10
Milwaukee, Wisc.	91	73	77	61	65	8	8	7	7
Tacoma, Wash.	62	54	59	47	51	6	6	5	6
Minneapolis-St. Paul, Minn.	74	64	68	54	57	7	7	6	6
Des Moines, Iowa	94	91	97	77	82	10	11	8	9
Wichita, Kansas	82	67	75	58	64	7	8	6	7
Oklahoma City, Oklahoma	70	68	74	59	64	7	8	6	7
Dallas, Texas	102	93	100	80	86	10	11	9	9
New Orleans, La.	74	63	70	54	59	7	8	6	6
Houston, Texas	86	73	79	62	67	8	9	7	7
San Antonio, Texas	54	59	64	51	55	6	7	6	6
El Paso, Texas	149	122	133	105	114	13	15	12	13
San Francisco-Oakland, Calif.	50	42	44	36	38	5	5	4	4
Denver, Colorado	122	109	115	94	99	12	13	10	11
Salt Lake City, Utah	82	76	82	66	70	8	9	7	8

Table 12.—Continued

Urban areas	1970[a]	Continuation of present abatement policy 2000				Active abatement policy 2000			
		B-H	E-H	B-L	E-L	B-H	E-H	B-L	E-L
Los Angeles-Long Beach, Calif.	95	95	99	81	84	10	11	9	
San Diego, Calif.	73	76	81	73	77	8	9	8	
Percent of these urban areas that do not meet the primary ambient air quality standard (annual geometric mean of 75 micrograms per cubic meter)	77	57	68	32	40	0	0	0	
Percent of these urban areas that do not meet the secondary ambient air quality standard (annual geometric mean of 60 micrograms per cubic meter)	94	89	91	68	79	0	0	0	

[a] U.S. Environmental Protection Agency, Division of Air Quality and Emission, Air Quality Control Office, unpublished data

more directly attack resource and environmental problems would result in greater savings. We can add that because the price system operates reasonably effectively to regulate the consumption of resources, but hardly at all to ration the use of waste disposal media like air and water, there should be greater savings from policies directly attacking pollution problems than from those, such as recycling, that attempt to conserve on resources.

But several qualifications should be borne in mind in assessing this material. First, direct attacks on the problems—for example, an effective and equitable abatement policy—may be very difficult to implement; and once implemented we may not like some of the social and institutional consequences. The last section of Chapter 1 discusses some of these issues.

Second, this analysis has not considered all resources and pollutants. While the picture for omitted resources is likely to be similar to that presented here, the situation for omitted pollutants could be quite different. To contain the cumulative effects of some long-lasting pollutants may require that they be banned altogether; this may be very difficult to do without reductions in population or economic growth. But more important, the pollution problems of the future may involve toxic substances undreamt of today, the identification and control of which may require considerable time. Slower rates of growth would provide more time.

Third, we have limited ourselves to a 30- to 50-year time horizon. While we have found ways to cope with problems generated by rapid growth within this period,

continued exponential growth could eventually overwhelm these solutions, making reductions in growth the only alternative. We cannot know for sure since technological capabilities this far in the future cannot be predicted. But certainly we can say that a reduction in growth today would minimize the risk involved in case adequate technological breakthroughs do not come along when needed.

For these reasons, there are benefits to be derived from reductions in population and economic growth that do not show up in the numerical estimates of savings presented in this chapter. A slowdown in growth reduces the need for application of solutions the secondary consequences of which we may not like; it buys time so that acceptable solutions can be found; and it reduces the risk that we may not find acceptable solutions.

For related reasons, in the long run at least, reductions in population growth are probably more important than reductions in economic growth. Growth in the economy can be utilized for different ends than it is currently put to; it results in additional capacity to solve problems as well as adds problems that need solution. But it is difficult to believe that similar kinds of offsetting advantages could be derived from additional population growth.[18]

The importance of these qualitative points can be overstated. Even if population and economic growth were to slow down or cease, we would still be faced with growing environmental and resource problems, as a consequence of our own activities as well as pressures emanating from population growth and struggles for higher standards of living in the rest of the world. More direct attacks on these problems will be required in any case.

REFERENCES

1. Clopper Almon, Jr., *The American Economy to 1975* (New York: Harper and Row, 1969).

2. U.S. Bureau of the Census, Current Population Reports, Series P-25, No. 448, August 1970. Labor force projections comparable with these population series were provided in unpublished form by the Bureau of the Census.

3. It is sometimes argued that, for women with fewer children, the opportunity cost of working is less; but this effect is likely to be at least partially offset by the family's need for less income. Nevertheless, it is likely that the same forces inducing women to have fewer children are also likely to induce them to participate more in the labor force.

4. Edwin Vennard, in *The Electric Power Business,* (New York: McGraw-Hill, 1970), pp. 139-40, for example, fits a Gompertz curve to kilowatt hours per capita (kwhpc) for the past 90 years of data plus projections to 1980 (the latter having a high degree of accuracy because of construction time lags). The curve starts with zero in 1880, reaches an inflection point in the mid-21st century, and an upper asymptote around 2200. In 1968, per capita consumption was 7,167 kwhpc; in 2000, it would reach 19,000-20,000 kwhpc. Multiplied by our population projections, this gives 6.4 billion kwh for B and 5.3 billion kwh for E in 2000, or annual compound growth rates since 1968 of 4.75 percent and 4.15 percent.

5. The concept of elasticity we are aiming at by this procedure is one that asks what percent change in a given resource use would result from a one percentage point change in population or GNP per capita, holding as much else constant as is possible (and reasonable). The simplest way to hold technology, tastes, and so on constant is to make the comparison between different scenarios in the year 2000, rather than making the comparisons between different points in time.

6. B. T. Bower, G. O. G. Löf, and W. M. Hearon, "Residuals Generation in the Pulp and Paper Industry," *Natural Resources Journal,* 1971, Vol. 11, No. 4, pp. 605-623.

7. Of course, there will be an offsetting increase in waste generation from the added electricity utilized, but this is more easily controlled than is generation from thousands of individual homes and offices.

8. A more detailed discussion of methodology can be found in relevant portions of Chapters 11 and 12, plus their footnoted references.

9. The impression of rapidly rising trends in pollution may be incorrect, influenced more by heightened concern than by hard data. In large part, the empirical basis for this impression comes from casual observation in a few urban centers. Data representative of the nation as a whole are not available for a sufficient number of years to establish a reliable national trend.

10. These are discussed in L. Ayres, I. Gutmanis, and A. Shapanka, "Environmental Implications of Technological and Economic Change for the United States 1967-2000: An Input-Output Analysis," IRT-229-R (Washington, D. C.: International Research and Technology Corp., Dec. 1971).

11. To reduce sulfur emissions to standards, with a few exceptions, the assumption was made that low sulfur coal and oil would be used; and cost estimates were based on the difference between low and high sulfur fuels. For a few sectors, however, it was assumed that sulfur would be removed from fuels by pilot methods currently being used, and cost estimates were taken from studies of those methods. In the case of nitrogen oxides, we assumed that modest modifications in the design of internal combustion engines will be introduced to reduce their emissions at the expense of increased emissions of hydrocarbons and carbon monoxide; the latter will then be treated by currently known methods.

12. The large difference in particulates generated with 1970 technology and 2000 technology is explained by the continuation of the current trend away from the use of coal for heat and power generation, plus better design of combustion chambers which will reduce ash content. There has been some talk about coal coming back into its own, but if it does it would be in new forms: gasification and direct conversion through fuel cells.

13. Assuming 1.25 passengers per car and 20 per bus. Derived from Robert U. Ayres and Richard V. McKenna, *Alternatives to the Internal Combustion Engine* (Baltimore: Johns Hopkins Press for Resources for the Future, 1972).

14. The five production sectors directly or indirectly responsible for the most sulfur oxides emission account for 56.6 percent of total emissions; and final consumer expenditures on these items account for 22.8 percent of GNP (both figures referring to 1970). A one-percentage-point reduction in GNP all coming out of consumer expenditures on these five commodities would reduce emissions from production by $(1 \div 228)(56.6)$ or 2.48 percent compared to 0.87 percent for a one-percent reduction in GNP generally.

15. On the influence of population density on automobile air pollution concentrations, see C. Peter Rydell and Douglas Collins, "Air Pollution and Optimal Urban Form" (paper presented at the 60th Annual Meeting of the Air Pollution Control Association, Cleveland, Ohio, June 11-16, 1967).

16. In addition, some aspects of regional water quality are discussed in Chapter 8. There, however, the emphasis is on adequacy of water supplies of a particular quality, rather than on quality per se.

17. But it should be interpreted with caution. We are implicitly assuming that emissions per person, except for the effect of higher incomes, are the same no matter what the density of population. This may not be so. If passenger car miles per person is constant, higher densities will slow down traffic resulting in greater emissions per vehicle mile. If higher densities mean less passenger car miles (e.g., more use of mass transit) or more use of apartment buildings (and hence some economies of scale in space heating) the result will be less emissions per person. These changes could offset the effects of changes in unit emissions indicated above.

18. Some have suggested that there are additional economies of scale to be exploited. While this argument could easily be supported in the United States of the past, as we look into the future, it is difficult to imagine whatever such economies remain to be exploited, or may arise in the future, cannot be reaped—if we feel it is worthwhile to do so—through international trade, larger urban centers, more homogeneous tastes, and so on.

Chapter 3

Waste Material Recovery and Reuse

by
Frank Austin Smith
Center for Environment and Man

COMMISSION ON POPULATION GROWTH AND
THE AMERICAN FUTURE, *RESEARCH
REPORTS, VOLUME III, POPULATION
RESOURCES AND THE ENVIRONMENT,*
EDITED BY RONALD G. RIDKER

CONTENTS

TABLES

Waste Material Recovery and Reuse

INTRODUCTION

"Recycling" is not a new idea, either in principle or in practice. However, it has only recently achieved widespread public recognition as a possible solution to both the current environmental quality and potential natural resource supply problems of economic growth in our mass-production, mass-consumption society. Because the subject has not received much research attention in the past and also because it is so broad and complex, considerable diversity of opinion and uncertainty persists regarding the extent to which we can look to this form of material conservation as an economically feasible solution to these natural resource problems.

Our specific tasks in the present chapter are two-fold. The first is to provide conceptual and empirical perspective on the nature of material recovery as a special class of economic activity—that is, its place in the economy in relation to other primary production and consumption activities, the factors which condition its viability, and an impressionistic overview of the present materials recovery picture for the United States economy. Based on this, our second task is to provide some crude but reasoned speculations regarding what its future role might be.

We have chosen to define our subject quite broadly to include any situation in which any residual physical output of production or consumption that would otherwise constitute a waste material of zero or negative value in the economy is instead somehow put to additional productive use somewhere within the economic system. The residual product or material may be reused either by the residual producer himself or by some other decision unit in the system; it may or may not be subject to reprocessing or repair prior·to reuse; and it may be reused either for essentially the same technical and economic function which it originally served, or for an entirely different function in the same or a different reprocessed form. This general definition allows for inclusion of a variety of special cases, some of which might otherwise go entirely unrecognized, but which nevertheless constitute important aspects of the general material recovery phenomenon within the overall materials utilization and resource conservation picture.

Three broad categories of material recovery may be conveniently distinguished for introductory purposes of definition. The first is the common case of secondhand goods transfers, in which durable consumer or producers goods retired from use by present owners are acquired for further direct use by new owners. The second category is that of recycling, per se, which we define as the return of a particular material from later stages of production or final use to be reintroduced as a raw material at an earlier stage of its original production cycle, destined to serve its own prior function. The third category is that of by-products production, which differs from recycling primarily in that the uses and markets to be served by the recovered material are essentially different from those giving rise to the material's original production as a residual.

Each of these three broad categories of material recovery activity will be expanded upon, in turn, in the three sections which follow. Our discussion then concludes with some general observations on the major economic and public policy factors expected to influence the rate and direction of future material recovery developments and some speculative observations on its potential role in the nation's future natural resources conservation picture.

SECONDHAND GOODS AND DURABLE GOODS REPAIR

Although not generally recognized as a form of material recovery, secondhand goods transfers and durable goods repair constitute most important aspects of economic activity in terms of prolonging the economic life of both household and producers durable goods.[1] As such, they thus divert substantial quantities of final-product residuals from the nation's annual waste flow; and at the same time, they also serve to substantially reduce demands on material resources for new goods production that would also engender additional residuals. Although significant portions of some kinds of secondhand goods are transferred as gifts (children's clothing being a notable example), the preponderant volumes are exchanged in secondhand goods markets. Thus, in a very real sense, secondhand goods markets should be considered (along with repair industries) as an integral aspect of society's institutional organization for material recovery.

Although the structural relationships of secondhand goods markets have not received much attention in the economic literature, certain characteristics are relatively obvious. First, substantial quantities of most items are sold directly by owners in non-organized market fashion via word of mouth and classified newspaper advertising. A second avenue includes the "tag-sale," "rummage sale," and auction methods, frequently for charitable as well as private-profit purposes. The third and undoubtedly most important includes the commercial secondhand goods retailers, both those who specialize entirely in used items as well as new goods dealers who accept trade-ins. Both of these, and especially the latter, also typically perform repair and servicing functions. With the exception of automobiles and rebuilt automobile components and the "antiques" categories, there appears to be relatively little used goods wholesaling. Of some interest as a special case is the used clothing market. Although engaged in to a limited extent by commercial retailers, the largest proportion of this market seems to be accounted for by organized nonprofit agencies, such as the Goodwill Industries and local church groups, who canvass households for used clothing to be sold for charity or other welfare revenue purposes. Goodwill Industries and the Salvation Army are particularly notable in that they perform both large-scale collection and repair of clothing (as well as certain other items) and also serve as substantial collector-suppliers of pre-sorted materials to specialized secondary materials dealers.

It is not at all clear at this time whether, on balance, secondhand goods have been maintaining their relative competitive position vis-a-vis new goods, or whether the economic feasibility of commercial repair as an alternative to replacement has been changing significantly in recent years. To our knowledge, neither of these issues has been systematically investigated, nor has it been possible to do so in the present project. However, there are some reasons for pessimism regarding their future prospects.

First, as average real family incomes rise (and especially if average family size declines), the general abilities of households to purchase new durable goods in preference to old may be expected to increase. Further, since durable goods transfers largely involve a "trickling down" from higher- to lower-income groups in the society, one may speculate that, if incomes become more equally distributed in the future (especially through raising the incomes of the lowest groups), then there is additional reason to believe that relative demands for secondhand goods will decline. Finally,

there is some evidence to indicate that typical repair costs relative to new goods prices have been increasing; and since repair activities tend to be highly labor intensive, one may suppose that these costs will continue to rise in the future. Although there may be partially offsetting technological changes in repair possibilities for certain items—for example, the modular design of electrical and other equipment components for ease of servicing and factory repair—our present guess is that if historical trends continue, both secondhand goods transfers and repair are more likely to decline than to increase in relative future importance. This implies that either durable goods waste disposal problems will grow faster than they otherwise would, or other forms of material recovery activity will have to be expanded in order to compensate.

MATERIALS RECYCLING

As previously noted, we have reserved the term "recycling" to apply to the special category of material recovery in which residuals from later stages of manufacture or consumption are returned to an earlier processing stage to be used again as raw material in producing essentially the same line of product. Whatever the source of the residual, there are at least three technological prerequisites for recycling. The first and most obvious is that the material must not have become physically dissipated into the environment by its prior use—it must be physically recoverable in a literal sense. As we shall note later, a very substantial part of our total material requirements—on the order of one-quarter to one-third by weight—are presently utilized in physically dissipative product uses (for example, fuels, pesticides, cosmetics), and are therefore unavailable for reuse. A second prerequisite for recycle is that the material and its utilization allows for physical and chemical reversibility, such that it can be returned to its original (approximate) form. Finally, the engineering knowledge must exist to perform the process of reversibility. Given these technical prerequisites, the recovered material must then be capable of competing in both price and quality with similar primary or virgin raw material.

Recycle may be accomplished within an individual production establishment (such as, the remelting of "home scrap" in integrated steel mills); it may involve the return of "new" or "prompt" industrial residuals from converting and fabricating mills to an earlier reprocessing stage; and it also includes recovery of specific material values from "old" or "obsolete" final-product residuals from household, general business, and demolition sources. The discussion will deal first with recycling within the individual plant or production enterprise and then consider recycling at the inter-industry level.

In-Plant Recycling

Recycling within the individual plant may be directed either at reworking the residuals of a "through-put" material to recover lost raw material feedstock; or it may involve the recovery of non-throughput processing chemicals, process water, or other "ancillary" inputs which are required in production but are never intended to become physically embodied in the marketable product. Quantitative data on the extent of in-plant recycling in major United States industries is extremely sketchy, at best, and generalization for entire industries or material categories based on scattered examples must be taken with caution.

Although in-plant recycling of one kind or another can and does occur at virtually any stage in the industrial production sequence, from initial raw material extraction through final manufacture, its most important and widespread applications are observed at the earlier raw material extraction and primary processing levels. A few selected examples will suffice to illustrate the nature and significance of some of these recycle activities.

One of the most obvious examples, and perhaps the single most significant one from a national conservation standpoint, is the traditional farming practice of returning organic residuals in the form of crop residues and animal manures to the soil. However, here the widely noted shift in animal raising methods towards concentrated feed-lot operations and "broiler factories" suggests a major case where the recycle proportion has been declining.[2]

In comparison to the organic materials recycling of agriculture, internal recycling within the mineral ore mining and milling sector presents a picture different in both kind and degree. First, it seems evident for many if not most of the major nonpetroleum mineral products, that mining, washing, and milling wastes per unit of marketable product have been historically increasing and can be expected to increase further in the future, due in part to the necessity of resorting to continually lower grade ores at increasingly less accessible and/or more narrowly veined deposits, and in part to increasingly strict controls on quality of product delivered.

Second, unlike the organic residuals of farming, mine residuals are largely inert and accumulate continuously at points of storage. A recent Bureau of Mines survey indicated that in excess of 15 billion tons of mining, washing, and milling residuals, exclusive of overburden deposits, had accumulated in the United States between 1942 and 1965.[3] Of this total, it was estimated that some 60 percent involved "enough value

attached to prohibit their removal simply for the sake of removal," although presumably not high enough to warrant current reworking. These waste piles were also said to be associated with varying degrees of environmental damages. An additional 37 percent of the accumulated waste piles were considered worthless in terms of presently known recovery potentials, but to be of present significance in terms of the external costs. A very small third category, involving 3 percent of accumulated waste, was considered both worthless in terms of minerals recovery and not to present significant external damage problems. As previously indicated, these waste piles are generally expected to increase more rapidly than marketable production of the mines.

It also appears evident that, relative to quantities of residuals involved, little internal recycle activity is associated with current extraction and milling operations. There is, of course, some activity of an internal recycling nature carried on in connection with washing and milling for some of the materials. In certain instances, however, the major present recovery activities are directed not at currently produced residuals, but rather at the exploitation of previously accumulated mine dumps and mill tailing piles that have become economically workable due to the combined effects of improved technology and the decreasing richness of alternative new mineral deposits. Thus, currently, some 30 percent of anthracite coal production comes from the exploitation of previously accumulated culm banks,[4] and modest amounts of copper and other nonferrous metals are being derived from mine and mill tailings through relatively new processes such as acid leaching. We anticipate that the reworking of historically accumulated waste piles will continue to be the single most important form of materials recovery in the mining sector. In this connection, however, the principal social benefit is likely to reside in the value of minerals recovery rather than from associated reductions in environmental damages, since the recoverable minerals content is often a very small fraction of the total material involved. Indeed, local environmental damages are perhaps more likely to be increased by this activity than decreased, due to the fact that reworking involves a considerable increase in activity at otherwise stabilized sites, and because certain methods of recovery such as acid leaching of copper ores can often raise more significant damage potentials than those of the original situation.

Turning from extraction to the basic raw materials processing and refining, the primary metals offer a number of significant illustrations of internal recycle. Considering first the recovery of basic metals, the most obvious and often the largest tonnage metallic recycle item is the remelting of "home" or "mill revert" scrap from the forming mills. In steel mills, for example, upwards of 25 to 30 percent of the gross metallic input to the furnace may be in the form of this mill-generated scrap, and there are also up to five additional sources of in-plant recovery of ferrous metallics in integrated iron and steel mills.[5] Three of these are related to blast-furnace residuals: fines from ore-charging operations and recovered blast-furnace flue dust are both reverted to sintering operations, along with iron concentrates derived as a by-product from the processing of blast furnace slag. In addition, steel mill residuals contribute two other sources of recycled metallic inputs to the sintering mill, that is, surface scales from finishing mills and (in a few cases, at least) metallic concentrates derived from steel slag processing. The output from sintering is then fed back as a metallic input to the blast furnace. Data on these in-plant recycle items is scarce and often ambiguous, however, it has been estimated that blast-furnace slags alone accounted for over a half-million tons of concentrated slag iron returned to blast furnaces in 1968.[6]

Internally recycled metallics for the nonferrous metals are less well documented, although it can be assumed that home scrap is well recovered from most finishing mills where it occurs. Additional examples of substantial recycle in the nonferrous field include the secondary recovery of aluminum from the "red mud" silicate residuals at certain bauxite-processing (alumina) plants, and the recovery of zinc from smelter and retort-refinery fumes.[7]

Although we do not have definitive, industry-wide data on which to base a firm conclusion, it seems doubtful that many major unexploited opportunities exist within the primary metals industry group for expanded internal recovery of metallics. Two possible exceptions are steel furnace slags (as distinct from iron blast furnace slags), only recently beginning to be exploited for by-product and iron recovery values, and copper smelter slags. However, for the most part metallic residuals appear to be already highly exploited internally for recycle values.

Internal recycle of non-throughput process inputs in the primary metals industries is associated principally with the recovery and regeneration of caustic and acid leaching solutions, spent electrolytes, and pickling liquors from various plant operations after removal of their built-up solids concentrations. Although generally widely practiced for most such operations, there are some instances where regeneration of chemical processing solutions has not been economically profitable in private market terms, and many other instances where the degree of reuse has been only partial. In both types of situations, significant water pollution problems have remained. An example of the former case can be found in the sulfuric acid pickling liquors widely used in steel finishing; however, the introduction of substitute processes, such as pickling with hydrochloric acid in vertical towers with acid regeneration and possible recovery of by-product salts, may provide a solution.[8] In general, we may expect to see increased efforts in the direction of recovering both metals and processing chemicals from dilute leaching, pickling, rinse water, and other solutions. However, in most cases, the additional recovery values will tend to be relatively small, and the major impetus as well as the major social value will derive primarily from the side of water quality control benefits.

Further significant examples are to be found in the pulp and paper industry, where in-plant recycling takes predominantly three forms. In chemical pulping, considerable emphasis is placed on recovery and reuse of pulping chemicals, particularly for the sulfate and soda chemical-pulping processes which constitute about 70 percent of total wood pulping. In spite of this, many million tons of make-up chemicals for pulping as well as bleaching are required annually to compensate for losses. In the paper and board mills, where the wood pulp and other fibrous materials are formed into paper and board, significant decreases in both fiber and filler losses have been achieved over the past two or three decades by the installation of save-alls for the recycling of paper machine residuals. In addition, it is the usual practice in paper and board mills to recycle most if not all non-marketable product (trimmings, rejects and overrun) back through the mill. It would appear that relatively little technological potential exists for material savings from additional recycling in the paper making process, since the more modern installations appear to have achieved very high input transformation efficiencies, probably on the order of 95 to 99 percent.[9]

Other industries could be cited in more or less detail. The food processing industries as a group, for example, do not appear particularly amenable to in-plant throughput recovery, although a few exceptions, such as increased sugar recovery in beet sugar refining, have been noted in the literature, and many plants in the canning and other wet food-processing industries have undertaken programs of wastewater recovery and reuse as an integral aspect of water pollution control. On the other hand, petroleum refining, petrochemicals, and other organic and inorganic chemicals provide numerous cases of throughput recovery via internal recycle.

However, it is well to point out that the significant issue here is not whether particular plants and industries exhibit high or low internal recycle ratios, per se.

Rather, the significant question is that of efficient materials utilization in the broader sense—in other words, whether plants and industries are producing high rates of residual wastes in relation to their net raw material inputs, and whether these wastes are technically and economically capable of being reduced by in-plant production changes, of whatever kind. In this respect, changes in processing technology and/or raw material input substitutions may often serve the same ends as in-plant recycle, and at lower cost. Thus, we do not wish to leave the impression that there is anything inherently superior, either from a technical or an economic standpoint, about high levels of in-plant recycle. Rather, it should be regarded as one class of methods, potentially applicable to both throughput feedstock and ancillary input recovery, which may or may not be a superior alternative in particular cases. Further, it should not be confused with by-products production, discussed below, as a means of utilizing nonrecyclable residuals.

If the particular industries and in-plant recycling cases reviewed—examples of which were discussed above—constitute a representative sample, and if our general observations and inferences regarding them are reasonably correct, what general impressions emerge? First, there are obviously a great many cases of successful and privately profitable internal recycle, relating to a wide variety of materials and applied under a number of quite different industrial production contexts. Further, and of more fundamental importance, we have thus far found no instances in the basic raw materials industries of really large throughput losses of potentially recoverable primary product—that is, losses exceeding, say, 5 to 10 percent of the potential product content of the input. Although our data here is very sketchy, the inference is that the potential for improving throughput yields of basic raw-material commodities, although not negligible in absolute terms, would not, even if completely exploited, augment primary supplies in most of the major industries by more than a few percent of annual output. In short, increases in internal recycle (or other alternatives for increasing throughput yields) would not seem to promise a major unexploited general solution to possible future material supply problems.

On the other hand, there may well be a quite significant potential in a number of industries for engineering significant reductions in process-chemical and other ancillary input requirements (for example, pulping and bleaching chemicals in the wood pulping industry, sulfuric acid for pickling in the steel industry). In both throughput and ancillary input cases, reductions in residuals may in many instances be quite significant from an environmental quality standpoint, although

relatively nonsignificant from the standpoint of raw material savings.

Inter-Industry and Inter-Sector Recycle

This category is defined broadly to include all cases of recycling in which residuals from later manufacturing or final use stages of the economy are returned across industry boundaries to different processing plants for recovery of the basic material. It thus includes the recycling of current manufacturing residuals originating at converting and fabricating mills (variously termed "new" or "prompt industrial" scrap) as well as "old" or "obsolete" materials from demolition activity, households, and other final-user sources. The list of materials involved includes all the major metals as well as paper and cloth fiber, glass, rubber, plastics, and used lubricating oils.

For the most part, this class of recycling is carried out by a group of specialized industries, often collectively referred to as the "secondary recovery industries" or the "secondary materials industries." The group as a whole includes a large number of firms, more or less narrowly specialized both by function and by material, which perform the functions of collection, preparation and pre-processing (sorting, separating, cleaning, sizing, baling, and so forth), marketing, and shipping of the scrap materials, as well as the industrial enterprises which ultimately purchase the scrap and subsequently transform it into a finished raw material. For want of a better term, we will refer to the latter as the secondary material "users," to distinguish them from the earlier processors or dealers. A brief introduction to the structure of some of the alternative inter-firm and inter-industry relationships may be instructive at this point.

In the simplest cases, the larger independent converting and fabricating plants may sell their new scrap residuals directly to primary or secondary users, while other mills vertically integrated by company ownership sometimes transfer their scrap mainly to user-mills of the same company. However, there are apparently no hard and fast rules in this regard, and specialized independent secondary materials wholesalers and dealers may handle material of both of these larger source categories as well as the bulk of the new scrap generated in the smaller independent establishments. Old scrap, on the other hand, passes almost entirely through the specialized scrap processors and dealers on its way to users. Thus, small collectors and scavengers specialize in collection from low volume sources (usually along with refuse handling services), and supply local dealer-processors, who in turn sell to larger dealer-wholesalers or directly to users. Larger local dealers also service many larger source-clients directly. There are also some firms who specialize solely as brokers. Closely related as intermediate sources of supply to the secondary materials industries are the auto wrecker-dismantling firms (who specialize mainly in the sale of secondhand parts), the demolition industry, automobile service stations (which serve as collection points for tires, batteries, and crankcase drainings), nonprofit organizations such as the Salvation Army and Goodwill Industries (which continuously supply waste paper and waste cloth from organized collection). A small number of city sanitation departments have also constituted collection and sorting agencies and, more recently the community "recycling center," under either private or public aegis, has entered the collection field.

Interesting variation is also evident at the user stage of the recycle industry structure. In many respects, this is the key stage in the system, inasmuch as it is here that the recovered scrap material comes into direct competition with its counterpart primary or "virgin" material. It is this stage that largely determines the competitive quality and price characteristics that the recovered material must meet; and it is the demand curve for scrap as determined at this point that has such an important bearing on derived price and quantity relations all the way down through the scrap supply network. The secondary material users may be grouped roughly into three general classes.

The first class is represented by the integrated iron and steel mills, unique among the primary metals industries in that the predominant blast furnace and steel furnace technologies have developed in such a way that they have virtually required the consumption of substantial quantities of scrap, along with iron ore and/or pig iron, for efficiency in melting. Thus, the bulk of purchased iron and steel scrap has always been remelted within the primary industry itself. The same is also true of the relatively small proportion of purchased glass cullet remelted by the primary glass industry, there being no significant secondary-specialist users of glass cullet. In contrast to the case of steel, most of the nonferrous scrap is remelted and/or re-refined in specialized secondary smelter mills, so designated in the Standard Industrial Classification. One branch of the steel industry—that employing electric furnaces rather than open hearth, basic oxygen or other types—has also traditionally depended on scrap (over 95 percent of its total metallic raw material) and is more closely comparable to the secondary nonferrous metals industries, in that it is composed of a larger number of smaller independent firms operating relatively small units in competition with the larger, integrated primary producers. Rubber reclaiming has also been accomplished

almost solely by a specialized secondary industry segment; whereas in paper recycling we find a variety of forms: deinking mills that process close to 100 percent old paperstock, fine paper mills that blend quantities of high grade pulp substitute paperstock, paperboard mills that use widely varying proportions, and building paper mills that use close to 100 percent old paper.

The full implications of these variations in user industrial organization characteristics have not been thoroughly explored in terms of their meaning for the strength, stability, and growth potential for secondary scrap use.

Available data on these recycle quantities is generally somewhat better than for other classes of recovery activity, at least for a number of the more important materials, and recent quantitative trends for seven basic materials are summarized in Table 1.

For all seven materials, the recycled quantities are substantial in both absolute magnitudes and in terms of their relative importance to total national supply. The data indicate that in absolute quantity terms, total scrap recovery has increased over the past 10 to 15 years for all of the materials except tin and rubber. However, old scrap recovery expanded at a less rapid rate than did new scrap for the three metals for which comparative data is shown. It should also be noted that, in all cases except lead, old scrap constituted less than 18 percent of the current total supply of material in 1968.

The relative contribution to total United States supply, as indicated by the total scrap recycle ratio (the final columns on the right of Table 1), shows some decidedly mixed trends: moderate increases in aluminum, copper, and lead; a stable proportion for iron and steel; and decreasing proportions in tin, paperstock, and rubber. Considering trends in recycle ratios for old scrap alone, specific data is available only for aluminum, copper, and ferrous metals, all of which show either constant or slightly declining proportions; however, significantly declining proportions of old scrap recycle may also be safely inferred for paperstock and rubber.

Among the general conclusions that one can draw from this data is that the secondary recycling industries generally held their own in competition with primary metals during this recent 10 to 15 year period, but that with respect to the "soft goods," both recycled paper and rubber showed distinct declines in market share.

It is generally conceded that the secondary recovery industries are extremely efficient in exploiting the new-scrap residuals of the converting and fabricating industries, and these are obviously the most commercially desirable scrap materials from the standpoint of quality, dependability of supply, and individual point source volume. Although detailed data are not available,

Table 1.—Inter-Sectoral Recycle Comparisons for Selected Materials, 1954-58 and 1968

Materials	Quantity of material recovered or of scrap processed (thousand tons)[a]				Ratio of recycled material to total current supply or consumption[b]					
	Old scrap		Total scrap[c]		Old scrap		New scrap[c]		Total scrap[c]	
	1954-58 annual avg.	1968	1954-58 annual avg.	1968	1954-58 annual avg.	1968	1954-58 annual avg.	1968	1954-58 annual avg.	1968
Aluminum	69	155	255	622	3.3%	3.3%	12.2%	14.2%	15.5%	17.5%
Copper	449	521	880	1,218	18.6	17.0	17.8	22.8	36.4	39.8
Lead	n.a.	471	476	551	n.a.	34.9	n.a.	5.9	37.3	40.8
Tin	n.a.	16	32	26	n.a.	17.3	n.a.	12.0	34.0	28.3
Ferrous metals	19,236	22,999	70,591	86,766	13.9	13.3	8.0	8.0	21.9	21.3
Paper stock fiber	n.a.	n.a.	8,580	10,290	n.a.	n.a.[d]	n.a.	n.a.[d]	24.8	18.7
Rubber[e]	n.a.	126	291	288	n.a.	4.1	n.a.	5.2	19.0	9.3

[a] For Aluminum, Copper, and Lead, represents annual quantity of metal recovered from scrap, including the content of the individual metal recovered in the form of alloys in combination with other metals. For Tin, data represents consumption of tin recovered from scrap. For Ferrous metals and Paper stock, quantities of scrap consumed as input in final recovery process.

[b] Total supply or consumption includes total domestic production or consumption of material from domestic and imported raw materials, both primary and secondary, plus net imports of refined materials. For Ferrous metals, based on total metallic input in iron and steel, including home scrap.

[c] Excludes home-scrap and other internal-establishment recycle.

[d] Midwest Research Institute estimates that old waste paper constitutes 60 percent and converting industry residuals 40 percent of total paper stock supply.

[e] Data for rubber reclaiming only, excludes tire retreading. Earlier figure for 1958 only.

n.a. = Not available.

Sources: Nonferrous Metals: Derived from U.S. Bureau of Mines, *Mineral Facts and Problems, 1965,* and *Minerals Yearbook, 1968.* Ferrous Metals: Adapted from U.S. Dept. of Commerce, Business and Defense Services Administration, *Iron and Steel Scrap Consumption Problems,* 1966, and updated data. Paper Stock: American Paper Institute, *Statistics of Paper: 1970 Supplement* (Washington, 1970). Rubber: Pettigrew and Roninger, *Solid Waste Management and Rubber Reuse Potential in the Rubber Industry,* 1970.

it is likely that over 90 percent of new scrap is already being exploited for recycle for most of the major recyclable materials, suggesting relatively little opportunity for increased recycling ratios based on new scrap.

The major potential for increased inter-sectoral recycling thus appears to depend upon old or obsolete scrap. A number of points can be made in this regard. First, in contrast with new scrap, obsolete material frequently involves very long turn-around times, from the time the final product goes into use until the time of its retirement as a residual available for recycle. For most of the metals other than lead, the average turn-around time is measurable in decades rather than in years. Thus, much of the current old scrap metals supply represents the primary output of steel, copper, etc., of 20 or 30 years ago. As a consequence, the availability of potentially recyclable obsolete scrap will be less relative to total current material consumption for a primary material experiencing a more rapid growth rate over time than it would be for a material whose total consumption is relatively stable. Thus, materials with very rapid growth rates and relatively long turn-around times (such as aluminum) may reveal low old-scrap recycle proportions simply because old scrap availability lags so far behind new materials production. Conversely, a material with a declining growth rate could exhibit an increase in its ratio of old-scrap recycle to current total material supply, even without any increase in the relative exploitation of old scrap sources, so long as recycle at least keeps pace with residuals availability.

A second point, previously noted, is that substantial quantities of many materials are consumed in dissipative uses and thus never become available for recovery in the form of old scrap. A good example of this is lead, for which 30 to 40 percent of total current output is consumed in the form of gasoline additives, pigments, and other inherently dissipative products. For such materials, increased recovery from obsolete sources may ultimately depend in large measure on a decrease in the relative proportion consumed in dissipative forms.

What is the nature and type of these remaining obsolete sources "available" for recycle? Apparently, these must consist primarily of remaining demolition residuals, junked farm implements, motor vehicles, and other small-lot industrial equipment, paper and miscellaneous refuse from commercial establishments, and household solid wastes. Although precise data are lacking on many of these individual sources, much of the material is farily well accounted for in household and other municipal refuse categories.

At present, the only items recycled in significant quantities from household sources are the scrap metal content of automobiles (probably already utilized up to 80 percent or more of availability in most regions), auto batteries (over 90 percent utilized), auto tires (less than 25 percent utilized in retreading and reclaiming), old newspapers (perhaps 25 percent utilized at present), and some used clothing which finds its way into the reweaving industries along with other by-product cloth and fiber uses. One may also choose to include here the rapidly disappearing refillable glass bottle as an item of recycle. Virtually all of this recovery activity, it should be noted, represents material diverted from municipal solid waste collection and disposal systems. As a general rule, only negligible quantities of material have typically been salvaged, either privately or publicly, after entering the municipal collection system of all but a few cities.[10]

In considering the relative quantities of material involved, we would find, for example, as a rough estimate, that the equivalent of 10 to 12 percent of the nation's current annual steel consumption is currently disposed of in the municipal solid waste disposal system. Corresponding estimates for some other materials would include 25 percent of current aluminum consumption, less than five percent of other nonferrous metals, 35 percent of plastics, 70 percent of paper, and 75 percent of total annual glass consumption for all purposes.[11] Considerable additional proportions of rubber and other nonmetallics are also accounted for as the unrecycled components of the auto-wrecking industry.

It is clear that the remaining obsolete sources are the most difficult and costly to exploit for recycle, for precisely the opposite reasons that new scrap supplies represent the most commercially desirable and most profitable sources. On the one hand, the materials collected in municipal refuse invariably exist in highly nonhomogeneous mixtures of dozens of different materials that are extremely difficult and expensive to separate into component categories. On the other hand, the remaining obsolete materials not collected in municipal refuse tend to be extremely scattered and in small volumes of sporadic occurrence, making them almost equally difficult and expensive to acquire. Even after collecting and sorting, many obsolete items (such as consumer appliances) still represent complex combinations of many different component materials that must be separated chemically or physically prior to reuse.

The major unexploited sources of material for recycle thus present challenging technological and managerial problems. For the most part, however, the problem is not one of absolute technological incapability to recover or reclaim the material. In virtually all instances, technological feasibility exists at all scrap processing stages to produce a marketable recycled product. Rather, the problem is that typically faced in the short run at the margin of all production endeavors, namely, that the costs of further exploitation under existing technology exceed the market value of the next increments of supply that could be brought forth. For more of the marginal available scrap to be recycled within the private market context, either demand must increase, thereby causing price to rise by a sufficient amount to cover the higher cost of the added supply, or one or more cost factors must somehow be reduced in order to make additional supply profitable. We will pursue the longer term price and cost issues further in a later section.

BY-PRODUCTS PRODUCTION

In general, production of by-products as a form of material recovery involves the use of residuals from one industrial production or consumption activity as the raw material for other, non-similar, products or functions. To one degree or another, all by-products utilize residual materials that would continue to be produced as waste (although perhaps not in the same volume) in the absence of a secondary opportunity for their economic use. By-products presently represent an almost bewildering variety of materials, technologies, inter-industry market relationships and final product uses; and they are particularly significant from a recovery stand-point in that they typically utilize material that is technically incapable of being recycled.

Individual firms may internally utilize residuals generated at one processing stage or operation in by-product applications within the same plant. The most typical industrial example of this is the burning of organic throughput residues as a fuel source for heat recovery, for example in sugar cane refineries and wood-pulp mills; but in other instances, by-product processing chemicals may be also similarly appropriated for internal reuse. The feeding of crop residues to livestock is an obvious example from the farming sector.

Most by-products, however, must compete in external markets. Some are technically identical to, and compete as perfect substitutes with, the primary outputs of other basic industries (for example, sulfuric acid from nonferrous metals smelting, natural gas from oil wells, etc.). In other cases, however, they constitute the only supply source of unique materials, as with a number of the minor metals that would not be economical to produce at all if they did not occur in association with major metal in ore deposits. As was true of inter-industry recycle, we find a number of variations in the patterns of production and marketing relationships for different by-product materials, and often for different sources of the same material. Some materials may be highly processed at their source establishments, while others are shipped in crude residual form and processed by users, and others may require no intermediate processing at all. In a number of instances, there have evolved specialized intermediate processing and market-ing firms corresponding to the secondary materials recycling industries—for example, the rending industry, cotton wiping rags dealers, and iron smelter-slag and utility coal-ash processors.

As might be expected from the nature of the operations, the largest volumes and widest varieties of by-products originate in the basic extraction sector and, especially, in the primary crude-materials processing industries, where the materials processed contain large proportions of impurities or components and where the heaviest uses of ancillary processing inputs are con-sumed. A few examples will suffice to further illustrate the diversity and order of magnitude of some of the materials involved.

The primary iron and steel industry provides a variety of ready examples, among the best known being the by-products from coke-oven residuals which have constituted the major historical source of raw material feedstock for the organic chemicals industries as well as manufactured gas. A perhaps less well known but extremely interesting by-product development in this industry is that of blast furnace and steel furnace slags.

Blast furnace slag, composed of iron ore impurities (largely silicates and aluminates), fluxing material, and coke ash residuals from the blast furnace is produced at the rate of up to one-half ton per ton of pig iron produced. It has always had some use as a road construction fill, and railroad ballast material, although prior to World War II only a relatively small proportion was utilized. However, during the past two decades, its utilization has increased to about 28 to 30 million tons per year, equaling and exceeding current annual produc-tion, to the point that historically accumulated stock-piles at a number of locations have been gradually reduced and in some places eliminated.[12] Its major uses are as a construction aggregate—in portland-cement concrete, bituminous paving, and concrete block, as a base material for pavement, as railroad ballast, fill, and as a roofing material—but it has also found interesting applications in mineral wool, ceramic materials, and a number of other uses. As noted previously, the processing of slag for by-product uses has facilitated the

annual recycle, via magnetic separation, of over a half million tons of concentrated slag-iron back to the blast furnaces.

In contrast to blast-furnace slag, steel furnace slags have been relatively little used historically. However, due partly to the decreased availability of blast-furnace slags, their processing has increased considerably in recent years to an estimated 12 million tons in 1968, primarily for use in the lower-valued fill and pavement-base applications. Both of these slags offer classic examples of materials that once constituted essentially valueless wastes, but that under slightly altered economic circum-stances (and with relatively modest developmental and promotional expenditures) became privately profitable to exploit.

From the standpoint of averting environmental damages, the by-product recovery of nonferrous smelter flue-gas constituents, especially sulfur, is of particular interest. It also provides a classic illustration of some of the problems facing potential by-products expansion. Most of the primary copper, lead, and zinc production in the United States is based on sulfide ores. A recent evaluation covering the 26 nonferrous smelters west of the Mississippi estimated gross sulfurous residuals equiva-lent to 2.5 million tons of elemental sulfur per year at these plants.[13] Presently, less than one-fourth is recovered as by-product sulfuric acid (1.6 million tons of sulfuric acid, equivalent to 550 thousand tons of elemental sulfur), with the remainder emitted to the atmosphere. Unfortunately, from the standpoint of profitable exploitation, these western smelters are surrounded by the largest low-cost sulfur producers— Texas Frasch mines; Arizona, Montana, and Utah pyrites sources; and recovered sulfur from Canadian natural gas and United States west coast oil refinery streams.

In addition, the production cost of by-product elemental sulfur from nonferrous smelters was estimated to be three to four times that of conventional sources; and local markets for this low-valued, bulk material are not large relative to potential smelter supply. Although it was estimated that smelter sulfuric acid—which is closely competitive in production costs to conventional sources—could be somewhat expanded beyond present production levels on at least a break-even cost basis, it appears evident that significant expansion in this by-product area will be largely dependent on air-pollution control exigences rather than natural market developments.

The wood pulping industry offers an additional instance in which by-product development efforts have been important in relation to pollution control. Continu-ous efforts over the years to create a major by-products chemical industry based on organic wood residuals contained in spent pulping liquors have met with mixed success, although it was reported in the mid-1960's that some 2,600 silvichemicals had been identified and extracted from wood pulp materials.[14]

In the kraft (or sulfate) wood pulping process, which now accounts for two-thirds of all wood pulp production, the major portion of lignin and wood sugar residuals are burned (with recovery of heat) as an integral part of the technology for recycling pulping chemicals. A relatively small portion (a half million tons in the mid-1960's) is recovered as sulfate turpentine and crude tall oils. These are either sold directly or processed further by distillation and other methods to yield purified tall oil, rosin, pitch, and a wide variety of lower volume chemical products.

In the older sulfite chemical pulping process, which has declined in relative importance to about six percent of current wood pulp production, efforts at by-products development have produced a large array of products; however, only about 20 percent of the spent-sulfite liquor material was estimated to be productively utilized. The two principal uses of concentrated sulfite liquor have been as a road binding material (mainly chargeable to the mill as a waste disposal method) and as an oil well drilling fluid. Other products include ethyl alcohol, vanillin, acetic and formic acids, and a variety of other chemical products used as binders in ceramics, animal feed pellatizing, lenoleum paste, and ready mixed concrete products. A small number of plants have utilized biological conversion processes to convert sugars into torulla yeast, a high protein animal feed supplement.

A virtually endless number of additional examples could be cited; however, our time will better be spent in summarizing some of the major problems and potentials of this general material recovery category. We can begin by saying that by-product expansion shares all of the same general problems faced by any material recovery activity—that is, development of lower cost technologies, difficult competition with existing virgin materials, possible locational disadvantages of residuals generation sources compared with markets, and the like. In addition, there may exist two particular kinds of difficulties unique to this special category (or at least to particular segments of it).

The first is the range of difficulties faced, especially in the development of new by-products, by the firm which often finds itself in a completely foreign technological and marketing arena from its traditional lines of production. Many individual firms and some entire industries may find it especially difficult to orient themselves successfully to the production and marketing challenges posed. What we are saying essentially, is that

the by-products development area may pose uncommonly high requirements for invention and innovation.

A second point is that, in some selected by-product areas at least, the absolute size of the relevant regional market may pose an absolutely limiting constraint on particular by-product growth. This has been clearly demonstrated in at least a few instances where the potential by-product supplies of only two or three plants in a particular industry are apparently sufficient to supply the entire national market for a particular product—vanillin from sulfite wood pulp mills and monosodium glutinate from beet sugar refineries, to cite two instances. We have already seen that the potential sulfur production of the western United States nonferrous smelters would equal a very substantial portion of the nation's total sulfur market. The sulfur potentially produceable from the stack gases at United States coal-burning power plants alone would be sufficient to supply the nation's total sulfur requirements in about a decade (given present relative growth rates of sulfur consumption and utility coal consumption).

It is evident that processed by-products represent the broadest field for potential innovation in the production and marketing of recovered materials. It also presents some of the greatest challenges to would-be entrepreneurs.

FACTORS AFFECTING THE FUTURE PICTURE

Preceding sections have attempted to define and review the present status of material recovery activity in the United States, and also to point out some of the more important potentials for future expansion. The purpose of the present section is to highlight briefly at a very general level some of the key factors likely to influence the degree to which recovery potentials are exploited over the coming decades.

Assuming the continued existence of competitive domestic and international commodity markets, recovered materials must obviously compete with virgin material supplies for their relative share of material-user market demands, both in price and quality terms. Clearly, future changes in these competitive relationships will depend both on virgin commodity cost trends and recovered material cost trends; and these may be influenced both by the natural workings of the dynamic private market system as well as by the direct and indirect effects of public policy actions.

As a very general proposition, the higher the marginal production cost or supply price of virgin materials and the lower the production cost of competing recovered materials, the stronger will become the relative market share of the latter. This emphasizes that one needs to look at both sides of the competitive picture in projecting relative market shares.

On the side of what is likely to happen to the costs of producing primary natural resource commodities over the next 30 to 50 years, we are not prepared to say very much in the present chapter, since this is treated in considerable depth and detail in the following chapters. However, we may note that relatively few virgin materials are projected to show significant upward cost trends by virtue of diminished natural resource bases, and those that do tend to occur relatively late in the projection period. On the other hand, no major primary commodity groups appear slated for long-term trend decreases in their real costs of supply.

However, another factor to be entered here is that of the possible cost increases in primary materials due to the increased imposition of environmental quality protection measures upon the mines and mills—requirements for mine safety, strip mine surface reclamation, erosion control, air and water pollution control, and the like. Clearly, these kinds of cost increases could be substantial in a nmber of particular cases. Further, they have a tendency to be pyramided, from mine through mill and smelter, each adding its increment to finished commodity price. In contrast with possible cost increases due to long-term depletion of the resource base, those due to environmental quality protection are both much more pervasive (affecting virtually all primary materials to some degree), and also much more immediate in their occurrence (many are already being reflected). It is easy to overplay this case, since secondary recovery operations, many of which have themselves historically been relatively high-polluting industries, are also subjected to the same kind of new or increased cost factor.

Nevertheless, on balance, there is the suggestion of at least a modest shift in the competitive relationship in favor of inter-industry and inter-sector recycle (and possibly also certain by-product materials) due to a heavier differential impact of environmental protection measures on direct costs of primary materials. This shift is currently underway and should continue to work itself out over the near-term future as the backlog of abatement measures gets caught up. On the other hand, those primary material cost increases due to increased scarcity of high grade mineral or other natural resource bases will apparently be much more selective, and their impacts will not generally begin to provide a direct stimulus to secondary recovery until quite some time in the future.

Regardless of whether projections for specific materials are right or wrong, the important principle here is that, if and when a primary material becomes scarcer (exerts upward pressure on price), there will in most instances be an automatic tendency on the part of secondary suppliers to fill as large a part of the gap as their own marginal cost conditions allow in response to the price change. This in turn mitigates the price rise, but at a larger resulting secondary material output.

This takes us to the other side of the question, namely, what should we expect in the future of recovery costs, per se? In other words, can one foresee substantial shifts in recovery cost functions playing a major independent role in improving the relative competitive position of secondary materials and by-products vis-a-vis primary commodities? The answer here is a somewhat guarded yes.

Decreasing the real economic costs of collecting, moving, sorting, separating, processing, and finally refining or reusing recovered materials (whether internal to the enterprise or on an inter-sectoral basis) almost necessarily implies some form of innovation—either in engineering technology, management organization, industry structure, or social institutions. The same could be said for improving the quality (technical attributes) of recovered materials (at the same or reduced unit costs), or for devising and marketing new materials or products, or for profitably exploiting previously nonrecoverable materials. In the longer-run time perspective of our present study, it is factors such as these that will have the major bearing on the role of materials recovery 30 to 50 years hence, and not the close calculations at the margin of cost and revenue of existing technologies so crucial to an understanding of what to expect over the next five years.

Therefore, one's position on the longer-term future possibilities should depend much more on one's estimate of the system's capabilities for creative invention and innovation, as well as the system's incentive structure for stimulating and guiding the rate and direction of innovative activity, rather than a detailed exploration of the current state of the art.

From a very cursory reading of the historical evidence, various elements of the nation's materials recovery structure exhibit wide variations in innovative capabilities. Regarding the major industries and their in-plant recycle and by-product potentials, one can be relatively confident that the innovative requirements can be met, provided that sufficient incentives are provided to assure that reasonable quantities of internal resources are allocated in this direction. As one moves towards smaller, less diversified firms, one becomes less sure about the internal capabilities.

Considering the secondary recovery industries themselves, one also has the impression of a very mixed picture. Many segments of these industries have traditionally been small-scale, family operations—notably in the collection and preprocessing of old scrap, and even with respect to final-user stages, many of the specialized user-processors are by modern standards small scale operations, lacking a solid research and development capability or the financial resources to develop them. Some of these industry groups, as noted earlier, appear to be on the demise, while others are expanding. Of all the elements of the recovery scene, municipal waste collection and disposal agencies (both refuse and wastewater) have, as a group and with very few exceptions, historically exhibited the least managerial or organizational capability to innovate in the area of material recovery. On this reading, it seems evident that at a number of key points in the overall economic and institutional structure, either the managerial capabilities or the financial resources or appropriate incentives, have been weak or absent.

Our reasons for optimism about the future relate not so much to where the system stands at present, but rather to how rapidly certain aspects of it have evolved only within the past decade, and the directions that they appear headed in.

Undoubtedly, the major new incentive presently operating to enhance materials recovery prospects over the near-term future resides in the Federal and state air and water pollution control policies introduced during the 1960's, and to a large extent still in an early stage of implementation. For literally the first time, these waste disposal restrictions have begun to reverse historical conditions of zero or very low-cost waste-disposal for most major residuals producers. As environmental disposal for some kinds of residuals becomes entirely prohibited, and as treatment and disposal costs for others become more significant, the opportunity costs to residuals producers of not recovering marketable values from their residuals become both more obvious and of more direct concern in both private and public decision-making. There can be little question but that this is the major new incentive factor operating on in-plant recycle and industrial by-products development. However, it also operated in the area of inter-industry recovery.

Adding its weight to this factor is the increasing scarcity of land-disposal sites in major metropolitan areas, reflected both in rising land prices and in frequent political opposition to any large-scale disposal operations. Since most wastewater treatment and air-pollution control devices transform previously transported materials into solid residuals, the land disposal situation is even further aggreyated, thus adding to the recovery stimulus.

The specific effects of these new incentives on waste recovery and reuse over the coming decades will depend not only on the strength of abatement policy and its particular mechanisms of implementation (still in a formulative stage in many respects), but also of course on the relative costs of alternative means of compliance. Nevertheless, pollution control policy may be rightly regarded as the cornerstone of material recovery policy.

Although it is a little too early to judge the full response of the system to these policies, there is considerable evidence of a new awakening in the private sector—new trade associations of material-recovery-related interests both within and across industry boundaries; new "industries" of consulting firms; new divisions, services, and products in the larger companies; increased interest in the investment houses; revisions in thinking within many consumer goods and packaging goods industries regarding the corporate interest and advantage in recycling the consumer's discard. Although much of this may be peripheral to the question of whether the 1970-75 by-products and recycle trends show an increase in slope compared to earlier years, it does seem indicative of new private sector resources entering the innovative process, and a revision in the private sector's sense of priorities.

There are, of course, a number of additional public policy options that might be introduced over the near future in an attempt to influence material recovery more directly, such as specific waste disposal taxes, direct operating subsidies to public and private recycle enterprises, and many, many more. Since it is not our point here to devise recycle policy alternatives, nor even to anticipate what they might be, it will suffice merely to emphasize that, with the exception of publicly supported research, development, and demonstration funding (mainly in the areas of municipal solid waste management), we have not yet formulated or implemented extensive material recovery policies of a comprehensive nature. This is probably the major single unknown element in the near-term future of material recovery.

Another factor that remains quite open to questioning is what to expect from the municipal sanitation systems. Successful exploitation on a self-sustaining basis of even a relatively small fraction of the total collected solid refuse and sewage sludge would represent major historical breakthroughs in the national picture. Fortunately, there are some signs of a new awakening in this sector also, partly in response to Federal Government research and demonstration initiatives and partly to steeply rising costs of many of the traditional waste disposal options. However, it remains to be seen whether successful institutional reforms can be carried out which either provide the city departments the capability to be strengthened as public material recovery operations, or provide for a new integration between city regional collection agencies and private sector recovery industries. Next to these questions, and those of how to credit waste disposal cost savings against recovery costs in municipal accounting systems, the questions of new technology may seem relatively easy to overcome over the next 10 to 20 years.

CONCLUDING COMMENTS

One should not be so optimistic regarding the practical potentials of materials recovery and reuse as to consider this a panacea for all problems of environmental quality and materials supply. To begin with, some extremely important groups of environmental problems are simply not amenable to mitigation via materials recovery. These include the whole range of ecological problems associated with the destruction of natural areas due to large-scale construction and other developmental activities, as well as many of the soil conservation and water quality problems stemming from various causes of soil erosion. They also include many of the conventional air and water pollutants—those related to inherently dissipative materials uses such as chemical pesticides and most residuals from fuel combustion. If these types of problems are to be dealt with, they must largely be approached in other, more directly preventative, ways. In addition, the fact that material recovery activities, just like any other production activities, are subject to diminishing marginal returns and increasing marginal costs means that there will always be technically recoverable quantities beyond the margin of privately profitable or socially worthwhile possibilities for reuse.

Finally, it should be kept in mind that other viable options for more conservative materials utilization will frequently exist—for example, material substitutions, technical process changes, product redesign—and that these may often offer superior means for achieving the same ends.

Keeping these necessary caveats in mind, we have nevertheless seen that materials recovery in its various forms already performs a major role in our economic life, both from the material welfare and the natural resource conservation perspectives, and we have suggested that there may be at least equally significant practical potentials for its socially efficient expansion over the next 30 to 50 years. The economic system already contains a solid technological base for materials recovery, as well as an industrial structure and specialized marketing organizations that are at least partially attuned to exploiting these potentials. We have argued further that the economy's incentive system for recovery can be expected to operate much more fully and effectively in the future than it has in the past, now that our political system has begun to rectify the major historical failure of the market system to reflect the social costs of waste disposal back to their private and public sources as incentives to more efficient materials use and reuse.

For the most part, then, we should be able to rely on the market system and the private profit mechanism to move in the right directions, at least, if not always to the desired degree, in its future recycling and by-products development activities.

In any event, we do not expect to see our material recovery activity perform any less well in the coming decades than in the past, with the possible and noteworthy major exception of the secondhand goods markets and consumer durable-goods repair components of the economy. On the contrary, we should expect to see most elements perform at least modestly better, even if left alone at this point from a public policy standpoint. Beyond this, there is considerable scope for well-designed public policy to provide appropriate incentives to make the economic system take greater advantage of its potentials. There also appears to be a clear and strong case for continued and probably increased Federal research and development support, as well as needs in certain areas for institutional change, if material recovery is to perform significantly better over the next half century than it has in the past.

There are a number of major unknowns in the future materials recovery picture, particularly in the area of technology, but also in the field of city government and regional waste management agency responses to the newly evolving Federal incentives and local citizen pressure groups. The uncertainties, of course, complicate the process of assaying the future contribution of material recovery to the continuance of material prosperity and maintenance of a livable environment.

However, one of the major conclusions to be drawn from all this is that the existence of substantial unexploited material recovery opportunities, though presently beyond the margin of profitability, provides a considerable element of flexibility to the future of the system. As such it provides a capability to absorb at least some future shocks over a relatively long period of time, as and if they occur, thus allowing considerably more time and resources to discover what the future world resource and population picture may hold forth.

REFERENCES

1. The broader question of how the socioeconomic system determines the effective economic life (durability) of the durable goods which it designs, produces, and utilizes has not received the attention it deserves among social scientists, although some aspects have received somewhat more popular partial treatment under such rubrics as the "hidden persuaders" and "planned obsolescense." The importance of the question for resource conservation and residuals generation is quite evident.

2. The water pollution and control-cost implications of this trend have been widely noted. See for example, U.S. Federal Water Pollution Control Administration, *The Economics of Clean Water,* Vol. II, *Animal Wastes Profile,* 1970.

3. U.S. Bureau of Mines and Illinois Technology Research Institute, "The Economic Factors of Mineral Waste Utilization," by William A. Vogely, in *Proceedings of the Symposium: Mineral Waste Utilization* (Chicago, Illinois, 1968), p. 9.

4. *Ibid.,* "Mining and Milling Waste Disposal Problems—Where Are We Today?" by Lewis M. McNay, pp. 126-30.

5. Based on H. C. Bramer, "Iron and Steel," in *Industrial Wastewater Control,* C. F. Gurnham, ed. (New York: Academic Press, Inc., 1965), ch. 14.

6. U.S. Bureau of Mines, "Slag—Iron and Steel," by John W. Thatcher, *Minerals Yearbook,* Vol. I-II, 1968, p. 1020.

7. John A. Tallmadge, "Nonferrous Metals," in *Industrial Wastewater Control, op. cit.,* ch. 15.

8. H. C. Bramer, *op. cit.*

9. A crude aggregate materials balance for the entire paper and board industry, based on published U.S. Department of Commerce data, indicates a virtual equality between the weights of total fibrous and chemicals inputs and the weight of total industry paper and board output.

10. For discussion of typical practices see American Public Works Association, *Municipal Refuse Disposal* (Chicago, Ill.: Public Administration Service, 1966). For more recent survey information on historical and current municipal salvage, see: U.S. Bureau of Mines, *Resource Recovery from Incinerator Residue,* by the American Public Works Association Research Foundation, 1969.

11. Author's estimates based on reviews of municipal refuse composition studies and current final user consumption data for materials in question.

12. U.S. Bureau of Mines and Illinois Technology Research Institute, "The Successful Utilization of Iron and Steel Slags," by H. K. Eggleston, *Proceedings of the Second Mineral Waste Utilization Symposium, op. cit.,* pp. 16-22.

13. F. A. Ferguson *et al.,* "SO_2 From Smelters: By-Product Markets A Powerful Lure," *Environmental Science and Technology,* July 1970, Vol. 4, No. 7.

14. L. C. Bratt, "Trends in Production of Silvichemicals in the United States and Abroad," *Tappi,* July 1965, Vol. 48, No. 7. Also see: "Chemicals From the Other Half of the Tree," *Chemical and Engineering News, Feb. 1963.*

Chapter 4

Adequacy of Nonfuel Minerals and Forest Resources

by
Leonard L. Fischman
Economic Associates, Inc. and
Hans H. Landsberg,
Resources for the Future, Inc.

COMMISSION ON POPULATION GROWTH AND
THE AMERICAN FUTURE, *RESEARCH
REPORTS, VOLUME III, POPULATION
RESOURCES AND THE ENVIRONMENT,*
EDITED BY RONALD G. RIDKER

CONTENTS

Adequacy of Nonfuel Minerals and Forest Resources

INTRODUCTION

Concern with mineral resources has long been couched in such terms as "adequacy of resources for economic and population growth," "mineral shortages," a "healthy mineral industry," and "self-sufficiency." Interest in the subject is more than justified. Evaluation of the nature and severity of mineral problems, however, and the formulation of solutions requires more precision than the foregoing terminology suggests.

"Adequacy," for example, is far from a simple concept, either on the requirements side or the supply side. Just what is the long-range "requirement" for a given mineral? How long is "long"? Is "need" defined as the volume of materials to satisfy the same input ratio for the same kinds of end products and services as are in use today, or only enough to meet demand at a given price? Or should one perhaps be concerned only with a "hard-core" requirement, that would persist even in the face of major increases in the material's cost? If so, how much is "major"? Should one possibly be concerned only with whatever amounts of the mineral are absolutely necessary to our not having to do without the end product or service altogether? Which would lead one to inquire how much of the end product or service is itself a "requirement" to begin with: today's per capita consumption, or the trends in per capita consumption? What per capita consumption would be attained if everyone could have the product or service they wanted. What about labor-saving devices, investment, research and development, science, art, and culture? Is it a "requirement" that man should not have to indulge in physical labor if there is technology to avoid it, regardless of the cost to man or the environment? Are the quantities "required" that would not be used if we were more conservationist in our consumption habits? Do we really "require" higher-speed highways, supersonic airplanes, leisure cities, Kennedy Centers, subways, bigger colleges, etc.? How much of a military establishment do we "require"? How much of a foreign-aid program? Is it a "requirement" that we go to the moon, split the atom, conquer cancer?

How much of a "requirement" do we assign to the world outside the United States? As much as they can afford? The quintupling of their per capita consumption which would bring them abreast of the United States? By when?

What is to be the relative valuation of a requirement today and a competing requirement 20, 40, or 100 years hence, or of preemptive consumption by the United States today of supplies needed elsewhere in the world some years hence?

What is a "shortage," and what is "adequacy"? Is the supply of a given mineral "adequate" only if it continues to be forthcoming in the "required" amounts at present relative prices, or at prices rising no more rapidly than has been the trend, even if that trend reflects increasing supply stringencies? What if the only means of avoiding marked price change is the initiation of unaccustomed efforts at conservation, reuse, and recycling, or the making of major investments toward technological advance? Is adequacy measured in terms of current levels of minerals exploration, evaluation, and development, or trend levels? May a mineral be considered adequate just because it can be geologically inferred to exist in sufficient quantity, even if it takes major new outlays in exploration, evaluation, and development to find this quantity and get it into production?

Is a mineral adequate in supply only if it exists within the borders of the United States? Or is it adequate even if located outside of the United States, but "securely" available to us? Or only if the import component of supply causes no major balance-of-payment problems? Or only if the United States does not increase its already-large share (some 20 percent in value, for non-energy minerals overall) of the world's consumption? Is United States supply "adequate" if we can preempt it in competition with other claimants only by paying a higher price?

Basic Standards

The answers to these questions depend upon the establishment of a set of reference standards—ethical, pragmatic, or other. Moreover, each requirements/supply balance can usually be profitably examined from the standpoint of a number of standards; and, different sets of standards will be particularly relevant to different mineral resources.

If the notion of "shortage" is to have enough specificity to permit rational discussion, at least a minimum set of reference standards is essential. The following normative propositions may serve as a starting point:

1. Any difference between actual (or probable) and possible per capita welfare (market goods plus "quality of life") which can be attributed in significant measure to a mineral supply problem is to be regarded as indicating a shortage of that mineral.

2. Any shortfall in the supply of a mineral from locations militarily, politically, and economically secure is a shortage as far as the United States is concerned.

3. Shortages are relative, not absolute.

4. In determining relative shortage, United States requirements are to be accorded a higher value than foreign requirements.

5. In determining relative shortage, the welfare of the current generation is to be accorded a higher value than that of the next generation, the welfare of the next generation a higher value than of the one succeeding it, etc.

Arbitrary (and possibly distasteful) as some of these propositions may appear to be, nothing less will suffice; and they only begin to set the necessary normative framework for evaluation. Relative values must still be assigned. Following are some considerations of the elements behind these propositions.

Supply vs. Demand

Even historically, let alone in projection, we know very little about the actual demand and supply circumstances for minerals. It may be taken for granted, however, that whatever the consumption of any given mineral might have been, its availability at a lower price would ordinarily have led to greater consumption. Similarly, a higher price would have led to lesser consumption. These differences might or might not have had anything significantly to do with ultimate per capita welfare, for they might merely have represented alternative ways of producing an identical aggregate amount of goods and services and associated non-market satisfactions. Somewhere up along the price scale, however, aggregate production would, in fact, have been seriously limited by the amounts of raw material available. Though we cannot know its exact location, we have to accept that there is such a point. Ascertainment of a mineral "shortage" in a sense is identical with identification, as well as possible, of that point or range.

National Security

An essential element in human welfare is personal security. Since personal security is, in some measure, a

reflection of the collective security, it follows that military security is an element in personal welfare. At some point along a diminishing scale, the contribution of collective military security to welfare must become perceptible, and even farther down the scale, potential jeopardy to the raw-material supply associated with security must significantly affect that security. Thus, there is some minimum "requirement" for geographical distribution of sources of mineral supply desirable for security reasons.

The proposition also holds more directly—in terms of output of civilian goods and services. If a lesser output (without compensating extra-market income) signifies less welfare than a greater output, so must any pattern of mineral supply which holds the risk of a lesser output.

"Shortage" is Relative

This follows necessarily from the fact that each of the criteria we have been discussing involves a continuum. The proposition obligates the analyst to inquire into the consequences of shortage, in order to determine its relative seriousness, with special attention to compensatory features or trade-offs.

United States vs. Foreign Requirements

Simply by the impact of its demand on world mineral prices (or effective control of a share of foreign supplies), the United States has inevitably imposed a pattern of mineral exploitation and trade upon others. Some maintain that it has done so at the expense of other countries; others say that it is bound to do so in the future. This appears to be a question subject to proof, and one beset with all the problems of questions that inquire into the implications of a rearranged history. There is, however, no escaping a working decision as to the relative priority to be accorded self, community, and nation as against other individuals, communities, and nations. Even to postulate a right to equality—a kind of resource egalitarianism—on a per capita or any other basis, represents such a decision. Ascertainment of true equality necessitates the factoring in of subjective differences in enjoyment of material consumption as well as of the virtually unevaluable "welfare" quantities embodied in satisfactions of the spirit. In any case, the mere proposition that raw materials ought to be equally shared in a world in which per capita GNP ranges from less than $100 in Southeast Asia, to nearly $5,000 in the United States, cannot be seriously contemplated except in the context of a revolutionary rearrangement of the world economy that far transcends any difficulties one might wish to contemplate in the field of mineral resources. This is apart from the fact that those enjoying a higher than proportionate share would claim this as a prerogative earned through history. We shall return to this point below in a slightly different context.

Present vs. Future Generations

Much the same type of reasoning applies to any conflict between present and future generations. Few would abjure responsibility for the welfare of future generations, but almost as few would accept an obligation of major current sacrifice for the benefit of as yet unborn generations. Particularly, they would not do so if the future benefit were conservation of per capita welfare which, though it might be lower than its potential by reason of minerals shortage, would—history suggests—still be much higher than that of the present generation.

Present vs. Distant Values

Reinforcing the judgment in both of the foregoing cases is a legitimate distinction between the here and now and the farther off—both in time and in space. The application of discounts to the future and the unknown is common practice. Whether it takes the form of sacrifice of interest on an investment or sacrifice of present enjoyment, a present loss is sure and knowable; the future gain—or the gain of distant populations—is less measurable and is subject to greater uncertainty. What assurance is there that far-off countries and future generations will be able to take advantage of any given level of specific mineral input made feasible by abstention among present users. Would we be better off—and by how much—if past generations had been more sparing in their use of, say, copper and tin? And what would they have used instead, and what would have been the consequences? Obviously, whatever they did or did not do, they opened up a road toward technological accomplishments that, in retrospect, seem to dwarf any drain on resources. To pursue the argument, what assurance is there that the "others" will attach similar values to the corresponding output? What assurance is there that they will not have alternative—and more efficient—means of accomplishing the same ends and thereby rendering any present sacrifice redundant (as has happened to us versus past generations)? These are all legitimate questions.

A partially countervailing consideration, at least insofar as time discount is concerned, is "lead time." It is widely recognized that no matter how uncertain our knowledge of the future, action must be taken sufficiently in advance to avert any calamitous occurrences. These are the kinds of occurrences where the benefit of insuring against loss, even when discounted, is judged to outweigh the opportunity cost of timely action. Evalua-

tion of the balance depends on the certainty that the viewer attaches to the outcome, and how grave he regards the calamity. Thus, at the extreme, there are those who now see ultimate consequences sure enough and dire enough (often seen as irreversible outcomes) to warrant an immediate commencement of zero population growth and an immediate and sharp diminution of physical consumption. At the other extreme are those who think it far more certain that "something will turn up" than that calamity will befall. In between are those who prefer to consider both the discounted risk and the lead time necessary to avert it. Following the comments on specific resource situations, we shall return to the lead time question more fully.

A Pragmatic Approach

To recapitulate, it is reasonable to look to the future with feelings neither of impending doom nor of complacency; to discount the distant, both in place and in time; and to regard any identifiable shortfall in aggregate output due to stringency of minerals supply as a loss, though not necessarily a significant one.

How does one apply these principles to an evaluation of mineral requirements and supply prospects, as they affect the interests of the present residents of a country (in this instance the United States) allowing for a reasonably discounted assumption of responsibility toward the future and the rest of the world? A practical start toward an answer is through an initial "screening"—one that will quickly, even if roughly, distinguish the "non-problem" minerals from the "problem" minerals and the "critical-problem" minerals. The problem cases can then be examined in depth. The approach requires a normative assumption as to the general character of past mineral supply-demand balances—in other words, actual minerals prices and consumption.

Since some mineral prices have risen and others have fallen, relative to one another and to the general price level, it may be deduced that some minerals have been getting scarcer in relation to "requirements" and others have been getting more plentiful. At the same time, since consumption in nearly all cases has been growing, the price responses may be assumed to be mostly a matter of relative supply and relative preference in application. As a whole, mineral prices have not exhibited a particularly rising trend, and there have been no sustained individual rises of such magnitude as to indicate that a mineral is on the verge of "running out" (though some have surely run out for some uses, but that is how the market reacts to changing relative costs and prices). In fact, year after year, the "reserves" for all minerals (defined as ore in the ground which is profitably minable at current prices) have tended to remain a relatively constant multiple of annual consumption. Thus, there is basis for an a priori presumption that scarcity of minerals has not so far had a significant impact on the aggregate production of measurable goods and services (GNP).

A second indication that mineral supplies have not so far impeded the rate of growth of the United States economy is the small, and falling, proportion they constitute of GNP. Currently, the value of primary minerals consumption, including energy materials, is only about three percent of GNP; that of nonenergy minerals is only a little more than one percent. Such low percentages have held in times of full employment as well as slack. Except for miners' strikes and other special occurrences, slack employment has never been attributed to mineral shortage. In times of full employment, scarcity of minerals could have been the limiting factor on aggregate output only to the extent that a more plentiful minerals supply might have enabled the labor force to function at a generally higher level of productivity—which is rather unlikely—or to the extent that lower real cost of minerals would have permitted diversion of mining labor to other effort. But the extent of such diversion is obviously limited, especially in the short run, and given the small role of mining labor in the GNP generally.

Trend Projections of Demand

By and large, it seems safe to postulate that past trends in aggregate mineral consumption in the United States have come rather close to a "non-shortage" situation. If there have been shortages—disregarding wartime emergencies—they certainly could not have been characterized as "serious." Can the same assumption be made, however, about projections based on trend? Is it not possible that, in the future, there will be less opportunity to compensate for declining availabilities of one or another raw material by substitution or by increases in cost that are negligible in terms of the economy as a whole? And is this not especially so because, even at no increase in rates of growth, the mere scale of production leads into different realms of materials consumption and depletion?

Our method has been to seek the answer to that question in two stages. The first stage is to project a mix of total and individual mineral consumption which would represent no future drag on GNP. Only those substitutions will have been incorporated in the mix that we believe to be visible on the basis of current trends. If then, as a second stage, we examine the individual minerals in the mix, we have a basis for initial conclusions as to whether there is prospect of shortage. Should we find that supplies are prospectively available,

at no increase in cost, for each of the individual mineral items, we can immediately proceed to a conclusion of "no shortage." Should we find that one or another falls short, we need to look further into the supply expansion and substitution possibilities only for those individual items.

The projections we have made for the foregoing purpose represent no simple extrapolation of past growth rates. As described in Chapter 2, use was made of a complex input-output model, projected into the future under varying sets of assumptions as to demographic trends and overall productivity growth as determined by factors quite independent of raw materials supply. The "trend" element in the projections lies essentially in the coefficients assumed to represent the input-output relationships among the model's 185 activity sectors, as well as in the macroeconomic determinants of "final demand." The projected domestic output (and the imports, segment by segment, to complement it) of the materials-producing sectors in the model is the end result of the whole complex of such trend relationships, plus postulated demographic and productivity assumptions used to represent different versions of the future.

Using base-year conversion ratios between the "constant dollars" of the input-output model and the physical quantities of primary domestic consumption of specific minerals, we arrived at projected physical consumption of these minerals, under each of the sets of assumptions, for intervals into the future, up to the year 2020. Ten-year intervals were used in some cases. In others, where the "basket" nature of the input-output activity category made conversion into physical units difficult, projections were made from the model for the year 2000 only, and the year 2020 was extrapolated by means of the implied 1968-2000 growth rates.

Table 1 shows the resultant United States projections for each of four "futures," defined in Chapter 2 (B-high, high population and economic growth; E-low, low population and economic growth; and B-low and E-high). The projections are shown in the table for the years 2000 and 2020, with corresponding 1968-1970 demand for comparison.[1] In each case, the figures represent domestic primary-metal consumption, on the assumption that the rates of use of secondary (scrap or recycled) material would be no greater than in the base period.

The subsequent entries under "U.S. demand" show the implications of the projected annual consumption levels for cumulative demand through the year 2000 and the year 2020, respectively. The cumulations were made on the assumption of a constant rate of growth for the mineral in question either within each decade or within

Table 1.—Current and Projected U.S. and World Requirements for Principal Nonfuel Minerals under Various Assumptions as to Population and Economic Growth[a]

Mineral, unit of quantity, and time period[c]	United States[b]				Rest of the world		World total	
	"B" pop.		"E" pop.					
	High	Low	High	Low	High	Low	High	Low
Iron (million tons) 1968	96				344		440	
1969	100				n.a.		n.a.	
1970	95				n.a.		n.a.	
2000	219	180	197	161	758	537	977	698
2020	432	314	337	243	1,242	709	1,674	952
1968-2000	4,879	4,389	4,678	4,193	17,320	14,314	22,199	18,507
1968-2020	11,293	9,325	9,956	8,222	37,164	26,778	48,457	35,000
Aluminum (million tons) 1968	3.8				6.4		10.2	
1969	3.8				n.a.		n.a.	
1970	3.7				n.a.		n.a.	
2000	17.5	14.3	16.0	13.1	68	32	86	45
2020	38.7	27.6	30.4	21.7	300	88	339	110
1968-2000	302	268	292	259	878	533	1,180	792
1968-2020	853	685	751	607	4,121	1,670	4,974	2,277
Copper (million tons) 1968	1.6				5.8		7.4	
1969	1.7				n.a.		n.a.	
1970	1.6				n.a.		n.a.	
2000	4.0	3.2	3.6	2.9	34.9	16.8	38.9	19.7
2020	8.1	5.8	6.3	4.5	107.8	32.8	115.9	37.3
1968-2000	87	76	84	75	538	341	625	416
1968-2020	206	166	182	148	1,867	827	2,073	975
Lead (million tons) 1968	0.8				2.6		3.4	
1969	0.8				n.a.		n.a.	
1970	0.8				n.a.		n.a.	
2000	2.4	2.0	2.2	1.7	5.3	4.3	7.7	6.0
2020	4.8	3.4	3.8	2.7	8.4	5.8	13.2	8.5
1968-2000	47	42	46	40	124	110	171	150
1968-2020	117	95	105	85	260	211	377	296
Zinc (million tons) 1968	1.5				4.0		5.5	
1969	1.5				n.a.		n.a.	
1970	1.3				n.a.		n.a.	
2000	4.4	3.5	3.9	3.1	11.2	8.8	15.6	11.9
2020	9.3	6.4	7.1	4.9	21.4	14.4	30.7	19.3
1968-2000	85	75	80	70	233	201	318	271
1968-2020	220	174	189	149	554	432	774	581
Manganese (million tons) 1968	1.2				7.1		8.3	
1969	1.6				n.a.		n.a.	
1970	1.6				n.a.		n.a.	
2000	2.9	2.4	2.6	2.1	21.3	15.2	24.2	17.3
2020	4.4	3.1	3.6	2.7	42.4	24.4	46.8	27.1
1968-2000	70.0	62.9	65.8	59.7	428	351	498	411
1968-2020	143.0	117.9	127.8	107.9	1,052	745	1,195	853
Chromium (million tons) 1968	0.4				1.5		1.9	
1969	0.5				n.a.		n.a.	
1970	0.5				n.a.		n.a.	
2000	1.1	0.9	1.0	0.8	4.3	2.8	5.4	3.6
2020	2.0	1.4	1.7	1.2	8.2	4.2	10.2	5.4

Table 1.—Continued

Mineral, unit of quantity, and time period[c]	United States[b] "B" pop. High	"B" pop. Low	"E" pop. High	"E" pop. Low	Rest of the world High	Rest of the world Low	World total High	World total Low
1968-2000	23.6	21.3	22.3	20.1	89	69	113	89
1968-2020	53.8	44.2	48.5	39.8	212	138	266	178
Nickel (million tons) 1968	0.16				0.3		0.5	
1969	0.14				n.a.		n.a.	
1970	0.15				n.a.		n.a.	
2000	.44	.36	.40	.32	1.1	0.8	1.5	1.1
2020	.89	.65	.75	.53	2.4	1.3	3.3	1.8
1968-2000	8.8	7.9	8.3	7.4	20.4	16.3	29.2	23.7
1968-2020	21.8	17.9	19.5	15.9	54.2	36.7	76.0	52.6
Tungsten (thousand tons) 1968	6.4				28		34	
1969	7.8				n.a.		n.a.	
1970	7.5				n.a.		n.a.	
2000	41	34	37	30	70	55	111	85
2020	125	94	108	76	122	84	247	160
1968-2000	620	550	580	510	1,515	1,337	2,135	1,847
1968-2020	2,160	1,750	1,940	1,520	3,410	2,715	5,570	4,235
Molybdenum (thousand tons) 1968	24				41		65	
1969	25				n.a.		n.a.	
1970	22				n.a.		n.a.	
2000	120	98	107	87	196	145	316	232
2020	361	259	299	213	522	317	883	530
1968-2000	1,870	1,640	1,740	1,530	3,304	2,731	5,174	4,261
1968-2020	6,350	5,030	5,570	4,410	10,131	7,208	16,481	11,618
Vanadium (thousand tons) 1968	5.5				11.2		16.7	
1969	6.2				n.a.		n.a.	
1970	10.0				n.a.		n.a.	
2000	46.0	38.0	41.0	34.0	40	29	86	63
2020	126.0	93.0	104.2	78.0	88	52	214	130
1968-2000	760	670	700	620	744	617	1,504	1,237
1968-2020	2,380	1,920	2,080	1,710	1,983	1,419	4,363	3,129
Cobalt (thousand tons) 1968	6.4				15.0		21.4	
1969	7.5				n.a.		n.a.	
1970	6.6				n.a.		n.a.	
2000	17.8	10.9	15.8	9.9	28.0	20.5	45.8	30.4
2020	34.7	14.9	28.7	12.9	41.5	25.0	76.2	37.9
1968-2000	360	280	340	270	692	583	1,052	853
1968-2020	880	540	780	500	1,386	1,039	2,266	1,539
Tin (thousand tons) 1968	66				211		277	
1969	65				n.a.		n.a.	
1970	60				n.a.		n.a.	
2000	97	83	93	79	437	211	534	290
2020	135	103	126	95	689	211	824	306
1968-2000	2,520	2,320	2,460	2,270	10,238	6,948	12,758	9,218
1968-2020	4,840	4,190	4,650	4,020	21,429	11,160	26,269	15,180
Magnesium[d] (million tons) 1968	1.2				4.1		5.3	
1969	n.a.				n.a.		n.a.	
1970	n.a.				n.a.		n.a.	

Population, Resources, and the Environment

Table 1.—Continued

Mineral, unit of quantity, and time period[c]	United States[b]				Rest of the world		World total	
	"B" pop.		"E" pop.		High	Low	High	Low
	High	Low	High	Low				
2000	3.0	1.5	2.7	1.3	9.4	5.8	12.4	7.1
2020	5.3	1.7	4.5	1.4	15.8	7.2	21.1	8.6
1968-2000	65	44	62	41	210	162	275	203
1968-2020	147	76	134	68	461	292	608	360
Titanium[d] (million tons) 1968	0.5				1.0		1.5	
1969	n.a.				n.a.		n.a.	
1970	n.a.				n.a.		n.a.	
2000	2.4	1.0	2.2	0.9	5.0	2.2	7.4	3.1
2020	6.4	1.5	5.5	1.3	14.1	3.6	20.5	4.9
1968-2000	40	24	38	23	82	50	122	73
1968-2020	123	49	112	45	263	108	386	153
Sulfur[d] (million tons) 1968	10.2				28		38	
1969	n.a.				n.a.		n.a.	
1970	n.a.				n.a.		n.a.	
2000	41.4	25.8	37.3	23.2	140	95	181	118
2020	99.8	45.7	83.3	38.8	379	204	479	243
1968-2000	742	552	688	523	2,313	1,819	3,055	2,342
1968-2020	2,099	1,258	1,856	1,138	7,230	4,729	9,329	5,867
Phosphorus (million tons) 1968	3.4				8		11	
1969	3.4				n.a.		n.a.	
1970	3.6				n.a.		n.a.	
2000	14.2	11.5	13.0	10.5	62	32	76	43
2020	35.7	24.7	30.9	21.4	223	77	259	98
1968-2000	253.5	217.8	239.4	206.1	878	582	1,132	788
1968-2020	477.3	351.7	423.0	311.3	3,473	1,631	3,950	1,942
Potassium (million tons) 1968	3.6				11		15	
1969	3.9				n.a.		n.a.	
1970	3.9				n.a.		n.a.	
2000	18.2	14.7	16.7	13.4	60	40	78	53
2020	50.4	35.4	43.8	30.7	175	89	225	120
1968-2000	305.5	261.9	288.4	247.5	944	742	1,250	990
1968-2020	653.4	481.1	579.4	426.2	3,151	1,995	3,804	2,421
Nitrogen (million tons) 1968	9.7				25		35	
1969	9.9				n.a.		n.a.	
1970	10.3				n.a.		n.a.	
2000	57.5	46.4	52.7	42.5	150	90	208	133
2020	181.1	126.7	156.7	109.5	463	201	644	311
1968-2000	924.0	805.8	861.2	750.5	2,339	1,687	3,263	2,438
1968-2020	2,215.8	1,649.8	1,962.2	1,459.2	8,053	4,506	10,269	5,965

[a]Unless otherwise indicated, projections for the United States are derived from a combined macroeconomic/input-output projection model of the U.S. economy. Quantity-conversion coefficients were applied to the constant-dollar values generated by the model for the appropriate input-output classifications. The coefficients are based on the quantity data for 1970 compiled by the U.S. Bureau of Mines and dollar-value data in the model for the same year. Except where there is no basis for distinguishing between primary and total requirements, the data for metallic minerals represent primary requirements only. For purposes of this table, relative recovery from secondary materials is assumed unchanged from 1970, except as otherwise noted. "Rest-of-the-world" projections are taken from U.S. Bureau of Mines, *Mineral Facts and Problems, 1970.* The Bureau made no specific world population assumptions, but the context indicates that assumptions as to economic growth, rather than population,

Table 1.—Continued

essentially accounted for the high-low range. The Bureau projected only to the year 2000; 2020 projections shown herein are by extrapolation at the 1968-2000 growth rate.

[b]"B" and "E" refer to the high and low population variants used by the Population Commission. "High" and "low" refer to the respective assumptions as to overall rate of productivity growth used in the RFF projection model.

[c]Data for 1968, 1969, and 1970 are actual, as compiled by U.S. Bureau of Mines or derived from Bureau of Mines data. Other years projected. Cumulative totals include the year 1968 and are calculated on the assumption of a constant geometric progression—in most instances for the entire time period, but for the first five minerals for each decade, based on figures not shown in the table but derived from the RFF projection model. (For these minerals, the I-O classification system permitted relatively more reliable quantity conversions.) All data are in short tons.

[d]Projections from U.S. Bureau of Mines, *Mineral Facts and Problems, 1970*. Since the population assumption in this source was similar to the "B" series of RFF, the high and low projections were taken as the "B-high" and "B-low" for this table. The approximate relative change caused by population differences in the consumption of other metals was used to estimate the "E-high" and "E-low" values.

the total elapsed period, depending (as explained above) on how the particular mineral was projected.

These, then, are the domestic demand levels which, in the light of our discussion above, would correspond to a situation of no serious minerals shortage, provided this demand could be satisfied by visible mineral supplies. A first comparison may be made between these cumulative figures and the estimates of domestic mineral reserves shown in Table 2. As would be expected from the fact that the United States is a net importer of most of these minerals, projected cumulative demand to the year 2000, let alone to the year 2020, exceeds domestic reserves in most instances.

"Rest-of-the-World" Demand

If we are to judge how much the United States can continue to rely on foreign supplies, non-United States demand and reserves must also be brought into the picture. Projections and estimates of both have recently been published by the United States Bureau of Mines.[2] Because independent rest-of-the-world demand projections could not practically be carried out by RFF for purposes of this analysis, we relied on the Bureau of Mines projections.

Like the RFF projections of domestic demand, the Bureau of Mines projections of rest-of-the-world demand lean heavily upon trend extrapolation. Such trend extrapolation is on a more direct and aggregative basis than in the RFF projections. As explained above, these projections confine the extrapolation primarily to the coefficients of relationship among economic-activity categories rather than applying it to minerals consumption directly. However, to the extent that the historical record of prices and relative consumption, among other indicators, suggests that neither worldwide nor domestically have mineral "shortages" been a long-term limiting factor upon total output, the Bureau of Mines rest-of-the-world projections may similarly be considered as denoting "non-shortage" consumption levels. Still, for

the developing countries particularly, it is difficult to project the levels that future national output might reach if deficiencies in investment, organization, education, motivation, and other constraints should rapidly disappear. Thus, it is hazardous to rely too securely even on "high" trend projections of such countries' consumption as being the limits of "non-shortage" demand for minerals, since such projections can take no account of unexpectedly accelerating economic growth. On the other hand, "rest-of-the-world" includes—and indeed may be assumed to a major extent to consist of—the consumption by developed countries; a sudden spurt in one, or a few, of the developing ones would not drastically and rapidly change the aggregate levels of rest-of-the-world requirements.

What would greatly change (increase) rest-of-the-world requirements is a condition under which all other countries suddenly reached United States per capita consumption levels. For purposes of ascertaining whether world supplies are adequate to demand, or whether the United States—as is frequently contended—is unfairly preempting world supplies, various analysts have occasionally made such a hypothesis. As suggested above, however, the assumption is unrealistic. Minerals consumption does not exist apart from the overall industrial production, transportation, etc., which generate it. A further, perhaps crucial, flaw of this mode of demand projection, especially in the long run, is the implicit assumption that the less-developed countries' economies and production mixes will be more or less faithful carbon copies of those of the now industrialized ones. Such an assumption may serve to illuminate one possible path of development but hardly exhausts the range of possibilities.

One need only compare the technological opportunities open to, say, the United Kingdom a hundred years ago, the United States at the turn of the century, and India, Brazil, or Nigeria at this time to perceive the shakiness of any assumption based upon a worldwide

Table 2.—U.S. and World Reserves of Selected Non-Fuel Minerals, ca. 1968

RESERVES, BY LOCATION

Mineral	Unit[a]	U.S.	Rest-of-world	World	Three principal locations	
Iron	Bil. tons	2	95	97	USSR So. America Canada	31 18 12
Aluminum (bauxite)	Mil. tons	9	1,159	1,168	Australia Guinea Jamaica	400 240 120
Copper	Mil. tons	86	222	808	United States Chile USSR	86 59 39
Lead	Mil. tons	35	60	95	United States Canada Australia	35 12 10
Zinc	Mil. tons	34	90	124	United States Canada East/West Europe, ea.	34 25 14
Manganese	Mil. tons	68 (see basis)	729	797	Rep. of S. Africa USSR Gabon	300 200 96
Chromite	Mil. tons	2	773	775	Rep. of S. Africa S. Rhodesia USSR	575 175 15
Nickel	Mil. tons	0.2	73.3	73.5	Cuba New Caledonia Canada/USSR, ea.	18.0 16.5 10.0
Tungsten	Thous. tons	95	1,317	1,412	China (mainland) United States So. Korea	1,050 95 51
Molybdenum	Thous. tons	3,150	2,265	5,414	United States USSR Chile	3,150 1,000 875
Vanadium	Thous. tons	115	10,000	10,115	USSR Rep. of S. Africa Australia	6,000 2,000 1,500
Cobalt	Thous. tons	28	2,377	2,405	Congo (Kinshasa) New Caledonia Zambia	750 440 383
Tin	Thous. tons	58 (see basis)	4,851	4,909	Thailand Malaysia Indonesia	1,570 672 616
Magnesium	Mil. tons	15	2,565	2,580	China (mainland) No. Korea New Zealand	1,370 820 165

Table 2.—Continued

Mineral	Unit[a]	U.S.	Rest-of-world	World	Three principal locations	
Titanium	Mil. tons	25	122	147	Norway U.S./Canada, ea. USSR	30 25 25
Sulfur	Mil. tons	342	2,425	2,767	Near East & So. Asia East. Europe United States	1,226 437 342
Phosphorus	Bil. tons	6.8	15	21.8	Morocco United States USSR	3.2 6.8 2.6
Potassium	Bil. tons	.8	109	110	USSR/Canada, ea. E. Germany W. Germany	41.5 8.3 7.9
Nitrogen	Mil. tons	In limitless supply from atmosphere, provided energy for recovery is available.				

[a]All tons are short tons.

Source: U.S. Bureau of Mines, *Mineral Facts and Problems, 1970.* Terminology is that used by Bureau of Mines. The term "known and potential reserves" presumably refers to total resources. Meaning of terms used, in context of narrative, is not in all instances unequivocal. The basis of measurement or estimate for each mineral is as follows:

Iron — Reserves in terms of recoverable iron (Fe). Potential ore easily twice as large.

Aluminum (bauxite) — Reserves of bauxite, including inferred, in Al equivalent. Potential bauxite resources (Al equivalent) ore estimated at an additional 2.1 billion tons.

Copper — Principal commercial copper reserves in Cu content.

Lead — Measured, indicated and inferred reserves of lead in ore.

Zinc — Measured, indicated and inferred reserves of zinc in ore.

Manganese — U.S. deposits are low-grade resources, not reserves. Rest-of-world figure refers to principal reserves. All data in contained Mn. Excludes potential from sea-bottom nodules.

Chromite — Principal and potential reserves of chromite ore, in terms of Cr content.

Nickel — U.S.: measured, indicated and inferred reserves of nickel in ore. World reserve estimates probably low. Considerable potential reserves throughout the world, of currently uncertain status.

Tungsten — Reserves of contained tungsten. U.S. estimate based on price of $63 per short-ton-unit (20 lbs.) of WO$_3$. At current price of $43, reserves would be only 83,000 tons. At prices up to $80: 150,000 tons additional. U.S. resources estimated at 155,000 tons.

Molybdenum — Molybdenum contained in ores. Substantial amounts of sub-marginal grade ores are presumed to exist throughout the world.

Vanadium — Reserves of contained vanadium. U.S. vanadium resources estimated at an additional 3.5 million tons.

Cobalt — Principal known reserves. U.S. resources estimated at an additional 100,000 tons. Resources elsewhere, different types of minerals and deposits many times larger than reserves.

Tin — U.S. figure refers to resources. Reserves alone are only about 6,000 tons. World reserves could be as high as 7.8 million tons, with some price increase, inclusion of other countries, and off-shore sources.

Magnesium — Limited to reserves of magnesite, in magnesium equivalent. Dolomite, seawater, and well and lake brines, the sources of most of the world's magnesium and magnesium compounds, are virtually unlimited, given energy.

Titanium — Reserves of ilmenite and rutile, in titanium equivalent. Additional resources of both with an estimated titanium content of 200-300 million tons are judged to exist, about half of which are located in the U.S. and Canada.

Sulfur — Includes native; by-product from petroleum, natural gas, sulfide ore smelting; Frasch sulfur, and pyrites.

Phosphorus — U.S. figure consists of 1.0 billion tons "known" and 5.8 billion tons "potential" reserves. Rest of world and world figures are "known and potential reserves." All data in phosphorus content (P).

Potassium — U.S. figure: Known plus inferred. Rest-of-world and world: indicated reserves. All figures in K content. Ultimately sea water and other sources could provide virtually unlimited supply.

Nitrogen — In limitless supply from atmosphere, provided energy for recovery is available.

Population, Resources, and the Environment

reaching of United States or Western European per capita consumption levels or even a continuation of past trends. Just the availability of light metals, of synthetics, and of nuclear energy are bound to exert a significant impact in altering the materials mix in the less-developed countries. Even assuming that developing countries universally wished to achieve the same style of life and production mix as prevails today in the United States, there is no reasonably conceivable GNP growth rate that would bring them abreast of today's United States consumption levels in less than half a century—and in much longer time for many and the larger ones among them. At that point, they would still be at a small fraction of the then current United States per capita consumption. Only by sharply decreasing per capita consumption in the United States while the least developed countries sharply increased theirs could there be even an approach to "equality" during the time span of this or the next generation. It may easily be argued that a sharp decrease in United States standard of living (which, involving a heavy decline in raw materials input, would have the likely effect of stilting economic growth elsewhere) would not represent equal sacrifice with accelerated increases elsewhere.[3] The Bureau's "high" trend projections thus appear to afford a much more reasonable starting point than "equality" for a first screening of the adequacy of world mineral supply to world requirements.

Comparison With Reserves

The initial screening compares United States and world requirements (cumulatively projected) with United States and world reserves. On the assumptions outlined above, this provides the first crude measure of whether, for any given mineral, there is a possible problem and when, within the two time periods surveyed (1968-2000 and 2000-2020) it might crop up. Or more precisely, if the "high" United States and rest-of-the-world projections combined cumulate to less than estimated world reserves, it may be concluded, as a practical matter, that for the time span specified there is "enough to go around." Conversely, if the "low" (low population and low productivity growth rates) projections of requirements exceed estimated reserves, we may initially assume that the problem may be serious enough to require sacrifice of otherwise attainable economic growth. In neither of these circumstances, however, is one necessarily relieved of further evaluation. In particular, unless domestic reserves alone are in excess of domestic demand plus customary exports, one cannot eliminate the possibility of at least a strategic or a trade-adjustment problem.

Where further evaluation is necessary, the first task is to look more closely into the estimate of "reserves." It is not just the scarcity of reliable information that dictates close scrutiny,[4] but the definition of the concept itself. Basically, "reserves" refers to the amounts of a mineral commercially recoverable by known technology at current prices. The amounts themselves need not be fully and certainly known (that is, "proven," or "measured"), but do include quantities merely estimated or "inferred." As has been pointed out, however, by V. E. McKelvey of the U.S. Geological Survey,[5] though "the definition of *inferred* reserves employed by the Survey and the Bureau of Mines permits inclusion of completely concealed deposits for which there is specific geologic evidence and for which the specific location can be described, it makes no allowance for ore in unknown structures or undiscovered districts." In other words, there is some amount of as yet completely undiscovered "reserves"—minerals which could satisfy tomorrow's demand at today's technology and prices—that are not included in the reserve estimates. The amount is unknowable, but in view of the paucity of exploration in many parts of the world, must be presumed to be large. The presumption is reinforced by the knowledge—often erroneously termed a "paradox"—that, in the face of rising production, total reserve estimates for particular minerals, decade after decade, tend to be maintained and even expanded, the reason in part being the discoveries not included, by definition, in the earlier estimates.

But reserves are maintained and expanded also for another reason—the continuing development of new technology. The best known example is copper, which, because of developing technology, can be mined today at 0.4 percent content in ore at costs not materially different from those encountered when content was running at one and two percent. The technology involved is not one which was developed at "forced draft," to meet emergencies, but has for the most part unfolded over the years with normal investment, research, and development.

There is still more to the supply story. Minable at just above current cost levels are quantities of each mineral which McKelvey refers to as "paramarginal resources." These he defines as the quantities "recoverable at prices as much as 1.5 times those prevailing now." With time, as he points out, this is a small gap for technology to make up; moreover, it is within historically common ranges of fluctuation of mineral prices. Suppose, however, that a permanent price rise of 50 percent was what it actually took for the demand for a particular mineral to be satisfied. Undoubtedly, the gap between demand and supply would then be closed in part because of decreased relative use of the particular mineral. But would this signify a minerals-created shortfall in aggregate output? On the contrary, there would likely be another mineral or nonmineral or synthetic material to substitute for part of the demand. If not, and if all minerals simultaneously had to undergo a 50 percent price rise in order to be in adequate supply, how much, starting from an initial (and declining) three percent of GNP could the extra real effort implied detract from the nation's total output potential?

McKelvey goes on to talk of "submarginal" resources, which might cost "two or three times more than those produced now . . . ." Even these, in a 30- or 50-year perspective, are potential reserves: "Many of the fuels and minerals being produced today would once have been classed as submarginal . . . and it is reasonable to believe that continued technologic progress will create recoverable reserves from this category."

What is particularly important about these distinctions and prospects is that for many, if not most, minerals, the addition of currently paramarginal and submarginal resources would increase the "reserve" category, not by modest amounts, but by multiples of itself. Mineral supply, in other words, tends to be highly elastic in terms of price. The concentrated mineral deposits which man has been working so far are, for the most part, rarities in the earth's crust. Though solid evidence has been adduced[6] to dispute the specific hypothesis that arithmetic decreases in mineral grade consistently produce geometric increases in available quantities, geological processes are such, that, allowing for discontinuities, the more widely disseminated occurrences of minerals do in fact tend to be more plentiful than the more concentrated quantities.

Somewhere in the earth's crust (or in its air and its ocean waters) are vast quantities of many minerals which might not be considered even submarginal resources. Moreover, the ultimate transmutability of much of the undifferentiated earth and rock of the world into useful energy sources and raw materials is less and less to be discounted. If one is to be concerned about the demands on resources of the developing economies and expanding populations of the next century, one must also make allowance for the technology of the next century, even though he cannot be nearly as persuasive as when totting up the demand picture.

In this connection, it is useful to note that, except for the negligible amounts shot off into space, the resources of this earth are never finally "consumed." They may be widely dissipated, into the air, seas, or over the surface of the earth; they may be changed in chemical, or even in elemental form; they may tempo-

rarily be retired from availability while they remain part of an increasing stock of things in use. But the vast bulk of the mineral wealth of the earth, once used, remains as much a part of the earth's resources as if it had never been mined. As costs of newly mined materials rise, it is not only additional virgin material that takes on the character of "reserves," but additional obsolete material as well. And since technology, either normally evolving or purposefully directed, increases the proportions of virgin resources economically minable at constant prices, it may do exactly the same for the resources that have already served man one or a hundred times in the past. In both cases, costs set the limit of what is practical; for example, there is a world of difference between recovering lead from wall paint, gasoline, or batteries! The theoretical point, however, is not to be ignored, for in a progression of times and places, it also becomes a practical one.

Time and Place Discount

In effect, we have been speaking of time and place discount. Both amount essentially to the same thing, even in respect to the claims of other nations: Of concern are not today's but tomorrow's claims that consumption today might foreclose them.

What is needed is a concept of "lead time"—the time needed to adapt to a future situation or to an unforeseen one. By projecting foreign requirements that, while not static, are based on a realistic pace of economic development, one obtains a manageable lead time needed for adjusting to foreign needs. By the same token, acceleration of rates of foreign development, should it occur, will be visible long before the actual need would arise for any adjustments (whatever these might be) that the United States might feel constrained to make in the interest of "fair shares." This is because it takes an extended period of unanticipated acceleration in current consumption to make any significant change in projected cumulative demands.

So far as the far-off future goes, one need but look backward 50 years and consider what was then known about such matters as petrochemicals, atomic energy, travel to the moon, exploration of the ocean depths, etc. to realize that the currently unimaginable (at least in practical terms) may be more important to man's adjustments in the year 2020 and beyond than that which we think we can clearly foresee. Considering the rate at which the pace of change keeps quickening, prudence suggests that one allow for a heavy dose of unexpected solutions when actions are formulated now to meet problems of even the year 2000.

In any case, the diversity of minerals demand and supply balance is such that no comprehensive shift in behavior just to meet future mineral shortage is either necessary or desirable, and perhaps not even feasible. The rest of this paper discusses some typical individual situations and means of adjustment. For general guidance, it uses the requirements projections shown in Table 1 and the reserve estimates shown in Table 2, without any pretense that either have a very high order of reliability. As a general screening device, however, these estimates and projections do suggest where continuing analytical and resource-management attention should most importantly be directed.

APPARENT NON-SHORTAGE SITUATIONS

A comparison of Tables 1 and 2 indicates eight minerals for which currently estimated world reserves are equal to or in excess of cumulative world requirements through the year 2020. These are chromium, iron, nickel, vanadium, magnesium, phosphorus, potassium, and cobalt.[7] A ninth mineral, nitrogen, has no reserve figure shown; but, since the present method of nitrogen production is to "fix" it by separating it from liquefied air, this, too, represents no resource problem on a world basis, except for the investment and energy required. In addition to fixed nitrogen, natural and byproduct nitrates are also used both in the United States and elsewhere.

However, of the nine foregoing minerals, only four—nitrogen, phosphorus, potassium, and magnesium— are (on the surface) also without problem in terms of domestic supply. The reason for inclusion of magnesium, despite the excess of cumulative United States demand over the domestic reserves figure shown, is that the principal and most economic source of magnesium in the United States is not mineral reserves in the ordinary—terrestrial—sense, but the sea. About 90 percent of United States magnesium supply is produced by extracting the metal from sea water at Dow Chemical Company installations at Freeport, Texas.

For practical purposes, iron may be added to the domestic "non-shortage" list. In recent years, imports have accounted for about one-third the total iron supply; but, at least half the imports are from Canada, with most of the rest coming from well-established, reliably accessible sources in the western hemisphere. Canadian reserves alone are sufficient to support joint United States-Canadian iron and steel production through the year 2020. In addition, there are very large paramarginal and submarginal resources within United States borders.

Nickel may also be added. This is an example of a mineral of which the United States produces hardly any, but the strategic problem is nonetheless minimal. Nearby Canada has more than sufficient reserves to cover United

States consumption to around the year 2020. Not all supplies need, however, come from Canada. Even now, the United States obtains about 10 percent from other sources. With further diversification of sources, secure supplies for the United States could be extended well beyond the end of the century.

SITUATIONS OF SERIOUS UNITED STATES IMPORT DEPENDENCY

Among the situations that present the United States with apparently serious self-sufficiency problems, two subsituations may be distinguished: (1) those in which world reserves are generally adequate through the year 2020 to meet world demand, and (2) those in which world demand is projected to outrun reserves by that date. For the first subsituation, satisfaction of United States cumulative demand out of world reserves might involve problems of security—in both political and economic terms—but not preemption. For the second group, both types of problems might be involved.

World Reserves Adequate

Among the minerals for which world, but not United States, reserves are apparently adequate through 2020 are iron, chromium, nickel, vanadium, cobalt, and potassium. Iron and nickel were discussed above. Three of the other minerals are ferroalloys; as such, they are, in different degrees, interchangeable with one another and with other ferroalloys. Their applications are such that all may be considered to have strategic significance. Each of the three represents a somewhat different kind of security problem.

Chromium

A negligible share of the world's reserves is located in the United States, and this country currently imports all of its supplies. The Republic of South Africa and the Soviet Union are the two leading United States suppliers. Of these, the first, as may be seen in Table 2, possesses about three-fourths of the world reserves.

There is little that the United States can do to increase its long-range security with regard to chromium by developing different current supply sources abroad; we already have a number of minor supplying countries, and the bulk of the reserves are in South Africa and Rhodesia.[8] There are a variety of other actions possible. One of these—stockpiling—is a long-standing but basically a short-term measure tailored to meet a specified contingency. Over the longer haul, substitution, increased secondary recovery, and development of technology to permit resort to lowgrade domestic ores[9] are additional approaches. Research and development have been carried on in all of these aspects, and the principal requirement is that such research and development be kept sufficiently up-to-date to permit minimum-cost satisfaction of emergency requirements in the event of interruption of foreign supplies and exhaustion of stockpiles. In the meantime, the continued import of chromium and its incorporation in products is, of course, building up an "above-ground" stock that will enter the scrap cycle and, in time, add to supplies and security.

Vanadium

The security problem here consists in the fact that the great bulk of world reserves—about 60 percent— are in the Soviet Union; the Republic of South Africa accounts for 20 percent, and Australia accounts for three-fourths of the balance.

What makes for considerably less of an ultimate problem, however, is that the United States has large quantities of lower-grade resources (not currently classifiable as reserves) which could far more than cover cumulative needs. Moreover, up to this time, the United States has been an exporter rather than an importer of vanadium ore and generally also a net exporter of ferrovanadium. The reason is that vanadium is recovered, both here and abroad, principally as a byproduct of other ore and metallurgical processing; in this country, it has been largely a byproduct of uranium ores. Vanadium is one of the most common elements in the earth's crust, and since it occurs in combination with a number of other minerals, will continue to be turned out as a byproduct. Thus, it may be some time before the United States becomes a net importer of vanadium, let alone runs into serious supply difficulties. If difficulties occur, it would take only relatively minor changes in price to increase domestic mining and promote greater byproduct recovery. As with chromium, however, attention needs to be given to timely performance of any relevant research and development. Lead time then is an important element. For short-term security purposes, lower-grade domestic resources are probably of little avail; but, in the long supply perspective, they loom importantly.

Cobalt

This is another element whose lower-grade resources, if brought into play by moderately higher prices, would greatly multiply reserves. The multiplication would not be enough, however, to permit the United States, given current trends in consumption, ever to rely on domestic supplies. At present, reliance is wholly on imports—directly or indirectly from the Congo (Kinshasa), Canada, Morocco, and Zambia. Should security problems arise, of too extensive a nature to be dealt with by utilization of the strategic stockpile, the principal adjustment would have to take the form of substitution of other alloys. Though there is need for further technical research, it appears that cobalt can probably be replaced, at little or no economic loss, by nickel, vanadium, molybdenum, tungsten, and/or chromium in the great bulk of its uses.

World Reserves Inadequate

Among the minerals with respect to which estimated world reserves are inadequate to meet high projections of world cumulative demand through 2020, there is no instance where there is not also a shortfall of United States reserves with respect to high projections of United States demand. Thus, these minerals—manganese, molybdenum, tungsten, aluminum, copper, lead, zinc, tin, titanium, and sulphur—present both a world problem and something of a United States domestic security problem. There are, however, wide differences in emphasis.

Molybdenum

Molybdenum, for example, has not been regarded as a strategic problem in the United States so far, despite the fact that a strategic stockpile has been maintained. Domestic production has been enough to meet domestic demand, with ample surpluses for export. Moreover, there are large reserves in Canada, as well as in the United States; the two together would last at least beyond the year 2000, even at a high estimate of future United States and Canadian consumption.

The real question for molybdenum is whether the United States should restrict exports, at the expense of the rest of the world, in order to maintain its own strategic security. The question is underlined by the fact that molybdenum would be the prime fallback metal if tungsten and a number of other steel alloying elements which are not plentiful in the United States should become a problem. The companion question is whether the rate of United States molybdenum consumption should be held down by substitution of other alloys while they remain available.

Part of the answer would seem to lie in the fact that chromium, vanadium, and cobalt are all in apparently ample world supply even past the year 2020. To the extent that these could be substituted in current United States alloy production, it would concurrently improve both United States security and the world's long-range mineral supply/requirements balance. The more compelling element in the situation, however, would appear to be the still distant date of potential molybdenum shortages. The situation bears continued watching, but immediate action to restrict United States molybdenum use or exports seems unwarranted.

Sulfur

The United States has also been a supplier to the world of elemental sulfur; it is able to produce this element from its Frasch mines in Texas and Louisiana more cheaply than most competitors. Yet the United States has experienced recurrent sulfur supply crises. It imports elemental sulfur from Mexico and byproduct sulfur and pyrites (alternative source of sulfuric acid) from Canada. Sulfur prices have fluctuated widely in response to world and domestic situations of alternating surplus and shortage.

Sulfur is probably the prime example of what one might call a "wait-and-see" mineral. It has happened more than once that just when low-cost reserves appeared to be petering out, a discovery in Mexico, or under the waters of the Gulf, or, most recently, in an area of western Texas considered well outside the likely producing zones, suddenly added large quantities to the total. Sulfur recovered as a byproduct of oil and natural gas production, especially from Canadian sour gas, has in recent years added a large new source and will continue to do so. Further, not disconcertingly above long range price levels lie huge quantities of sulfur recoverable from gypsum. And finally, if the nation's moves toward reduction of air pollution result in the recovery of marketable sulfur, from smokestacks and elsewhere, this could completely flood the market and might well relegate today's standard sources to a standby status!

It might be added that this widely used inorganic chemical also has ready substitutes in some major uses. Other acids are substantially substitutable in fertilizer and metallurgical applications—two of sulfur's large-scale uses. At least phosphatic fertilizer can also be produced electrically, without use of acid, and the sulfate compound has long ceased to be the principal form of consumption of ammonia (nitrogen).

Tungsten

This is an example of a mineral which appears to present serious prospective problems. Largely because of its use in the cutting edges of machine tools, it is a key element in industrial societies. Yet currently estimated reserves are inadequate to world demand, as early as the year 2000 and even on a "low" projection of requirements. Moreover, roughly three-fourths of world reserves are located in mainland China, and even the total estimated resources—that is, material irrespective of cost considerations—available in the United States are insufficient by themselves to sustain United States consumption for more than a couple of decades.

The United States strategic stockpile has accumulated tungsten when prices were low and released it when prices were high. There have been periods of

extensive subsidization of marginal tungsten producers—with only moderate results. On the whole, domestic production has come from two large mines, where it is extracted jointly with molybdenum. Extensive imports have been obtained, over a period of time, from Bolivia, South Korea, Portugal, Canada, Australia, and Peru. (Some of these amounts may have been reshipments of material received from Communist China or North Korea.)

While data are incomplete, secondary recovery (recycling of industrial products like used cutting tools, rock bits, and welding rods) already represents a substantial source of tungsten, and additional supplies from this source are probably fairly limited, largely because a good deal of the tungsten used in these applications is dissipated beyond possibility of recovery.

Thus, tungsten is clearly a commodity where, sooner or later, substantial adjustments will have to be made in the face of waning supplies. Price rises will probably accomplish most of this adjustment, partly by stimulating exploratory activity and recourse to lower-grade deposits; partly by increased substitution of molybdenum, nickel, cobalt, titanium, and other minerals (for some of these, relatively smaller price rises would open up large additional supplies); and partly by greater recovery than is probably currently practiced from industrial dust and sweepings, stacks, and other sources. (Such recovery is, in any case, in the interest of reduced environmental pollution.) Shifts toward powder metallurgy, plastics, and other methods and products would reduce demand by diminishing the need for machining, where use of tungsten is important to high-speed operation. Slower-speed machining, at some decrease in efficiency, may permit the substitution of molybdenum in many applications. A switch to fluorescent lighting is already reducing the relative need for tungsten for electric lamps (though lamps represent only a little over five percent of tungsten demand), and there are possible substitutes in other of its electrical, chemical, and miscellaneous uses.

In short, while adequacy of tungsten cannot be now foreseen with any degree of confidence (given higher prices and relatively modest sacrifices in terms of real cost of ultimate output, coupled with reasonable attention to the research and development required for timely solutions), supply difficulties need not become a significant stricture either on United States or on rest-of-the-world welfare.

Tin

Tin represents another situation of both United States and worldwide shortages. Even at a "low" projection, cumulative world requirements just through the year 2000 are more than double currently estimated reserves; comparable United States requirements add up to 400 times United States reserves. So far, the United States has depended for its tin supply almost wholly on imports and a high proportion of secondary recovery. The latter source is subject to significant extension, and there are important possibilities for replacement of tin by other materials—especially in containers where a great deal of substitution has already taken place[10] and where recycling, because of the mechanics of collection and cleaning, presents some of its most difficult problems. (This, of course, could change in the next few years, given the new focus on solid waste management.) Subtle forms of conservation also offer potential savings—for example, through the development of welded or seamless cans (rather than soldered), which would in turn be more acceptable as steel scrap.

Probably the most important adjustment in the case of tin, however, is the extension of reserves. There is little prospect of such a development in the United States. The Bureau of Mines estimates that it would take a very large increase in price for the roughly 6,000-ton—and hitherto almost unexploited—reserve in Alaska (the only substantial United States deposits) to be raised to anywhere near the 40,000 tons which are the estimated resources in Alaska. But elsewhere in the world, the reserve-extension possibilities are considerable. The "rest-of-the-world" reserve figure of 4.9 million short tons shown in Table 2 is that estimated by the International Tin Council. The Bureau of Mines considers this conservative and judges that the reserve figure is located nearer seven million short tons (assuming a modest price increase and technological development, as well as the inclusion of omitted, smaller sources). An additional eight million short tons is credited to lower-grade resources by the U.S. Geological Survey. Assuming all of this were to become minable at a cost not radically higher than historical levels, it would just about cover cumulative world demand through the year 2020 according to the "low" set of projections and somewhat beyond the year 2000 according to the "high" set of projections.

Since a price rise in the wake of developing stringencies would promote the exploitation of these additional resources, as well as substitution and secondary recovery, there is a strong presumption that tin supplies, on a world basis at least, will not become a troublesome scarcity problem.

Even these supply estimates may be conservative. The nature of tin deposits is such that undiscovered resources could be very large indeed. Much of the occurrence is in areas very inadequately explored, and much lies in old river beds buried beneath the seas, but

likely to become increasingly accessible with developing offshore mining techniques. Moreover, the U.S. Geological Survey estimate of lower-grade resources includes neither the Soviet Union nor mainland China, both of which may have sizable additional amounts of paramarginal and submarginal resources.

Of the quantity of tin reserves currently identified, about one-third is in Thailand, and about three-fifths, in total, in Thailand, Malaysia, and Indonesia. The United States does not have entirely secure long-term access to these places, but all are currently available sources of supply. In fact, United States firms are involved in much of the exploration and mining activity. Bolivia also has substantial reserves, and is still the world's second most important producer. All of these countries—but particularly Malaysia and Thailand—have been supplying the United States in recent years. Since they also supply others, it cannot be said that reserves are visible for meeting United States needs without impact on either price or consumption by others or both, even at a low projection level to the year 2000; but, as noted, the currently estimated reserves appear to fall well short of expressing long-range total availabilities.

It does not follow that the United States need be unconcerned about adequacy of tin. In fact, it maintains a strategic stockpile in this metal to guard against shortages. Furthermore, intensified conservation and recycling measures, even if they turn out not to be actually needed to avert outright shortage, should receive continuing consideration as ways of avoiding the possibly greater economic burdens engendered by environmental pollution and rising tin prices. Fundamentally, however, tin's end use pattern, and consequent potential for substitution and secondary recovery, remove it from the roster of ultimately critical problem materials.

Other Minerals

Other minerals short both on a United States and a world basis generally fall between the extremes of, say, tungsten, on the one hand, and sulfur on the other. Some of them, like aluminum, are backed up by probably very large undiscovered reserves and by even larger resources that only gradually deteriorate in desirable characteristics. But the need for large amounts of electric power for the final extraction of aluminum from the ore might someday present a problem; so, the resource problem here (as also in magnesium and titanium) shifts to a different field.

Rather than discuss the remaining materials individually, we turn now to a consideration of general ways of dealing with mineral shortage, as well as to the general significance of differences in population growth, economic growth, and measures to reduce environmental pollution.

MINERAL SHORTAGE PROBLEMS, POPULATION GROWTH, AND ECONOMIC GROWTH

Above, we suggested reasons why comprehensive solutions to prospective mineral supply problems are neither necessary nor desirable. One such comprehensive solution is conservation of minerals through the deliberate limitation of population growth. While there may be good reasons for taking early steps toward the limitation of population growth, minerals conservation, even on general grounds, is not one of them. Tables 1 and 2 afford some more specific grounds for this conclusion.

It has already been noted that a number of important minerals are not in prospective shortage, either in the United States or elsewhere, within the next 50 years even on assumptions of high population growth. Others are in short supply in the United States; but they are in sufficient supply in the world at large, so that stockpiling and other security measures would provide adequately for United States needs without unfair preemption. Where worldwide statistical shortages are indicated, the preceding evaluation points to relatively modest investment in research and development plus the incurrence of relatively modest increases in real costs as affording an adequate solution to prospective problems.

Table 1 also shows, however, that substitution of low for high rates of population growth in the United States would improve prospective shortage problems but little. Specifically, substitution of the "E" for the "B" levels of population growth reduces cumulative demand through the year 2020 by no more than 14 percent (average of about 11 percent). Through the year 2000, it reduces it by only one to eight percent (average of about four percent). These are negligible savings in terms of solving long-range minerals shortages should these in fact develop along the lines that statistical analysis suggests that they might.

It should be noted that our method of projection assumes that aggregate economic output would not decline in proportion to the difference in population—especially not before the year 2000. This is because the population of labor-force age through that date is for the most part already born and therefore would not be altered significantly by an immediate lowering of United States birthrates. Even by 2020, the response of labor force to immediately lower birthrates, though considerably more complete, would not have been in existence long enough to have had much impact on cumulative demand.

Voluntarily to cut down on the growth of consumption of goods and services in the United States—by methods not entirely clear, in any event—would, according to the projections in Table 1, offer but little greater prospect for relief of any prospective minerals shortages. Through the year 2020, the difference between low and high output projections yields a potential saving in cumulative demand for minerals ranging, with few exceptions, between 18 and 26 percent. Through the year 2000, the saving would generally be on the order of 10 to 14 percent. The longer-range savings begin to look interesting, but the great bulk of them would not begin to accrue until large volumes of annual demand are reached beyond the end of the century. These savings might well back up other reasons for supporting modest efforts at conservation in our consumption habits, but not major sacrifices in level of living when the same or greater savings could be accomplished by slightly more input into minerals exploration; research and development in extraction, processing, manufacturing, secondary recovery, and substitution; and real costs of extraction.

The combination of lower population growth and lower economic productivity would produce a combined saving through the year 2000 for most minerals in the range of 14 to 19 percent. The cumulative saving through the year 2020, if we started right now to cut back on both our population growth rate and on our potential growth in level of living, would generally come to 27 to 35 percent. These are, of course, substantial amounts, but again most of the saving would not accumulate until past the year 2000. Whether such savings make it necessary or advisable to push for immediate adjustments in both the population and the output direction (save for modest exercise of restraint) is, of course, a political decision. The foregoing analysis suggests ample management opportunities, and history suggests that we have consistently underrated available resources and the technology to make them accessible. In combination, they promise to be more effective than major societal remedies.

This is not to say that the per capita level of living implied in the low-economic-growth projection is "necessary." The comparisons just made do not refer to any particular absolute level of consumption. Their relevance is to the amount of exhortation, regulation, or regimentation that may be justified to change the immediate-future course of economic growth to achieve far-off accommodation to the strictures, as we currently perceive them, of the resources of the earth upon which we live. Our conclusion is "some, but very little."

RECYCLING AS A SOLUTION TO SHORTAGES

If the word "recycling" had any original precision, it has been quickly lost with its widespread application to various types of secondary minerals recovery. For precision, it is necessary to distinguish between six different kinds of dispositions of materials that have been initially mined or extracted, all of which involve actual or potential recycling:

1. Material is mined and processed. A certain part of it (punchings, clippings, cuttings, chemical residue, dusts, etc.) never reaches the point of final consumption, but is immediately "recycled" for reprocessing. Although such material is sometimes referred to as "waste" (as in "waste" paper), in the metals field it is called "scrap," with such additional adjectives as "new," "prompt industrial," "home," and "run-around." The particular adjective used depends on the customs of the trade and whether the material is recycled within the same establishment or company or passes from one establishment to another as an article of commerce.

2. Same situation as "1" except that the material is not immediately recycled but is accumulated as waste. Examples are "dump" ore, slag piles, settlement ponds, waste dumps, etc. These may be gone back to, under suitable conditions, and "mined."

3. Same situation as "1" except that the material is customarily disposed of in such "dissipative" form as being sent up a chimney or flushed down a river. By definition, such material is neither recycled nor "mined," but to a large extent could be subjected, if it were so desired, to processes that would recover some or all of the valuable constituents.

4. Material is "finally" consumed, either as a durable good or a nondurable good or construction put in place. The differences among these forms of consumption is one only of degree—length of useful life—although the ephemeral (e.g., food) and least durable (e.g., apparel) forms also tend to be the most dissipative. Much of "consumed" material is customarily "recycled"—either for "re-use" (e.g., used clothing, returnable bottles, second-hand books) or for reprocessing (e.g., used auto batteries, old newspapers, drained lubricating oil). "Consumed" recycled metals are customarily referred to as "old," or "obsolete," scrap.

5. Same situation as "4" except that the material is "dumped" instead of being immediately recycled (e.g., in city dumps, automobile "graveyards"). Like that in mining and industrial dumps, such material can later be gone back to and "mined" in one way or another. Given appropriate circumstances—like higher prices for the recoverable content, large enough accumulations to permit economic processing, or "clean-up" campaigns—

such dumped waste is frequently mined or reprocesse[d]

6. Same situation as "4" except that the discard[ed] material is dissipated (e.g., incinerated, flushed in[to] rivers, etc.). Conditions of disposal can be altere[d] however, so as to permit processing of such materi[al] with varying degrees of recovery of valuable const[it]uents.

Available statistics for distinguishing among the various types of recycling are generally either poor [or] nonexistent. Minerals recovered out of dump-ore pi[les] are generally counted in the statistics as part of new[ly] mined quantities, since mining statistics customari[ly] refer only to quantities processed or shipped to marke[t] rather than the total amounts extracted from the eart[h.] Data on "old" scrap do not distinguish between quan[ti]ties immediately recycled and those extracted fro[m] long-standing junk piles. Scrap consumption data som[e]times do not even distinguish between "new" and "old[."] Data on "home" scrap are generally not available at a[ll] except for the steel industry. Data on "new" metal scr[ap] generally distinguish such scrap by sources (includi[ng] amounts recovered from flows usually associated wi[th] dissipative use), but there are no direct data on the rat[io] of scrap reprocessed to the total scrap (or "waste[")] potential.

On Table 3, which shows potential saving throug[h] recycling, we confined ourselves to merely a simp[le] breakdown between "new" and "old" scrap. Moreove[r,] we made the arbitrary assumption that the potential f[or] return flow of new scrap was already sufficient[ly] exploited; therefore, no appreciable error would b[e] entailed in our assuming that the new-scrap contributi[on] to future production of any given metal would remain [in] the same proportion as it was in 1970. On the othe[r] hand, we have made a moderately more sophisticate[d] analysis of the potential contribution that might b[e] made by increased old-scrap "recycling," be it current[ly] recycled or mined from waste dumps.

The calculations were carried out illustratively, on[ly] for iron, aluminum, copper, lead, and zinc, and only fo[r] the United States. To test out the possible impact on ol[d] scrap of an "active recycling policy," we took int[o] account the following factors:

1. Useful life of metal-containing items "finally["] consumed. For the "dissipative" uses of metals (gasolin[e,] paints, etc.), we assumed a useful life of zero. T[o] estimate average lifetime of articles in use, we use[d] approximate consumption mix circa the year 2000 a[s] projected in other work in progress at Resources for th[e] Future.

2. Approximate amounts likely to be "retired["] from use in the year 2000. Using consumption a[s] projected for that year and for whichever earli[er]

Table 3.—Impact of an Active Recycling Policy on Five Major Metals
(million tons)

I. U.S. requirements for primary metal under "active recycling policy"	Year or period	Metal				
		Iron	Aluminum	Copper	Lead	Zinc
"B" population, high growth	2000	212	12.2	3.2	2.2	3.5
	2020	409	20.4	5.7	4.3	6.1
	1968-2000	4803	247	76	46	75
	1968-2020	10931	576	166	111	171
"B" population, low growth	2000	175	9.9	2.6	1.8	2.7
	2020	297	14.6	4.1	3.0	4.2
	1968-2000	4326	219	68	40	66
	1968-2020	8986	467	136	88	136
"E" population, high growth	2000	191	11.1	2.9	2.1	3.1
	2020	319	16.0	4.5	3.4	4.6
	1968-2000	4607	239	75	44	70
	1968-2020	9669	513	148	98	147
"E" population, low growth	2000	156	9.1	2.4	1.6	2.4
	2020	230	11.4	3.2	2.4	3.2
	1968-2000	4131	212	67	39	62
	1968-2020	7992	419	124	79	119
II. Conservation of primary metal by "active U.S. recycling policy"						
"B" population, high growth	2000	7	5.3	.8	.2	.9
	2020	23	18.3	2.4	.5	3.2
	1968-2000	76	55	11	1	10
	1968-2020	362	277	40	6	49
"B" population, low growth	2000	5	4.4	.6	.2	.8
	2020	21	13.0	1.7	.4	2.2
	1968-2000	63	49	8	2	9
	1968-2020	339	218	30	7	38
"E" population, high growth	2000	6	4.9	.7	.1	.8
	2020	18	14.4	1.8	.4	2.5
	1968-2000	71	53	9	2	10
	1968-2020	287	238	34	7	42
"E" population, low growth	2000	5	4.0	.5	.1	.7
	2020	13	10.3	1.3	.3	1.7
	1968-2000	62	47	8	1.	8
	1968-2020	230	188	24	6	30

end-of-decade year (1970, 1980, or 1990) was most appropriate, we applied a rough estimating formula devised some time ago by the Battelle Memorial Institute.[11]

3. Proportions of the foregoing amounts which, under an "active recycling policy," it would be reasonable to assume might be collected for reprocessing. These proportions could theoretically exceed 100 percent, on the strength of the amounts collected from long-standing dumps; but, we interpreted an "active recycling policy" as meaning that such amounts would have been substantially recovered prior to the year 2000.[12]

4. Percentage recovery of the metal in question from the amounts reprocessed. These percentages were derived from the separate percentages for total metal

recovery and proportion thereof of the metal in question projected for the year 2000.[13]

The quantity of recovery from old scrap, derived in the foregoing manner, was then related to the gross consumption of the metal in the year 2000, to obtain the percentage which would be supplied by old scrap under an active recycling policy. This percentage was added to the unchanged percentage for new scrap to obtain total secondary contribution to requirements and, by subtraction, the lower primary requirements under active recycling. In combination, the assumed proportion of gross current requirements which might be satisfied from secondary sources[14] compares with the current proportion as follows:

	Current proportion	Proportion under active recycling policy
Iron	47.3%	48.9%
Aluminum	17.3	42.6
Copper	44.0	54.4
Lead	43.9	47.2
Zinc	16.5	34.6

The resultant primary requirements and conservation under an active recycling policy are shown in Table 3 for each of the four population/productivity variants given in Table 1. An examination of the table, in comparison with Table 2, reveals that the relative savings are negligible for iron, somewhat more interesting for lead (about one-tenth), still more so for copper and zinc (about one-fifth), and most of all for aluminum (about one-third). Only in the case of copper and zinc, however, would the savings do much for United States self-sufficiency; even here, the contribution is negligible when measured in terms of extending the life of reserves. If the United States were to depend entirely on domestic reserves, visible copper minable at present prices with present technology would give out around the end of the century. An active recycling policy would add only a few more years' worth of United States reserves—far less than could normally be expected to be added by technological evolution or a modest price rise. Around the same order of difference is entailed for reserves of zinc, although domestic zinc ores, at present prices and technology, would have given out well before the year 2000.

The importance of recycling, however, goes beyond the simple matter of United States reserves. The potential recycling increase in aluminum, for example, while not making the United States self-sufficient, would, over a period of 50 years, save 20 percent of the world's aluminum (bauxite) reserves (as now estimated). For copper, the comparable figure would be around 15

percent and for zinc, around 40 percent. If recycling were stepped up worldwide, it could make an even more important contribution. Even if less important than substitution and the utilization of lower-grade materials as a means of accommodation to increasing minerals consumption, its contribution cannot be ignored. Just as attention needs to be given to providing the subsidies and incentives required for timely exploration, research, and technological development, so is it distinctly useful to promote the growth of recycling at a faster pace than that at which it might otherwise evolve.

A NOTE ON FOREST PRODUCTS

Largely because of the lengthy depression in the home-building industry, recent demand levels for forest products have suggested surpluses rather than shortages. "Catch-up" in housing requirements, by the same token, will be among the factors eventually contributing to an accelerated demand. Eventually, demand levels for both paper and wood are expected to rise to the point of putting a much heavier burden on the nation's forests—so much so that if one assumed the present forest acreage as given, without also assuming: (1) relative shifts in softwood cut from east to west, with resulting increases in western forest productivity; (2) further shifts toward the relative use of hardwood for pulping; (3) increased relative use of smaller trees, cull trees, forest residues, and cut from areas not classified as "commercial" (because of sparseness of cover or withdrawal for other uses); (4) replanting of eastern hardwood acreage with softwood; and (5) continually increasing imports; one would, by the end of the century, arrive at a disastrously depleted forest cover in the eastern part of the United States. Avoidance of such an eventuality rests on all of the measures enumerated, as well as continuing replacement of forest products with non-forest products. This was essentially the analysis and conclusion set forth in *Resources in America's Future* a decade ago.[15]

For the present analysis, we postulated that the size of commercially forested acreage was not inflexible, and we sought to project what changes in acreage would be required to support a reasonable projected increase in annual cut. For this cut to meet forest-products demand, we also had to assume that the share of domestic softwood requirements supplied from commercial growing stock would decline from 83 percent in 1970 to 59 percent by the end of the century (hardwood from 95 percent to 90 percent) under the high population assumption, and to 68 percent (90 percent for hardwoods) under the low population assumption. This change would be accompanied by a considerable redistribution of commercially forested acreage, with the west (the more productive area) growing from 132 to 144 million acres over the 30-year time span and with the compensating decline in eastern acreage being accompanied by a substantial shift from hardwood to softwood cover. The decline in proportion of supply coming from commercial growing stock would be compensated by increasing imports and by increasing relative utilization of timber not classified as commercial growing stock (residues, cull trees, and so forth).

The need for these acreage adjustments could be obviated in part by greater improvement of conservation practice at all stages of harvesting and processing, greater recycling of waste paper, more extensive re-use of used lumber and plywood, increased substitution of agricultural residues (bagasse, etc.) as a source of cellulose fibers (for paper, etc.), and accelerated replacement of wood by plastics and other materials, especially in construction. Better management, fertilization, rainmaking, pest control, and so on, could also be directly applied to increasing forest productivity.

One can speculate about the practicability, efficiency, and side effects of such measures, as well as about exploiting the vast forest reserves in some of the less-developed and poorly explored countries. But such general prescriptions raise specific questions that need to be pursued in research. One of especial interest and complexity is the degree to which one should advocate accelerated substitution in order to lighten the burden put upon United States forests. For one, the forest is, after all, a renewable resource, while, by and large, minerals are not. Should one not, therefore, press forests into service to the limit that environmental considerations, in their broadest sense, permit? Secondly, what are the environmental and other trade-offs between using forest products and mineral-derived materials? The answer is by no means clear but could perhaps be approximated by means of an input-output analysis or some other "systems" approach. Transportation, energy use, differences in degradation and in recycling ease, and other factors are involved.

The answers to be obtained are important. It is only because residential construction activity lagged so conspicuously and because types of housing with low lumber needs have come into prominence that the lumber market, except in short-term supply crises, has not thrown forest product adequacy into great prominence so far, and may not do so for yet another score of years to come. In the projections made a decade ago, lumber supply was flagged as an area to watch closely for scarcity that would develop unless the cut could be shifted increasingly from east to west and from softwood to hardwood, and unless productivity per acre could be greatly increased.[16] Should we move toward

actual satisfaction of current ambitious housing goals— ambitious not in terms of needs but in terms of past performance—the problem would still be very much before us and still without a satisfactory solution.

What then is the short answer to the question of adequacy of United States timber resources? It is that, with increased imports, increased substitution, increased productivity, and probably increased cut from virgin forests, we can meet demand; but, each of these partial answers contains a package of questions that we must confront. To these might be added the speculation that a lower rate of population growth, if associated with higher per capita income, could exert greater pressure on timber demand, as it might lead to relatively more single-dwelling homes—that are lumber-intensive—as against apartment houses.

CONCLUSION

Having sorted out the problems by degree of concern, we have found, by and large, that in the near perspective of three decades none loom threateningly. However, because some of these problems may assume somewhat more serious proportions in a 50-year perspective, one is left with a few nagging misgivings. The first relates to the practical impossibility of pursuing this kind of exercise over a longer time horizon, for the simple reason that demand projections are bound to seem more plausible—because on the surface at least more precise and systematic—than supply projections— whose degree of precision tends to diminish rapidly as one carries them into the remote future. We know of no way in which these cards can be unstacked, especially for those who find reference to past accomplishments unconvincing and are unwilling to put their bets on a combination of continued technological advance and adjustment of want satisfaction to availability of materials, where the adjustment includes not only substitution between alternative materials but also between alternate ways of filling needs (for example, telecommunication as a substitute for transportation).

A second concern relates to the absence of a mechanism that sets in motion adjustments which the market does not bring about. Let us suppose, for an instance, that the newly asserted problem of exhaustion of the earth's phosphorus resources within less than 150 years rests on solid ground and thus poses a grave problem for mankind's future food supply. Surely, the market does not react to such circumstances except near the end. Phosphate fertilizers will not rise in price and their use will not become more efficient. Yet, the discounting of remote contingencies that we have talked about should be paralleled by attention in some other context, as yet not visible.

Thirdly, while in contemplating substitution opportunities it is comforting to deal with one material at a time, one cannot pursue this line too far for too many materials. Before long, one will find himself engaged in circular reasoning. That point was made above with respect to the alloying metals and nonferrous materials generally. *Mutatis mutandis* it holds true for materials as a whole. Unfortunately, little systematic research has been undertaken to establish substitution thresholds and options, taking into account availability of the substituting resource. And in the final analysis, perhaps the ultimate substitute is energy, thought of as an input into production of materials. One should again note that the market operates on the margin and on one switch at a time (though it performs with great rapidity). A systematic view of substitution, for both materials and functions, is badly needed to illuminate the subject—and to get away from two tunnel visions—one that deals with a single material in isolation and is apt to predict its exhaustion at a specified time, and the other that deals with substitution in isolation and, by stopping short of pursuing the implications of that substitution, can extend availability into the remote future.

Finally, there is the matter of "lead time" (to which allusion has been made at various points in the discussion). When the extent of adequacy is judged by comparing cumulative requirements (however defined) with estimated reserves, an important element is lost: the time it takes to bring about adjustments to close gaps that result from the comparison. That is, one easily falls into the habit of citing various options (increased recycling, greater efficiency in use of low-grade resources, substitution, etc.) as reasonable escape routes from shortfalls indicated by the arithmetic. What is neglected in this approach is the combination of institutional obstacles, general inertia, technical adjustments, supplier-purchaser relations, and so forth, that tends to delay the theoretically feasible adjustments. Recent experience in stepping up recycling is a good example. But the time consumed in moving to substitute materials may be equally long, that in moving to functional substitutions extremely long, and where legislation is needed (codes, ordinances, etc.), one needs to count on a great deal of waiting. Thus, just because one can contrive to equate projected demand with estimated supply plus escape routes, one cannot be assured that the latter will in fact become feasible at the right time and in the right volume. On the other hand, our analytical tools are not anywhere sharp enough to become more predictive about these outcomes at any given time in the future. One cannot, therefore, rule out the emergence of situations in which the necessarily short-sighted market is temporarily overwhelmed by a developing shortage. Such situations may be associated with price increases that might at times be steep, followed by rapid development of new sources, substitutions, and so forth. Price levels may possibly remain permanently higher; but, experience shows, they will more likely not be different from previous levels. (In the energy field, discussed separately, events may not be leading to a basically different pattern of future prices.)

Such fluctuations are not the most efficient way of making adjustment to divergences between demand and supply when it seems clear that, over the long run, there is enough to go around. But one must ask what price society might reasonably pay for avoiding such situations. On inspection, that price might turn out to involve a sufficient modification of the market system, howsoever it is even now constrained, to suggest that temporary inefficiency of adjustment is by far the lesser evil.

REFERENCES

1. For lack of directly comparable data, only the 1968 comparison is shown for the "rest of the world."

2. U.S. Bureau of Mines, *Mineral Facts and Problems, 1970*, Bulletin No. 650.

3. The "high" Bureau of Mines trend projections of "rest-of-the-world" consumption already have unequal sacrifice built into them, if for no other reason than that the underdeveloped world has been far slower than has the United States in limiting its rate of growth in population.

4. U.S. Congress, Joint Committee on Defense Production, testimony by the Acting Director of the U.S. Geological Survey, 91st Cong., 1st Sess., Aug. 2, 1971. He characterized the reliability of reserve data outside the United States as "good" for four commodities, "fair" for 10, and "poor" for 67, out of a total of 81 mineral commodities, with an overall 83 percent having inadequate data. Surprisingly, the domestic picture is only slightly better: 13 commodities having "good," two "fair," and 66 having "poor" reserve data, for an overall 81 percent having inadequate data. "Accurate reserve data are known only to the mineral producers and then only for the mines under their control," the witness testified.

5. For example, V. E. McKelvey, "Mineral Resource Estimates and Public Policy" (Seventh McKinstry Memorial Lecture, Harvard University, Feb. 23, 1971).

6. See, for example, T. S. Lovering, "Non-Fuel Mineral Resources in the Next Century," *Texas Quarterly*, 1968, Vol. XI, No. 2, especially pp. 131ff.

7. Recent questions raised about phosphorus appear to relate to a much longer time horizon (see below).

8. The United States is currently abiding by a United Nations embargo on purchases from Rhodesia.

9. U.S. Congress, Joint Committee on Defense Production, testimony by Harold B. Scott, Acting Assistant Secretary of Commerce, 92nd Cong., 1st sess., Sept. 22, 1971, in which he described at least one such process as "well along in commercial development" and estimated that by 1975 "... virtually all stainless steel produced in the United States will be made by this

new process." This would enable United States consumers to add the Republic of South Africa as a supplier, if this were to appear desirable.

10. One of the substitutes, glass, would represent a reversal of historical trend and at the same time substitute a plentiful mineral—glass sand—for a scarce one.

11. The formula, cited *inter alia* in Landsberg, *et al., Resources in America's Future* (Baltimore: Johns Hopkins, 1963), footnote 4 to Table A16-33, p. 902, estimates the potential scrap "crop" in any one year (quantities retired from consumption) as: $1/L$% of that year's consumption, plus $L - 1/L$% of the consumption one average life cycle earlier, where L represents the average life cycle in years.

12. More precisely, we assumed that the increasing applications of recycling activity and the declining relative availability of accumulated obsolete-scrap inventory for reprocessing would be more or less offsetting. This, in turn, was reflected in the assumption of proportionate contribution of secondary material to total supply over the whole projection period. More precise assumptions were not considered useful for the illustrative purpose at hand.

13. Landsberg, *et al., op. cit.,* pp. 859-939.

14. Assumed constant over the whole projection period.

15. Landsberg, *et al., op. cit.*

16. *Ibid.*

Chapter 5

Energy

by
Joel Darmstadter
Resources for the Future, Inc.

COMMISSION ON POPULATION GROWTH AND
THE AMERICAN FUTURE, *RESEARCH
REPORTS, VOLUME III, POPULATION
RESOURCES AND THE ENVIRONMENT,*
EDITED BY RONALD G. RIDKER

CONTENTS

TABLES

Energy

INTRODUCTION

Economic history attests to the critical role played by the consumption of inanimate energy in advancing the material well-being of mankind—both by providing an essential input into economic growth and by satisfying a diverse range of wants made possible by the resultant increases in real income. The Industrial Revolution and the growth of industry in the nineteenth century are almost synonymous with the significant contribution of coal to the development of the iron and steel industry, to railways, and to factory mechanization. In the twentieth century, electrification and motorized transport, while reshaping society in ways which we know produced also serious detrimental effects, nonetheless served to sustain this historic process and, on balance, to step up tangible economic progress. And even as one ponders the potentially harmful environmental consequences of expanding levels of energy consumption in the years ahead, it is important to note that, quite apart from conventional applications, energy resources may in fact have to be increasingly deployed to deal with pressing environmental and other problems in the United States and around the world—for example, materials recycling and waste management, minerals extraction, and water desalination.

In the United States, as elsewhere, then, growth in the aggregate demand for inanimate energy supplies bears a close relationship to growth of the economy in general. But while there is a broad parallelism between economic growth and energy growth, it is important to pin down the relationship as precisely as possible, given the compounding effect of even a narrow spread in growth rates. Whether a four percent rate of growth in GNP means a 4.5 rather than a 3.5 percent rate of growth in energy consumption can spell over a third higher annual level of energy requirements by the year 2000. So both from the standpoint of environmental impacts as well as resource use, there is more than academic curiosity over this by now widely-debated concern with factors determining the future growth of the nation's energy needs.

A necessary underpinning to a consideration of future developments is some basic information pertaining to the historic and recent role of energy in the United States economy. We will therefore look at the record, as reflected in the broad statistical aggregates dealing with population, GNP, and energy consumption and review the role played by energy (in its totality as well as in terms of the different energy sources and forms employed) within particular sectors and activities of the American economy. The relationship between energy and national output growth, and the key role of the electricity sector, are looked at in some quantitative detail.

Next, we consider the matter of projected growth of energy demand in the United States over the next three decades, with emphasis on a discussion of factors likely to play a dominant role rather than on specific quantitative estimates. We also touch on the effect of alternative assumptions and "scenarios." We then look at the prospects for energy supply in the United States, and, in the course of this discussion, examine energy demand-supply outlook in the world as a whole—primarily, however, as that impinges on the position of the United States.

The final section deals with selected critical issues raised by the preceding discussion with respect to environmental implications and to the subject of research and public policy.

THE UNITED STATES HISTORICAL RECORD
Long-Term Trends in Major Aggregates

Expressed in quantity of heat contained, the consumption of energy resources in the United States in 1970 amounted to some 69 quadrillion Btu's.[1] This level of consumption was far in excess of the amount of energy consumed by all the countries of Western Europe (with a population 75 percent above that of the United States) taken together. A somewhat less abstract impression is gained if Btu's of heat value (which for analytical reasons are the preferred formulation) are expressed in terms of their underlying 1970 resource components: 527 million short tons of coal (used largely in the generation of electricity) were consumed in the United States in that year, 22 trillion cubic feet of natural gas,

Table 1.—Total U.S. Energy and Electricity Consumption, Gross National Product, and Population Selected Years, 1920-1970

Year	Total energy consumption (trillion Btu)	Electricity consumption (billion kwh)	GNP (billion 1958 dollars)	Population (million)	Per capita			Per $1 of GNP	
					Energy consumption (million Btu)	Electricity consumption (kwh)	GNP (1958 dollars)	Energy consumption (thousand Btu)	Electricity consumption (kwh)
1920	19,782	57.5	140.0	106.5	185.8	540	1,315	141.3	0.41
1930	22,288	116.2	183.5	123.1	181.1	944	1,490	121.5	0.63
1940	23,908	182.0	227.2	132.6	180.3	1,376	1,720	105.2	0.80
1950	34,154	390.5	355.3	152.3	224.3	2,564	2,342	96.1	1.10
1960	44,960	848.7	487.7	180.7	248.8	4,967	2,699	92.2	1.74
1965	53,785	1,157.4	617.8	194.6	276.4	5,948	3,175	87.1	1.87
1970	68,810	1,648.3	724.1	205.4	335.0	8,025	3,525	95.0	2.28

Notes and Sources: Total energy consumption, 1920-1940, from U.S. Bureau of the Census, *Historical Statistics of the United States, Colonial Times to 1957* (1960); 1950-1960, from U.S. Bureau of Mines Information Circular 8384, *An Energy Model for the United States* (1968); 1965 from U.S. Bureau of Mines, *Minerals Yearbook, 1969*; 1970 from U.S. Bureau of Mines News Release, March 9, 1971.

The data on electricity consumption represent net generation by privately- and publicly-owned utilities as well as other generation (e.g., industrial firms' own electricity production) and, in addition, include net imports of power. The 1920-1965 data are from the U.S. Bureau of the Census and the Federal Power Commission, shown in Edison Electric Institute, *Statisti-cal Yearbook of the Electric Utility Industry for 1969* (New York, 1970) and *Historical Statistics of the Electric Utility Industry* (New York, 1963). Figure for 1970 is preliminary estimate.

GNP for 1920 from U.S. Bureau of the Census, *Long-Term Economic Growth, 1860-1965* (1966); 1930-1965, U.S. Department of Commerce data shown in *Economic Report of the President, January 1971*; 1970 figure from U.S. Department of Commerce, *Survey of Current Business*, May 1971.

Population for 1920-1965 from U.S. Bureau of the Census, *Statistical Abstract of the United States* (annual); for 1970 from *Economic Report of the President, January 1971*.

nearly 5.5 billion barrels of oil products, 245 billion kilowatthours of electricity generated by falling water, and around 19 billion kilowatthours generated by nuclear energy (in addition to the 1.4 trillion kilowatthours based upon fossil fuel generation and covered in the foregoing primary energy consumption statistics).

The quantitative dimensions, within the economy, of the industries which are responsible for producing, processing, delivering, and marketing these resources to the point at which they heat and light homes, power factories, fuel the private and industrial transport system, and satisfy a variety of other demands, cannot be unambiguously specified. While the energy producing and conversion sectors per se (principally coal mines, crude petroleum and natural gas production, oil refineries, electric and gas utilities) constitute only a modest proportion[2] (not much over five percent) of the nation's GNP—and partly this is a consequence of abundance of relatively low-cost energy resources available to this country—other measures, reflecting energy-related activities, signify considerably greater relative importance. For example, these same energy industries, which, moreover, exclude some sectors involved in the energy field (for example, water and rail transport), in some years account for as much as one-fifth of the nation's capital investment spending.

And, energy supplies constitute a far more significant input to certain economic activities than to others (such as, iron and steelmaking and nonferrous metals).[3]

The long-term growth of total energy use in the United States bears a predictably close parallel to the nation's overall economic expansion, even though—as we shall see—the two trends have not always proceeded in lock-step. The twentieth century record in its entirety is one showing a 3.2 percent yearly growth rate for aggregate consumption of primary energy resources, compared to an only slightly higher one of 3.3 percent for a constant dollar GNP. On a per capita basis, energy's long-run growth rate amounts to 1.7 percent per annum; GNP per capita, to 1.8 percent. For the more recent 50-year (1920-70) period shown in Table 1, a wider gap in growth rates prevailed: Energy consumption grew at the annual average percentage rate of 2.5 percent and GNP, at 3.3 percent; the respective per capita figures were 1.2 and 2.0 percent. These trends are reflected in the persistent long-term decline in the ratio of Btu's of energy consumed for each $1 (in constant prices) of GNP—down from 141,000 Btu's in 1920 to 95,000 in 1970. As Table 1 indicates, however, a reversal to this energy-GNP trend occurred during the 1960's and much interest centers on the meaning and resultant implications for the future of this apparent turnabout. More concerning this point a little later.

Steadily rising shares (from eight percent in 1920 to 25 percent in 1970) of total energy resources have been devoted to production of electricity. (See the percentage share of Table 2.)[4] Hence, electricity, with a long-term average annual growth rate of around seven percent, has expanded at a pace far greater than either total energy consumption or GNP and much faster still, obviously, than the long-term one to two percent population growth rate in the United States. Indeed, if we view the growth of electricity consumption for the period, say, since 1950 (7.5 percent yearly) as the product of a 1.5 percent per annum growth in population and a six percent growth in electricity consumption per capita, it turns out that only about one-fifth of total electricity growth is attributable to population increase and as much as 80 percent to growing levels of per capita use. (As a corollary calculation, one can say that a halt to production growth, everything else equal, might scarcely

have affected the rising volume of electric power use; while an unchanged volume of electric power use since 1950 would, in order to accommodate rising per capita standards, have required a 1970 population level of around 50 million—the figure of the year 1880.)

The Changing Importance of Different Primary Energy Sources

Major shifts have taken place in the relative contribution to total consumption of the major energy resources—coal, natural gas, oil, hydro, and most recently (and as yet insignificant within this overall perspective), nuclear power.[5] The major long-term shifts are spelled out in Table 2.

Coal's dominance in the various energy markets (households, industry, transport and commerce) persisted well into the 1920's, even though by then, its supremacy in the nation's fuel and power base was beginning to be challenged—particularly by the growth

Table 2.—Total U.S. Energy Consumption, by Source and Form of Use, Selected Years, 1920-1970

Year	By source[a]					By form used			As raw material
						Fuel and power			
	Coal	Natural gas	Petroleum	Hydro and nuclear	Total	Total	Electricity	Other	
In trillion Btu									
1920	15,504	827	2,676	775	19,782	n.a.	1,663	n.a.	n.a.
1930	13,639	1,969	5,898	785	22,288	n.a.	1,965	n.a.	n.a.
1940	12,535	2,726	7,781	917	23,908	n.a.	2,458	n.a.	n.a.
1950	12,914	6,150	13,489	1,601	34,154	32,712	5,142	27,570	1,442
1960	10,414	12,699	20,067	1,780	44,960	42,715	8,387	34,328	2,245
1965	12,358	16,098	23,241	2,088	53,785	51,140	11,104	40,036	2,645
1970	13,792	22,546	29,617	2,855	68,810	64,910	16,967	47,943	3,900
1920	78.4%	4.2%	13.5%	3.9%	100.0%	n.a.	8.4%	n.a.	n.a.
1930	61.2	8.8	26.5	3.5	100.0	n.a.	8.8	n.a.	n.a.
1940	52.4	11.4	32.4	3.8	100.0	n.a.	10.3	n.a.	n.a.
1950	37.8	18.0	39.5	4.7	100.0	95.8%	15.1	80.7%	4.2%
1960	23.2	28.2	44.6	4.0	100.0	95.0	18.7	76.3	5.0
1965	23.0	29.9	43.2	3.9	100.0	95.1	20.6	74.4	4.9
1970	20.0	32.8	43.0	4.1	100.0	94.3	24.7	69.7	5.7

[a]Coal includes bituminous coal, anthracite, lignite; petroleum includes natural gas liquids; the nuclear component (not shown separately) amounted (in trillion Btu) to six in 1960, 39 in 1965, and 208 (or 0.3 percent of total energy consumption) in 1970.

Source: Total energy consumption, 1920-1940, from U.S. Bureau of the Census, *Historical Statistics of the United States, Colonial Times to 1957* (1960); 1950-1960, from U.S. Bureau of Mines Information Circular 8384, *An Energy Model for the United States* (1968); 1965, from U.S. Bureau of Mines, *Minerals*

Yearbook, 1969; 1970, from U.S. Bureau of Mines News Release, March 9, 1971. Data on energy consumed in electric generation was based, for 1920, on data in U.S. Bureau of the Census, *Historical Statistics of the United States, op. cit.*; and for 1930-40 was obtained on the basis of data shown in Edison Electric Institute, *Historical Statistics of the Electric Utility Industry* (New York, 1963). The EEI series on total net electric generation (expressed in kwh) was multiplied by the EEI estimate of the heat rate (Btu per kwh) for all boiler fuels; the result was added to the hydro figures, shown above.

of automotive transport and, hence, the inroads of gasoline. Various circumstances sheltered coal's position. The steam locomotive was still preeminent; in merchant shipping, oil-fired vessels had only recently begun to displace coal-burning ships. Coal was the preponderent fuel in thermal electricity generation, and it had a virtually complete grip on space and process heating. In fact, not until after World War II did coal relinquish its 50-percent-and-over share of the nation's energy consumption. By 1970, it accounted for a fifth of nationwide energy.

During the past two decades, the use of natural gas has made the most rapid strides among the basic energy sources. With an average growth rate of over seven percent, the natural gas share of overall energy consumption rose from around 14 percent after World War II to one-third by 1970. Oil already occupied a one-third share during and immediately after World War II; its postwar growth was therefore more modest. Reaching around a 45-percent share in 1960, its subsequent percentage place has been one of relative stability. Hydro's share—scarcely ever above 4.5 percent of total energy consumption—rose during the first 50 years of the century, but has levelled off in the last two decades, since the practical potential for developing new hydroelectric sites in the country is limited.

The Changing Importance of Different Sectors of Consumption

Available statistics make it possible to distinguish among four major energy-consuming sectors of the economy, as shown in the lefthand panel of Table 3. From this presentation, it is evident that, with the exception of the increasing relative importance of the electric utility sector as a consumer of primary energy resources (already alluded to) no really drastic distributional changes are evident over the postwar period. Households and commercial users (combined) increased their share of nationwide energy consumption slightly, while industry and the transport sector (the latter including private automotive fuel consumption) reduced theirs. Even so, the respective sectoral shares in recent years—one-fifth for households and commerce, a bit under one-third for industry, and close to one-fourth for transportation—stood not far from their level two decades earlier. Electric utilities, by contrast, raised their proportion from 15 percent in 1950 to 25 percent in 1970.

A somewhat different perspective emerges when input into power generation is apportioned among final consumers rather than as a separate end-use sector. This adjustment, made in the righthand panel of Table 3 shows the industrial sector to remain the largest customer, again with slightly declining shares since 1950. Because transportation is effectively out of the electric power market, it slips markedly below the household and commercial sector in its share of energy consumption, retaining, however, its only slightly declining postwar relative position in total energy markets. The household and commercial segment, on the other hand, now reflecting its rapidly rising demand for electric power both lifts its share substantially for any given year

Table 3.—U.S. Energy Consumption, Shares of Major Consuming Sectors, Selected Years, 1950-1970 (percent)

Year	Electric utilities treated as consuming sector					Electric utility energy consumption allocated to ultimate consumers of electricity[a]				Total energy consumption (trillion Btu)
	Households & commercial	Industrial	Transportation	Electric utilities	Total[b]	Households & commercial	Industrial	Transportation	Total[b]	
1950	22.2%	36.1%	25.2%	15.1%	100.0%	29.5%	43.5%	25.5%	100.0%	34,154
1955	21.6	35.3	24.6	16.7	100.0	29.2	44.3	24.8	100.0	39,956
1960	22.7	33.1	24.1	18.7	100.0	31.8	42.5	24.2	100.0	44,960
1965	22.1	32.6	23.6	20.6	100.0	33.2	42.0	23.7	100.0	53,785
1970	20.5	30.7	23.9	24.7	100.0	34.3	41.5	24.0	100.0	68,810

[a]That is, the primary energy input into the electric utility sector (e.g., 5,142 trillion Btu in 1950—see Table 2) is apportioned according to sectoral purchases of kilowatthours of utility output, and is then added to each sector's direct (non-electric) fuel consumption shown in the lefthand panel above.

[b]Including small amount of "miscellaneous and unaccounted for," not shown separately.

Note: See also the notes to Table 4, which provide further definitional remarks.

Source: Total energy consumption, 1920-1940, from U.S. Bureau of the Census, *Historical Statistics of the United States, Colonial Times to 1957* (1960); 1950-1960, from U.S. Bureau of Mines Information Circular 8384, *An Energy Model for the United States* (1968); 1965, from U.S. Bureau of Mines, *Minerals Yearbook, 1969*; 1970, from U.S. Bureau of Mines News Release, March 9, 1971.

Population, Resources, and the Environment

Table 4.—Total U.S. Consumption of Energy Resources, by Source and Consuming Sector, 1950, 1960, 1970 (trillion Btu)

Consuming sector[b]	Primary energy source[a]				Total sector inputs of primary energy	Utility electricity[f]	Total sector inputs of primary energy and utility electricity[g]
	Coal[c]	Natural gas	Petroleum[d]	Hydro and nuclear[e]			
	(1)	(2)	(3)	(4)	(5)	(6)	(7)
Household and commercial:							
1950	2,912	1,642	3,038	. . .	7,593	546	8,139
1960	1,023	4,268	4,923	. . .	10,214	1,262	11,476
1970	399	7,350	6,349	. . .	14,098	2,904	17,002
Industrial:							
1950	5,957	3,728	2,642	. . .	12,326	559	12,885
1960	4,898	6,287	3,682	. . .	14,867	1,306	16,172
1970	5,560	10,500	5,069	. . .	21,129	2,275	23,404
Transportation:							
1950	1,701	130	6,785	. . .	8,616	24	8,640
1960	91	359	10,372	. . .	10,822	18	10,840
1970	9	671	15,756	. . .	16,436	18	16,454
Electric utilities:							
1950	2,228	651	662	1,601	5,142	1,129	
1960	4,257	1,785	564	1,780	8,387	2,586	NOT APPLICABLE
1970	7,824	4,025	2,263	2,855	16,967	5,197	
Miscellaneous and unaccounted for:							
1950	115	. . .	362	. . .	477		
1960	145	. . .	526	. . .	671		
1970	. . .	. . .	180	. . .	180		
Total primary energy inputs:							
1950	12,914	6,150	13,489	1,601	34,154		
1960	10,414	12,699	20,067	1,780	44,960		
1970	13,792	22,546	29,617	2,855	68,810		

[a]Represents energy content of all primary (domestic and net imported) energy sources and their derivatives (e.g., gasoline) at the time they are incorporated into the indicated consuming sectors of the economy, and irrespective of whether used for fuel and power or other (nonenergy) purposes. (Strictly speaking, fossil-fuel based electricity is a derivative energy source—analogous to gasoline—but it is represented statistically as being incorporated at the fuel-input stage, prior to conversion.)

[b]Energy consumption arising from operation of household passenger cars is included in the transportation sector, which also includes commercial transport services, bunkers, and military. Nontransport government energy consumption is distributed largely between the household and commercial sector (e.g., lighting of government buildings) and the industry sector (e.g., electricity purchases for Atomic Energy Commission nuclear enrichment plants).

[c]Largely bituminous coal, but also including anthracite and lignite.

[d]Including natural gas liquids.

[e]Includes net imports of electric power, however fueled. The nuclear component applies only to 1960 (six trillion Btu) and 1970 (208 trillion Btu). Hydro- and nuclear-based electricity are not distributable by consuming sectors, because only aggregate electric energy purchases from utilities (col. 6) can be allocated to end uses. Thus, hydro and nuclear electricity—converted to theoretical fossil-fuel inputs using the prevailing fuel-per-kwh requirements at central electric stations—are assigned entirely to the electric utility sector.

[f]Represents utility electricity delivered to the indicated consuming sectors, computed at 3,412 Btu per kwh, the direct calorific value of electricity. The sum of this column, shown in the "electric utility" sector panel, falls short of the total primary energy inputs into the electric utility sector by the amount of conversion losses experienced by fossil fuels and those ascribed (theoretically) to hydro and nuclear. The column excludes power generated by nonutility plants. Correspondingly, fuel inputs for nonutility power is excluded from the electric utility sector. Such nonutility power and its primary fuel requirements are included within the other consuming sectors.

[g]Represents sectoral energy resource inputs, including direct fuels and electricity furnished by utilities. The sum of this column (not shown) plus electricity conversion losses (the difference between columns (5) and (6) in the electric utility sector panel) plus the miscellaneous and unaccounted-for totals equals the grand total of column (5).

Sources: U.S. Bureau of the Census, *Historical Statistics of the United States, Colonial Times to 1957* (1960); 1950-1960, from U.S. Bureau of Mines Information Circular 8384, *An Energy Model for the United States* (1968); 1965, from U.S. Bureau of Mines, *Minerals Yearbook, 1969*; 1970 from U.S. Bureau of Mines News Release, March 9, 1971.

Table 5.—Total U.S. Consumption of Energy, by Source and Consuming Sector, 1950, 1960 and 1970

A. Percent Distribution of Total Energy Consumption, by Sector and Source

	Coal	Natural gas	Petroleum	Hydro and nuclear	Total
Household & commercial:					
1950	8.5%	4.8%	8.9%	(a)	22.2%
1960	2.3	9.5	10.9	(a)	22.7
1970	0.6	10.7	9.2	(a)	20.5
Industrial:					
1950	17.4	10.9	7.7	(a)	36.1
1960	10.9	14.0	8.2	(a)	33.1
1970	8.1	15.3	7.4	(a)	30.7
Transportation:					
1950	5.0	0.4	19.9	(a)	25.2
1960	0.2	0.8	23.1	(a)	24.1
1970	...	1.0	22.9	(a)	23.9
Electric utilities:					
1950	6.5	1.9	1.9	4.7%	15.1
1960	9.5	4.0	1.3	4.0	18.7
1970	11.4	5.8	3.3	4.1	24.7
Total energy[b]:					
1950	37.8	18.0	39.5	4.7	100.0
1960	23.2	28.2	44.6	4.0	100.0
1970	20.0	32.8	43.0	4.1	100.0

B. Percent Distribution of Energy Sources, by Sector

	Coal	Natural gas	Petroleum	Hydro and nuclear	Total
Household and commercial:					
1950	22.5	26.7	22.5	(a)	22.2
1960	9.8	33.6	24.5	(a)	22.7
1970	2.9	32.6	21.4	(a)	20.5
Industrial:					
1950	46.1	60.6	19.6	(a)	36.1
1960	47.0	49.5	18.3	(a)	33.1
1970	40.3	46.6	17.1	(a)	30.7
Transportation:					
1950	13.2	2.1	50.3	(a)	25.2
1960	0.9	2.8	51.7	(a)	24.1
1970	0.1	3.0	53.2	(a)	23.9
Electric utilities:					
1950	17.3	10.6	4.9	100.0	15.1
1960	40.9	14.1	2.8	100.0	18.7
1970	56.7	17.9	7.6	100.0	24.7
Total energy[b]:					
1950	100.0	100.0	100.0	100.0	100.0
1960	100.0	100.0	100.0	100.0	100.0
1970	100.0	100.0	100.0	100.0	100.0

Table 5.—Continued

C. Percent Distribution of Sectors, by Energy Source[c]

	Coal	Natural gas	Petroleum	Hydro and nuclear	Total
Household and commercial:					
1950	38.4%	21.6%	40.0%	([a])	100.0%
1960	10.0	41.8	48.2	([a])	100.0
1970	2.8	52.1	45.0	([a])	100.0
Industrial:					
1950	48.3	30.2	21.4	([a])	100.0
1960	32.9	42.3	24.8	([a])	100.0
1970	26.3	49.7	24.0	([a])	100.0
Transportation:					
1950	19.7	1.5	78.7	([a])	100.0
1960	0.8	3.3	95.8	([a])	100.0
1970	0.1	4.1	95.9	([a])	100.0
Electric utilities:					
1950	43.3	12.7	12.9	31.1	100.0
1960	50.8	21.3	6.7	21.2	100.0
1970	46.1	23.7	13.3	16.8	100.0
Total energy[b]:					
1950	37.8	18.0	39.5	4.7	100.0
1960	23.2	28.2	44.6	4.0	100.0
1970	20.0	32.8	43.0	4.1	100.0

[a]Not shown, since only aggregate electric energy deliveries can be allocated to end uses. See Table 4.

[b]For convenience, and because of the small magnitudes involved, we do not show the "miscellaneous and unaccounted for" category.

[c]It should be remembered that the percentage shares of panel C distribute only sectoral purchases of *fossil* fuels. If we add to the household and commercial and the industrial sectors their respective electricity utility purchases as well, the following percentages result for 1970:

	Coal	Natural gas	Petroleum	Utility electricity	Total
Household & commercial	2.3	43.2	37.3	17.1	100.0
Industrial	23.8	44.9	21.7	9.7	100.0

Source: See Table 4.

as well as showing distinctly rising shares.

But, the end-use breakdown of Table 3 should be recognized as exceedingly broad, with each identifiable sector covering a multitude of different activities. "Defense uses, agriculture, and use of energy materials for non-energy purposes, are all included in one or the other of the three specifically designated economic segments. Compounded with ambiguities in the data as originally collected and classified, these categorizations should not be looked at as more than rough suggestions of change ...."[6] For clues as to some underlying factors obscured by these sectoral aggregates, it is useful to look at the behavior of specific energy sources within each of the end-use sectors. This is taken up next.

Shifts Among Energy Sources in Different Sectors of Consumption

The way in which each fuel source has positioned itself in the broad energy markets of the economy during the past two decades is shown in Table 4. This table represents the standard aggregative statistical framework developed by the U.S. Bureau of Mines for examining the sectoral disposition of energy resources. To probe somewhat beneath these rather unwieldy totals, it is useful to refer to the three-part summary presentation shown in Table 5, where we have translated the 1950, 1960, and 1970 absolutes of Table 4 into percentages, once again reverting to the treatment of electric utilities as a consuming sector and omitting utilities' electric sales to their customers because these mostly represent secondary energy based on the primary fuels (coal, oil, gas) whose trends we are first interested in depicting.

From the top panel (A) of these summary data, we see that—based on this broad classification scheme—petroleum consumption in the transportation sector (accounting for nearly a quarter of nationwide energy consumption) represents the single most important sectoral purchase of an energy resource in 1970. Just after World War II, petroleum consumed in the transportation sector had also been very important (20 percent of United States energy consumption of all types), though in that year industrial consumption of coal ranked a close second with 17 percent. Among other numerically important consumption flows in 1970, there were coal deliveries to the utility sector (11 percent of the nation's energy consumption), natural gas consumption by industry (15 percent) and by the combined household and commercial sector (11 percent). Along with the 23 percent accounted for by petroleum deliveries to the transport sector, these flows aggregated to 60 percent of nationwide energy consumption in 1970.

The middle panel of the table shows the changing importance of the different consuming sectors for each energy source. For coal, the virtual disappearance of the household, commercial, and transportation market was offset—but amidst a falling absolute volume of coal consumed (see Table 4)—by the electric utility sector. The industrial market (essentially iron and steel) continues to represent an important share of total coal consumption. Electric utilities and the household and commercial sectors both increased their relative importance (the former not noticeably) to natural gas; while for petroleum, the 1970 distribution of its sectoral deliveries was rather similar to its 1950 sectoral breakdown, the most striking change being the relative increase in deliveries to utilities—a consequence of a shift within the past few years towards environmentally less objectionable fuels.

The bottom panel in Table 5 discloses striking shifts in shares of the different energy sources in given markets—for example, coal's decline from nearly two-fifths of household and commercial energy consumption in 1950 to a mere three percent in 1970; and, conversely, the rise of natural gas to over 50 percent in 1970 from 22 percent in 1950. Comfort heat is, of course, the main source of demand for these fuels in the household and commercial sector. In the industrial sector, both petroleum and (in particular) natural gas gained at the relative expense of coal, though in this

market—due to coal's continuing importance in steelmaking—each fossil fuel retains important shares. In transport, the trend could not be more concise: Largely because of the disappearance of steam railroads (which right after World War II gave coal over one-third of the transportation market), coal declined from 20 percent of the market in 1950 to the point (in 1970) where petroleum enjoyed a virtually captive market, with a 96 percent share. In the electric utility sector, the story is interesting, for what we see are relatively unchanged shares for both coal (43 percent in 1950, 46 percent in 1970), and oil (13 percent in both years), with a rising natural gas share (from 13 to 24 percent) offsetting the declining hydroelectric proportion. This offset was, of course, statistical—in the sense that the rising utility share taken by natural gas would not otherwise have largely gone to hydro. We must also note that these terminal-year comparisons are slightly misleading since they obscure some ups and downs during the period. Thus, coal's share of the utility sector was somewhat higher in 1960, while that of oil was a bit lower. Shifts since then reflect in part the already mentioned rising demand for low-sulfur fuel oil at the expense of coal.

Energy Consumption and National Output

Although more research is needed to shed light on the correlation between economic growth and energy consumption, one's judgment may be guided by some broad suggestive evidence from the past. During the 40-year period of intensive industrialization occurring in the United States between 1880 and 1920, yearly energy consumption growth averaged 5.6 percent, substantially exceeding annual GNP growth of 3.4 percent. By contrast, over the ensuing four decades, United States energy consumption growth steadfastly fell below GNP growth—the annual figures for the period 1920-1960 averaging out to 2.1 percent and 3.2 percent, respectively. In both periods, of course, energy and GNP each grew more rapidly than population, yielding per capita growth for both indicators.

Sorting out the factors at work in the contrasting trends for these two periods of American history is a complicated business, which need not detain us here, but a couple of summary observations are worth making. The steeper rise of energy consumption than of GNP in the closing decades of the nineteenth century and in the early part of the twentieth century almost certainly reflects the disproportionately fast growth of manufacturing in the economy—a sector requiring far higher energy input per unit of activity than the agricultural component which had dominated the economy in the past. (This phenomenon is at work presently in developing parts of the world: There, consumption of energy rises at rates considerably in excess of output in general, when compared to most of the advanced countries.)

The forces making for relatively slower growth in energy consumption than in GNP for the United States after World War II—or, to put it differently, for progressively less energy used per constant $1 of GNP—are more difficult to unscramble; but, at least several distinct elements appear to have played a role.[7] An important contributing factor was the rapid rise of electrification which greatly enhanced the efficiency of factory operations formerly dependent on, and constrained by, the limitations on plant layout imposed by the coal-burning factory steam engine. And this occurred in spite of the fact that the generation of a kilowatthour of electricity required many times the caloric input of electricity produced. This disadvantage was, however, moderated in a very important respect by the fact that the thermal efficiency of electricity generation improved

substantially over the years: In 1925, it took over two pounds of coal to produce one kwh of electricity, while by the 1960's, the figure was down to under one pound. Another important instance of improved energy conversion later in this period was the replacement of railroad diesel engines—with their greater efficiency—for steam locomotives.

With this brief historical backdrop, we can look at developments during the decade just ended, recognizing that, as against the long-term developments just reviewed, observations based on 10 years should not carry an undue amount of interpretive weight. Between 1960 and 1965, things continued pretty much as they had in preceding decades; United States energy consumption increased at the average annual rate of 3.6 percent, while GNP increased by 4.8 percent. Energy consumption per $1 of GNP (expressed in constant 1958 prices) continued its prior downward path, falling from 92 thousand Btu to 87 thousand Btu. But then a sharp reversal occurred. Between 1965 and 1970, energy

Table 6.—Contributions of Different Components to Changes in U.S. Energy Consumption, 1960-1965 and 1965-1970

End-use sector and type of energy consumed	1960 share of total U.S. energy consumption (percent)	1960-1965		1965 share of total U.S. energy consumption (percent)	1965-1970		Change between 1960-1965 and 1965-1970 in the contribution of different components (col. 6 minus col. 3)
		Average annual percent rate of change	Contribution to average annual percent rate of change in total energy consumption[a]		Average annual percent rate of change	Contribution to average annual percent rate of change in total energy consumption[a]	
	(1)	(2)	(3)	(4)	(5)	(6)	(7)
Households and commercial:							
Fossil fuels	22.7	3.05	0.69	22.1	3.51	0.78	0.09
Electricity	2.8	9.08	0.25	3.6	8.31	0.30	0.05
Industry:							
Fossil fuels	33.1	3.37	1.12	32.6	3.78	1.23	0.11
Electricity	2.9	4.58	0.13	3.0	6.84	0.21	0.08
Transportation:							
Fossil fuels	24.1	3.28	0.79	23.6	5.27	1.24	0.45
Electricity conversion losses .	12.9	5.29	0.68	14.0	9.42	1.32	0.64
Total energy	100.0	3.65	3.65	100.0	5.05	5.05	1.40
In fuel and power uses	95.0	3.67	3.49	94.9	4.88	4.63	1.14
In nonenergy uses	5.0	3.33	0.17	5.1	8.07	0.41	0.24

[a]Weighted by relative contribution to nationwide energy consumption in 1960 and 1965, respectively, as shown in cols. (1) and (4).

Note: Components of cols. (1), (3), (4), (6), and (7) do not quite add to totals because of rounding and because of omission of electricity consumption in Transportation (a statistically insignificant sector) and a minor "miscellaneous and unallocable" component.

Source: U.S. Bureau of Mines, *Minerals Yearbook* and various U.S. Bureau of Mines releases.

consumption rose by five percent yearly, GNP by 3.2 percent, or from a level of 87 thousand Btu per $1, to one of 95 thousand Btu per $1—a level left behind in the early 1950's and, until 1970, never again recorded. (In 1970 alone, energy consumption rose by over 4.5 percent while GNP actually declined.)

The figures in Table 6 provide some insight into the anatomy of this acceleration in United States energy consumption during the 1960-1970 decade. The last column, showing how the 1.4 percentage point increase (from the 3.6 average annual rate during 1960-1965 to the 5.0 rate for 1965-1970) was distributed, is of particular interest. We see that a major thrust (an 0.64 percentage point portion—or 45 percent of the increment) came from the line marked "electricity conversion losses." This item refers to the thermal losses associated with electricity conversion at power plants.[8] Contrary to long-term historical experience, during which electric-generating efficiency exhibited persistent improvements, the 1965-1970 years showed a stoppage to such improvements. Indeed, there was a decline: Electric-generating efficiency was 32.5 percent in 1965, around 30 percent in 1970.[9] Note that, in itself, electric power use by the household-commercial and industrial sectors, though exceedingly high (especially by earlier projection standards) did not drastically change between the two periods (for all sectors combined, the average annual rate went from 6.7 percent to 7.2 percent), and so did not materially contribute to the accelerated rate of growth in energy consumption.

The transportation sector was the next most important component to the stepped-up energy growth rate, accounting for one-third of the 1.4 percentage-point increment. In the case of transport, almost solely involving oil consumption, the significant contribution resulted from a fairly substantial increase in the consumption growth rate (from 3.3 percent per annum to 5.3 percent), coupled with the large weight occupied within the nation's total energy use.

Although the overwhelming portion of basic energy resources are consumed in fuel and power uses, in recent years their use in nonenergy applications (e.g., as raw materials for the petrochemical industry) has tended to rise. The last line of the table shows that energy sources so used grew at the rate of 3.3 percent during 1960-1965, but rose to 8.1 percent during 1965-1970. From the last column, we can calculate that this acceleration contributed about 17 percent to the increment in growth rates in total energy consumption between the two periods, although the nonenergy sector's weight in overall energy consumption, and even in its contribution to the overall five percent 1965-1970 growth rate, was far below this. (Nonenergy applications are largely contained within fossil fuel consumption in the industry sector.)

We will offer some conjecture about the meaning of some of these rather distinct recent changes in United States energy consumption and their implications for the future when we turn to the subject of projections, below.

Table 7.—Electric Utility Sales, 1960-1969

Year	Billion kwh				Percent of total			
	Resi-dential	Com-mercial	Industrial	Total	Resi-dential	Com-mercial	Industrial	Total
1960	195.6	114.4	344.1	681.2	28.7	16.8	50.5	100.0
1961	208.2	134.4	346.6	718.6	29.0	18.7	48.2	100.0
1962	225.5	143.6	373.0	773.7	29.1	18.6	48.2	100.0
1963	240.7	165.9	387.4	828.2	29.1	20.0	46.8	100.0
1964	261.0	182.9	408.3	887.5	29.4	20.6	46.0	100.0
1965	279.8	201.4	432.2	950.4	29.4	21.2	45.5	100.0
1966	305.4	225.1	463.8	1,035.6	29.5	21.7	44.8	100.0
1967	330.2	241.7	484.7	1,103.5	29.9	21.9	43.9	100.0
1968	366.2	264.2	517.3	1,198.4	30.6	22.0	43.2	100.0
1969	402.0	290.0	557.3	1,303.8	30.8	22.2	42.7	100.0

Source: *Electrical World* data shown in U.S. Congress, Joint Economic Committee, *The Economy, Energy and The Environment,* by the Environmental Policy Division, Legislative Reference Service, Library of Congress, Joint Committee Print, September 1, 1970, p. 73. The 1969 breakdown is estimated. A sectorally unallocable "other" component is not shown above. Apart from the fact that the figures of Table 4 are expressed in Btu's and those above in kwh's, the two tables are not precisely comparable.

The Key Role of Electricity

A relentlessly high growth rate coupled with major environmental ramifications has made electricity a focal point in public discussion on energy matters. It is therefore desirable to single out electricity for particular, though limited, consideration. Sectoral trends in electric utility sales are depicted in Table 7.

Growth rates based on the figures in Table 7 show these annual averages for the period 1960-1969:

	Annual average growth rate
Residential	8.3%
Commercial	10.9
Industrial	5.5
Total sales	7.5%

Per residential customer, sales went up from 3,851 kwh in 1960 to an estimated 6,550 kwh in 1969—or by approximately six percent per year (the difference from the 8.3 percent total growth being essentially due to the growth of customers).

In spite of the attention that has been directed to household demand for electricity, it is the commercial sector of the economy (office buildings, shopping centers, public facilities, and the like) which the table shows to have been in the forefront of electricity consumption growth, even though that sector's purchases are still substantially exceeded in absolute levels by residential and industrial purchases. Still, residential customers have expanded their electric power use faster than the economy as a whole; and since that market's growth has been so widely singled out in discussions of electricity's environmental consequences, it is useful to take a somewhat closer look at those components of household electricity consumption which can be said to have provided particular thrust to this growth.

As a point of departure, let us indicate the way in which the 195 billion kwh of residential electricity purchased in 1960 was apportioned among different household uses.[10] (See Table 8.)

It is interesting to see that eight separately identifiable sources of electricity demand within the home accounted for 90 percent of residential consumption in 1960. That is, in spite of what one often hears about the proliferating range of frivolous household electrical gadgets, these could not possibly have contributed a great deal to electricity consumption in 1960. Of course, one person's necessity is another's luxury; and over time, luxuries become necessities. All that we want to establish is that, in 1960, the preponderant share of

Table 8.—Apportionment of Residential Electricity by Major Uses, 1960

	Billion kwh	Percent of total
Lighting	43	22
Ranges[a]	21	11
Water heaters[a]	45	23
Air conditioners[a]	8	4
Space heating[a]	12	6
Refrigerators and T.V. sets	28	14
Home freezers	9	5
Clothes dryers[a]	9	5
All other	20	10
	195	100

[a]Gas constitutes an alternative energy source.

Source: From Hans H. Landsberg et al., *Resources in America's Future* (Baltimore: Johns Hopkins Press, 1963); taken from tables in Chapter 10 Appendix. The "all other" category was increased slightly in order to adjust Landsberg's overall total of 193 billion to our figure of 195 billion.

household electric power demand originated in what had, by then, come to be viewed as fairly basic uses and excluded many of the items commonly singled out as typifying the runaway craze for domestic electrification: toothbrushes, shoeshine kits, slicing knives, vibrators, and so on. (In the course of this research, the existence of an electric spaghetti fork came to light.) Moreover, it is likely that the overwhelming portion of the "all other" category in the preceding tabulations consisted of such resistance appliances—otherwise unidentified in the tabulations—as roasters, broilers, grills, and irons, as well as such lesser-wattage but nevertheless "basic" items as clothes washers and radio-phonographs.

What, then, explains the continued surge of household electricity consumption during the most recent decade? Although no systematic data were at hand at the time of writing, sufficient figures to permit some tentative judgments were available. In this connection, it is useful before proceeding to exotic explanations of electricity growth, to recall the extent to which, in 1960, American households were or were not equipped with such items as were catalogued in Table 8 (whether powered by electricity or other energy sources). For example, the "saturation factor" (the percentage of American households possessing the item in question) for central airconditioning was only one percent, that for room airconditioning, 14 percent. Some 60 percent had water heaters, of which about half were electric. A bit over 20 percent had freezers, a bit under 20 percent had clothes dryers—70 percent of the latter being electric. Although the overwhelming proportion of American homes were centrally heated, less than one percent had electric heat. And while 87 percent possessed some kind of television set, the proportion owning color could not have been much over one percent, if that.[11] The potentiality for a growing electricity demand arising from quite conventional needs was therefore present.

Indeed, in trying to account for the slightly more than 200 billion kwh increment in household electricity consumption between 1960 and 1969 (from 196 to 402 billion noted in Table 7), we find, first, that roughly 32 billion kwh (or 16 percent) of incremental growth was due to airconditioning alone.[12] A recent congressional report notes that "some utilities found during the summer of 1969 that as much as 25 to 35 percent of their peak loads were attributable to airconditioning or other weather related needs."[13]

Another major stimulus has come from the installation of electric heat—principally in new homes. In recent years, this has been the fastest growing component of residential sales, the 1960 figure of 0.9 million electrically heated homes having jumped to nearly 3.5 million by the end of 1968.[14] If, as a rough approximation, we assume that kilowatthours absorbed by electric heating multiplied by a corresponding factor of 3.5, then 36 million kwh out of the 1969 nationwide total of 402 billion can be ascribed to residential space heating in that year—up from 12 billion in 1960, the 24 billion increment accounting for another 12 percent of 1960-69 growth. Thus, 28 percent of household electricity expansion during the period 1960-69 can be traced solely to airconditioning and space heating. Put another way, compared to the total residential electricity growth rate of 8.3 percent per year, airconditioning and space heating (combined) went up by 14 percent, and all other uses by around seven percent. As a result, in 1969, airconditioning and space heating occupied twice their relative share in residential electric power consumption.

Statistics enabling us to distribute the balance of the 1960-69 residential growth among different uses are lacking. However, some ideas can be gotten by looking at changes in selected saturation factors.[15] (See Table 9.) As suggested earlier, the items among those which may be presumed to have provided particular stimulus to growing household electricity use are those—with heating elements—drawing substantial current. The lowly toothbrush—frequently the symbolic villain in our despair over relentless power growth—may prove something or other about man's hedonism. But it has not contributed to power shortages.[16]

Table 9.—Percent of U.S. Households Owning Electrical Appliances

	1960	1969
Blenders	7.5%	25.9%
Coffeemakers	53.4	82.9
Dishwashers	6.3	20.8
Disposals	9.5	20.5
Clothes dryers (incl. gas)	17.8	38.8
Freezers	22.1	28.5
Frypans	40.7	53.4
Irons	88.6	99.5
Mixers	53.4	80.5
T.V.—Black & white	89.9	98.5
T.V.—Color	2.9[a]	35.7
Clothes washers	83.1	90.8
Refrigerators	98.0	99.8
Toasters	70.4	89.3

[a]1965 figure.
Source: *Merchandising Week* data from U.S. Bureau of the Census, *Statistical Abstract of the United States, 1970,* p. 687.

THE DETERMINATION OF FUTURE UNITED STATES ENERGY DEMAND AND SUPPLY

The Projected Relationship of Energy Consumption and GNP

We noted earlier the fairly distinct reversal in long-term trends occurring in the mid-1960's, prior to which energy consumption growth had proceeded markedly below GNP growth and after which the opposite trend appeared to be taking hold. At this point, it is far too soon to speak with certainty about what, if anything, some of these rather marked recent changes portend for future long-term trends in United States energy consumption. It is probably correct to say that these unfolding developments have surprised many involved in projecting future energy requirements. The conventional approach, not only for the United States but numerous highly industrialized nations as well, had been to project long-term energy growth at a rate somewhat below that of GNP, even where the analysis probed into sectoral, rather than merely aggregative, relationships. This presupposed that factors operative throughout much of the present century (and we have earlier alluded to some) would continue to exert a heavy weight on the growth of energy needs. It was also thought that growth of an increasingly "service-oriented" society would entail proportionately fewer energy inputs. While it is possible that what we have been witnessing in recent years may be a transitory phenomenon, it is also worth pondering whether there are here the seeds of a more enduring phenomenon. Several points come to mind.

One should at least allow for the possibility that there is a short-term aspect to the recent experience. Earlier post-World War II retardations in the nation's economic growth (particularly the recessions of 1954 and 1958) did not produce anywhere near a corresponding retardation in energy growth. Thus, it is conceivable that the demand for energy has become insensitive to short-term fluctuations in economic activity and that, with a resumption of full-employment growth of the economy, more traditional relationships will reappear.

Behavior of the transportation sector in the past few years presents something of a puzzle. As we saw in Table 6, its 5.3 annual growth in energy demand during 1965-1970 was an important factor in overall energy growth. This 5.3 percent growth factor was far above any preceding five-year postwar period. Does this reflect the fact that the patterns of suburbanization and the ways in which the American people spend their leisure time will increasingly cause transport requirements to grow rapidly relative to total economic growth? On the other hand, what part have the transportation-fuel needs associated with the Viet Nam war played in this development. This subject, along with similar sectoral analyses requiring further study would benefit immeasurably from the development of more detailed statistical breakdowns of the end-use consumption of different energy sources than the very limited annual series produced by the Bureau of Mines (and summarized, for example, in Table 4 above).

Whether there are other aspects that would point to energy needs expanding either persistently faster or slower than the economy as a whole in the years ahead is an important topic for study. Tentatively, it may be suggested that the electric power branch of the energy industry is likely to exert a propulsive rather than a moderating impact in this respect. Out of the total consumption of primary energy resources in this country, 25 percent now go into the utility sector for generation of electricity (up from under 20 percent in just 1960). The well-publicized decadal doubling of electricity, amounting to a seven percent annual growth rate, shows as yet no serious sign of abating. Sharply rising demands for airconditioning and electric residential heating have played a large role in mounting electricity needs during the 1960's, and airconditioning, at least, will no doubt continue to do so. In time, of course, saturation points are likely to be approached, both with respect to the acquisition of electrical appliances not formerly owned and the conversion to

electricity (in homes as well as industry) in uses formerly dependent on fuels used directly. On the basis of Federal Power Commission (FPC) projections, however, such a state of affairs is still some time off: Even between 1980 and 1990, the FPC projects electric generation to increase at a rate of 6.6 percent a year.[17] At that point—in the last decade of the century—the share of nationwide primary energy consumption accounted for by the electric utility sector would probably begin to approach one-half.

Growth in the use of electricity as a source of comfort heating is almost certain to lead to a faster growth of energy than the direct use of fuels in the home furnace, by virtue of the thermal losses in generating electric energy. The extent to which this trend may, however, abort due to adoption of policies designed to discourage this development needs to be examined.

Beyond this, electricity's growth is of critical importance, because of the uncertain outlook for changes in electric-generating efficiency—that is, the "heat rate," which measures the Btu requirements to generate a kwh of electricity. Historically, as we noted earlier, there has been a persistent fall in the heat rate. For the postwar years as a whole, the heat rate declined by 1.4 percent annually; for 1955-1965, only slightly below that at 1.2 percent. Had the latter rate of improvement been sustained into 1970, rather than actually being reversed, overall energy consumption, due to lower input requirements by the utility sector, would have grown by only around 4.5 percent during 1965-1970 instead of the recorded figure of five percent. (To be sure, this would still have exceeded GNP growth.) The FPC, in its 1970 National Power Survey, foresees, for the future, half the historic heat rate improvement—a decline of about 0.7 percent per year. The difference between even that relatively modest figure and no improvement could, however, spell, say, half a percentage point difference in the average annual growth rate in total energy consumption.

More intensive examination of trends in electric generating efficiency is, therefore, an important element in analysis of overall energy consumption. Ultimately, of course, progressive improvements in thermal efficiency approach limits set by the thermodynamic principles associated with the nature of the equipment and the energy conversion process; but, since even today the actual efficiency approaches 40 percent in some plants while the prevailing national average was earlier seen to be still much closer to 30 percent, that constraint does not figure in calculations (at least from a technological point of view) for the foreseeable future, say two to three decades.

Whether, apart from electricity needs in particular, the pattern of economic life will evolve in a way that, compared to the past, is energy-intensive, energy-saving, or essentially neutral from an energy point of view, is a question that again is obviously unanswerable, but one that, on the basis of further study (including use of alternative assumptions), is susceptible to at least informed judgments. One prevalent viewpoint has held that an economy shifting towards services and leisure-time activities would tend to slacken its energy needs. But as one thinks about the numerous services and activities associated with an affluent society (for example, airplane and automobile vacation trips and at least some of the more energy-demanding household conveniences) that notion may not withstand critical scrutiny.

Again some insight might be gained from study of the past. An intensive study covering the period 1939-1954 sought to determine whether, at a given overall economic growth rate, shifting patterns of consumption in the United States economy (towards more services and leisure) tended, on balance, to raise or lessen the consumption of energy.[18] The finding was that the slower growth in energy compared to overall output was the result of efficiency improvements in energy conversion and utilization. The changing output mix, itself, with no change in the efficiency of energy conversion, would, in fact, have yielded a greater increase in energy consumption than in GNP. The study in question, of course, covered a period in which there were extraordinary changes in the efficiency of energy conversion, in electricity, as already noted, and in the dieselization of railroads, and therefore now too dated to stand as the definitive word. Indeed, a more recent study, extending this type of inquiry forward to the year 1963, produced findings which are in substantial agreement with the earlier study for the period ending in 1958, but yielded far less conclusive evidence for the years 1958-63.[19]

On the basis of still a third study, however, one is nevertheless tempted to suggest, at least tentatively, that in the current and foreseeable context of the American economy, shifting patterns of output are unlikely to exert dramatic impact on the volume of energy requirements. A recent effort of the U.S. Bureau of Labor Statistics (BLS), though not centrally concerned with energy growth, did construct a projected picture of the United States economy using a reasonably detailed input-output framework in which the energy sector is, for the most part, separately identified.[20] (Unfortunately, however, the utility sector embraces electricity and gas—the sector's dominant components—as well as water and sanitary services.) This study produced projec-

Table 10.—Average Annual Percentage Change in Output

	1965-80	
	BLS "Basic" model	BLS "High Durable" model
Gross National Product . .	4.3%	4.3%
Coal mining	1.8	1.7
Crude petroleum and natural gas	3.4	3.3
Petroleum refining	3.4	3.3
Utilities (electric, gas, water, sanitary)	6.6	6.5

Source: U.S. Bureau of Labor Statistics, *Patterns of U.S. Economic Growth,* 1970, Bulletin 1672, p. 97. The percentage growth rates refer to constant dollars and, for that reason and because of other conceptual factors, are not entirely comparable to the physical energy growth trends discussed elsewhere in our paper. Also, the industry gross output figures on which the above rates are based involve some double-counting insofar as some mine, gas, and refinery output, for example, is delivered in part to utilities and crude oil output is delivered to refineries.

tions of the United States economy in 1980 under various alternative assumptions. The two alternatives of greatest interest here both assume a 4.3 percent GNP growth rate—substantially above, it must be recognized, the longer-term "medium-range" 3.5 percent rate used throughout this discussion. Both BLS cases assume an end to the Viet Nam war and partly, but not wholly as a consequence, a significant decline in Federal purchases as a share of GNP. Both cases project a continued rise in the state and local government share of GNP. One of the two models (labeled "basic" by the Bureau of Labor Statistics) projects otherwise a continuation of past trends in national expenditure patterns, reflecting a long-term shift towards services and away from goods. Another model emphasizes a disproportionately higher share of expenditures on durable goods and investment on construction. We mention these features in the BLS models so as to underscore the fact that neither modest to marked departures from past spending patterns nor alternative distributions of the GNP for the future influence very significantly prospective trends in energy growth, no matter what may have been United States experience in earlier times. Some key BLS results are summarized in Table 10.

But much more intensive research is needed to suggest whether the growth of activities other than manufacturing—even the growth of leisure—can be relied

Table 11.—U.S. Consumption of Energy Resources: Total Consumption, Consumption in Electric Generation, and Consumption in Other Sectors, 1969, and "Standard" Projection, 1980-2000

(In trillion Btu unless otherwise specified)

	Total energy inputs					Total gross energy inputs	Utility electricity generated and distributed[a]	
	Coal	Natural gas	Petroleum	Hydro	Nuclear		Billion kwh	Trillion Btu
Total energy inputs:								
1969	13,538	21,322	28,419	2,635	141	66,055	Not Applicable	
1980	17,935	27,329	37,266	3,145	9,470	95,145		
1990	16,728	35,005	48,337	3,956	30,660	134,687		
2000	26,185	47,097	59,671	5,498	51,563	190,014		
In sectors other than electric utility generation:								
1969	6,082	17,710	26,816	. . .	. . .	50,608	1,442	4,920
1980	6,221	22,478	35,117	. . .	. . .	63,816	3,110	10,613
1990	2,774	29,424	46,253	. . .	. . .	78,452	5,920	20,198
2000	2,000	37,570	56,739	. . .	. . .	96,308	10,802	36,858
In electric utility generation:								
1969	7,456	3,612	1,603	2,635	141	15,447	1,442	4,920
1980	11,714	4,851	2,149	3,145	9,470	31,329	3,110	10,613
1990	13,954	5,581	2,084	3,956	30,660	56,235	5,920	20,198
2000	24,185	9,527	2,932	5,498	51,563	93,706	10,802	36,858

[a]The breakdown by major consuming sectors of electric utility deliveries follows:

	Billion kwh	Trillion Btu
Household and commercial:		
1969	786	2,681
1980	1,852	6,318
1990	3,316	11,314
2000	5,855	19,977
Industrial:		
1969	650	2,219
1980	1,245	4,248
1990	2,580	8,802
2000	4,915	16,771
Transportation:		
1969	6	20
1980	14	47
1990	24	81
2000	32	110

Notes and Sources: The classification in this table is a condensed version of the more complete sectoral and energy source breakdown for historical years in Table 4.

The projections are an adaptation based on several different sources. The kwh data on electric generation through 1990 are based on preliminary (unpublished) materials from the updated and forthcoming Federal Power Commission, *National Power Survey* (1971). (For further detail, see Table 12.) For the decade 1990-2000, it was assumed that electric power consumption would decelerate from the 1980-90 annual rate of 6.6 percent to 6.2 percent.

For the sources of energy used to generate the projected levels of electricity, as well as for projected data on the non-utility sectors of energy demand, we relied to a considerable extent upon a preliminary and unpublished updating by the U.S. Bureau of Mines staff of its earlier Information Circular 8384, *An Energy Model of the United States*, 1968. In our adaptation of this document, and of Bureau of Mines revisions we made a number of modifications to insure a reasonable measure of consistency with the FPC electric power projections.

upon to lead to a significant lowering in the growth of energy consumption relative to national output. If the answer is "no," and a reduction in energy consumption is conceived to be important, other means for bringing it about might usefully be investigated—for example, the consequences of internalizing energy's social costs, or the effect of other consumption disincentive mechanisms.

A "Medium-Range" Projection of Energy Consumption to the Year 2000

In light of the foregoing and for want of a better basis of estimation, let us accept, as a perhaps reasonable judgment, the assumption that GNP growth rates within the range of historical experience and those postulated as assumptions for this study—that is, a spread of between about three and four percent per annum—will mean roughly commensurate growth rates in total energy consumption. For working purposes, we shall adopt the midpoint growth-rate assumption, illustrating the projected implications for energy use to the year 2000 of a 3.5 percent per annum growth rate in national output. (We shall frequently refer to this as a "medium-range" or "standard" projection.) In a quantitatively less precise way, we shall also refer to the implications of the low and high growth-rate assumptions used in the study—these being associated, in turn, with alternative premises regarding population.

The "medium-range" projection of United States energy consumption over the next three decades, summarized in Table 11, represents a composite adaptation of long-term energy projections prepared by two Federal Government agencies deeply involved in energy matters—the Bureau of Mines and the Federal Power Commission.[21] Since, in their main features, these agencies' projections did not appear to differ markedly from what a more independent analysis might have yielded, it seemed convenient to rely on their estimates as the basic framework for the figures presented here. Moreover, the FPC projection of future United States power growth (which is constructed from regional subtotals) is commonly viewed as an important reference point for decisions about generating requirements in different parts of the country. It is an interesting question—and by no means an academic one, from an environmental point of view—whether there is an element of "self-fulfillment" in this power forecasting process; thus, the assumption of a rather substantial continuation in electric power growth might especially deserve closer scrutiny. While this and other particulars within the projections might be open to criticism, the figures in general seemed satisfactory as a basis for drawing out broad resource and environmental issues in which we are primarily interested here.

The major characteristics of this projection may be briefly noted. For the period 1969-2000, the projected 3.5 percent per annum growth of nationwide energy consumption in the United States is slightly above its long-term historic rate (since 1900) of 3.2 percent, though below the average figure of 4.3 percent, recorded during the 1960's. The consumption of electric power alone (about which more detail will be found in Table 12) is expected to continue rising far more rapidly. The average rate of increase to the year 2000 works out to 6.7 percent per year, with the rate during the current decade somewhat higher than this, and growth during the last decade of the century decelerating to around 6.2 percent per annum. As with total energy, the projected electricity growth rate falls somewhat below its rate of increase in recent years. The fact, however, that the consumption of electric power will continue to rise at a rate exceeding that for energy in its entirety means, of course, that the historical expansion in the share of primary energy consumption going into electricity will persist for the remainder of the twentieth century. As can be quickly calculated from Table 11, the nearly one-fourth of primary energy consumption going into electric power generation in 1969 is expected to rise to one-third by 1980, to over 40 percent by 1990, and to essentially one-half by the year 2000. Some leveling off by that time reflects the present assumption that the types of energy demand which can be met in the form of electricity will, in the absence of technological break-throughs (such as electric vehicles recharged by utility electricity) cease to grow.[22]

In their more specific aspects, the energy projections summarized in Table 11 are "surprise-free" in most respects, novel in some others. In the following paragraphs, examples of both cases (not all of which are directly evident in the tabulation) are highlighted:

The different sectors of demand are all projected to share fully in future electricity growth—as they have in the past. Growth in residential electricity consumption is expected to parallel overall electricity growth—that is, at an annual rate of 6.7 percent for the time span 1969-2000, as noted earlier. This implies a per capita growth of five percent yearly, or per household (or, essentially, residential customer) of 4.7 percent yearly. The average residential customer's electricity consumption would grow from 6,550 kwh in 1969 to 27,200 kwh in 2000. The Federal Power Commission is not explicit—no one can be—on all types of residential demands reflected in this figure; obviously, saturation factors far short of 100 percent today (e.g., color T.V.) could easily denote complete satiation by the year 2000 (generating largely a replacement and "multiple ownership" demand), while other still unanticipated needs and still undeveloped products remain to be established. The Federal Power Commission is specific with regard to future expansions in electrically heated homes: The Commission expects 40 to 50 percent of new residential construction during 1970-90 to involve electric heating, compared to around 15 percent in the latter part of the 1960-70 decade. In this respect, the FPC cites the

Table 12.—U.S. Electric Utility Industry: Installed Generating Capacity Net Generation, and Equivalent Energy Resource Inputs, 1969 and Projected to 1980, 1990, and 2000

	Installed generating capacity (megawatts)	Net generation[a] (billion kwh)	Energy resource inputs[b] (trillion Btu)
1969: Fuel-burning plants	251,563	1,178.0	12,670
Nuclear plants	3,980	16.3	141
Hydropower plants[c]	57,069	250.1	2,635
Total	312,612	1,444.4	15,466
1980: Fuel-burning plants	396,000	1,890.8	18,714
Nuclear plants	147,000	902.0	9,470
Hydropower plants[c]	125,000	317.6	3,145
Total	668,000	3,110.4	31,329
1990: Fuel-burning plants	559,000	2,445.0	21,619
Nuclear plants	500,000	3,066.0	30,660
Hydropower plants[c]	201,000	408.5	3,956
Total	1,260,945	5,919.5	56,235
2000: Fuel-burning plants	984,270	4,311.1	36,644
Nuclear plants	955,550	5,859.4	51,563
Hydropower plants[c]	288,580	632.0	5,498
Total	2,228,400	10,802.5	93,706

[a]The plant factors used to translate generating capacity into net generation are as follows for 1969 and 2000:

	1969 Actual	2000 Projected
Fuel-burning plants	53%	50%
Nuclear plants	47	70
Hydropower plants	50	25
Total	53	55

[b]Obtained by applying to net generation figures the average historical and projected heat rates for fuel-burning plants, and theoretical heat rates for hydropower and nuclear plants, based on average rate of Btu's of fossil fuels per kwh at central electric stations. The implicit nationwide heat rate thus derived was 10,712 Btu/kwh in 1969, and is projected to fall to 8,670 Btu/kwh by 2000.

[c]Comprising conventional hydro and pumped storage, but also including small quantities of internal combustion and gas turbines.

Sources: See notes and sources, Table 11.

environmental virtues of replacing fossil-fueled residential furnaces by efficient central station electric generation embodying the latest anti-pollution devices. Similar advantages could be ascribed to a significant switch to electrically-powered vehicles, although no such shift is embedded in the projections. Finally, the figures of Table 11 reflect a significant rise in the electric power share of energy requirements by industry.

Fundamental changes are in prospect in the mix of energy sources used to generate electricity. As can be seen from Table 12, nuclear power is expected to be the dominant source of power in the United States well before the end of the present century. The extent to which this nuclear power forecast is tied to a precise timetable for development and operation of advanced

reactors and breeders is not specified by the Federal Power Commission, although it may reasonably be assumed that there is a necessary connection.[23] Energy inputs into electric generation are estimated to rise to 94 quadrillion Btu by the year 2000, compared to 15 quadrillion Btu in 1969. (The implicit annual rate of increase—6.1 percent—falls somewhat below the projected 6.7 percent growth for utility electric generation, owing to a modest improvement factor expected in the heat rate. If such an improvement materializes, as assumed, it would spell a resumption—albeit slight by past standards—in electric generation efficiency advances; as noted earlier, such advances have been notably absent in the last few years.) The make-up of attendant resource inputs looks as follows (based on absolute figures in Table 11):

Energy Resource Inputs Into Utility
Electric Generation
(percent distribution)

	Coal	Natural gas	Petro-leum	Hydro-power	Nuclear	Total
1969 . .	48.3	23.4	10.4	17.1	0.9	100.0
2000 . .	25.8	10.2	3.1	5.9	55.0	100.0

Overall energy consumption is likewise assumed to undergo a sharp shift in its constituent fuel mix. To some extent, of course, this follows from the rising weight in total energy of electricity, both because of new uses for electricity and substitution of electricity for direct fuel use, all accompanied by shifts in the electricity fuels mix, just mentioned. Shifts are also foreseen in non-utility sectors of the economy (e.g., a marked decline in the relative importance of coal in industrial activity).[24] The overall results (from Table 11) appear as follows:

Overall Energy Consumption, By Source
(percent distribution)

	Coal	Natural gas	Petro-leum	Hydro-power	Nuclear	Total
1969 . .	20.5	32.3	43.0	4.0	0.2	100.0
2000 . .	13.8	24.8	31.4	2.9	27.1	100.0

Some Alternative Energy Growth Paths

Alternative GNP and Populations

In earlier discussion, we looked at the uncertainty surrounding the energy-GNP relationship, from which it follows that, even if we could pinpoint fairly precisely the future part of the national economy, there would still be considerable unknowns about what this would portend for energy use. With the assumed independent variables (population, GNP, industrial production, etc.) themselves subject to considerable uncertainty, the course of future energy consumption may be more problematical still.

Thus, as mentioned earlier, the projected 3.5 percent annual growth rate in energy consumption was assumed to coincide with a similar growth rate in GNP—that is, the approximate mid-point in the range of GNP assumptions governing this study. Under those conditions, total energy consumption was projected as rising from 66 quadrillion Btu in 1969 to a level of 190 quadrillion by 2000—a nearly threefold increase. At the

most simplistic level, one might assume that variations in the assumed rate of economic growth would mean corresponding variations in the rate of increase in energy use—that is, that the "one-for-one" relationship between energy and GNP growth, which was adopted for the "medium-range" projection, would be equally appropriate at varying rates of GNP growth, irrespective of the component sources (demographic, productivity) of that growth. Thus, four percent GNP growth—corresponding roughly to assumption "B-H"—would mean around 220 quadrillion Btu of energy in 2000; three percent GNP growth—corresponding to assumption "E-L"—might signify energy use of 165 quadrillion Btu. If the same share of total energy would go to electric utility generation in these two alternate cases as in the "medium-range" projection, it would mean electric power output in the year 2000 of about 12.5 trillion kwh (or a growth rate of 7.2 percent yearly from the 1969 level of 1.44 trillion kwh) in the "B-H" variant; and a figure of 9.4 trillion kwh (growth rate of 6.2 percent) in the "E-L" alternative. The "medium-range" assumption depicted in Table 12 showed electricity use of 10.8 trillion kwh by 2000—up by 6.7 percent yearly from recent levels of consumption.

These, of course, are crude computational exercises designed to illustrate orders of magnitude: In point of fact, since overall energy growth is significantly affected by the (faster) growth rate for electricity, it might be reasonable to expect that the low energy growth variant might be associated with an electricity share somewhat below the "medium-range" proportion of around 50 percent; while the opposite would hold for the high-growth variant. In that case, the respective growth rates for electric power use might be a bit lower or higher than the indicated 7.2 and 6.2 percent growth rates. But no matter, the variance is not likely to be significant.

Of more interest than these essentially mechanical calculations is the question of whether long-term energy growth would, in fact, be so closely proportional to overall growth at different assumed growth rates for the latter, and irrespective of varying underlying determinants. One can do little more than conjecture about some of the possibilities. In doing so, let us draw a schematic distinction between two aspects of energy use: (1) energy required as a precondition for the levels and types of organization of production needed to produce a stipulated GNP (or alternatively, manhour productivity); and (2) energy needed to satisfy given levels of income and spending patterns.

To deal with the first aspect, let us note that the projected GNP growth rate, which serves as the springboard for assumed trends in energy demand, is compounded of assumptions regarding primarily population, labor force, and hours worked, and employee productivity—output per manhour. Historically, the sustained growth in productivity has been closely associated with growing amounts of energy per worker (often reflected in time series on installed horse-power)—a particular feature of the capital-labor substitution which has characterized United States economic growth. There appears to be no offhand reason why such a relationship should not be expected to continue to apply. Suppose the economy embarks on a pronounced shift towards service- as opposed to goods-producing industries. Under traditional production practices in services, this could imply lowered overall productivity advance—precisely because such technological processes as presuppose important energy applications would be absent. In other words, a deceleration in productivity growth would be accompanied by more slowly growing needs of energy per worker. But now assume that the shift to services involves a concerted effort to raise productivity in that traditionally low-productivity sector: computerization in medical services, programmed learning, information retrieval in administration of justice, enhanced efficiency in retail inventory control. Each example suggests an energy-intensive technological adaptation. There is, in other words, some basis for the expectation that variations in future productivity advance would also presuppose variations in energy requirements, with forces at work—at least in the case of this particular relationship—that would not break sharply with the historical experience.

As to the other component of energy consumption—that needed to accommodate the disposition of income rather than the wherewithall needed to generate it—we have already commented on the lack of decisive postwar evidence bearing on the consequences for energy of a changing output mix and taste patterns. We should, however, ask what might be the separate implications of alternative population growth assumptions, even though manhour productivity advance—clustered, in each of the alternatives for this study, around 2.75 percent annually—does not depart significantly from historical trends. Take an extreme case as an example—Alternative "E-L" which postulates 0.9 percent per annum population increase and an unprecedented sharp decline in working hours per employee. Beyond the general proposition that a slowing-down of national income expansion would also mean more slowly growing energy needs, one can speculate on the particular effects of new demographic and sociological features of the population. Sharp declines in the length of the work week would expand leisure opportunities with a substantial energy content—for example, boating, automotive trips, and airplane travel. Reduced family size

might impel more accentuated trends in female labor-force participation with a heightened dependence on household labor-saving (and heavy energy-using) devices. But one can also visualize counter trends: more emphasis on adult education, cultural affairs, volunteer welfare activities—none especially energy demanding.

Though these ruminations must end on an inconclusive note, we can at least suggest the following: Economic growth per se—whatever its constituent sources—is likely to mean a closely related growth in energy consumption. For major ways in which that relationship could conceivably be altered in an energy-saving manner, one would want to address himself to technological potentialities not inherent in the trends so far discussed, and in disincentive mechanisms that might be devised specifically to meet this objective. Some alternative technological possibilities are discussed next; the question of policy devices designed to effect energy demand is taken up in a later section of this paper.

Alternative Technologies and Efficiencies at Given GNP Growth Rates

Another group of alternatives which we might consider relates both to the effect of various assumed developments in technology and efficiency, and to the form in which energy is desired by ultimate consumers. (Here we look at energy flows at a given level of GNP—the assumed 3.5 percent growth rate in the "medium-range" assumptions spelled out earlier.) By "form," we have in mind principally electrical energy versus fuels consumed directly (for example, electrically heated homes versus gas-fired furnaces).[25] The reader will appreciate that the form in which energy is provided is partially dependent on the technological advances assumed. That is, the circumstances under which vastly higher proportions of primary energy would be in the form of electricity would also be those under which great forward strides in technology would make such a development economically feasible. This is apparent from the different possibilities which were considered and which are summarized in Table 13. Except for the first two cases (alternative assumptions regarding the heat rate in thermal generation), which may be viewed within a context of continued evolutionary change, the different situations whose effect on levels of energy consumption is explored here all presuppose either some major breakthrough (in addition to those implied in the "medium-range" forecast, such as the nuclear component) in the technology and economics of energy conversion (for example, a fuel-cell oriented society), or some fairly radical departure from evolving trends and patterns (such as, the largely conventionally fueled all-electric economy). The variations in the projected

Table 13.—Energy Consumption in 2000 under Alternative Technological Assumptions

Case	Energy consumption in 2000 under assumed 3.5 percent GNP growth rate	
	In quadrillion Btu	Average annual percentage growth rate from 1969
"Medium-range" projection . .	190	3.5%
Rapid improvements in electric generating efficiency (1-1/2 percent annual decline in heat rate	170	3.1
No change in electric generating efficiency (1969 heat rate prevails)	210	3.9
Single fuel (natural gas) economy; transportation sector features electric vehicles recharged by utilities	205	3.8
Single fuel (natural gas) economy; all-electric transportation sector as in preceding case; energy inputs into central power stations via hydrocarbon-air fuel cells	186.5	3.4
No purchased utility electricity; sectoral needs (including fuel-cell powered vehicles) supplied by natural gas-fired hydrocarbon-air fuel cells	133	2.3
All-electric economy, based on utility power plants fueled by conventional sources, hydro, and nuclear	241	4.3
All-electric economy, based on utility power plants, fueled by natural-gas hydrocarbon-air fuel cells; transportation sector features battery electric vehicle system recharged by utility power	211	3.8
All-electric, all-coal economy with MHD technology of centrally-operated utility power plants	190	3.5

quantity of primary energy resources consumed by the year 2000 within this range of alternatives is not insignificant. The highest amount estimated (predictably for an all-electric economy fueled by conventional as well as nuclear resources, and therefore implying relatively great waste in heat use) is over 80 percent above the lowest energy-demanding hypothesized (one featuring a fuel-cell based economy without the intermediation of central power plants). The highest model is 27 percent above our "medium-range" case, while the low model is 30 percent below it. A more detailed review of the alternative case follows.

As the first set of examples, we take the simple illustration of energy consumption growth under circumstances where improvements in electric generating efficiency are either much more rapid than those assumed in the "medium-range" model or where such improvements are zero, without varying in either case the amount of electricity consumed. (In the "medium-range" forecast, we assumed average annual declines in the heat rate of about 0.7 percent.) Say future efficiency improvements averaged an annual decline of 1.5 percent—close to the post-World War II record. In that event, due to the fact that less primary energy resources would be required at utility plants than otherwise, total energy consumption by 2000 could be only about 170 quadrillion Btu—11 percent below the "medium-range" figure of 190 quadrillion Btu. (The average annual rate of increase in total energy consumption would be 3.1 percent instead of the assumed figure of 3.5 percent.) If, in addition, technology were to materialize which could lead to significant use of the waste heat now rejected at power plant—say, for district heating, or for certain types of process heat uses in manufacturing—even less growth in raw energy consumption might be the case.

An assumed stagnation in the heat rate, on the other hand, might mean energy consumption of over 210 quadrillion Btu by 2000—11 percent over the "medium-range" figure, or a yearly rate of growth of 3.9 percent. (It is, of course, possible that in the first situation, substantial efficiency improvement might, via price attractiveness, increase the demand for electricity above levels otherwise desired. And this might mean primary energy needs not falling all the way to the level shown. Under circumstances of no improvement, the opposite might hold.)

Turning next to a number of alternative contingencies spelled out in the 1968 U.S. Bureau of Mines study,[26] we consider one case where the situation assumed is such that (1) fuel and power needs are supplied entirely by natural gas (adequately supplied from domestic sources), and (2) "revolutionary technology will provide an economic electric car and that the entire needs of the transportation sector [including aircraft] will be met from utility electricity."[27]

This model implies a level of primary energy consumption about eight percent above our "medium-range" forecast to the year 2000 of 190 quadrillion Btu because such a large portion of primary energy (around 75 percent) is needed to supply electric utilities. (This in spite of the fact that the electric vehicles are assumed to operate at a higher degree of efficiency than gasoline-driven cars.)

A variant of the preceding model assumes, similarly, an all-natural gas fuel and power economy (including an all-electric transport sector) but one featuring, this time, energy inputs into central power stations using hydrocarbon-air fuel cells, with a maximum system efficiency of 50 percent, as compared to efficiency of only around 40 percent assumed in our "medium-range" forecast. Because of this higher level of assumed efficiency in electric generation, primary energy inputs required are actually somewhat lower in spite of the fact that the electric sector here too represents a disproportionately large portion of primary energy cconsumption—over 65 percent compared to the figure in our "medium-range" forecast of 49 percent. (See Table 11.) The level of nationwide energy consumption in 2000 implied in this case is about 186.5 quadrillion Btu, compared to the "medium-range" forecast figure of 190 quadrillion.

Another U.S. Bureau of Mines case speculates on the possibility of a future economy involving no purchased utility electricity, and where, rather, natural gas is assumed as the single fuel serving the fuel and power needs of all sector requirements (including transport featuring fuel-cell powered vehicles) via gas-fired, hydrocarbon-air fuel cells. Such a contingency envisages in the year 2000 a level of nationwide energy consumption of approximately 133 quadrillion Btu—roughly 30 percent below the "medium-range" projection of 190 quadrillion Btu. The lower figure would imply an average annual long-term rate of energy consumption of only 2.3 percent, compared to the "medium-range" figure of 3.5 percent. The "saving" in primary energy inputs is made possible by the elimination of the electric utility sector whose efficiency under conventional technology is estimated as far below, and whose efficiency even under centrally operated fuel cell power plants (the preceding case considered) is significantly below, the efficiencies assumed for the all fuel cell, nonutility economy specified in the present alternative.

Still another possibility worth considering is an all-electric economy, based on utility power plants, fueled—as in our "medium-range" case—by conventional fuels, hydro, and nuclear, and assuming (also as in the "medium-range" case) a modestly improving heat rate. The results show a total energy consumption in the year 2000 of 241 quadrillion Btu, 27 percent above the "medium-range" figure of 190 quadrillion Btu, and implying a total energy growth rate of 4.3 percent rather than 3.5 percent.

An interesting contrast to the preceding case is another all-utility based electric economy but one featuring, in this illustration, utility electricity fueled by natural gas-based hydrocarbon-air fuel cells. (The transport sector would involve a battery-electric vehicle system recharged by utility power.) Because of high fuel-cell efficiency, this version of the all-electric economy would require only 11 percent or so more primary energy resource inputs (211 quadrillion Btu all told) than the 190 quadrillion Btu in the "medium-range" model. Annual energy growth would amount to 3.8 percent.

The final illustration involves once more an all-electric economy (with a battery-electric vehicle system), this time envisaging bituminous coal as the fuel source with magnetohydrodynamic (MHD) technology at centrally operated utility power plants. With a heat rate assumed to be even lower than the system embodying a central station fuel-cell technology, this model works out to a level of primary energy consumption in 2000 (all coal) virtually identical to the quantity resulting in the "medium-range" projection. In the various all-electric models we have discussed, the electricity growth rate would, of necessity be enormous—roughly 10.5 percent per annum.

UNITED STATES ENERGY DEMAND AND SUPPLY IN A WORLDWIDE CONTEXT

Growth of Total and Per Capita World Energy Consumption

Some broad indicators of worldwide and regional trends in total and per capita energy consumption appear in Tables 14 to 16.[28] The growth of total world energy consumption from 44 quadrillion Btu in 1925 to 190 quadrillion Btu in 1968 (see Table 14) is the same thing, calorically, as going from a level of 1.6 billion metric tons of coal (or about 1.1 billion metric tons of oil) in 1925 to a level of approximately seven billion metric tons of coal (or 4.5 billion metric tons of oil) in 1968. Actually, the preponderant worldwide energy source in 1925 had been coal, while the leading component in 1968 was oil. Some period growth rates, reflecting this expansion of world energy consumption, are as follows:

Average Annual Percentage Rates of Change

	Energy consumption	
	Total	Per capita
1925-50	2.2	1.1
1950-60	4.9	3.1
1960-68	5.5	3.5
1925-68	3.4	2.0

If there is an inherent accelerating trend in the growth of international energy consumption, these figures should not necessarily be viewed as corroborative, for the slow growth during the first 25 years occurred during a period marked by worldwide depression and terminated in a year still characterized by war-induced industrial dislocation. (Indeed, the period 1925-29—preceding the Great Depression—discloses annual growth rates in total and per capita energy consumption of nearly 4.5 percent and two percent, respectively.) Still, the rather fast pace of expansion in energy use has now persisted for nearly two decades, and according to numerous analyses, is not judged likely to abate soon.

Changing Regional Shares of World Energy Consumption

Accompanying this growth in total world energy utilization, there have been some rather striking post-World War II geographic shifts. In a number of areas, these shifts represented a continuation of trends in progress even earlier. For example, the Soviet Union's share of world energy consumption stood at under two percent in 1925; just before World War II, it was up to 10 percent; and from its early postwar share of around 11 percent, it rose to approximately 15 percent in 1968.

The figures in Tables 15 and 16 (particularly the percentages in the latter presentation) point to rising shares occurring elsewhere in the world in the past several decades: The other Communist countries, Latin America, Africa, and Asia all exhibit long-term increases in their relative standing. The postwar rise of Asia reflects in part the growing share of the region's developing countries; but to an even greater extent, it reflects the phenomenal momentum of energy growth in Japan, whose annual postwar growth rates of between 10 and 15 percent have been sustained to the most recent years for which figures are available.

A principal offset to these long-term increases in regional shares of worldwide energy consumption has been the declining relative position of North America. Although North America retains its leading world share (with the United States occupying the top-ranking country share), that region's proportion of world energy consumption (which had been as high as 50 percent in the mid-twenties) fell from 45 percent in 1950 to approximately one-third in 1968. The relatively slight decline of Western Europe's share of world energy consumption since 1950 reflects the fact that in 1950, the area was still in the midst of postwar recovery; in 1925, its world share had been around 35 percent.

Regional Trends in Per Capita Energy Consumption

These distributional shifts in total energy among different parts of the world have also been accompanied by disparate trends in the growth of per capita energy consumption; as shown in the last column of Table 16, numerous regions of the world have exceeded—in some

Table 14.—World Energy Consumption and Population, Selected Years, 1925-1968

Year	Total energy consumption (trillion Btu)	Population (million)	Energy consumption per capita (million Btu)
1925	44,249	1,890.1	23.4
1950	76,823	2,504.5	30.7
1955	99,658	2,725.6	36.6
1960	124,046	2,989.9	41.5
1965	160,722	3,281.2	49.0
1968	189,737	3,484.5	54.5

Notes and Sources: The table represents the addition of data for the United States and for the rest of the world. U.S. data from Table 1 or sources cited there. Rest-of-world data for the period 1925-1965 adapted from Joel Darmstadter and associates, *Energy in the World Economy* (Baltimore: Johns Hopkins Press for Resources for the Future, 1971).

For purposes of the present table (and succeeding tables), the scope of the rest-of-world total energy-consumption measure (shown in the RFF study cited above) was broadened in three ways: (1) to include the consumption of bunker fuels; (2) to include nuclear energy for years when applicable (1960 and beyond) and for areas for which data shown in the United Nations, *Statistical Yearbook* were available (for the U.S.S.R., none were); and (3) to calculate primary electricity (hydro, nuclear, geothermal) not by the heat value produced, but rather, by the estimated (higher) fuel inputs required at fossil-fueled thermal electric power stations. Also, data expressed in coal equivalents in the RFF study were converted into Btu's at the rate of 27.3 million Btu's per metric ton of coal equivalent. (The U.S. data, which, for overlapping years, are those of Table 1, already embody each of these characteristics.)

Rest-of-world data for 1968 were derived from United Nations, *World Energy Supplies,* Statistical Papers, Series J, No. 13, 1970; the 1968 energy estimate was constructed by linkage to the earlier figures at 1965.

"Energy" comprises the so-called "commercial" fossil fuels and primary electricity; it excludes firewood, animal wastes and other "noncommercial" fuels.

Table 15.—World Energy Consumption and Population, by Major Regions, 1950, 1960, 1968

Region	1950 Total consumption (trillion Btu)	1950 Population (million)	1950 Consumption per capita (million Btu)	1960 Total consumption (trillion Btu)	1960 Population (million)	1960 Consumption per capita (million Btu)	1968 Total consumption (trillion Btu)	1968 Population (million)	1968 Consumption per capita (million Btu)
North America[a]	36,860	166.1	221.9	48,701	198.7	245.1	68,594	222.0	309.9
Canada	2,707	13.7	197.6	3,885	17.9	217.0	6,162	20.8	296.3
United States	34,153	152.3	224.3	44,816	180.7	248.0	62,432	201.2	310.3
Western Europe[b]	17,483	302.4	57.8	26,066	326.5	79.8	41,584	350.6	118.6
Oceania	890	12.2	73.0	1,398	15.4	90.8	2,240	18.3	122.4
Latin America	2,397	161.9	14.8	4,939	212.4	23.3	8,034	267.4	30.0
Asia (excl. Communist)	3,804	805.4	4.7	8,228	970.6	8.5	16,757	1,182.7	14.2
Japan	1,739	82.9	21.0	3,672	93.2	39.4	8,691	101.1	86.0
Other Asia	2,063	722.5	2.9	4,556	877.4	5.2	8,066	1,081.6	7.5
Africa	1,297	217.0	6.0	2,162	276.0	7.8	3,343	336.5	9.9
U.S.S.R. & Com. East Europe	12,842	269.8	47.6	25,973	312.9	83.0	39,843	341.9	116.5
U.S.S.R.	8,427	180.0	46.8	17,898	214.4	83.5	28,628	237.8	120.4
Eastern Europe[b]	4,414	89.7	49.2	8,075	98.5	82.0	11,215	104.1	107.7
Communist Asia	1,250	569.8	2.2	6,579	677.5	9.7	9,342	765.2	12.2
World	76,823	2,504.5	30.7	124,046	2,989.9	41.5	189,737	3,484.5	54.5

[a]In some of our regional tables, "North America" may exceed very slightly the sum of Canada and the United States because of (statistically) minor territorial inclusions (e.g., Greenland).

[b]Yugoslavia is included in Western Europe throughout these tables.

Source: Same as Table 14 whose notes are also applicable here.

Table 16.—World Energy Consumption and Population, by Major Region, Percentage Distribution, 1950, 1960, 1968, and Average Annual Percentage Rates of Change, 1960-1968

Region	Percentage distribution 1950 Energy consumption	Percentage distribution 1950 Population	Percentage distribution 1960 Energy consumption	Percentage distribution 1960 Population	Percentage distribution 1968 Energy consumption	Percentage distribution 1968 Population	Average annual percentage rates of change, 1960-68 Energy consumption	Average annual percentage rates of change, 1960-68 Population	Average annual percentage rates of change, 1960-68 Energy consumption per capita
North America	48.0	6.6	39.3	6.6	36.2	6.4	4.4	1.4	2.9
Canada	3.5	0.5	3.1	0.6	3.2	0.6	5.9	1.9	4.0
United States	44.5	6.1	36.1	6.0	32.9	5.8	4.2	1.3	2.8
Western Europe	22.8	12.1	21.0	10.9	21.9	10.1	6.0	0.9	5.1
Oceania	1.2	0.5	1.1	0.5	1.2	0.5	6.1	2.2	3.8
Latin America	3.1	6.5	4.0	7.1	4.2	7.7	6.3	2.9	3.2
Asia (excl. Communist)	5.0	32.2	6.6	32.5	8.8	33.9	9.3	2.5	6.6
Japan	2.3	3.3	3.0	3.1	4.6	2.9	11.4	1.0	10.3
Other Asia	2.7	28.9	3.7	29.4	4.3	31.0	7.4	2.7	4.7
Africa	1.7	8.7	1.7	9.2	1.8	9.7	5.6	2.5	3.0
U.S.S.R. and Com. East Europe	16.7	10.8	20.9	10.5	21.0	9.8	5.5	1.1	4.3
U.S.S.R.	11.0	7.2	14.4	7.2	15.1	6.8	6.1	1.3	4.7
Eastern Europe	5.7	3.6	6.5	3.3	5.9	3.0	4.2	0.7	3.5
Communist Asia	1.6	22.8	5.3	22.7	4.9	22.0	4.5	1.5	2.9
World	100.0	100.0	100.0	100.0	100.0	100.0	5.5	1.9	3.5

Source: Calculated from figures in Table 14, whose notes are also applicable here.

cases, by a substantial margin—the per capita energy growth of North America and Western Europe, both during the long-range time span since the 1920's and during the briefer post-World War II period highlighted in the table.

Nevertheless, regional gaps in per capita energy use, while narrowing, remain dramatically wide, as can be seen by reverting to Table 15. In 1968, United States per capita energy consumption of 310 million Btu, and that of Canada, which was only slightly lower, was more than 2.5 times the level of the next ranking regions—Oceania, the Soviet Union, and Western Europe, all of which recorded per capita figures in the vicinity of 120 million Btu. And the more extreme disparity is reflected in the fact that North American per capita consumption was between 30 to 40 times the levels prevailing in Africa and the developing portions of Asia.

If North America's level of per capita energy consumption in 1925 (roughly 175 million Btu) had remained unchanged throughout the period 1925-68, it would still have been some 45 percent above the next highest areas tabulated for the year 1968. A simple computational exercise—one meant to illustrate rather than to forecast—dramatizes these regional trends and disparities: It would take another decade at per capita energy growth of close to 10 percent annually even for booming Japan to reach North America's 1925 per capita level of consumption. It would take Africa around 60 years and an annual per capita growth rate of at least five percent (a probably ambitious target) to achieve North America's figure of the mid-1920's. To be sure, trends and levels in per capita energy consumption are not synonymous with per capita income or GNP; nor are the latter measures, in turn, truly reflective of living standards, however, defined. (For example, numerous Communist countries' disproportionately high per capita energy levels are characteristic of their industrial structure as well as, in certain cases, an inefficient use of energy resources.) Nonetheless, there is unquestionably a sufficiently close connection between levels of per capita energy consumption and general economic development, that one can point to our simple calculation for Africa as yet another sign that substantial improvement in living standard in the years ahead will be difficult.

Demand-Supply Trends

A useful way of summarizing long-term energy demand-supply trends in different parts of the world appears in Table 17, where we present regional net import balances (shown as a percentage of energy consumption) to suggest the overall degree of import dependence; regional net exports are shown as a percentage share of production in order to denote

Table 17.—Net Energy Imports or Exports in Relation to Consumption or Production, by Region, 1925 and 1967
(Percent of net imports in energy consumption or net exports (–) in production)

	1925	1967
North America	−0.6%	7.2
of which: United States	−3.1	7.2
Western Europe	2.0	60.8
Oceania	7.4	39.9
U.S.S.R. and Com. East. Europe	−12.5	−7.5
U.S.S.R.	−6.1	−11.7
Eastern Europe	−15.2	5.0
Communist Asia	6.8	−0.1
Latin America	−27.3	−45.3
Caribbean	−55.9	−61.4
Other Latin America	60.3	31.4
Asia	−5.7	−45.8
Middle East	−64.9	−87.8
Japan	. . .	80.4
Other Asia	3.4	18.1
Africa	28.5	−61.3

Source: Joel Darmstadter and associates, *Energy in the World Economy* (Baltimore: Johns Hopkins Press for Resources for the Future, 1971).

export capacity.[29] Increased import dependence was experienced by such relatively developed parts of the non-Communist world as North America, Western Europe, Japan, Oceania, and South Africa. The increase in import dependence was fairly modest in the case of North America: In 1925, a very small share of total production (around one-half of one percent) was exported; in 1967, a bit over seven percent of consumption was accounted for by net imports.[30] Among the major energy-consuming regions of the world, North America and the Communist area as a whole came closest in recent years to energy self-sufficiency, as represented by these statistical measures. The emergent trend for the United States, however, points to a gradually rising relative external dependence as foreign petroleum supplies become increasingly significant in fulfilling domestic demand.

The increase in the net import/consumption share for Western Europe between 1925 and 1967 was enormously greater than that for North America. The region's net import/consumption share had been only two percent back in 1925; by 1967, it has risen to 60 percent. Of the areas shown in Table 17, Japan exhibited the most dramatic change of all—a zero trade balance in 1925 giving way four decades later to an import/consumption share of 80 percent. (Among the major industrialized countries, only Italy has in recent years been faced with a still higher degree of net import dependence.) Other areas with heightened net import dependence in 1967 as compared with 1925 include Communist Eastern Europe and the less-developed countries of Asia outside the Middle East.

The converse to the foregoing changes has of course been the increased export capability of the oil-producing nations of the Middle East, whose net export share of output rose from 65 percent in 1925 to nearly 90 percent of an enormously expanded output in recent years. North Africa and Tropical Africa both made a huge quantum jump from deficit to surplus areas— although the latter's role (involving primarily Nigerian oil) has so far remained relatively small in terms of recent levels of net imports. Soviet Russia's net export/production share of six percent in 1925 had doubled by 1967. Non-Caribbean Latin America

decreased the net component of its consumption between these years; though, with over a 30-percent net import dependence in 1967, the improvement nevertheless left the area in very substantial deficit status.

The picture emerging from this brief review is one of a growing geographical imbalance between the location of energy supply sources, on the one hand, and the central areas of energy demand, on the other. It is well to keep in mind the geopolitical issues bearing on this characteristic of the world energy economy: It has produced, for numerous fuel-deficient regions and countries, a sense of anxiety about the reliability and adequacy—under various circumstances—of their sources of energy supplies, while for major producing areas (such as the Middle East, North Africa, and the Caribbean), the assurances of stable and growing markets are a critical element in their aspirations for economic development. In view of recurrent political crises in the Middle East as well as an almost chronic uncertainty over contractual relationships between host-country governments and the concessionary international oil companies, such considerations have assumed heightened importance in recent years.

A final and somewhat different perspective on the value of world energy trade appears in Table 18, which

Table 18.—Energy Trade as a Share of the Total Trade of and Between Selected Regions, Selected Years, 1950-1967 (percent based on value)

	1950	1955	1960	1965	1967
Total trade (interregional plus intraregional):					
Total world	9.5%	10.7%	9.8%	9.4%	9.6%
From developed countries	4.4	5.0	3.9	3.2	3.3
To developed countries	8.5	10.4	10.2	10.1	10.2
From underdeveloped countries	19.4	24.2	27.4	30.4	33.0
To underdeveloped countries	12.0	12.2	10.2	8.7	8.6
From Communist countries	n.a.	12.1	10.9	10.6	9.8
To Communist countries	n.a.	8.7	7.1	6.5	6.0
Interregional trade between indicated groups of countries:					
From developed to underdeveloped countries	2.8	3.2	2.6	1.6	1.6
From underdeveloped to developed countries	14.8	20.6	26.1	31.9	34.2
From Communist countries to underdeveloped countries	n.a.	0.8	0.7	0.7	7.5
From underdeveloped countries to Communist countries	n.a.	. . .	. . .	. . .	0.4

Source: From United Nations, *Statistical Yearbook,* various issues, and *Monthly Bulletin of Statistics,* March 1969.

shows world energy flows in relation to the value of world merchandise trade as a whole.

A particularly striking statistic is the continuously rising share which energy comprises of the total exports of underdeveloped countries to developed regions of the world. From 15 percent in 1950, this figure has risen steadily, reaching over one-third in 1967. The absolute value of energy flows from underdeveloped (albeit a small and unique group of LDC's) to developed areas in 1967—virtually all due to petroleum—is estimated at $10 billion, one-half of this sum originating in the Middle East. Only a portion of this amount, of course, is retained by the host country in the form of taxes, royalties, and other earnings. The data nonetheless testify to the extent with which oil dominates an important sector of world trade. Particularly, the figures suggest that one need be cautious in dealing aggregatively with the export potential of the underdeveloped countries of the world taken as a group, for so large a portion of that potential appears to reflect only a single commodity originating in only limited parts of the world. Indeed, a recent analysis of trends in world trade finds that

> . . . the developing countries share in world exports of primary commodities has fallen continuously since 1953. If fuel exports are excluded, this trend is still more striking. World exports of fuels have grown at almost twice the rate of other primary commodities and the developing countries have managed to capture an increasing share of these exports. The developing countries' exports of nonfuel primary commodities have grown less than half as fast as world exports of these commodities. *Therefore, except for the fuel component, the decline in the developing countries' share of world primary exports would have been quite precipitous.* [31]

One additional percentage in the tabulation deserves mention. Only a handful of underdeveloped countries are net exporters of energy. Much of the underdeveloped world is energy-deficient and the nearly nine percent or close to $4 billion of underdeveloped nation's total merchandise imports accounted for by energy imports places a not inconsequential foreign exchange burden on such countries. Subject to the development of refining capacity (which can be to some extent foreign exchange-saving) and/or new discoveries in these countries, such foreign currency requirements for fuel import requirements seem destined to grow rapidly in the years ahead, and will constitute an important cost factor in programs for economic development.

Prospective Trends in Worldwide Energy Consumption

For a projection of the estimated growth in world energy consumption over the next 30 years, we have taken into account a number of different forecasts and analyses, and, as in the earlier case of our United States "medium-range" projection, shaped these into a composite picture of what might be regarded as the "medium-range" worldwide outlook. The results appear in Table 19.

One basic premise is that worldwide population growth will, for the time being, continue to hover around the two percent per annum mark, with some deceleration assumed toward the end of the century. If, as in our consideration of the United States scene, this produces a perhaps somewhat exaggerated picture of future energy demand, in the context of data assembled for the purpose of evaluating environmental consequences, erring on the side of over- rather than understating the future course of events might not be wholly inappropriate.

Total world energy consumption is projected at slightly over five percent per year during the next decade, with a 4.5 percent rate assumed thereafter. (The record during the 1960's was approximately 5.5 percent growth.) Electricity consumption is assumed to continue increasing around the world—sufficiently so, that by the year 2000, the average electricity consumption per capita in areas outside the United States would approximate the United States per capita level achieved in the latter 1950's. Overall energy consumption per capita outside the United States, however, would only approach what the United States experienced at the beginning of the present century.[32] (A bit over one-third of primary energy consumption would be destined to go into electric generation, compared to the nearly 50 percent share that is projected for the United States.) This suggests that any concern over the possibility of having overstated future worldwide energy growth may be misplaced, the more important issue being whether even this projected level is compatible with reasonable social stability through the world. Much may depend on the possibility of vastly raising energy supplies in poorer areas—far above levels here projected—through nuclear energy and the requisite associated industrial infrastructure. Such possibilities have been envisaged in schematic "scenarios" (for example, in connection with nuclear-based "agro-industrial" complexes); but, the technological and economic barriers are still such that such visions must be reckoned among possibilities rather than probabilities.

Table 19.—Energy Consumption, Electricity Consumption, and Population: Projections of Selected Data, United States and World, 1968, 1980, 2000

	Unit	1968		1980		2000	
		United States					
Energy consumption							
Coal	Percent and trillion Btu	21.3%	13,329	18.8%	17,935	13.8%	26,185
Oil	Percent and trillion Btu	43.3	27,052	39.2	37,266	31.4	59,671
Natural gas	Percent and trillion Btu	31.3	19,564	28.7	27,329	24.8	47,097
Hydro	Percent and trillion Btu	3.8	2,357	3.3	3,145	2.9	5,498
Nuclear	Percent and trillion Btu	0.2	130	10.0	9,470	27.1	51,563
Total	Percent and trillion Btu	100.0	62,432	100.0	95,145	100.0	190,014
Population	Million	201.2		229.3		284.5	
Energy consumption per capita . . .	Million Btu	310.3		414.9		667.9	
Electric generating capacity	mw	310,125		668,000		2,228,400	
Of which: nuclear	Percent and mw	0.9%	2,817	22.0%	147,000	42.9%	955,550
Electric generation	Billion kwh	1,434.9		3,110.4		10,802.5	
Of which: nuclear	Percent and billion kwh	0.9%	12.5	29.0%	902.0	54.2%	5,859.4
Electric generation per capita	kwh	7,133		13,565		37,970	
Resource input equivalent of electric generation	Trillion Btu	14,494		31,329		93,706	
Share of energy consumption .	Percent	23.2%		32.9%		49.3%	
		Rest of World					
Energy consumption							
Coal	Percent and trillion Btu	39.9%	50,841	20.4%	50,996	11.5%	73,560
Oil	Percent and trillion Btu	42.7	54,360	52.3	130,371	47.8	306,613
Natural gas	Percent and trillion Btu	9.6	12,246	16.0	39,879	16.0	102,521
Hydro	Percent and trillion Btu	7.4	9,484	6.6	16,479	6.0	38,332
Nuclear	Percent and trillion Btu	0.3	374	4.7	11,787	18.7	120,169
Total	Percent and trillion Btu	100.0	127,305	100.0	249,512	100.0	641,195
Population	Million	3,283.3		4,189.7		6,154.5	
Energy consumption per capita . . .	Million Btu	38.8		59.6		104.2	
Electric generating capacity	mw	662,116		1,520,000		5,520,600	
Of which: nuclear	Percent and mw	1.4%	9,223	12.0%	183,000	40.3%	2,227,450
Electric generation	Billion kwh	2,768.9		6,790.8		26,802.9	
Of which: nuclear	Percent and billion kwh	1.4%	37.4	16.5%	1,122.9	50.9%	13,655.6
Electric generation per capita	kwh	842		1,621		4,355	
Resource input equivalent of electric generation	Trillion Btu	27,969		67,888		232,265	
Share of energy consumption .	Percent	22.0%		27.2%		36.2%	

Table 19.—Continued

	Unit	1968		1980		2000	
		World					
Energy consumption							
Coal	Percent and trillion Btu	33.8%	64,170	20.0%	68,931	12.0%	99,745
Oil	Percent and trillion Btu	42.9	81,412	48.6	167,637	44.1	366,284
Natural gas	Percent and trillion Btu	16.8	31,810	19.5	67,208	18.0	149,618
Hydro	Percent and trillion Btu	6.2	11,841	5.7	19,624	5.3	43,830
Nuclear	Percent and trillion Btu	0.3	504	6.2	21,257	20.7	171,732
Total	Percent and trillion Btu	100.0	189,737	100.0	344,657	100.0	831,209
Population	Million	3,484.5		4,419.0		6,439.0	
Energy consumption per capita	Million Btu	54.5		78.0		129.1	
Electric generating capacity	mw	972,291		2,188,000		7,749,000	
Of which: nuclear	Percent and mw	1.2%	12,040	15.1%	330,000	41.1%	3,183,000
Electric generation	Billion kwh	4,203.8		9,901.2		37,605.4	
Of which: nuclear	Percent and billion kwh	1.2%	49.9	20.5%	2,024.9	51.9%	19,515.0
Electric generation per capita	kwh	1,207		2,238		5,840	
Resource input equivalent of electric generation	Trillion Btu	42,463		99,217		325,971	
Share of energy consumption	Percent	22.4%		28.8%		39.2%	

Source: Adapted, with minor changes, from Joel Darmstadter, "Energy, Economic Growth and the Environment" (unpublished paper prepared for the Resources for the Future Forum, April 1971), to be published in a somewhat revised form in a forthcoming RFF book. Complete details on assumptions and derivation will be found there.

We have not attempted to project the geographic distribution of world energy consumption all the way to the end of the century—a task which would be necessary to provide some substance to an exploration of this vital question. Some idea about the general drift of regional changes may be gotten from Table 20 in which energy consumption is projected for major parts of the world to 1980.[33] Not surprisingly, rising shares of worldwide energy consumption are most markedly indicated for the developing areas—Latin America, the less industrialized parts of non-Communist Asia as well as Communist Asia, and Africa; modestly declining proportions seem likely for the most advanced areas—the United States and Western Europe.

What are the prospects for the consumption of different energy sources for the remainder of the twentieth century. A further substantial reduction of coal's proportion in world energy consumption can be assumed; at least, that is the case barring large-scale conversion of coal to pipeline gas and gasoline—a development whose technological feasibility has been demonstrated, but whose economics remains in doubt.[34] On the basis of a range of estimates constructed by the United Nations Economic Commission for Europe, coal's energy share is projected to fall particularly sharply during the next decade—from one-third of world energy consumption in 1968 to one-fifth by 1980.[35] Beyond 1980, the projected decline in coal's share is dampened and, in fact, coal is assumed to revert to a phase of reasonable absolute growth; this assumes that there are practical limits in the extent to which coal can continue to be readily replaced. For example, steelmaking will probably be an important market for coal for years to come.

The most dramatically increasing share of projected world energy consumption to 1980 is taken by nuclear energy—rising from a mere three-tenths of one percent in 1968 to a figure of over six percent in 1980. The underlying 330 thousand mw of 1980 nuclear capacity (around 15 percent of worldwide electric generating capacity) on which this figure is based is a conservatively slanted version of the International Atomic Energy

Population, Resources, and the Environment

Agency's forecast of 350 thousand mw of capacity;[36] and even so, it still rests a good deal more in informed speculation and faith than on firmly-anchored judgments. It goes without saying that the further projected rise of nuclear energy to 20 percent of world energy consumption (representing an installed capacity of over three million mw—or 52 percent of estimated total electric generating capacity) by the end of the century is compounded of still greater uncertainty. The IAEA's underlying assumption is that "nuclear power would dominate the market for new power plants in advanced countries by 1980 and almost everywhere else by 1990."[37]

We shall not attempt here to question the reasonableness of this judgment nor to try and spin out the implications of the assumption for different parts of the world. However, acceptance of the assumptions for the projected role of coal and nuclear in total energy consumption is consistent with shares for oil and natural gas that appear not unreasonable in the light of past trends and of industry and governmental assessments of the future outlook. To 1980, as is seen in Table 19, oil and gas are both projected to increase their shares of world energy consumption. Oil is estimated to rise from 43 percent in 1968 to 49 percent in 1980, or from 81 quadrillion Btu (approximately two billion metric tons or nearly 40 million barrels per day) to a level of 168 quadrillion Btu (four billion tons or 80 million barrels per day)—representing an average annual rate of increase of six percent. Oil consumption growth may be expected to reflect a persistent substitution for coal in uses and areas where, until recently, the latter has continued to figure significantly. In addition, as suggested earlier, the potential market for automotive transport outside America remains enormous, with the impact of motorization in (particularly) the less urbanized portions of developing areas scarcely having yet been felt.[38]

The share of natural gas in world energy consumption is projected to grow from 17 percent in 1968 (32 quadrillion Btu or 875 billion cubic meters) to about 20 percent in 1980 (67 quadrillion Btu or 1.8 trillion cubic meters)—a yearly growth rate of close to 6.5 percent. Its attractiveness as a nonpollutant, coupled with the growth of new supplies (in such disparate areas as the

Table 20.—Distribution of World Energy Consumption by Major Regions, 1968 and Projected 1980

	1968		1980		Average annual % rate of growth
	Trillion Btu	Percent	Trillion Btu	Percent	
North America	68,594	36.2	106,124	30.8	3.7
Canada	6,162	3.2	10,979	3.2	4.9
United States	62,432	32.9	95,145	27.6	3.6
Western Europe	41,584	21.9	64,354	18.7	3.7
Oceania	2,240	1.2	3,743	1.1	4.4
Latin America	8,034	4.2	18,7.71	5.4	7.3
Asia (non-Communist)	16,757	8.8	38,666	11.2	7.2
Japan	8,691	4.6	17,715	5.1	6.1
Other Asia	8,066	4.3	20,951	6.1	8.3
Africa	3,343	1.8	7,236	2.1	6.6
U.S.S.R. and Com. East.					
Europe	39,843	21.0	80,073	23.2	6.0
U.S.S.R.	28,628	15.1	60,611	17.6	6.4
Eastern Europe	11,215	5.9	19,462	5.6	4.7
Communist Asia	9,342	4.9	25,690	7.5	8.8
World	189,737	100.0	344,657	100.0	5.1

Sources: Same as Table 19.

North Sea, Australia, and Siberia) and the feasibility (only now beginning to be realized) of liquefied tanker transport, should insure this growing market.

Beyond 1980, both oil and gas are seen in Table 19 to be projected at slightly falling shares of total energy consumption, as nuclear power is assumed by then to take a strong hold. Nevertheless, consumption of both fuels may be expected to record significant absolute growth in the closing decades of the century.

United States and Worldwide Energy Resource Outlook

The traditional concern in the United States (as indeed in most other regions) has been over the adequacy of the different energy sources (coal, oil, natural gas, waterpower, nuclear raw materials) to promote continued economic growth. Of course, "adequacy" referred not merely to the quantity of estimated fuel reserves or ultimate recoverable resources, but also to their relative prices and the degree of which foreign sources of supply could be relied upon. Until the past few years, United States energy policies have been mainly influenced by concern for adequacy and scarcity of supplies; with few exceptions, the environmental repercussions of energy supply (or of demand) figured neither in public discussion nor in policy formulation. The recognized importance attached to environmental questions has changed both the nature of the discussion and the kinds of policy prescriptions being advanced. As just one illustration, the quantitative assessment of energy reserves and resources (with all its difficulties) is judged incomplete if environmental-quality characteristics are ignored (such as the sulfur content of coal deposits).

The qualitative characteristics of a particular energy resource are not the only way in which environmental considerations intrude upon the question of resource adequacy. When environmental constraints severely curb the ability to produce, deliver, or convert energy (as may, for example, be what is currently happening with respect to the Alaskan pipeline and as no doubt accounts for some of the delays in bringing electric energy capacity on line in places like New York), the volume of energy Btu's in the ground, and ready for the taking, provides scant comfort. Not that the sheer physical volume of energy reserves and ultimately recoverable resources has ceased to be a matter of undue concern. The shortage of natural gas currently afflicting the United States reminds us that this is not the case. Nor does there appear to be substantially lessened vulnerability on the part of major energy-consuming regions of the world to the political and economic leverage of supply sources upon which they are dependent, as the

interruptions in Middle Eastern and North African oil flows during 1970 and the subsequent negotiations over new price, tax, and concession terms illustrate.

Let us look briefly at each of these aspects of the supply picture. Few persons question the underlying strength of the United States in its long-term energy resource adequacy. It is true that, judged by the estimated quantity of proved reserves of oil and natural gas (the two are the present mainstay of the country's fuel economy, accounting for a 75 percent share of United States energy consumption), there has been a pronounced weakening of that basic strength in recent years. United States proved oil reserves increased only slightly since the mid-1950's—from 35.5 billion barrels in 1955 to around 38 billion barrels in 1969; this at a time when United States production went up from 7.6 million barrels per day in 1955 to 10.8 million barrels per day in 1969 (an average annual increase of 2.5 percent). The United States proved reserve-to-production (R/P) ratio consequently fell markedly during this period, though this in itself may not be alarming before some "minimum acceptable" level of the R/P ratio is reached. Similarly, the concurrently still faster rise in United States oil consumption from 8.5 to 13.8 million barrels per day (an average annual rate of increase of 3.5 percent) has meant a United States oil import share rising from 15 to 23 percent, though here again there is no simple borderline between a tolerable and critical situation. Only during 1970 did the United States proved oil reserve estimates receive their first sizable boost in some years—the increase from 38 billion to 47 billion arising largely because of the first inclusion of portions of North Slope Alaskan oil.

In the case of natural gas (increasingly attractive for its low polluting features), there has been a drop in the United States reserves-to-production ratio in virtually every year since World War II, though until the late 1960's, yearly reserve additions always exceeded annual production (if by only a small margin). But for the past several years, reserves have actually fallen below production; and there is mounting evidence that the nation's readily available natural gas supply is falling to critical levels at given levels of demand. Attention is now being given to the possible need for upward revision of wellhead ceiling prices (regulated by the FPC) as a means of providing exploratory incentives.

There is no disputing the presence in the United States of vast undiscovered resources of both oil and gas of which the "proved reserves" measure (a basic minimum estimate) gives no clue. Proved petroleum reserves refer to the amount remaining in the ground which, on the basis of geological and engineering information, can with reasonable certainty be assumed recoverable in the future from known reservoirs and under current economic and technological circumstances. For purposes of assessing very long-term adequacy, the measure of proved reserve is regarded as too restrictive a concept and is augmented by estimates of "unproved reserves," which may comprehend knowledge about probable and possible reserves: that is, the amount of petroleum which can reasonably be assumed recoverable under today's economic conditions but which can only be approximated on the basis of incomplete geological, geophysical and other data. As one progressively relaxes further both the economic and technological assumptions (for example, to include an allowance for higher-cost marginal deposits or to allow for new recovery techniques) as well as assumptions about the degree of certainty (so as to allow for still undiscovered resources), still much higher estimates of total resources or "ultimate probable reserves" can be derived.

For example, United States oil resources (with which natural gas deposits are normally geologically associated) have been estimated at a level of "possible ultimate discoveries" ranging up to a trillion barrels, though the proportion recoverable by present economic and technological standards would have to be figured at substantially less than that. Of course, anyone wishing to cite the fact that, ultimately, resources are limited by finite crustal occurrences can scarcely be contradicted. But even estimators of petroleum resources governed in their analysis by this orientation have been known to make sizable upward revisions (within the span of a relatively few years) in their own figures, thus attesting to the highly dynamic character of petroleum resource estimation.

If, with the addition of estimated recoverable resources to existing proved reserves, the nation's petroleum position can be deemed adequate for well into the next century rather than merely for some decades, the inclusion of other energy sources extends that time horizon considerably further. United States coal resources (less subject to estimating uncertainties), are judged in the hundreds of billions of tons, using recoverability factors conforming to current underground mining experience in the United States. Whatever estimate of shale oil reserves one uses (the U.S. Department of the Interior cites oil shale with a content of at least 15 gallons per ton of rock in both private and public ownership as representing as much as 1.8 trillion barrels "that could be classed as 'known reserves'"), the fact is that the quantity is immense and a large multiple of proved United States reserves. North American energy supplies are augmented by an estimated 300 to 600 billion barrels of synthetic oil imbedded in the tar sands of Canada's Alberta province.

As for the reserves of nuclear fuels, the adequacy of fissionable raw materials is not likely to be a critical factor. Probably more important than the known magnitudes of economically recoverable reserves of uranium (or thorium) ores will be the development of conversion technology for advanced reactors, including the likely development of breeders as one looks several decades or more into the future. The latter achievement would reduce the problem of nuclear raw materials to insignificance for a long time to come, since it enhances raw materials use by a factor of 50 or more to nonbreeder systems. If (looking still further ahead) we assume that nuclear fusion can be controlled to produce power economically, the availability of the required resources (deuterium and lithium) appears to be still more staggering.

Although the picture that emerges here is one of vast quantities, implying adequacy of energy sources well into the distant future, the intent is not to convey a notion of complacency. After all, the enormity of coal resources means little if coal, in dwindling demand as a share of primary energy sources, cannot be supplied in a desirable form (such as converted to gasoline or high-Btu gas). But it is precisely on this score that the estimates provide reassurance. For they suggest ample lead times during which our continued reliance on energy conventionally supplied can simultaneously witness major efforts to surmount the considerable technological and economic problems inherent in the production, delivery, and conversion of these more novel energy sources, so that these, too, can be economically employed amidst safeguards to the natural environment and to the public health and safety.

As the nation seeks to insure energy adequacy in the years ahead, it is unlikely that it can, or would wish, to insulate itself from the world economy. For the foreseeable future, it is probable that the United States will elect to provide for at least some significant portion of its petroleum requirements through imports from abroad, since the economic cost of not doing so is unlikely to be acceptable. This means that the United States—to a far lesser extent, to be sure, than major energy importing areas like Japan and Western Europe—will be a decidedly interested party in issues affecting the terms on which petroleum, and perhaps to an increasing extent, natural gas as well, enters international markets. (This is apart from interests stemming from capital investments by American companies in foreign oil-producing areas.)

On this matter of securing adequate energy supplies, as in others we have reviewed, new forces have emerged on the scene. Producer countries, concerned in their actions to a degree that did not exist some years ago, have succeeded in winning sizable gains in their per-barrel oil revenues. Threat of a multi-country boycott in shipments figured prominently in the Middle Eastern and Libyan negotiations during the past year. The first round of Libyan price talks (in 1970) actually involved a severe curtailment of output by selected companies with the result that, apart from its possible effect as a negotiating tactic, there was a worldwide tanker shortage and an escalation of freight rates which significantly raised the cost of imported United States oil, irrespective of origin. In any such producer-country/company confrontation, it is doubtful whether the United States could altogether avoid economically inimical consequences.

Moreover, even though it is the Middle East and North Africa which are viewed as the most volatile oil-exporting areas (and only a relatively small proportion of United States oil imports originate there), other regions, of greater consequence for energy supplies, are not immune to pressures in which the self-interest of the producing country may, correctly or not, be viewed as in conflict with the interests of the United States. This country's major oil supplier, Venezuela, is moving towards sharply accelerated per-barrel revenues as well as greater domestic control over both its domestic oil as well as natural gas resources. And, it should be noted that, in liquefied form, natural gas prospectively may figure significantly in international energy trade in the years ahead. (Whether the trend towards increased control by producing countries is not injurious to the goal for increased profits is a question under debate.) And Canada, our second most important supplier, is engaged in internal soul-searching in which the importance of Canadian oil and gas to the United States (and hence their use in bargaining over broader joint issues) is given at least as much weight as the importance of these exports to the Canadian economy.

One could not fairly argue, on the basis of these observations, that United States energy supply adequacy faces overriding international challenges. But, the world setting within which United States energy problems are met and decisions made also comprehends the matter of resource adequacy on a global level, and some brief remarks should be addressed to this point as well.[39] As with the data cited above for the United States alone, enormous variability is possible in worldwide energy resource estimation depending on technological and economic assumptions and on the estimating technique employed. Thus, a bare minimum estimate of conventional fossil fuel reserves (employing a "proved reserve" concept for the petroleum component) might suggest not much more than a century's supply at current rates of production; with what some would regard as an entirely defensible relaxation of restrictive assumptions, a 1,000-year supply can reasonably be adduced. The addition of shale, tar sands, uranium (assuming breeding), and thorium would expand the resource picture manifold, even allowing for worldwide growth in consumption, including the disproportionately fast rate of increase foreseen outside the United States.

Even if the specter of absolute physical exhaustion of world energy resources may have ceased to the matter of chronic anxiety which it once was, other issues will continue to command close attention. The technology and economic cost of exploiting various energy resources and their respective degrees of utilization will be topics of vital interest. Also, the global perspective here employed—with emphasis on worldwide aggregates and adequacy—may have limited bearing for particular regions of the world: These world totals cannot be expected to relieve the concern of fuel-deficit regions whose satisfaction of fuel and power needs may periodically be jeopardized by supply interruptions such as have occurred in the past, or whose dependence on energy sources from abroad may impose severe foreign exchange burdens. These subjects may, in time, pall in the shadow of the environmental consequences which a rapidly expanding level of worldwide energy use may pose for mankind. That subject is considered in the concluding part of this paper.

CONCLUSIONS: SOME CONSEQUENCES OF EXPANDED ENERGY CONSUMPTION FOR THE ENVIRONMENT AND FOR RESEARCH AND PUBLIC POLICY

Summary of the Paper to This Point

It will be well to pull together the main strands of the preceding discussion prior to looking at some of the resultant issues raised thereby in the fields of environment and of public policy and research.

1. Historically, the growth in United States energy consumption has broadly parallelled the growth of the nationwide economy as measured by constant-dollar GNP; both measures have substantially exceeded the rate of population growth.

2. There have, nonetheless, been distinct period variations in the relationship between energy and GNP growth. The steeper rise of energy consumption than of GNP in the closing decades of the nineteenth century and in the early part of the twentieth century most probably reflects the disproportionately fast growth of manufacturing in the economy; while energy growth below that of GNP growth after World War I appears to be strongly related to the efficiencies induced by

electrification (both in the progressive improvements in its generation as well as those made possible by its use), dieselization and other processes.

3. Vast changes in the relative contributions of different primary energy sources accompanied these developments; in most uses, excepting electric generation, coal gave way to oil and gas as the preeminent fuels. And one form of energy—electricity—grew continuously at a much faster rate than energy consumption as a whole, with the result that, out of the total consumption of primary energy resources in this country, 25 percent now go into the utility sector for generation of electricity.

4. During the past five years, United States energy consumption has once again risen at rates above those of GNP—a phenomenon which, though it is too early to attempt to explain fully, may in part be connected with a halt (whether temporary or more enduring) to electric generation efficiency improvements. Also, contrary to what may at one time have been the presumption about future trends, there is at the present time no compelling evidence to suggest that "product mix" shifts in the United States economy are, in themselves, likely to be energy-saving rather than energy-intensive.

5. Prudent assumptions about the future would be, therefore, that energy consumption growth will in general conform closely to growth of the national economy; that both will continue to outstrip population growth; and that, to the end of the present century, electric power use will, as it has historically, expand fastest of all in line with developments of new electricity applications, shifts from other sources of energy to electricity, felt improvements in living standards, and, of course, population growth.

6. Variations in the assumed rate of population growth will, of course, affect the projected growth of energy demand, though less appreciably than would be the case if reinforced by assumed variations in the projected rate of productivity (GNP per manhour) growth. Interestingly, one can postulate a range of technological "scenarios" in energy conversion and utilization in which (at a given growth rate for GNP) the rate of primary energy consumption growth varies from 2.3 to 4.3 percent per annum—a wider spread than that flowing from the alternate population assumptions (and accompanying economic parameters) governing the present study.

7. Resource adequacy to meet demand is best viewed in a dynamic framework which, when allowing for changing economic and technological circumstances—such as synthetic fuel sources and breeder reactors, evolving at changing cost and price relationships—does not spell stringency as one looks to the year 2000 and even beyond. Moreover, the United States comes off well when placed in a context of worldwide energy interdependence, in which numerous developed and less developed regions are virtually all but deficient in indigenous energy supplies—at least fossil fuels.

8. Ultimately, of course, energy resources are nonrenewable assets whose conservation and prudent management are justified on that score alone. To the extent that a slowly rather than a rapidly growing population contributes (albeit only modestly) to that end, it may be judged beneficial, though it is likely to be dictated by a host of more persuasive considerations. It could turn out that environmental repercussions will constitute a much earlier constraint on energy growth than demographic factors.

Environmental Implications

Here, we are interested in noting those environmental concerns which, as a minimum, deserve consideration in any balanced perspective on likely or desirable trends and patterns in energy use. The fact is that virtually every facet of energy production, conversion, delivery, and use has some significant environmental ramification which must be brought into account. All too often, a restricted viewpoint highlights a particular form of environmental damage only to ignore the consequences of the implied alternative: An electric car may minimize gasoline-engine emissions only perhaps to compound the problem of central electric-generating plants. It is this pervasive presence of environmental implications which we wish to highlight in what follows. The treatment will be brief and is intended to call attention to problems rather than to discuss their essence.

Primary Energy Production

Fossil Fuels

As estimated in Table 19, fossil fuels will, in spite of the rapidly rising share of nuclear energy, continue to account for the preponderant share of energy consumption in the United States and throughout the world for the remainder of this century. Certain aspects of coal and petroleum production cause special environmental concern. In society where increasing amenities are associated not merely with one's personal life but are expected as well amidst one's working conditions, coal mining continues to be an occupation which is disproportionately susceptible to bodily injury, accidental death, and health hazards. Although productivity has advanced in United States mines, there has not been a significant reduction in injury rates.[40]

Coal mining exacts its toll on land and water as well. One-third of United States coal production has, in recent years, been mined by stripping; the proportion has, if anything, been rising slightly. In the absence of land reclamation, which is slowly beginning to be practiced under rising pressure from conservationists, public authorities, and citizens, the effects of surface mining are accumulated overburden, a scarred landscape, and water pollution from both acid mine drainage and erosion.

In addition, underground coal mining "can cause subsidence unless the mining systems are designed to prevent deterioration and failure of abandoned mine pillars. Underground fires may weaken or destroy coal pillars that support the surface, causing subsidence with consequent damage to surface structures. An additional threat is the possible collapse of buildings and opening of surface fissues and potholes."[41]

Irrespective of mining method, coal preparation (applicable to 62 percent of the coal mined in the United States and undertaken so as to improve the quality of the coal) produces large quantities of wastes which, if not returned to the mine, pile up in open slag heaps. At times, these may ignite. They may also contaminate nearby streams.[42]

The problems of crude oil production have in recent years focused particularly on oil pollution of the seas, though inland crude production has problems as well. The Santa Barbara offshore oil leak in 1969 and most recent blowouts in the Gulf of Mexico are among the more dramatic such occurrences.[43] Less publicized are the thousands of small leaks with unknown consequences over time. Scientists appear still to be relatively ignorant about the long-term and low-level effects of crude oil pollution on aquatic ecology and on human and animal health. There is uncertainty also about the most effective way to combat oil spillage that has occurred and about the best way to accelerate its dissipation or recovery. The potential environmental effects of oil spillage, although not fully understood, are bound to increase as more oil originates in offshore fields, as more of it is being transported across the oceans, and as the tankers carrying it grow to enormous size, possibly with diminished maneuverability.

It is estimated that, at the beginning of 1970, seven million barrels of oil a day (or 17 percent of the world's output) came from offshore wells. This represented an increase of 175 percent over a period of just four years. Rapid future growth in offshore production seems certain.[44]

Oil production operations on land also have environmental effects—such as combustion emissions and incomplete wastewater treatment at refineries—although here the control of damage is comparatively well in hand. If and when conventional fossil fuels begin to be supplanted by synthetic liquid fuels from America's vast store of oil shale, significant environmental problems will have to be dealt with, for the production process makes a large claim on water and generates enormous wastes. Underground fracturing by nuclear explosions presents an obvious environmental problem of its own. That would also be true of nuclear-assisted freeing and extraction of trapped natural gas formations.

Hydroelectricity

Hydroelectricity is a quantitatively minor source of primary energy here and in most industrially advanced countries; and, the outlook is for its relative importance to decline, even allowing for the growing relative importance of pumped storage. Its potentiality is greater in the less developed regions.

From an environmental standpoint, hydro offers the virtues of emitting no waste heat or contaminants. But the installations and the impounded water may intrude into natural, often spectacular, scenery. In addition, the modification of streamflow characteristics and other changes that accompany a major hydro project may be cause of significant disruption of aquatic ecology, and possibly even a threat to human health in some instances. Finally, the remoteness of hydro sites from load centers entails the presence of electric transmission lines cutting a long-distance swath across an otherwise unspoiled terrain.

Nuclear Fuels

Open-pit or underground uranium mining create problems of waste accumulation and injury to the landface that are similar to coal mining. However, the quantities involved, presently and even under the volume of requirements envisaged with rising nuclear capacity over the next several decades, are slight by coal-mining standards.

More important are the problems of radioactive contamination during the mining and processing of uranium ores. The uranium found in nature is slightly radioactive, emitting a radioactive gas (radon) from exposed rock surfaces. The gas can be ingested by the lungs of underground miners whose "excess incidence lung cancer . . . is believed to be induced by the exposure to radiation from the radioactive decay of the radon daughters in their lungs."[45]

In the milling process for the recovery of uranium oxide there is some risk of pollution of water supplies by radioactive constituents in liquid effluents. Safeguards are provided by impounding such effluents controlling their discharge into streams at controlled rates.[46] The production of uranium concentrates also results in accumulated piles of uranium mill tailings whose finer radium-containing particles can be carried away by wind and rain.

Energy Transport

Tankers. The delivery of energy to ultimate users and its shipment at intermediate stages of the production-consumption chain poses numerous environmental hazards. The possible magnitude of the environmental threat from ocean transport spillage is dramatized by events such as the grounding of the *Torrey Canyon* in 1967.

In recent years, some 60 percent of oil consumed in the world has involved ocean transport among major producing-consuming regions.[47] Around 24 million barrels per day represented inter-area ocean movement in 1968; by 2000 the figure may amount to 105 million.

The prospects are for this volume of oil to be moved in tankers of ever-increasing size. Indeed, with the increased size of tankers, the expanding volume of oil consumption is likely to be achieved with a smaller number of ships in service. Yet, much remains to be learned about the structural and operating properties of these huge ships.

Though at present still a minor factor in international energy flows, liquefied natural gas shipments promise to expand significantly in the years ahead. LNG tankers, which carry gas that, at a temperature of −160° C, has been compressed into a liquid at 1/600 of its normal volume in special tanks, have had operating experience for less than a decade. The economic characteristics of LNG lead to strong pressures to minimize transport costs. But the search for optimum design features (including some uncertain safety aspects) is still very much underway.

Pipelines. In the United States, there are over 165,000 miles of oil and 850,000 miles of natural gas lines. Breaks, explosions, and seepage do occur, of course; and there are efforts by various groups to secure tighter standards and enforcement authority. But, as far as one can judge, the safety record seems by and large to have been reasonably good. The intense debate over the proposed trans-Alaska oil pipeline is a special case, for it poses a combination of safety as well as aesthetic issues not encountered previously; permafrost subsidence, a scarred landscape, earthquake risks, intrusion into a "pure" ecological habitat. On the other hand, as the problem of securing energy supplies compels the extension of pipelines in still other more remote and hitherto unspoiled regions, the recent debate may simply be a foreshadowing of things to come.

Electric Transmission. When we come to the transport of electrical energy, the problems are almost entirely aesthetic. Even if electricity generation entailed no environmental problems, the trend toward ever-larger generating facilities and a cross-country network of multiple-strand transmission lines offers anything but a cheerful visual prospect. Power plants situated closer to load centers might, in many cases, reduce transmission requirements, but the trend—dictated by the cost of urban real estate, objections to fossil-fuel combustion emissions, anxiety over the location of nuclear plants in heavily populated areas, and facilitated by long-distance high-voltage technologies—is now towards more remote siting.

Of course, remote siting still presents emission problems (and it does mean somewhat more energy required per unit of load center demand met). One should note, however, that increased size of power plants in the United States achieves not only increased scale economies in operation, but will also reduce greatly the absolute number of plants required (compared to today), as well as lowering the required space per unit of power production capacity.[48]

Many feel that the problems of public acceptance of larger station size and more extensive transmission lines can be minimized by long advance planning, public participation in the decision, and perhaps by innovations in industrial design and landscaping. Efforts might also be made to integrate such facilities within broader industrial "complexes." It has also been suggested that stations may be located offshore on man-made islands or under water in coastal locations or underground on inland locations. Transmission line rights of way could be shared with pipelines or other carriers and landscaped or used for recreation. Already 300,000 miles of such lines occupy four million acres in the United States; by 1990, the 500,000 miles projected are expected to require seven million acres.[49] It may prove possible with advances in technology to achieve economic means of placing lines underground. Because of the varying governmental agencies and jurisdictions involved in siting, it has been suggested that the companies need a public authority that, while protecting the public interest can, nevertheless, give a positive response to a siting proposal instead of being left to deal with the many who can only veto it.

Nuclear Fuels. We saw earlier (in Table 19) that over one-half of electric power output both in the United States and worldwide may be atomic by the year 2000. According to Federal Government estimates, these projected trends will require that, by 1990, this country will have to locate sites for around 165 new nuclear plants, all of over 500 mw capacity, a significant portion exceeding 3,000 mw.[50] If our projection of worldwide nuclear generating capacity by the end of the century of 3.2 million mw is reasonable, it is equally reasonable to expect the presence by that time of some 3,200 large nuclear power stations (assuming average capacity of 1,000 mw) around the globe. Numerous environmental issues are implied by these developments, quite apart from problems (which many persons no longer believe to be unmanageable) regarding radiation emissions to air and water resulting from routine power-generating operations. As for transport, if approximately one-third of these plants are to undergo annual reloading of their fuel cores,[51] the volume of nuclear-fuel handling and management would be very great with a particular critical part of the process centering on transportation, reprocessing, and disposal of radioactive materials. The recent Massachusetts Institute of Technology-sponsored Report of the Study of Critical Environmental Problems (SCEP) notes that probably "the major potential for nuclear contamination of the environment will occur at the site of the fuel reprocessing plants. Here as the protective claddings and shields are removed to enable fuel recovery, fission and activation products are exposed and the potential for escape into the environment is increased."[52] SCEP cites one estimate that 99.9 percent of all radionuclides entering the environment are released from fuel reprocessing plants. Where nuclear fuel management occurs in countries with political instability or less sophisticated technological traditions, the normal problems of nuclear fuel handling may be compounded. As breeder reactors assume an important role, as these quantitative estimates assume, the monitoring and containment of plutonium will become an enormous responsibility. Finally, irrespective of reactor technology, technical and durable institutional approaches will have to be devised for the burial of radioactive wastes.

Energy Conversion and Utilization

Combustion in Stationary Sources: Fossil Fuels. The stationary sources burning coal, oil, and gas comprise power stations, coke ovens, blast furnaces as well as combustion associated with other iron- and steel-making operations, other manufacturing activities, refinery operations, and domestic and commercial establishments (the latter largely involving combustion for space heating). The major pollutants emitted from stationary fossil-fuel combustion (along with industrial processes) are seen, from lines 2 and 3 in Table 21, to be sulfur oxides, nitrogen oxides, and particulates, with the "industrial process" category contributing a sizable quantity of hydrocarbons and carbon monoxide (which we will, however, take up in connection with transport where they loom much larger). Along with transportation, these two groups of stationary sources are clearly a major United States national air pollution source. In addition to the pollutants indicated in the table, fossil-fuel combustion releases waste heat and carbon dioxide. The former is significant primarily because of increased temperature produced in water adjacent to power plants (and other stationary heat converters), while increased carbon dioxide in the atmosphere is of some concern to scientists because of uncertainty as to its long-term climatological consequences via the "greenhouse" effect. This refers to the heating up of the earth's atmosphere because ultra-violet rays from the sun penetrate, while infra-red rays from the earth are blocked by, the blanket of overhanging carbon dioxide. (There may, however, be some compensation because particulates may effect ultra-violet rays.)

Within the total of the stationary fossil-fuel combustion and industrial-process categories shown in the table, power stations (in terms of fuels consumed) are quantitatively the most important, accounting for about one-third of the total stationary combustion energy consumption in the United States and a roughly similar proportion for numerous other advanced countries, through in certain metropolitan areas, residential space heating is an important contributor to sulfur oxides in the area. Because of their disproportionately high requirements for water for cooling purposes (under prevailing "once-through" cooling methods) power stations are the major source of thermal effluents. (Waste heat release is the principal environmental effect common to both fossil-fueled and nuclear power stations; in fact, since the latter currently operate at substantially lower efficiencies than fossil-fueled generating plants, they produce relatively higher amounts of heat per kilowatt-hour of power generated.) Power plants also account for a preponderant share of the sulfur oxide emissions.

The effect of stationary combustion emissions varies with the type of pollutant, as does the technology and understanding necessary to deal with these effects. While the exact biological consequences of sulfur dioxide are not completely understood (complicating the specification of air quality standards) there appears to be widespread appreciation of the fact that sulfur dioxide can be harmful to persons suffering from lung ailments as well as other diseases. Of the three fossil fuels, natural gas has the least sulfur content, which explains why it is increasingly desired as fuel for steam electric plants; but natural gas is currently in short supply in the United States, a stringency which is likely to endure for some time. By contrast, many types of coal and oil are by nature excessively high in sulfur. The principal solution to the problem is believed to lie in technologies (now in various stages of research) for sulfur dioxide removal from the furnace gases produced during combustion, as,

Table 21.—Estimated Nationwide Emissions, United States, 1968
(million short tons)

Source	Carbon monoxide	Particulates	Sulfur oxides	Hydro-carbons	Nitrogen oxides
Transportation	63.8	1.2	0.8	16.6	8.1
Fuel combustion (stationary)[a]	1.9	8.9	24.4	0.7	10.0
Industrial processes[b]	9.7	7.5	7.3	4.6	0.2
Solid waste disposal	7.8	1.1	0.1	1.6	0.6
Miscellaneous[c]	16.9	9.6	0.6	8.5	1.7
Total	100.1	28.3	33.2	32.0	20.6

[a]Largely power plants, but including residential-commercial heating and minor items.
[b]Including, as major components, primary metals, chemicals, oil refining.
[c]Including, as major items, forest fires and agricultural burning.

Source: U.S. Council on Environmental Quality, as reproduced in U.S. Congress, Senate, Committee on Public Works, "Management of Fuels to Satisfy Environmental Criteria," by G. Alex Mills, Harry Perry, and Harry Johnson, in *Problems and Issues of a National Materials Policy*, 1970, p. 144.

for example, by stack scrubbing. Additional alternatives involve, on the one hand, the removal of sulfur from fuels beforehand, or, on the other, the dispersion and dilution of sulfur in the air following combustion. But an adequate amount of prior sulfur removal is believed to be quite costly, while post-combustion dispersal may not be sufficiently effective to meet stringent anti-pollution standards, particularly as the volume of emissions increases over time. In practice, a mix of these different methods may be appropriate, depending on particular circumstances. While for the moment, the feasibility of various measures is limited by technology, cost factors may in time constitute the major constraint.

A major component of particulate discharges are the fly and furnace ash from oil- and coal-burning power plants, the principal environmental impact being dirt emitted to surrounding property and—in the form of smaller-sized particles—into the atmosphere. The 297 million tons of coal burned for electric power in the United States in 1968 produced roughly 30 million tons of these wastes—a 10-to-1 ratio.[53] Of the 30 million tons, only around two million tons are actually emitted, the remainder being gathered by dust collectors. Different types of control equipment have been developed to combat particulate discharges (for example, electrostatic precipitators, scrubbers, and mechanical separators). There is a promise of steady improvements in the efficiency of these devices.

In emissions of nitrogen oxides, which are common to both stationary as well as automotive combustion, natural gas is again the least villainous fuel, coal the most, with oil in between. Nitrogen oxides are the chemicals incriminated in the formation of eye-irritating photochemical smog. They are also believed to be harmful to cell tissues, especially lungs. Research at control of nitrogen oxides is not at all well advanced and there is little promise of early success at a solution to the problem.

Heat emissions are particularly a problem of electric generating plants; and it is this concentrated dosage of heat rejection in particular areas (such as densely-populated metropolitan centers) which may, in some views, cause serious localized climatic perturbations long before the heat rejection which necessarily accompanies all energy use becomes a problem to be reckoned with. Fossil-fueled power plants convert only about 35 to 40 percent of heat input into electric energy (with nuclear plants, the proportion is still lower), the balance having largely to be discharged into the air or water in the vicinity of the plant. The resulting "thermal pollution" is not at all well understood with respect to the ecological effects. It is possible that the presence of waste heat in waters, with a severely limited temperature increase, is beneficial to some forms of water life (in certain stages of their life cycle) and detrimental to others.[54] Also its effects will vary greatly from place to place depending upon the original temperature of the waters, and will vary also with the seasons.

Given the projected United States demand for electricity (including the more-than-50 percent share for nuclear—see Table 19), one study speculates on the possibility that "more than 10 times as much heat will be rejected to cooling water in 2000 as is being rejected now. Even with greatly increased use of brines or sea water for cooling, the demands for fresh cooling water [that is, with once-through cooling] would be larger than could be supplied."[55] However, with sufficient investment in recirculation systems which are needed to avoid heat pollution by steam-electric power plants—and such expenditures may constitute a significant share of future steam-quality maintenance costs—a more sanguine outlook is warranted. The water monograph, which forms part of the present project, thus takes a reasonable position on this score.

Coping with the thermal pollution problem would seem to lie in the use, at an incremental cost, which has been estimated at 0.4 mills per kwh,[56] of cooling ponds and evaporative cooling towers (the latter are standard in Great Britain.) Dry cooling towers—considerably more costly—produce no evaporative water loss, giving off only dry heat to the atmosphere. In time, more efficient electric generating modes—such as, magnetohydrodynamics (MHD)—and more productive uses of waste heat (for example, dual purpose electric power-process steam plants) would serve to mitigate thermal pollution.

All energy-consuming activities (not merely the waste heat reflecting inherent energy-conversion inefficiencies) emit heat to the environment, of course. Whether the heat so released could in time constitute a sufficiently large fraction of the earth's surface as to threaten significant climatic alteration is a subject deserving serious study—notably as regards certain densely-populated areas where, some fear, these effects may first appear. (This ignores the use of solar energy as a possible energy source.)

Carbon dioxide emissions are directly related to the combustion of fossil fuels, varying somewhat with the respective carbon content of coal, oil, and gas, and the completeness of combustion achieved. As with nitrogen oxides, carbon dioxide emissions are common to both stationary and automotive energy consumption, except that in the latter case, release prior to absorption in the atmosphere is partially in the form of dangerous carbon monoxide gases. As pointed out earlier, carbon dioxide emissions are of concern because of their uncertain, long-range climatological impact. It is feared that, because of the "greenhouse effect," eventual overheating of the earth's atmosphere may occur. The M.I.T.-sponsored report (cited earlier) is sanguine about the absence of global climatic problems for the remainder of this century, even though in numerous countries fossil-fuel combustion, and hence carbon dioxide emissions may rise by a factor of 3.5 or four percent yearly (roughly calculated). The M.I.T. study does view with some apprehension the cumulative carbon dioxide release implicit in the combustion of world fossil-fuel resources as we look beyond the year 2000, and therefore urges that we undertake to learn more about this problem.[57] Here again it may be appropriate to assess the possibility of climatic effects which could conceivably occur sooner in specific areas.

Nuclear Power Plants. We have already mentioned environmental problems connected with the shipment and chemical reprocessing of nuclear fuels and wastes. Also, in the preceding section, we touched on the matter of heat dissipation in electric generation, a problem common to all thermal power stations except for the fact that present types of atomic stations, because of comparatively poor efficiency in generating electricity, emit larger amounts of waste heat. Here, we are concerned with the environmental aspects of nuclear power plant operations per se, a subject which has received, and continues to be the subject of, widespread attention.[58]

Concern over nuclear power plant operation arises from two factors: risk of major catastrophe involving accidental rupture of the reactor and its containment sphere and the dispersal of its radioactive contents to the surroundings; and anxiety over low-level, though persistent, radioactive emissions. While it is possible to conceive of accidents of catastrophic dimensions (in which case, no one disputes the fact that there might be widespread exposure to large doses of radiation, with all its well-publicized hazards), the probability of such accidents is said to be tiny by most of the experts on the subject. But not all are convinced of AEC and other scientific assurances on this score. The debate therefore is over the probabilities of major accidents, and whether even apparently negligible risks of catastrophic accident should be accepted by society.

In the case of low-level radioactive emissions during routine reactor operation, what is involved is the collection and venting to the outside air (generally from stacks or blowers on top of the power station) of radioactive gases, especially krypton and xenon. Small amounts of other radioactive wastes may also escape and be mixed in with cooling water leaving the station. These emissions are regarded as routine discharges, and are well within the radiation limits specified by United States standards. Though some scientists continue to argue, nevertheless, that all radiation, including natural radiation exposure in the environment, is dangerous to life and that the increase in radiation incidental to the proliferation of nuclear power plants should not be tolerated, many people now believe this aspect of nuclear power to have achieved a safe and manageable status.[59]

Combustion in Mobile Sources. Motor vehicles (automobiles along with trucks and buses) are the overwhelming source of the pollution ascribed to the "Transportation" sector in Table 21. Of the 90 million ton total of emissions for that sector in the United

States in 1968, 83 million tons come from motor vehicle operation.[60] Aircraft, railroads, vessels, and nonhighway motor fuels use account for the small remainder.

The principal emissions are nitrogen oxides (which, since they are common also to stationary fossil-fuel consumption, have already been covered), hydrocarbons, and carbon monoxide. To these should be added emissions of lead compounds, included within the "Particulates" column in the table. (Automobile exhausts are the principal source of lead emissions in the country.)

Hydrocarbons, the result of incomplete combustion of gasoline, are for the most part believed nonpoisonous in present atmospheric concentrations, although questions have been raised about the health hazards of the "aromatic" constituents of certain specific types of hydrocarbons, particularly where aromatics are used to preserve the octane rating of low-lead gasolines. Hydrocarbons also contribute to smog. Carbon monoxide, under conditions of sufficiently high concentration (such as inside closed, idling cars having exhaust leaks), is potentially deadly. But even short of fatal concentrations of carbon monoxide, those amounts encountered in congested areas are believed possibly sufficient to cause cardiovascular changes, dizziness, and headaches. The quantity of atmospheric lead compound concentrations have not yet been incriminated as a demonstrable threat to health, there being no scientific agreement on the exact danger point of such concentrations. But lead (a gasoline additive to raise the octane rating for high-compression engines) is known to be highly poisonous, and with the steadily increasing volume of automotive traffic, there is great apprehension about its possible effects. Moreover, compliance with Federal Government standards for 1975 emissions of carbon dioxide and hydrocarbons will most probably compel elimination or severe reduction of gasoline lead content, for lead has been found to impair efficiency of the catalytic converters designed to lower emissions of these pollutants.

The automobile has shaped our whole style of life and structure of metropolitan areas; and with a lag, it is imposing similar effects on the rest of the world. Even with automotive growth here and elsewhere assumed to fall below recent growth rates our projections imply that without a change in fundamental patterns, the world of the year 2000 would contain over one billion conventionally-fueled cars. If that were the case, emissions per car equal to 16 percent of those in 1968 would be necessary just to hold the total volume of emissions unchanged! It is impossible to say what cost the automobile imposes on society, or what the value is of the flexibility and convenience it also brings, although

its incremental value will no doubt for years to come be regarded more highly in the rest of the world than here.[61]

In the future, there is also the possibility of developing alternatives to the internal combustion engine. Other forms of propulsion receiving attention (each no doubt having at least some adverse characteristics), include steam engines, gas turbines, and battery-powered motors. More dependent on public policy and attitudes than on technological breakthroughs, a major increase in the uses of mass transit systems would have proportionally beneficial effects on emissions and energy resource savings. Such systems might appreciably cut down on pollution and reduce primary energy needs in transport (which accounts for about one-fourth of the nation's overall energy needs), quite apart from easing congestion on streets and highways. The following figures[62] show that the car ranks relatively low on a passenger-mile-per-gallon basis:

	Passenger miles/gallon
Automobile (sedan, two people)[63]	32
Conventional trains	80-130
Electric metroliner	50
Two-deck suburban train	200
Ten-car subway train	75
Buses	100-125
Jet planes	22

Some Issues for Research and Public Policy

The objective of economic growth and the recognized importance of steadily increasing amounts of energy in sustaining that growth has led past energy policy, to the extent that simplifications allows us to speak of "an" energy policy in the first place, to concern itself with the task of attaining essentially three desirable attributes of energy supply: current and future abundance, cheapness, and security of supply. There is, of course, some inescapable conflict among these objectives, as in the case where security of supply—achieved by oil import restrictions—leads to higher prices. Moreover, this conflict will surely become even more pronounced in the future, as environmental criteria take their place as yet another consideration in energy policy. The task for future research and public policy can be viewed as one which seeks to harmonize these objectives along the lines of some sort of socially optimum criteria.

Let us cite a specific example, which illustrates the nature of choices that have to be faced. America's most abundant fossil-fuel resource—coal—is also one which, as we have seen, stands severely incriminated from an environmental standpoint at both its production and combustion stages. The problem is complicated by the fact that low-sulfur coal is concentrated in the Western United States—a costly distance from major consuming centers—where it is extracted mostly by strip mining.

Industrial and government-fostered research in promotion of a viable coal gasification technology, if successful, could lead to an altogether changed outlook of United States resource potentialities and one, on balance, far less inimical to environmental interests than would otherwise be the case. A critical look at past government programs in support of energy research and development reveals, however, that these programs have unfortunately developed in an episodic and disjointed way, bare of any apparent overriding criteria such as might arise out of an overall energy outlook. In the past, vast sums have been poured into nuclear research and development; by contrast, only relatively modest amounts of money have been used in the development of shale oil and liquid and gaseous fuels from coal. In the future, analogous choices will have to be made among what may appear as more or less equally worthy programs: breeder reactors, thermonuclear fusion, synthetic sources of liquid and gaseous fuels, the gas-fired fuel cell, and others. Much will depend upon the underlying technological promise of the alternatives, and the social payoff to be expected; but, these will seldom yield unequivocal answers. Nonetheless, systematic study of the alternatives, using technical, economic, and social criteria, should provide useful guides to those engaged in national scientific management.

Another change in emphasis that may be called for is one which is directed not merely at the problem of mobilizing abundant, cheap, secure, and (now) clean resources to meet expected levels of demand (as suggested above) but one which critically questions projected demand levels. Electric power is the most frequently cited case where, largely because of detrimental environmental effects, critical scrutiny of demand-growth assumptions is called for.

Complex issues intrude here which can only be briefly alluded to in this respect. To the extent that the "internalization" of environmental costs preserves environmental purity even as electric power is being generated, no curtailment of power growth would appear to be called for.[64] Nor would this be the case if increased electricity prices suppress demand growth.

But "internalization" may not be feasible—perhaps because of disagreement on proper costs and standards, because of technological ignorance (such as nitrogen

oxide omission) or because of unacceptable costs (such as dry cooling towers). Moreover, some potentially harmful effects—for example, atmospheric heat emissions—are inherent in all energy use. The problem then becomes one of curtailing demand, a situation which will confront policy makers with what may be unprecedented problems of implementation and equity. For example, how can one discourage consumption of substitute energy sources which have their own harmful impacts? How does one apportion cutbacks among different classes of users (such as industrial versus residential) and different income groups, and with what impacts on the overall economy and society? What are the implications of curtailed growth for managerial innovations? For traditional regulatory institutions and practices?

There is no question whatsoever that the unfolding climate of concern over environmental deterioration and resource management will confront us with choices and problems which we have barely begun to grasp. This paper has sought to provide some minimal background understanding in the energy field that might assist us to start wrestling with this formidable and challenging task.

REFERENCES

1. By "energy" consumption or use, we refer to combined resource inputs (coal, oil, natural gas, hydro, and nuclear electricity) expressed in a common calorific measure (Btu's), irrespective of whether such resources are ultimately utilized in the form of fuels and power, on the one hand, or as raw materials (e.g., in the chemical industry), on the other. For hydro and nuclear, the Btu equivalent of the electricity generated is computed on the basis of primary energy inputs at fossil-fueled generating stations at prevailing rates of efficiency. In practice, about 95 percent of energy resource inputs go to fuels and power use. Readers are referred to various tabular footnotes for technical and definitional information.

2. Measured by these industries' value added.

3. See U.S. Bureau of the Census, *Annual Survey of Manufacturers, 1966.* The variability of energy's role in different industrial activities is illustrated by the following selected 1966 figures, showing the ratio of dollar purchases of fuels and electricity per $100 in output:

All manufacturing	$ 1.40
Primary nonferrous metals	5.50
Hydraulic cement	15.40
Basic chemicals	6.00
Steel rolling and finishing (inc. blast furnaces)	4.10
Machinery	0.65
Printing and publishing	0.50

4. The continually rising percentages of Table 2 reflect, moreover, a downward bias since, with rising thermal efficiency, progressively lower quantities of primary energy have been needed to produce a given amount of electric power. For example, if the nation's electric power output in 1969 (reflecting an efficiency factor of about 10,500 Btu per kwh) would have had to be produced at the 1940 efficiency rate (or 16,400 Btu per kwh), some 24 quadrillion Btu's of primary energy (rather than the actual 1969 level of 17 quadrillion Btu) would have been required, and one-third of all energy consumption would have been accounted for by the electricity sector, as against the approximately one-fourth that actually prevailed.

5. Note that, in this context, fossil-fueled electricity—being treated as a secondary energy form—is excluded from consideration.

6. Resources for the Future Staff Report, *U.S. Energy Policies: An Agenda for Research* (Washington, 1968), p. 14.

7. For a more elaborate treatment, see Sam H. Schurr *et al.*, *Energy in the American Economy, 1850-1970* (Baltimore: Johns Hopkins Press for Resources for the Future, 1960), especially Chapter 4.

8. Other energy-using sectors of the economy are, of course, also subject to efficiency losses not indicated in the table. Automotive energy consumption is a major example.

9. This anomaly might have been due to excessive use of old plant for peaking purposes.

10. From Hans H. Landsberg *et al.*, *Resources in America's Future* (Baltimore: Johns Hopkins Press, 1963); taken from tables in Chapter 10 Appendix. The "all other" category was increased slightly in order to adjust Landsberg's overall total of 193 billion to our figure of 195 billion.

11. Presumed from the fact that only 2.9 percent had color sets in 1965 (*Merchandising Week* data in U.S. Bureau of the Census, *Statistical Abstract of the United States, 1970*, p. 687).

12. Based on 8 billion kwh in 1960 (from Landsberg, *et al., op. cit.*, p. 747) and estimated 40 billion kwh in 1969. The latter figure was based on a *Merchandising Week* estimate (shown in U.S. Bureau of the Census, *Statistical Abstract of the United States, 1970*) on ownership of window units, and on Air Conditioning and Refrigeration Institute figures (oral communication) on central airconditioning. Landsberg's extrapolated kilowatthour estimate for each type of unit per household was then applied.

13. U.S. Congress, Joint Economic Committee, *The Economy, Energy, and the Environment,* by the Environmental Policy Division, Legislative Reference Service, Library of Congress, Joint Committee Print, September 1, 1970, p. 73.

14. *Ibid.*

15. *Merchandising Week* data in U.S. Bureau of the Census, *Statistical Abstract of the United States, 1970,* p. 687.

16. An electric toothbrush draws 2 watts of current. Thus, a household could have 30 toothbrushes whirring simultaneously throughout a 24-hour day without exceeding the current drawn by a single 60-watt bulb lit at all times. Some idea of the wattage rating and average annual kilowatthour consumption for home heating as well as selected household appliances appears below (unpublished data from Potomac Electric Power Company, Washington, D. C.):

	Average watts	Estimated annual kwh per home
Airconditioner (window)	1,300	1,265
Clothes dryer	4,800	1,100
Frying pan	1,170	190
Food freezer	300	1,560
Range	11,720	1,225
Refrigerator-freezer (14 cu. ft.)	330	1,330
Heat pump (medium-sized home)	9,600	17,000
Broiler	1,375	140
Vibrator	40	2
Radio	80	90
Shaver	15	2
Sewing machine	75	10
Clock	2	18

17. Based on preliminary data from the U.S. Federal Power Commission, *1970 National Power Survey* (December 1971).

18. Alan M. Strout, *Technological Change and United States Energy Consumption, 1939-1954* (unpublished Ph.D. dissertation, University of Chicago, 1966).

19. W. A. Reardon, *An Input/Output Analysis of Energy Use Changes From 1947 to 1958 and 1958 to 1963* (Richland, Wash.: Battelle Memorial Institute, Pacific Northwest Laboratories, June 1971). This document represents the preliminary version of a study which has been undertaken on behalf of the U.S. Office of Science and Technology, and which in its final form is slated to bring the analysis up to 1963.

20. U.S. Bureau of Labor Statistics, *Patterns of U.S. Economic Growth,* Bulletin 1672, 1970.

21. The U.S. Bureau of Mines, Information Circular 8384. *An Energy Model for the United States,* 1968, was supplemented by selective revised and updated Bureau of Mines materials, unpublished at the time of writing. The FPC data are preliminary projections and textual materials from its *1970 National Power Survey* (December 1971). However, the share of total electricity assumed for nuclear power represents an Atomic Energy Commission projection, adopted by the Federal Power Commission.

22. The projected proportion of energy resources going into electric power would level off more were it not for the "medium-range" assumption that we can expect only modest overall improvements in the efficiency of electric generation. Alternative assumptions, of course, need not be similarly constrained.

23. Indeed, in a recent speech dealing with forecasts of nuclear generating capacity to the year 2000, Glenn T. Seaborg, Chairman of the Atomic Energy Commission, stated that, of the nuclear capacity in 2000, about two-thirds is expected to be represented by fast breeder reactors, with lightwater and advanced reactors splitting the balance. See Glenn T. Seaborg, "The Plutonium Economy of the Future" (speech) Atomic Energy Commission Press Release, October 5, 1970.

24. In this "medium-range forecast," no significant role is assigned to coal gasification or liquefaction; either alternative could dramatically change the picture described below.

25. The third "form" (energy resources desired for raw material nonfuel and nonpower uses), while gradually increasing as a share of nationwide energy consumption, is not likely to vary its growth in a manner greatly altering the quantity of primary energy sources consumed from the levels which would otherwise prevail. Rather surprisingly, in fact, in the U.S. Bureau of Mines analysis (*An Energy Model of the United States, Featuring Energy Balances for the Years 1947 to 1965 and Projections and Forecasts to the Year 1980 and 2000, op. cit.,* pp. 114-15), the share of total energy consumption for the year 2000 ascribed to nonfuel and power uses is barely higher than that in 1969. As a projected share of U.S. petroleum consumption alone, however, it rises from 10 percent in recent years to 17 percent. It is, however, possible that a growing volume of energy sources used as raw materials may have more significant environmental repercussions.

26. *Ibid.* Specifically, the Bureau of Mines study (partly revised in this paper) qualifies no less than 22 alternative "cases" of future U.S. energy consumption: Two cases represent what the authors term a "basic" or "conventional" forecast to the years 1980 and 2000, respectively, and, in modified form, these have gone into the construction of the "medium-range" forecast in our paper; 11 cases involve for the most part relatively minor variations on the basic forecast to the year 1980; while nine cases deal with alternative technological contingencies to the year 2000. In referring to some of these cases on succeeding pages, we have so modified the Bureau of Mines computations as to render them comparable to our "medium-range" projection — the latter being itself a modification of the Bureau of Mines medium-range model.

27. *Ibid.,* p. 42.

28. As in the preceding discussion concerning the United States, world energy consumption is here defined to comprise coal (in its different varieties), natural gas, hydro and nuclear power (as well as negligible amounts of geothermal power). The so-called "noncommercial" fuels—e.g., firewood, animal and vegetal wastes—are excluded even though in some countries, such as India, they continue to represent as much as 30 or even 50 percent of total energy use (of all kinds). But even in such countries, their use is dwindling, and for the world as a whole, they probably do not account for more than five percent. Because of the substitution of commercial for noncommercial fuels, growth rates based on commercial energy forms only (as in this paper) may be somewhat overstated for certain less developed regions. However, the conspicuously low efficiency with which noncommercial fuels are commonly used makes their omissions a less serious matter than might be thought.

29. Both measures, relate, of course, to statistics which reflect the prevailing economic and policy circumstances for the area and year in question. Policy changes in such matters as import controls, fuel taxes, shut-in productive capacity, or subsidies can bring about a different statistical picture of net foreign "dependence."

30. However, this relatively mild degree of importance dependence was supported by U.S. policy, placing severe restrictions on oil imports. Moreover, more recently prevailing North American shares have been somewhat higher—in the neighborhood of 8.5 percent—than the seven percent figure shown in the table; the 1967 figure was down due to reduced net imports associated with the Middle East conflict of that year.

31. Federal Reserve Bank of Kansas City, "International Trade Policies—The Export Performance of Developing Countries,"

Monthly Review, July-August 1969, pp. 11-12 (italics added).

32. In explanation of this United States vs. Rest-of-World lag difference between total energy and electricity, it should be remembered that electrification was virtually non-existent even in the U.S. in 1900. Thus foreign 1968 per capita energy consumption represented the U.S. level of around 1875, while foreign per capita electric power production represented the U.S. level of the late 1920's.

33. The table was adapted from a study in which attention was directed to future trends in energy and GNP in specific regions. See Sam H. Schurr, *et al., Middle Eastern Oil and the Western World: Prospects and Problems* (New York: American Elsevier Publishing Co., 1971).

34. Any comprehensive projection effort, which this paper does not purport to be, should, however, consider as a serious "scenario" the possibility that coal gasification will be economically feasible long before the year 2000 in the United States, and may likely be in operation in other countries of the world by that time.

35. UNECE, "Symposium on the Future Role of Coal in the National and World Economies" (held in Warsaw, September 1969; released in Geneva, March 9, 1970, pp. 19-21.) (Mimeographed.)

36. See IAEA *Bulletin,* 1970, Vol. 12, No. 5, p. 12.

37. *Ibid.* We might note, however, that elsewhere, Dr. Sigvard Eklund, Director General of the International Atomic Energy Agency, has underscored the uncertainty in such estimates by indicating that even a "modest nuclear target of 330,000 mw by 1980 would imply, for developing countries, foreign exchange resources of $3 billion to $4 billion during 1970-80. "It is clear that unless adequate capital is available from the industrial countries and international financing organizations, even this modest target will not be achieved." (From a speech to the United Nations Economic and Social Council, quoted in IAEA *Bulletin,* 1970, Vol. 12, No. 4, p. 3.)

38. See "Motorization of the Developing World," *Petroleum Press Service,* June 1970, pp. 215-16.

39. For some quantitative detail, see Joel Darmstadter and Associates, *Energy in the World Economy* (Baltimore: Johns Hopkins Press for Resources for the Future, 1971).

40. Compare, for example, the record of growth in output per manday with that in injury per manhour, shown in U.S. Bureau of Mines, *Minerals Yearbook 1968* 1970, Vol. I-II, pp. 137, 301.

41. U.S. Congress, Senate, Committee on Public Works, "Management of Fuels to Satisfy Environmental Criteria," by G. Alex Mills, Harry Perry, and Harry Johnson, *Problems and Issues of a National Materials Policy,* 1970, p. 144.

42. *Ibid.*

43. In 1969, over 1,000 oil spills of over 100 barrels each were reported in U.S. waters, over one-half coming from vessels and about one-third involving pipelines, oil terminals, and main storage facilities. U.S. Council on Environmental Quality, *First Annual Report,* 1970, p. 38.

44. Projections of future trends vary, but on the basis of a range of estimates, one might reasonably—perhaps even conservatively—expect that around 30 percent of world oil output might be from offshore sources in 1980, with the proportion rising to at least 40 percent by the year 2000. Offshore production in 2000 might thus be 75 percent higher than the 40 million b/d of total world output in recent years. (*Oil and Gas Journal,* March

16, 1970, pp. 126-127).

45. U.S. Congress, Joint Economic Committee, *op. cit.,* p. 67.

46. U.S. Congress, Senate, Committee on Public Works, *op. cit.,* p. 145.

47. U.S. Department of the Interior, Office of Oil and Gas, *1968 Petroleum Supply and Demand,* 1970, pp. 10-11.

48. It is estimated that of the 255 new stations in the United States required by 1990, 27 out of 91 fossil-fueled facilities and 78 out of 164 nuclear plants will be of 2,000 mw size and over. See U.S. Office of Science and Technology, *Electric Power and the Environment* (Washington: Government Printing Office, 1970), p. 5.

49. *Ibid.,* pp. 21-22.

50. U.S. Office of Science and Technology, *Considerations Affecting Steam Power Plant Site Selection* (Washington: Government Printing Office, 1968), p. 5.

51. "From a 1,000 mw station, the fission product quantity after three years of steady operation is of the order of 4 tons, and can be physically confined in a single (albeit red-hot) carload." B. I. Spinrad, "The Role of Nuclear Power in Meeting World Energy Needs," in *Environmental Aspects of Nuclear Power Stations* (Proceedings of a Symposium, United Nations, New York, August 1970; Vienna: International Atomic Energy Agency, 1971), p. 70.

52. Massachusetts Institute of Technology, *Man's Impact on the Global Environment: Assessment and Recommendations for Action* (Cambridge: M.I.T. Press, 1970), p. 298.

53. U.S. Congress, Joint Economic Committee, *op. cit.,* p. 109.

54. *Ibid.,* p. 95.

55. U.S. Congress, Senate, Committee on Public Works, *op. cit.,* p. 146.

56. *Ibid.,* p. 133.

57. Massachusetts Institute of Technology, *op. cit.,* p. 54.

58. The interested reader will find an enormous amount of factual information as well as the representation of different viewpoints in U.S. Congress, Joint Atomic Energy Committee, *Environmental Effects of Producing Electric Power, Hearings,* Part I, 91st Cong., 1st sess., October-November 1969; and Part II, 91st Cong., 2nd sess., January-February, 1970.

59. In June 1971, the AEC announced a drastic reduction in the permissible amount of radioactive releases from routine operations of commercial nuclear plants. The new standards require that light water reactors limit the release of radioactivity to no more than would expose an individual at the plant boundary to one percent of the individual maximum allowed under previous standards.

60. A more detailed breakdown appears in Massachusetts Institute of Technology, *op. cit.,* p. 296.

61. Under the assumptions regarding automotive growth employed in the above paragraph (per annum growth of three percent in the United States and 7.5 percent elsewhere), by the year 2000 car ownership in the United States would reach 65 cars per 100 persons, whereas in the rest of the world it would be less than 15 per 100.

62. Estimated by Richard A. Rice, "System Energy as a Factor in Considering Future Transportation" (unpublished paper for American Society of Chemical Engineers, paper WA/Ener.-8). The figures probably reflect a minimum estimate of the efficiency advantages of buses over cars. (The estimates generally assume about a 50 percent lead factor—e.g., in the case of cars, an average of two cars per car; thus, seat miles per gallon are usually double the figures shown.)

63. On the assumption of 1.6-person occupancy—which appears to be nearer the mark—the automotive figure drops to around 28 pm/gallon.

64. An estimated 25 percent increase in electricity prices as a result of covering environmental costs seems, in the judgment of numerous persons, a highly plausible development. A considerably greater prospective increase is calculated in Philip Sporn, "Energy, Economic Growth and the Environment" (paper prepared for the 1971 RFF Forum). His paper, along with others presented at the Forum, will appear in a forthcoming RFF book.

Chapter 6

Outdoor Recreation and Congestion in the United States

by
Charles J. Cicchetti
Resources for the Future, Inc.

COMMISSION ON POPULATION GROWTH AND
THE AMERICAN FUTURE, *RESEARCH
REPORTS, VOLUME III, POPULATION
RESOURCES AND THE ENVIRONMENT,*
EDITED BY RONALD G. RIDKER

CONTENTS

Outdoor Recreation and Congestion in the United States

INTRODUCTION

During the postwar years, participation in outdoor recreation in the United States has grown by an average annual rate of between 10 to 15 percent.[1] During more recent years, a slowdown in this rate has been observed for some specific recreation activities; however, the overall annual rate of growth may still be close to 10 percent.[2] There have been several interdependent reasons for the dramatic growth in recreation participation.

Perhaps the foremost reason for the growth in participation in outdoor recreation has been the growth in population. At the same time that population size increased, the median age of the population fell. Accordingly, since most recreation activities have been observed to be more actively pursued by persons under 30 years of age, a younger and growing population was observed to have a per capita, as well as a total, increase in recreation participation.

During this same period, several socioeconomic factors which are important determinants in outdoor recreation participation were also observed to be changing. These factors include an increase in real per capita income, a greater level of educational attainment per person, a general increase in leisure time or at least a shorter work week, and a general reduction in travel cost. Each of these changes, as well as the population changes discussed above, have been identified as being positively related to recreation participation.[3] They are, in fact, the reasons for the observed high annual rates of growth in recreation participation.

An important question for the future is to estimate how these same factors are expected to change and then to assess indirectly the future levels of participation in outdoor recreation. While continued declines in work week, average age, or travel costs, as well as continued increases in real income, educational attainment, and population may not be expected to be as dramatic in the last quarter of this century as in the preceding 25 years, a somewhat diminished rate of growth may be expected. In addition, any nation which has a given level of recreation areas and a fixed supply of land and water

dedicated to outdoor recreation will find that a growing number of recreationists will place increasing demands on its existing recreation facilities. The congestion that might result from increased use is likely to cause a decline in the satisfaction or the utility of any single outdoor experience. Additionally, congestion may reduce the number of outdoor experiences that any individual would demand in its absence.

Overuse of recreation facilities that either reduces the satisfaction of recreationists or causes a consumer to reduce his consumption of recreation services may be dealt with in part by charging a user fee. This would be similar to using a peak-load price to redistribute use over a recreation season and thus increase the service flow from a given stock of recreation resources. In this way, the available spaces of a given quality or uncongested nature are rationed in a manner which insures that those consumers who are willing to pay the most are insured prior access to recreation areas. The social, cultural, and equity questions surrounding such price or other similar rationing schemes should not be dismissed too quickly. It is enough to point out that resource managers and planners may be able to increase the use of the nation's recreation resources by spreading growing demand more evenly over a season. The issues surrounding whether this be accomplished by price, chance, "first come first served," or any other plan are too complex to discuss at the present time.[4]

The reusable nature of a recreation facility is the key characteristic that permits the stock of recreation resources to provide a constant quality service flow of different magnitudes if use can be more evenly spread over a recreation season. However, an additional cost of increased use or congestion may be an ecological deterioration of the recreation resource stock. Such an erosion may reduce both the quality of recreation experience and the ability of a given area to provide the same quantitative level of services. For example, the ecological damage caused by overuse of Yosemite Valley may reduce both the carrying capacity of that resource and/or the level of satisfaction which that resource can provide; in this sense, the stock has been reduced and service flow diminished. Accordingly, we may think of the overuse of a national park, forest, or urban recreation area—which reduces the stock of recreation areas for some activities in the future by changing the natural environment of a given recreation area—in the same way we might view industrial pollution and "clearcutting" a forest which also reduce the available stock of recreation areas. Congestion then is a form of people pollution.

A second factor, which we can observe historically, is the movement of larger portions of our growing population into urban and suburban communities. As the members of the Outdoor Recreation Resources Review Commission warned in the early part of the 1960's:

> It [the outdoors] no longer lies at the back door or at the crowded end of Main Street. More and more, most Americans must traverse miles of crowded highways to know the outdoors. The prospect for the future is that this quest will be even more difficult.[5]

The implication of this warning is that, unless public planners and private developers insure adequate open space through zoning and acquisition in suburban and urban areas, the level of possible recreation areas will decline in the future. Additionally, as cities spread, the physical, temporal, and monetary distances separating the population from the existing recreation areas increase—a second negative effect on recreation participation.

By way of summary, whether the future pattern of growth in participation will remain constant (Y), increase with respect to the present rate (X), or decrease with respect to the present rate (Z) will depend upon (1) the relative, as well as absolute, importance of each of the aforementioned explanatory factors in determining recreation participation; (2) the size and direction of change in each of these factors; and (3) the type of management policy adopted for recreational facilities in the future. In graphic form, these three cases are represented in Figure 1. While it is important to be able to predict the future level of recreation participation under various future scenarios—population, economic, and supply of recreation facility—an issue of even more important interest is a determination of how individual welfare may be changing over time as population increases and other socioeconomic changes result in greater pressure on a given stock of recreation resources.

Such hard-to-quantify factors as the "quality of a recreation experience" or the "satisfaction derived from an encounter with nature" may be considered measures of welfare. When population increases and congestion at recreation facilities results, solely concentrating on such measures as total recreation participation or even days of recreation per capita may greatly underestimate the disutility of such congestion for the following reasons. First, even if congestion reduces the rate of participation, the magnitude of the population increase may cause total recreation participation to increase, while the "quality" of each individual's experience declines. Second, a decline in days of recreation per capita is an indication that increased congestion was severe enough to cause some individuals either to stop recreating or to reduce the number of times they participate; but, it does not measure the congestion costs which result in both a decline in quality of the experience and a reduction in the willingness to pay for those remaining recreation experiences.

These conclusions perhaps can be better appreciated by considering the following numerical example. If a country of 200 million people has a given stock of recreation facilities and the overall probability of swimming is 50 percent (P_a) and the average number of swimming occasions is 10 per swimmer (d_a), then we would estimate that there are 100 million swimmers and a total of one billion swimming occasions by members of that population. On the other hand, if the population of the country increases to 300 million people and the stock of recreation facilities remained the same as when the population size was 200 million, then we might estimate that the overall probability of swimming declines to 45 percent and the average number of swimming occasions might decline to seven occasions per swimmer. With such congestion-induced declines in the rate and intensity of participation, we would estimate the number of swimmers to be 135 million and the total number of swimming occasions to be 945 million.

The preceding example was constructed to demonstrate the quantitative importance population size may play on both the demand and supply side of the market. With a population that was 50 percent larger, the aggregate number of swimming occasions was lower, even though the total number of swimmers is larger. This dual role of population can be further shown diagrammatically in Figure 2, where both the willingness to pay to avoid "population pollution" or congestion costs and the expected value of swimming occasions demanded (probability of swimming × number of swimming days) are shown to depend upon the supply of recreation facilities available to individual "j." If the available supply of constant quality (uncongested) recreation facilities available to individual "j" declines from S_2 to S_3, then the expected value of the number of swimming days demanded declines from 5 to 3.15 days. Additionally, the welfare of each swimmer in the population declines by the amount indicated by the shaded area

FIGURE 6-1
TIME PATTERNS OF RECREATION GROWTH

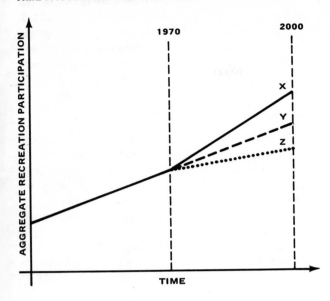

is meaningless. Our initial concentration of the discussion on recreation participation was intentional and, while we can say much about what the future will be like under future conditions and note some measures of lower welfare under alternative scenarios, the analysis below cannot be considered appropriate for measuring the welfare of future individuals under these various scenarios.

In order to make the fullest use of the reduced form model in the analysis below, we will adopt the following strategy. Rather than to simply list several scenarios and then forecast aggregate recreation participation for each of them, we hold several explanatory factors constant under future scenarios and "partialize on," that is, determine the effect of those factors which are varied. In this manner, it is felt that the powerful tool of reduced form forecasting models can be most usefully employed in considering the importance of various controllable and uncontrollable factors which will determine future recreation decisions.

ABCD. By summing such welfare losses over all swimmers, the aggregate cost of congestion or population pollution can be measured.

In order to determine the economic importance or meaning of future scenarios of population size, income, average age, etc., and to evaluate alternative levels of supply of recreation facilities or management strategy, a theoretical model, which is either just identified or which has been structurally estimated, is required. Structural models based upon individual consuming units or households have not yet been empirically estimated for two reasons. First, all the theoretical models of individual consuming units have been over-identified; second, data on the point of destination and prices or travel costs paid by individual consuming units have not yet been gathered at the national level. Accordingly, national recreation models have been estimated using ordinary least squares regression on a reduced form model.[6]

The implications of using a reduced form model for the analysis below are important to note at the outset, since they define the limits of the quantitative measures we may consider under future scenarios. Reduced form models of overidentified structural systems can be used to make unbiased forecasts of future levels of recreation participation. However, the parameters of such models cannot be interpreted as indicative of either solely demand or supply effects. Accordingly, direct benefit estimation or a quantification of a change in welfare under future population and supply of facility scenarios

FIGURE 6-2
CONGESTION INDUCED WELFARE LOSSES

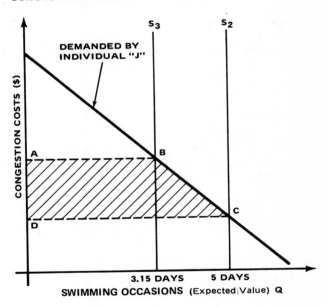

WHERE

S_2 = Supply of swimming occasions when population size is 200,000,000

S_3 = Supply of swimming occasions available for individual j when population is 300,000,000

D_j = Demand or willingness to pay function of individual j

ABCD = Welfare loss when supply is reduced from S_2 to S_3.

THE FORECASTING MODEL

General Comments

In the preceding section, we discussed briefly the forecasting model that we will use below. The model is more formally discussed in Appendix A below. This discussion is in two parts. First, we present a general mathematical model, which is analogous to the Ridker pollution model[7] and which also emphasizes the important dual role of population as both an indicator of potential demand as well as the degree of congestion on the supply of facilities. In the second part of the discussion, we review the historical background, survey of the literature, and data base that have been utilized to estimate this mathematical model.

The model utilized is a two-step reduced form forecasting model based upon individual respondents to a national recreation survey and inventory of recreation facilities. The first step is an equation, which is used to predict the probability of participation (p) in a given recreation activity. There are 24 different recreation activities, which we will consider below; therefore, there are 24 separate step-one equations. The second step is an equation, which is used to predict the number of times a participant in each activity will participate (d).

Forecasting total recreation participation is accomplished by assuming that the reduced form parameters estimated for this model in 1965 will remain constant into the "near" future. Forecasts, of different values for the explanatory variables, such as income, education, population size, and the supply of recreation facilities, are then made and various future scenarios are used in the empirical model to estimate the probability and intensity of participating for each of 14 different types of people, which correspond to the primed equations utilized for the general model in Appendix A. Race and age are the primary variables upon which the grouping has been based:

> There are three principal reasons for emphasizing these two variables as the foundation for our classification. First, they are usually the most statistically significant variables in the empirical equations. Secondly, the quantitative effect of changes in either age or race is usually large in absolute magnitudes. Finally, census projections for 1980 and extrapolations to the year 2000 are available most readily for these two socioeconomic variables. . . .[8]

A separate estimate of the probability of participation by any member of the group is estimated (p^j) given the underlying independent variables in a given scenario for 1965, 1980, and 2000. In any of these years, the estimated conditioned probability is multiplied by the number of people in the corresponding demographic group (N^j) and summed over all 14 cells to determine the total number of participants in each recreation activity. For example, the number of swimming participants (P) are determined by:

$$P = \sum_{j=1}^{14} p^j N^j$$

In the second step, the corresponding number of days (d^j) of participating in each activity for the same demographic group and year (1965, 1980, and 2000) are determined. By multiplying these values by the corresponding number of participants, aggregate recreation participation is determined for each activity and time period. For example, total swimming occasions (R) are estimated by:

$$R = \sum_{j=1}^{14} p^j d^j = \sum_{j=1}^{14} p^j N^j d^j$$

Specific Scenarios and Approach Utilized

In the scenarios considered below, whether or not the number of occasions of participating in any recreation activity will increase, decrease, or remain the same in any of the different future scenarios depends upon the following components of the reduced form forecasting model which we have selected:

1. Population size.

2. The demographic, i.e., age, race, sex, etc., distribution of the population under each different population size.

3. The geographic distribution of the population.

4. The sensitivity of the probability of participation to population-induced congestion (people pollution).

5. The sensitivity of the number of days of participation (intensity) per participant to the population-induced congestion.

6. The supply of recreation facilities.

7. The distribution of recreation facilities.

8. Cross elasticities of demand between different recreation activities and between other leisure time activities, that is whether a given recreation activity is complementary or a substitute for other recreation activities, whose volume may also be sensitive to population variations.

9. The aggregate and per capita levels of economic activity under different population scenarios.

As we indicated above we will concentrate on two different projections of population size, Census Bureau Series B and E. We will also consider three different assumptions or scenarios concerning the 1980 and 2000 supply of recreation facilities. In the first supply scenario (I), it is assumed that there will be no congestion; it is based upon forecasts of 1980 and 2000 recreation participation that were made with a model that did not include any supply variables and which, perhaps, unrealistically assumes the annual rates of growth in days per participant observed in the early 1960's would continue into the future.[9] Accordingly, it is assumed that the relative distribution of recreation facilities vis a vis the population and absolute level of recreation facilities per capita are identical in 1980 and 2000 to the distribution and level of recreation facilities in 1965. This assumption is an inverted microeconomic version of "Says Law" and quite unrealistically assumes that demand creates its own supply in outdoor recreation. Yet, it is an important case to consider for several reasons. First, it provides a useful benchmark and, second, it allows us to consider the suitability of various future goals or targets in outdoor recreation planning. Finally, this case is sometimes used to emphasize the development of a crisis in outdoor recreation.

The other two scenarios were described in detail in the Rutgers' study and are further outlined in Appendix B of this paper. We may summarize the distinctions as follows:

> ...Under the [second] hypothesis (II), land and water of different qualities will be increased at varying rates which are roughly proportional to the present regional distribution of the recreational resource and facility distribution. The [third] hypothesis (III) assumes that increases in land and water of different qualities will be based upon varying needs in the nation's nine Census Divisions. It is also assumed that 5 percent of the recreational water currently polluted (type C) will be converted by 1980 into acceptable recreation water (type A). The same assumption is made for the year 2000. The [third] hypothesis may be summarized by stating that it is based upon a relative increase in recreational resources, where population and resource distributions are not in balance...[10] [Parentheses indicate changes from the original text for consistency.]

The most important differences found are summarized in Table 1. The biggest difference in these two

Table 1.—National Recreation Needs under Supply Scenarios II and III

	Percentage increase 1965 to 1980		Percentage increase 1965 to 2000	
	II	III	II	III
Recreation water acerage ..	.3	57.0	.8	90.0
Recreation land acreage ...	.6	1.2	1.6	1.9
BOR Class I acreage	4.3	55.0	9.9	173.0
BOR Class II acreage	1.9	37.0	4.8	57.0
Water quality	0.0	5.0[a]	0.0	10.0

[a]The water quality plan under B is to convert five percent in 1980 and 2000 of all polluted recreation waters into water acceptable for swimming. Note the Bureau of Outdoor Recreation includes all offshore waters contiguous to national recreation areas, which are included in United States jurisdiction, in its water acreage data.

scenarios is the amount of land being converted to or acquired for high density recreation, and the amount of water being converted to recreation as one of several possible uses. While both plans are possible, they differ in direction. As we pointed out above, supply scenario II increases recreation roughly in proportion to the present geographical distribution of recreation land and water, as well as roughly in proportion to the present quality or types of recreation acreage. On the other hand, supply scenario III represents an attempt to bring recreation facilities to the people in a form that encourages active high density recreational pursuits.

In the broadest sense, supply scenario II represents the conventional wisdom that existed before the studies performed by the Outdoor Recreation Resources Review Commission and the Bureau of Outdoor Recreation's Land and Water Conservation Fund. Supply scenario III represents a plan similar to that which would be provided under the Land and Water Conservation Fund if its authorized expenditures were appropriated. This was not the case during the early period of the Fund, which coincided with the Viet Nam War build-up. However, President Nixon has instituted a "Parks to the People" program and has appropriated the differences between past authorizations and appropriations to the Fund and has also requested that Congress increase the authorization to $280 million per year for land acquisition and development at the Federal, state and local levels. In addition, the Fund is matched; if it is fully financed, there would be some $150 million to $180 million of state and local additional money which would bring the total to nearly half a billion dollars per year. Emphasis is also now being given to urban states and Standard Metropolitan Statistical Areas. If these trends continue and an active planning strategy is adopted, we might expect scenario III as the more likely of the two hypotheses.

Since the number of possible combinations of the nine factors which we outlined above would be unmanageable, we will adopt the following strategy for the other components of the model. We will use the same relative geographic distribution of the population for census Series E, as that which has been forecasted for census Series B. Since we are using a national model, except for swimming, this assumption will not cause much quantitative variation in the results. The sensitivity of the probability of participation and intensity of participation, as well as the cross elasticities of demand, depends upon the parameters of the model which we have adopted. In the present section, we will assume that these parameters will remain constant into the future.

Finally, the future aggregate and per capita levels of economic activity and the demographic characteristics of the population have initially been assumed to be the same under each of the six population and supply of facility scenarios after adjusting for population size. However, in the succeeding section, we will consider the effect that variation in such other variables as per capita income, age, and leisure time, will have on the analysis. These assumptions are summarized in Appendix B of this paper and are discussed in the Rutgers' study in more detail.

By way of summary, we will consider two different population size scenarios and three different supply of recreation facility scenarios to emphasize the effect of congestion, population size, geographic distribution of facilities, and the absolute level of recreation facilities. These six different scenarios will be presented for 1980 and 2000; 1965 will be used as the base year, since that is the year the data were gathered. In all, 24 different recreation activities will be forecasted under the various future scenarios.

THE FORECASTING RESULTS

Supply Scenario I

The results of the forecasting exercise under the six different population and supply scenarios are shown in Tables 2 through 4. In the first column of each table, the 1965 or base year estimates of recreation participation are shown. The next two columns are the 1980 population Series B and population Series E results for the given supply scenario. The last two columns contain the 2000 Series B and Series E recreation forecasts for the given supply scenario.

In Table 2, the results are presented for the case in which the supply of recreation facilities was to be made responsive to population increases (supply scenario I) and historical trends in days of participation were to continue unrestricted until the turn of the century. In all cases, total recreation participation under population Series B exceeds total recreation participation under population Series E. This result was anticipated, since the implicit assumption under supply scenario I is that no congestion effects are present. Accordingly, the positive effect of a larger population is not offset by a reduction in the per capita supply of recreation facilities. Furthermore, Table 2 shows that any population dependent socioeconomic variables which might have an offsetting negative effect are assumed to be unimportant; and, per capita levels of recreation participation are unrealistically assumed to increase to 56 days per capita and 110 days per capita in 1980 and 2000 respectively. One last result in Table 2 should be emphasized; that is, the increases in recreation participation shown between 1980 and 2000 are generally much larger in both absolute and relative terms than similar changes between 1965 and 1980.

In 1980, under population Series B, there would have to be a 40 percent increase in recreation land and water, and under Series E, the increase in recreation facilities would have to be 38 percent. In contrast to this rather close comparison in 1980, under Series B the expanded facilities' requirement would be a 100 percent increase in contrast to an 83 percent increase in Series E. The differences in requirements increase further under each series when the requirement to provide the same acreage per recreation occasion is met. Under Series B and E in 1980, such a requirement would mean increases of 95 percent and 90.5 percent, respectively. For the year 2000, the requirements are for an approximate tripling in the amount of recreation lands and water, since the requirements for Series B and E in 2000 would mean increases of 229 percent and 190 percent respectively.

To put such requirements or "needs" into perspective, it is important to note that, if the 1965 Bureau of Outdoor Recreation estimates of recreation land and water are converted to a percentage of the total land and water acreage of the 50 United States, land set aside for recreation would make up approximately 15 percent of the total land, while water classified for recreation would make up approximately 28 percent of the total.[11] Given the most extreme percentage increase in Table 1 for Series B of 229 percent, this would mean

Table 2.—Supply Assumption Scenario I

Activities	Total recreation use (in millions of activity days)				
	1965	Series B 1980	Series E 1980	Series B 2000	Series E 2000
I.					
Swimming (NE)	352.2	758.9	723.9	2,096.3	1,745.1
Swimming (NC)	217.2	468.0	446.4	1,292.7	1,076.1
Swimming (W)	181.0	390.0	372.0	1,077.2	896.8
Swimming (S)	297.3	640.6	611.0	1,769.3	1,472.9
Swimming (national)	1,047.7	2,257.5	2,153.3	6,235.6	5,190.9
Water skiing	63.4	150.8	143.9	484.6	403.4
Fishing	310.7	512.0	488.3	1,013.0	843.3
Sailing	29.9	123.0	117.4	746.0	621.1
Other boating	274.9	541.4	516.4	1,352.3	1,125.7
Canoeing	28.5	83.7	79.8	337.6	281.0
II.					
Hunting (annual)	131.8	123.3	117.6	337.0	280.6
Camping (remote)	19.4	38.6	36.8	97.2	80.9
Hiking	52.7	97.6	93.1	227.5	189.4
Bird watching	188.0	n.a.	n.a.	n.a.	n.a.
Wildlife and bird photography	26.9	n.a.	n.a.	n.a.	n.a.
III.					
Picnicking	469.5	1,167.3	1,113.4	3,715.8	3,093.3
Sight-seeing	521.8	1,165.0	1,111.3	3,354.9	2,792.8
Camping (developed)	75.4	150.0	143.0	377.5	314.3
IV.					
Bicycling	444.6	658.9	628.5	1,142.4	951.0
Horseback riding	103.9	141.9	135.3	216.8	180.5
Playing outdoor games or sports	906.6	2,413.1	2,301.7	8,532.6	7,103.1
V.					
Attending outdoor sports	206.1	311.5	297.1	555.3	462.3
Attending outdoor concerts	54.6	91.1	86.9	268.4	223.5
VI.					
Driving for pleasure	982.0	1,244.7	1,187.2	1,743.4	1,451.3
Walking for pleasure	1,021.1	1,891.5	1,804.2	4,390.0	3,655.3
VII.					
Snow skiing (other 9 months)	31.0	n.a.	n.a.	n.a.	n.a.
Ice skating (other 9 months)	69.5	n.a.	n.a.	n.a.	n.a.
Sledding (other 9 months)	97.4	n.a.	n.a.	n.a.	n.a.
Totals	7,157.4	13,162.9	12,555.2	35,127.9	29,243.7
Days per capita	36.8	56.0	56.0	110.0	110.0

Table 3.—Supply Assumption Scenario II

Activities	Total recreation use (in millions of activity days)				
	1965	Series B 1980	Series E 1980	Series B 2000	Series E 2000
I.					
Swimming (NE)	352.2	443.5	436.2	705.2	609.
Swimming (NC)	217.2	430.8	411.3	917.0	766.
Swimming (W)	181.0	212.0	202.2	354.6	295.
Swimming (S)	297.3	437.8	417.6	808.5	673.
Swimming (National, computed separately) . . .	1,047.7	1,524.0	1,465.1	2,785.3	2,344.
Water skiing	63.4	76.4	73.3	128.4	110.
Fishing	310.7	361.7	347.5	405.2	341.
Sailing	29.9	58.2	55.7	129.9	109.
Other boating	274.9	378.0	363.8	737.9	629.
Canoeing	28.5	30.7	29.3	42.0	35.
II.					
Hunting (annual)	131.8	129.2	123.6	98.7	83.
Camping (remote)	19.4	16.7	16.2	11.3	10.
Hiking	52.7	71.5	68.9	127.8	110.
Bird watching	188.0	235.7	224.8	341.7	284.
Wildlife and bird photography	26.9	33.1	32.6	50.4	53.
III.					
Picnicking	469.5	786.3	756.7	1,617.1	1,389.3
Sight-seeing	521.8	798.1	761.3	604.7	503.4
Camping (developed)	75.4	120.2	116.2	331.7	299.3
IV.					
Bicycling	444.6	597.4	569.8	914.3	761.1
Horseback riding	103.9	159.7	152.3	361.7	301.1
Playing outdoor games or sports	906.6	1,262.3	1,204.1	1,995.8	1,661.4
V.					
Attending outdoor sports	206.1	268.3	255.9	409.3	340.7
Attending outdoor concerts	54.6	85.1	81.2	153.1	127.4
VI.					
Driving for pleasure	982.0	1,235.0	1,178.9	761.9	634.3
Walking for pleasure	1,021.1	1,462.6	1,395.1	1,510.0	1,257.1
VII.					
Snow skiing (other 9 months)	31.0	44.8	42.8	85.9	71.8
Ice skating (other 9 months)	69.5	75.5	72.0	104.9	87.3
Sledding (other 9 months)	97.4	149.7	142.8	87.2	72.6
Totals	7,157.4	9,961.1	9,529.9	13,796.2	11,627.6
Days per capita	36.8	42.0	42.3	43.0	44.3

Table 4.—Supply Assumption Scenario III

Activities	Total recreation use (in millions of activity days)				
	1965	Series B 1980	Series E 1980	Series B 2000	Series E 2000
I.					
Swimming (NE)	352.2	616.0	605.8	851.1	736.1
Swimming (NC)	217.2	438.7	418.9	931.7	778.7
Swimming (W)	181.0	212.1	202.3	354.7	295.3
Swimming (S)	297.3	439.9	419.6	812.4	676.3
Swimming (National, computed separately)	1,047.7	1,706.7	1,642.7	2,949.9	2,482.7
Water skiing	63.4	82.4	79.1	148.4	127.2
Fishing	310.7	398.2	383.0	429.9	361.3
Sailing	29.9	60.7	58.1	136.2	114.4
Other boating	274.9	418.3	402.6	832.5	709.6
Canoeing	28.5	31.3	29.9	43.0	35.9
II.					
Hunting (annual)	131.8	132.1	126.4	102.5	86.5
Camping (remote)	19.4	18.7	18.2	15.4	14.4
Hiking	52.7	77.0	74.3	143.3	124.3
Bird watching	188.0	236.5	225.6	343.1	285.6
Wildlife and bird photography	26.9	41.8	41.3	88.6	93.6
III.					
Picnicking	469.5	839.4	807.8	1,755.4	1,508.1
Sight-seeing	521.8	776.9	741.0	582.4	484.8
Camping (developed)	75.4	132.4	127.9	410.6	370.5
IV.					
Bicycling	444.6	568.7	542.5	845.5	703.8
Horseback riding	103.9	159.5	152.1	361.2	300.7
Playing outdoor games or sports	906.6	1,265.4	1,207.0	1,999.4	1,664.4
V.					
Attending outdoor sports	206.1	269.7	257.2	404.9	337.1
Attending outdoor concerts	54.6	84.5	80.6	153.4	127.7
VI.					
Driving for pleasure	982.0	1,237.0	1,179.9	761.1	633.6
Walking for pleasure	1,021.1	1,461.8	1,394.3	1,509.2	1,256.3
VII.					
Snow skiing (other 9 months)	31.0	45.3	43.2	86.2	71.8
Ice skating (other 9 months)	69.5	75.0	71.5	103.8	86.4
Sledding (other 9 months)	97.4	149.8	142.8	87.2	72.6
Totals	7,157.4	10,269.1	9,829.0	14,292.6	12,053.3
Days per capita	36.8	43.3	43.5	44.5	46.0

that, by the year 2000, some 49 percent of all land and 93 percent of all water must be dedicated to recreation. The conclusion is clear. When we speak of recreation, we cannot consider holding the line or improving the quantity of land and water in absolute numbers as population increases; we would just run out of both commodities soon after the turn of the century.

Supply Scenarios II and III

The nation's recreation plans must be based instead on redistributing the public lands with relatively small net increases in recreation lands. In order to consider such plans for these same population series, we will now consider supply scenarios II and III and refer to Tables 3 and 4. These plans are described in detail in Appendix B, and partially presented above in Table 1.

In all the cases shown in Tables 3 and 4, the forecasted participation levels for population Series B exceed the corresponding results for population Series E except for the wildlife and bird photography activity. This means that, until the year 2000, if population Series B occurs rather than population Series E, the positive effect of a larger population for any of three supply scenarios more than makes up for any congestion-induced negative effect on either the probability of participation or days per participation in its effect on total recreation participation levels. It is important to note that this is a reflection of the aggregate quantity consumed; however, the overall per capita days of recreation is lower under population Series B than E in both 1980 and 2000. Additionally, the total welfare of individual j may also decline as indicated in Figure 2 above. In fact, the aggregate level of welfare that comes from the service flow of a given stock of recreation facilities may be higher under a smaller aggregate quantity of use, if the inflated use is the result of a larger population but at higher levels of congestion. Accordingly, the observation that total use under Series B exceeds total use under Series E should not be given any unqualified normative significance. Furthermore, whether or not such a pattern would continue beyond the year 2000 cannot be assessed from these results.

A second generalization is that the levels of use in Table 2 (supply scenario I) exceed those found in Tables 3 and 4 (supply scenarios II and III, respectively). This result is of course directly related to the fact that supply was assumed to be perfectly elastic with respect to increases in demand at 1965 quality levels and that historical rates of change in recreation days per capita were forecast to continue until the turn of the century.

The effect of supply differences are shown in two ways: First, a comparison of Tables 3 and 4 may be

made for each population size; second, the decline in days per capita may be examined for each supply scenario under different population assumptions. In those activities which are dependent upon recreation facilities, recreation land, and recreation water (namely those activities in categories I, II, and III, excepting sightseeing), the levels of total recreation participation are systematically higher under supply scenario III than under supply scenario II. Additionally, the days per capita for different population scenarios are higher under E than under B for each supply scenario. Since these two scenarios differ with respect to (1) the levels of recreation land and water, (2) their quality, (3) their level of development, and (4) their proximity to population centers, it is not surprising to find that those recreation activities most sensitive to these attributes are most significantly affected by the different supply scenarios.

When supply is held constant and population alone is varied (for example, in scenario III in Table 4), then the overall elasticity of recreation participation to congestion induced by increased population can be derived. Thus, with a population that is 17 percent greater under Series B than Series E, the resulting per capita decrease in total recreation is only 3.3 percent less under Series B than Series E (44.5 days per capita as compared to 46 days per capita). The implied overall elasticity of recreation participation to supply deflated by population is approximately 0.195. Several reasons can be given for this relatively low or inelastic measure of the effect of congestion. First, the coefficients of the model are linear and are estimated using data gathered in 1965. For some activities and recreation facilities, congestion may not have been important in the mid-1960's. Accordingly, we might expect the recreation participation-congestion parameters to be under-estimated. Therefore, it would be inappropriate to apply such parameters to future periods in which congestion may become severe. Second, the model utilized in the above analysis was, for the most part, restricted to publicly provided recreation facilities. Therefore, since some of the recreation activities may be less sensitive to congestion than others, these possible biases may be minimized. Additionally, there is substantial variation in the estimates of these congestion elasticities among the different recreation activities. For example, the swimming to supply/population elasticity for the northeast region is approximately 0.232 and the wildlife and bird photography to supply/population elasticity is 1.42. In the former case, population increases result in aggregate increases in total recreation; but in the latter case, if supply is constant, population increases cause a decline in total recreation days for this activity. Such a result may be found in both Tables 3 and 4 for this latter activity, since the value of its congestion elasticity exceeds unity.

Generally, the other summer activities, which are found in categories IV, V, and VI do not require particular recreation facilities. The differences between the two supply scenarios are generally not large and can be attributed to the substitute and complementary effects between activities, which were described above. For example, if the level of good quality recreation water is higher we would expect a higher total number of swimming activity days. Additionally, if swimming and bicycling compete for an individual's leisure time, then we would also expect a lower volume of bicycling days, and vice versa.

While nearly all activities will grow (albeit at different rates) up to the year 2000, driving for pleasure grows only until 1980, but declines from 1980 to 2000. The reasons for this exceptional behavior are the negative effects of a growing real income, as well as an increasing population and density in the year 2000. Each of these factors interact after 1980 to induce recreationists to substitute other activities for driving for pleasure during the available leisure time. While driving for pleasure is especially sensitive to population density, it was not possible to include the effect of differences in population density under Series B and E in the above calculations. Accordingly, there is a systematic underestimate of the driving for pleasure that Series E forecasts. Similarly, the effect of crowding and/or population density after 1980 leads to some decline in sight-seeing and hunting. Finally, although remote camping declines both in 1980 and 2000 relative to 1965, the decline is more than offset by the growth in developed camping over the period.[12]

The supply scenarios considered in the above analysis differ most importantly with respect to the supply of "developed" recreation lands and waters provided. Therefore, it is important to underscore the fact that declines in such activities as wildlife and bird photography, hunting, and remote camping—all particularly sensitive to congestion—should be taken as a serious warning to public officials responsible for planning our nation's primitive and wilderness areas. While plans that bring "parks to the people" will have positive effects, offsetting to a large extent the congestion effects of an increasing population, concern must also be given to that segment of the population which demands a low-density-of-use or resource-intensive recreation facility. If the demands of such individuals are not taken into account, then the declines forecast for such activities as bird watching, hunting, and remote camping will be realized in the future.

Finally, the regional differences shown for the swimming results in Tables 3 and 4 should be examined. In the northeast, where population density and urbanization are increasing, the higher level of recreation facilities in supply scenario III causes a large increase in participation in swimming when compared with similar results for this same region under supply scenario II. Additionally, under supply scenario III, the number of swimming days per capita is about one-half a day lower per capita under population Series B than population Series E. In contrast, in the western region, which includes the sparsely populated mountain states, the difference between the two scenarios is very small indeed. These results are as one should expect and they indicate the importance of distributing facilities over regions in a manner similar to the population distribution if one desires to maximize the number of recreation activity days.

Income and Age Effects Under Population Series B and E for Supply Scenario III

Up until this point, it has been assumed that per capita income and median age are identical for population Series B and E. It was stated previously that one reason for such an assumption was to hold certain variables constant in order to "partialize on," that is, determine in a *ceteris paribus* manner, the effect of other variables in the system separately. We now want to take these variables into account. The percent differences calculated for per capita income[13] are summarized in Table 5. Similarly, the percent differences in median age are summarized in Table 6.

By considering the percent changes in Tables 5 and 6, we can conclude, in both 1980 and 2000, that while the population under Series E is forecast to have a higher per capita income than Series B (some 6.6 percent and 11.1 percent respectively), the same population is also expected to have a higher median age under Series E than Series B (some 5.3 percent and 22.2 percent in 1980 and 2000 respectively). Populations that have higher incomes are likely to participate more than populations with lower incomes; but, populations who are older are less likely to participate as much as younger populations. Thus, taken together, the age and income effects tend to offset one another. Therefore, there is a second reason for omitting age and income from the above analysis: We could determine if there is a systematic effect on per capita levels of participation in recreational activities under the different population Series E and B, only if we were to consider the magnitude of the age and income elasticities of participation for each activity.

Table 5.—Percent Differences in Per Capita Income

	Series E − Series B / (Series E + Series B)/2	(High − Low) Productivity / (High + Low Productivity)/2
1980. .	+6.6%	+7.0%
2000. .	+11.1%	+21.6%

Table 6.—Percent Differences in Median Age

	Series E − Series B / (Series E + Series B)/2	2000 − 1980 / (2000 + 1980)/2
1980	+5.3%	Series B = −2.2%
2000	+22.2%	Series E = +14.9%

Table 7.—Swimming in the Northeast, Age and Income Effects

	Percent change in participation for Series E relative to Series B		
	Age +	Income =	Net effect
1980	− 9.7%	3.2%	− 6.5%
2000	−40.6%	5.5%	−35.1%

Since young people are also likely to participate in activities which do not require the purchase of expensive ancillary equipment or large transportation expenditures, we might conclude that those recreation activities which have low income elasticities (approximately 0.5) are also likely to have a high age elasticity (approximately −1.5). While the reverse situation—high income elasticities and inelastic age parameters—is possible, it is less likely to be found with any set pattern. As an extreme example, swimming in the northeast region of the United States has been found to have an income elasticity equal to +0.49 and to have an age elasticity of −1.82. The implications of these elasticities when applied to the percent differences in median age and per capita income between population Series B and Series E are shown in Table 7.

The calculations shown in Table 7 may be extreme for most activities since swimming is one of the most age-elastic activities, and some activities have higher income elasticities. If a population in 2000 is on average more than 22 percent older as the present forecasts for Series E and B imply, then, for many recreation activities especially popular among the young, this is quantitatively more important than a population difference of 17 percent or a per capita income difference of 11 percent. For such activities, this implies that the pressure on and need for recreation facilities, which young people prefer, will be drastically reduced, perhaps by as much as the 52 percent found for swimming in the northeast.

The quantitative importance of these effects in general can be estimated by considering several factors. First, the percent difference in age between 2000 Series B and E is twice as large as the percent difference in income in 2000 under Series B and E (22.2 and 11.1 percent, respectively). Second, the absolute value of most, but not all, age elasticities is greater than the corresponding income elasticities. Accordingly, if all recreation age and income elasticities were to equal unity, this would imply that a 17 percent smaller population that was 22.2 percent older but 11.1 percent wealthier in per capita income would require recreational facilities for approximately 30 percent fewer recreation occasions. The importance of this result for recreation planners cannot be overemphasized.

CHANGING STRUCTURAL MODELS IN THE FUTURE

The most questionable assumption concerning the future recreation forecasts presented in the last section was that the parameters estimated by using the 1965 National Recreation Survey will remain constant until 2000. To put it another way, the previous recreation forecasts were based upon a model in which it is implicitly assumed that excluded factors will not affect recreation and leisure-time habits in 1980 and 2000. Having pointed out this fact, does it negate the entire exercise?

The answer to this question depends upon the use to which a simulation of future recreation patterns are to be put. If the planner is interested in good hard forecasts, a planning horizon out to the year 2000 for a sector of the economy, which is almost hypersensitive to population size and its characteristics, is foolhardy. However, if the purpose, as in the present exercise, is to compare quantitatively what is surely a qualitative set of circumstances, where relative differences rather than absolute forecasts are the goal, then the model and the assumption of constant structure or parameters should not cause much over concern.

Low Density versus Urban Needs

In addition, there have been two studies which have further examined this general forecasting model and its assumptions. Both studies have used additional data to question the consistency of various parameters. The first study concluded that continuing to forecast future recreation participation based upon different rates of participation between whites and nonwhites was probably incorrect and might make as much as a 20-percent difference in the estimated total recreation demand.[14] Therefore, an underestimate of facility requirements in urban areas by the same percentage would result. The second study concluded that low-density recreationists who prefer a pristine wilderness experience generally grow up in urban areas (participating in recreation of a higher density when they are children), are highly educated, and have above average incomes.[15] Overall, these factors point up a very important planning question which must be raised, but which as yet cannot be resolved: "Will there be a shift in demand towards the low density recreation areas in the future?"

The evidence gathered thus far is affirmative for some people, but we do not know yet whether this will encompass the entire population. An explicit conclusion in the previous section was that supply scenario III which brought recreation facilities to the people was superior to supply scenario II. This short-run goal should be lauded. But, if the long-run effect is to convert primitive and wilderness areas into high-density recreation areas then the irreversibility of such a plan would mean that we had an inefficient long-run use of our recreation resources. Therefore, there is value in preserving the option either to develop or to maintain an area in its pristine state: Long-run and short-run alternatives must be compared and irreversibilities considered by the recreation planner. Land should be acquired for high-density recreation in a manner that avoids irreversibilities of the type described above until more information is available. The possible changing degree of substitution and complementarity between activities must be investigated further if the inefficient use of resources is to be avoided.

Leisure Time Changes

Perhaps the biggest miscalculation of the absolute level of recreation participation in the future is not taking into account changes in the work week and work schedules and any concomitant changes in demand for recreation resources in the future. In part, this has been deliberate, since it is not enough to know whether leisure time may increase; it is also important to know the form this increase may take. For example, a four-day work week might exert greater pressure on our national parks and camping areas, while a shorter work day might put greater pressure on activities such as swimming, hiking, boating, golf, or tennis which might be accessible close to home.

In Table 8, a breakdown by the percent of participation in each activity when Americans were on vacations, overnight trips, outings, or had "just a few hours" is shown for 1965. If leisure time increases in the future, the values in Table 8 would provide an estimate of the possible effect on the demands that would be placed on recreation facilities. Shorter work weeks would be most likely to increase overnight trips and outings; shorter working days are more likely to increase those activities appropriate when only a "few hours are available." Increased leisure time may, however, mean less real income; in that case, some forms of recreation, particularly those requiring large personal expenditures, may be affected differently than others.

Perhaps the amount of leisure time may not increase in the future, but more substitutions in the distribution of leisure time may be possible. For example, an individual might be permitted to choose to work four days of 10 hours each; therefore, his income would not be affected. But, his total yearly travel time to and from work will be reduced and his number of free days will increase; so, his opportunities for a larger number of recreation experiences will expand. For some individuals, this may mean the substitution of more trips and outings for those activities closer at home; for others, this may be a way to avoid congestion and queues at such close-to-home leisure-time facilities as tennis courts, golf courses, libraries, museums, theaters, etc. This latter phenomena would be particularly true if individuals who select a four-day work week have freedom of choice over which day they may elect not to work and all affected individuals do not select the same days. If this last phenomena occurred, there would be less congestion on commuter highways and mass transit facilities—a result that would probably have social value in itself and may also increase leisure time by reducing commuter traveling time.

In addition, we have implied that changes in leisure time will have two effects which move in the opposite direction, much like variations in population size. More leisure time means more participation; but, more participation probably means more congestion, unless it is redistributed more evenly over the recreation season. Therefore, if facilities are not expanded, a decline in quantity per person or quality per experience is likely. In fact, the effect of different assumptions about leisure time may be determined in a manner proportional to changes in the population, if we ignore the differences in

Table 8.—Outdoor Recreation Activities: Percent Distribution of Total Days of Participation in Selected Activities by Type of Occasion, Summer 1965

Activity	Total	Vacations	Overnight recreation trips	Outings	Few available hours
Total	100%	13%	12%	52%	23%
Bicycling	100	10	6	14	70
Horseback riding	100	15	9	28	48
Playing outdoor games or sports	100	9	8	49	34
Golf	100	13	9	31	47
Tennis	100	8	9	32	51
Fishing	100	12	20	49	19
Canoeing	100	19	35	27	19
Sailing	100	19	19	46	16
Other boating	100	14	22	50	14
Swimming	100	10	11	64	15
Ocean	100	11	8	72	9
Lake, pond, stream	100	10	15	62	13
Pool	100	13	5	48	34
Water skiing	100	10	20	59	11
Camping	100	35	65	n.a.	n.a.
Remote camping	100	21	79	n.a.	n.a.
Mountain climbing	100	24	13	46	17
Hiking	100	20	18	42	20
Walking for pleasure	100	16	12	46	26
Bird watching	100	14	15	43	28
Wildlife and bird photography	100	32	6	43	19
Nature walks	100	18	15	48	19
Picnics	100	7	6	73	14
Driving for pleasure	100	16	8	41	35
Sightseeing	100	25	10	47	18
Attending outdoor sports events	100	10	6	28	56
Attending outdoor concerts, plays	100	17	5	28	50
Hunting	100	10	22	20	48

n.a.—Not applicable.

Source: U.S. Department of the Interior, Bureau of Outdoor Recreation, *1965 Survey of Outdoor Recreation Activities.*

the form (be it a shorter work week or shorter working day) that the increase in leisure time might take.

Other Issues

Additional issues which should be weighed in any analysis of future recreation patterns include the conversion of farmlands in the northeast (which has difficulty competing with the emerging agro industries) and grazing lands in the west into possible recreation resources. The trade-offs between suburban development and recreation needs must be given greater attention in the years ahead. The continued subsidizing of public recreation facilities, which has a definite impact on the emergence of private recreation facilities, should be examined in the future as population growth continues to exert pressure on our nation's limited recreation resources.

SUMMARY AND CONCLUSIONS

In the above analysis, we have stressed the importance of population as a factor which jointly affects the aggregate level of recreation demand and, via congestion or "people pollution," the quality of recreation experiences. We have utilized a reduced form forecasting model to examine six future scenarios with different population and recreation facility data. We have also considered which of the underlying assumptions of the model we feel are least likely to hold in the future.

The overall conclusions of the exercise are straightforward. At least until 2000, holding supply constant, more people means more total recreation days, although this effect was found to be diminishing for those activities more sensitive to congestion. Similarly, by holding population constant, more recreation facilities means that more total recreation days will be consumed. The effect of this phenomena is most profound in those activities which are heavily dependent upon the use of public lands and recreation waters. Furthermore, those activities which are either passive in character or can take place in almost any environment may be negatively affected by additions to the stock of public lands and recreation water.

Those supply scenarios which bring the "parks to the people" in both urban areas and relatively undersupplied census regions, that is to say the areas where congestion is presently most severe, are most notably affected by increases in recreation facilities. Additionally, it was found that the most important quantitative effect of diminished population growth in the future is not the reduced population size or higher income expected under series E; rather, the important factor was the negative effect that scenario E's older population will have upon total recreation demand generally and more specifically in those recreational activities most avidly pursued by younger people. In fact, we can conservatively expect that Series E would result in at least a 30 percent reduction in the demand for public recreational facilities and perhaps as much as a 50 percent reduction in the demand for recreation facilities than an otherwise similar (*ceteris paribus*) population Series B estimate of facility requirements.

We also considered the possible implications of increased leisure time in the future and concluded that changes could occur in several ways. First, the work week might be reduced to four days and individuals might work only 32 hours a week. This would increase leisure time but would also probably decrease income; its net effect on recreation demand is, therefore, uncertain, since these are opposite effects. However, it is likely to shift demand to more distant recreation facilities. Second, the work week may be reduced to four days of 10 hours each; this would change the distribution of leisure time, but would probably not reduce income. The expected effect is to shift demand from those activities which are pursued when there are a few hours available to those activities likely to be participated in while on an outing or trip away from home. Finally, the work day may be reduced, for example from eight to seven hours. Because income may also fall, the net effect might be uncertain; but, demand would be expected to shift to those activities which are participated in either close to home or work.

Finally, we must caution that measuring the level of use for which a reduced form model is particularly well suited does not permit the planner to gauge two very important additional factors: We can neither estimate the possible reduction in welfare if congestion reduces utility nor can we determine in some simple benefit-cost manner whether investments or public expenditures, to avoid such a deterioration in satisfaction, can be socially justified. We leave such decisions to our collective value judgments and we enter the world of "second" best.

REFERENCES

1. See Marion Clawson, "The Crisis in Outdoor Recreation," *American Forests* (Washington: Resources for the Future, Inc., Reprint No. 13, March 1959); and Outdoor Recreation Resources Review Commission (ORRRC), *Outdoor Recreation for America,* A Report to the President and to the Congress (Washington, January 1962).

2. See U.S. Dept. of the Interior, *Selected Outdoor Recreation Statistics,* March 1971; and *The Demand and Supply of Outdoor Recreation,* by C. J. Cicchetti, J. J. Senaca, and P. Davidson, July 1969.

3. U.S. Dept. of the Interior, *The Demand. . . , op. cit.*

4. For a discussion of some of these issues as applied to outdoor recreation, see C. J. Cicchetti, "Some Economic Issues Involved in Planning Urban Recreation," *Land Economics,* Winter 1970. For a more general discussion of rationing public services, see C. J. Cicchetti and R. H. Haveman, "Optimality in Producing and Distributing Public Outputs" (paper presented at the joint American Economic Association and Public Choice Meetings in December 1971).

5. ORRRC, *op. cit.,* p. 1.

6. For a discussion of the various theoretical and empirical models used by econometricians for the outdoor recreation market, as well as an interpretation of the terms used above, see C. J. Cicchetti, *et al.,* "The Identification Problem: A Clarification for Recreation Studies" (Washington: Resources for the Future, Inc., July 1971). (Mimeographed.)

7. R. G. Ridker, "Population and Pollution in the United States" (Washington: Resources for the Future, Inc., Sept. 1971). (Mimeographed.)

8. U.S. Dept. of the Interior, *The Demand. . . , op. cit.,* pp. 202-203.

9. U.S. Department of the Interior, *A Study of the Demand for Outdoor Recreation Based on an Analysis of the National Recreation Surveys of 1960 and 1965,* Interim Report by Rutgers Univ., Bureau of Economic Research, July 28, 1967; and *A Study of Participation in Outdoor Recreation Based on an Analysis of the National Recreation Survey of 1965,* Interim Report by Rutgers Univ., Bureau of Economic Research, January 1, 1968.

10. U.S. Dept. of the Interior, *The Demand. . . , op. cit.,* pp. 205-206.

11. *Ibid.*

12. *Ibid.* pp. 210-211.

13. As shown in Appendix B, Table B-1.

14. C. J. Cicchetti, "Some Economic Issues Involved in Planning Urban Recreation," *op. cit.*

15. C. J. Cicchetti, "Some Economic Issues Included in Planning Wilderness Recreation Areas" (presented at Resources for the Future Multidisciplinary Workshop on Recreation in Wildlands, Wildlife and Scenic Resources, Missoula, Montana, Summer 1971).

APPENDIX A

General Model

The purpose of this appendix is twofold. First, a general model, which is intended to be overly simple, will be described to explain the analytical machinery of the empirical and forecasting models utilized in the preceding analysis. Second, this general model will highlight the central role that population plays in determining the aggregate level of participation in outdoor recreation. It will be developed in such a manner that the similarities and differences between its form and the population and pollution model described by Ridker may be emphasized.[1]

Participation in outdoor recreation depends upon two broadly defined arguments, which we will denote as demand (D) and supply (S). Each of these terms is more accurately considered as a vector of heterogeneous characteristics. For example, demand (D) factors which influence recreation might include such demographic factors as age, race, sex, family size and life cycle, and such socioeconomic factors as income, education, profession, and occupation. Similarly, the supply of recreation facilities (S) may include various types of recreation facilities, land and water, which may differ in both quality and topography.

As a first step, the probability of any individual in a given population participating in outdoor recreation (p) will depend upon his demand characteristics and the supply of facilities available to him deflated by the other possible users of such facilities, which we will represent by N for the total population, to measure the effect of possible congestion or "people pollution" as described above. It follows that equation (1) is a shorthand way of expressing this relationship algebraically.

$$p = a_1 + b_1 \cdot D + c_1 \cdot (S/N) \qquad (1)$$

where a_1, b_1, and c_1 are the parameters of equation (1) which are used to show how changing demand and supply conditions affect the probability of participating in outdoor recreation generally. Additional variables may be added to equation (1), when we recognize that outdoor recreation itself is not a homogeneous commodity, but instead is comprised of many different service flows from environmental and capital resources. The importance of this extension is that some recreation activities may be complementary to one another, for example swimming and picnicking. Others may be more or less substitutes for one another, for example motor boating and fishing. Participation in other activities may have a neutral effect on one another.

We will denote the complementary, substitute, and neutral terms by the following change in equation (1).

$$p_a = a'_1 + b'_1 D + c'_1 (S/N) + \sum_{i=1}^{m} i_1^{\sigma} p_i \qquad (1')$$

where

p_a = probability of participating in activity a

p_i = probability of participating in activity i and m = the number of such other outdoor activities

and

i_1^{σ} = is an interaction term and when it is greater, equal to or less than zero, we will define activities i and a to be complementary, independent and substitute recreation activities.

In order to determine the total number of participants in any given period of time we can calculate the expected value of participation by summing the product of the probability of participating by each type of person in the population (assume n types) and the number of people of that type. Equation (2) then follows:

$$P = \sum_{j=1}^{n} p^j N^j \qquad (2)$$

where

P = total number of outdoor recreation participants;

n = the number of different types of people who have the same demand and supply characteristics;

p^j is derived from equation (1) for the jth type of individual, $j=1,n$;

N^j is the number of people with the jth characteristics.

If all people were alike or equation (1) was solved for the average demand and supply characteristics in the population, equation (3) would follow:

$$P = pN = a_1 N + b_1 DN + c_1 S \qquad (3)$$

If differences between individuals concerning preferences for different activities are allowed to affect the slopes and constants as in equation $(1')$, we would similarly derive different equations (2) and (3) for each activity, as:

$$P_a = \sum_{j=1}^{n'} p_a^j N^j \qquad (2')$$

$$P_a = p_a N = a'_1 N + b'_1 DN + c'_1 S + \sum_{i=1}^{m} i_1^{\sigma} p_i N \qquad (3')$$

A second step is to determine the intensity of participation in outdoor recreation, or the days of recreation per participant (d). In equation (4), we can represent the effect of demand characteristics D and supply characteristics S deflated by the number of other recreation participants (P) to measure the actual congestion effect as opposed to the potential congestion effect in deciding whether to participate as in the first step where we used the population size N as a measure of "people pollution":

$$d = a_2 + b_2 D + c_2(S/P) \qquad (4)$$

In order to determine the aggregate number of recreation days we will multiply the days per participant of a given type of person by the number of participants of a given type and sum over the number of classifications, as shown in equation (5):

$$R = \sum_{j=1}^{n} d^j p^j = \sum_{j=1}^{n} d^j p^j N^j \qquad (5)$$

We can also determine an equation similar to (3) above, as:

$$R = dP = dpN = \left[a_2 + b_2 D + c_2 \frac{S}{P} \right] \cdot [a_1 N + b_1 DN + c_1 S] \qquad (6)$$

$$= a_2 a_1 N + a_2 b_1 DN + a_2 c_1 S + b_2 a_1 ND + b_2 b_1 ND^2 +$$

$$b_2 c_1 SD + c_2 a_1 N \frac{S}{P} + c_2 b_1 DN \frac{S}{P} + c_2 c_1 \frac{S^2}{P}$$

We can also add to both the complexity and reality of the model by realizing that a separate "d" or days per participant equation may be determined for each activity ($i=1$, $m+1$). The result would be similar to equation $(1')$ above:

$$d_a = a'_2 + b'_2 D + c'_2(S/P) + \sum_{i=1}^{m} i_2^{\sigma} d_i \qquad (4')$$

where:

i_2^{σ} and d_i are defined in a manner similar to the step 1 counterparts. Finally, a function may be determined to estimate the total number of recreation days in any given recreation activity by:

$$R_a = d_a P_a = \sum_{j=1}^{n} d_a^j p_a^j N^j \qquad (7)$$

If we assume all the parameters of these equations remain constant, then a structure similar to equations (6) and (7) can be used to estimate the effect of changing population size (N), its characteristics (D) and the available supply of recreation facilities in a given geographic area (S) in a manner similar to Ridker's damage functions.[2] Furthermore, the addition of interaction variables between recreation activities compounds the role played by population since it is a causal factor in each p_i and d_i equation.

From equations (5) through (7) above, we see that as the population increases, we might expect an increase in the total recreation days. However, since both the probability of participation and number of recreation days per participant depend upon the amount of congestion or "people pollution." It follows that increases in population will have two effects. While the direct effect of population increases $\Delta N > 0$ is to increase R, the indirect effect is to decrease the uncongested supply of recreation facilities as measured by $\Delta(S/N) < 0$ and $\Delta(S/P) < 0$, unless there is a concomitant increase in land and water dedicated to recreation of a greater or equal amount. We also conclude that population size, while the key variable in the recreation model, is not the only population factor to consider, since the socioeconomic and demographic characteristics of the population as indicated by "D" are also important determinants in the general recreation model.

In the succeeding section an empirical model which was based upon this approach will be discussed. It was utilized to forecast future levels of recreation participation using this methodology in the text above.

A Two-Step Reduced From Econometric Model for Outdoor Recreation

National Background

In the late 1950's, the Congress and the President formed the Outdoor Recreation Resources Review Commission (ORRRC). The purpose of this commission was to assess the country's present and future relationship between the demands for outdoor recreation and the supply of outdoor recreation facilities. After uncovering the areas of greatest need, the Commission made legislative recommendations to the President and the Congress to carry out a coordinated Federal, state, and local recreation plan to meet the expected increased pressure for additional facilities from a growing population.

As a direct outgrowth of the ORRRC recommendations, the Bureau of Outdoor Recreation of the U.S. Department of the Interior was established on May 28,

1963, when the President signed Public Law 88-29. The Bureau of Outdoor Recreation's planning and coordinating functions were further outlined in Public Law 88-578, which established the Land and Water Conservation Fund to acquire, plan, and develop recreation facilities. In order to carry out these planning and coordinating functions, the Bureau of Outdoor Recreation began two large data gathering efforts.

The first effort was to develop a complete inventory of all public recreation lands, state, local, and national. The information gathered as part of this public recreation facility inventory by the Bureau of Outdoor Recreation included the following data at each publicly operated recreation area:[3]

1. Total recreation land acreage.
2. Total recreation water acreage.
3. Total recreation wet land acreage.
4. Recreation water acreage with none or minor pollution (A).
5. Recreation water acreage polluted but acceptable for recreation use (B).
6. Recreation water acreage polluted and not acceptable for recreation use (C).
7. High density recreation acreage (Class I).
8. General outdoor recreation acreage (Class II).
9. Natural environment acreage (Class III).
10. Outstanding natural areas acreage (Class IV).
11. Primitive areas acreage (Class V).
12. Historic and cultural areas acreage (Class VI).
13. Total day use.
14. Total overnight use.

The second data gathering effort of the Bureau of Outdoor Recreation was a national recreation survey to assess the participation habits of Americans and to determine the socioeconomic factors that might be important in explaining participation in outdoor recreation.[4] In 1960 and 1961, the first *National Recreation Surveys* were sponsored by ORRRC. They sponsored four quarterly *National Recreation Surveys* covering the period from June 1960 to May 1961.[5] Approximately 4,000 respondents were interviewed in each of these four surveys.

In 1965, the Bureau of Outdoor Recreation sponsored another *National Recreation Survey*. Based upon the experience gained in the 1960-61 National Recreation Surveys and advances in planning techniques in outdoor recreation, the 1965 National Recreation Survey was slightly altered during the intervening period,[6] while substantial comparability was maintained to aid trend analysis. There were over 7,000 respondents in the single 1965 National Recreation Survey and, although questions concerning recreation participation for the entire year were asked, the survey was concerned primarily with the summer season of 1965 (June, July, and August).

The individuals chosen for each of the various National Recreation Surveys were residents of households where the head of the household was previously interviewed as part of the Monthly Labor Survey. Information about the socioeconomic characteristics of the National Recreation Survey sample person and the head of the household was therefore available for analysis. This data included information on the age, race, sex, place of residence, marital status, family composition, occupation, and employment status. These data were further supplemented by a set of questions on each National Recreation Survey dealing with the level of education and family income of the sample person and the head of the household, as well as the relationship between the head of the household and the sample person.

The respondent was asked to indicate the activities he preferred and if he participated as often as he would like in each season of the year. If he indicated his participation was constrained, the respondent was asked to explain the reasons why he did not participate more often. The major part of the various national recreation surveys both in the quantity of information and the intent of the surveys dealt with whether the respondent participated in some 20 to 25 outdoor recreation activities and with the frequency of that participation. Each sample person was asked to indicate the number of times he participated in each of the various activities while on a vacation trip away from home, other overnight recreation trips, one-day trips or outings, and any other occasions not included in the first three categories. Participation in an activity for any portion of a day, whether for several minutes or several hours, was counted as one "activity day." During any one day, an individual may have participated in several different activities; for example, a respondent participating in fishing, picnicking, and swimming all in the same day would then count as three "activity days."

A Two-Step Population Specific Demand and Supply Analysis

In an attempt to make use of the techniques which proved beneficial in the previous empirical studies and to consider jointly the supply and demand conditions in the outdoor recreation market as directed in Public Law 88-29, the Bureau of Outdoor Recreation financed a major study of the 1960-61 and 1965 National Recreation Surveys and the 1964 public inventory of recreational facilities. This study was conducted by Paul Davidson, Joseph Seneca, and Charles Cicchetti at

Rutgers University and has resulted in several publications.[7]

The study conducted at Rutgers University contained a separate analysis of each of the 25 principal outdoor recreational activities which were included in the 1960-1961 and 1965 National Recreation Surveys. A major point of departure of this study was that, for the first time, the basic National Recreation Survey data for each respondent were expanded by adding variables representing the relative availability (quantity) and relative quality of recreation facilities at the county and state of residence levels from the Bureau of Outdoor Recreation's facility inventory. These supply-related or facility variables were analyzed jointly for each respondent along with the traditional socioeconomic variables to explain the levels of participation in the various outdoor recreation activities.

In the Rutgers study, an empirical model was estimated, which incorporated and tested the hypotheses described in the general model presented in the previous section of this study. The authors of this study present a detailed discussion of the interpretation of these equations, which economists call "reduced form" along with a discussion of the identification problem which arises from the joint determination of both the quantity demanded and the quantity supplied for cross section data of the type found in the National Recreation Surveys. These details and the precise meaning of these terms are discussed in the Rutgers study.

The technique adopted to expand the National Recreation Survey data was to focus on the states and county in which the respondent lived at the time of the survey. This supply information was aggregated into county and state totals by the Rutgers researchers and along with aggregate socioeconomic variables for both the county and state were added to the National Recreation Survey records for each of the nearly 25,000 respondents in each survey.

Among the principal accomplishments of the Rutgers study was the derivation of a two-step equation for each activity, which corresponds to equations (1') and (4') above. In the first step, an equation of the (1') type was developed and a zero-one binary dependent variable was utilized. These equations can be used to estimate the conditional probability of participating in each of the 25 activities in 1965 summer, 1960 summer, and 1965 annual (p_a). The explanatory variables in these equations included both the socioeconomic characteristics of each individual (D) and various indices of the availability of recreational facilities deflated by population (S/N).

In the second step an equation of the (4') type was determined for each of the 20 summer activities, these equations can be used to estimate the number of days of participation in each activity for those who participated one or more days (d_a). These equations were estimated by using facility variables deflated by the total number of recreation participants (S/P) along with the socioeconomic variables (D).

The empirical results found by the Rutgers researchers, substantiated and made more general the results of past recreation studies, that is: (1) a sharp negative effect of age was observed in both step one and step two equations, (2) income and income-related variables showed a positive but generally an increasing at a decreasing effect on participation, (3) the supply or facility variables proved to be a more important set of constraints in determining the intensity or number of days of participation (d_a) than on the probability of participation (p_a) and were positively related in quantity and quality to participation patterns, thus confirming a priori expectations, and (4) significant differences in participation rates between white and nonwhite individuals were observed in both step one and step two equations for most activities and these differences were quantitatively greater in 1965 than in 1960.

The final objective of the Rutgers study was the formation of a 50-equation multivariate (some 150 independent variables) population specific forecasting model used to show the relative effects of two different possible future national recreational plans on the levels of recreation participation. This was accomplished by using the two step population specific recreation model similar to that outlined by equations (6) and (7) above along with facility variables in a simulation analysis. This model was used in the text of the present study to compare several future population and supply of recreation facilities scenarios.

APPENDIX A
REFERENCES

1. R. G. Ridker, "Population and Pollution in the United States" (Washington, D.C.: Resources for the Future, Inc., April 23, 1971). (Mimeographed.)

2. *Ibid.,* equations 5a and 5b, p. 8.

3. For a full discussion of both data-gathering efforts, see U.S. Dept. of the Interior, *The Demand and Supply of Outdoor Recreation,* by C. J. Cicchetti, J. Seneca, and P. Davidson, June 1969.

4. *Ibid.*

5. For a discussion of population rotation groups and sampling techniques, see U.S. Bureau of the Census, Current Population Reports, Series P-23, No. 13, *Concepts and Methods Used in Household Statistics on Employment and Unemployment from the Current Population Survey,* June 1964; and *The Current Population Survey: A Report on Methodology,* Technical Paper No. 7, 1963.

6. For further details, see U.S. Bureau of the Census, *Th Current. . . , op. cit.*

7. C. J. Cicchetti, "An Applied Econometric Analysis of th Outdoor Recreation Market" (unpublished doctoral dissertation Rutgers University, March 1968); U.S. Dept. of the Interior, *op cit.;* and a study that C. J. Cicchetti and J. J. Seneca hav undertaken with Robert R. Nathan Assoc., in which they hav applied this model to some 60 countries in the state of Nev York entitled *Water-oriented Recreation Study of the Osweg River System* (Washington, April 1970). Also, J. J. Seneca, "Ar Analysis of Outdoor Recreational Activities and A Case Study o the Oswego River Basin," Discussion Paper No. 3 (Rutgers Univ. Bureau of Economic Research, October 1969).

APPENDIX B

Table B-1.—Population Series B and E Differences

	Series B	Series E
National population size 1980 .	236,797,000	225,510,000
North East census region size 1980	50,248,600	47,846,500
National population size 2000 .	320,780,000	266,281,000
North East census region size 2000	64,573,000	53,575,700
High productivity per capita income 1980	$3,397	$3,627
High productivity per capita income 2000	$5,552	$6,203
Low productivity per capita income 1980	$3,167	$3,383
Low productivity per capita income 2000	$4,481	$5,006
Median age 1980	27.8 years	29.3 years
Median age 2000	27.2 years	34.0 years
Mean household size 2000 . . .	3.18 persons	2.66 persons

Source: U.S. Bureau of Census.

Table B-2.—Projections of Various National Socio-Economic Factors Used in the Recreation Model

	1960	1965	1980	2000
Number of persons in family	3.67	3.71	3.65	3.60
Employed in government service	12.5%	13.9%	19.0%	24.0%
White collar workers . . .	55%	58%	62%	67%
Percent of population living in SMSA's . . .	63%	65%	75%	87%
Percent of SMSA population living in the central city	51.4%	48.1%	35.9%	24.7%
Family income	$5,620	$6,957	$8,900	$13,800
Index of education	1.76	1.85	2.07	2.28
Percent of population living in rural areas	30.1%	28%	23%	17%
Percent of the population with income below $3,000	22%	16%	8%	2%

Source: For definitions and further references see, U.S. Dept. of the Interior, Bureau of Outdoor Recreation, *The Demand and Supply of Outdoor Recreation,* by C. J. Cicchetti, J. J. Seneca, and P. Davidson, July 1969.

Table B-3.—Age, Sex, and Color Distribution of the Population of the United States in 1965, 1980, and 2000

	Percentage of population (age 12 and over)					
Age and sex	1965		1980		2000	
	White	Non-white	White	Non-white	White	Non-white
Male						
12-17 years	12.5	1.9	10.7	2.8	10.4	3.5
18-24 years	13.3	1.1	14.6	1.2	14.0	1.3
25-44 years	28.9	3.7	31.5	4.6	31.4	5.5
45-64 years	24.5	2.7	21.2	2.4	21.4	2.1
Over 65 years	10.5	0.9	10.0	0.9	9.4	1.0
Female						
12-17 years	11.2	1.6	9.5	2.3	9.1	3.1
18-24 years	12.6	1.0	13.6	1.3	12.6	1.6
25-44 years	29.6	3.7	29.5	4.4	29.0	5.8
45-64 years	23.5	3.0	22.0	2.7	21.0	2.2
Over 65 years	12.8	1.1	13.5	1.3	14.0	1.6

Table based on U.S. Bureau of the Census, Population Census Series B (Population by Age, Sex, and Color).

Table B-4.—Area, Population and Density of the United States by Section and Region, 1965, 1980 and 2000

Section and region	Area (square miles)			Population (thousands)			Population density (persons per square mile)		
	1	2	3	4	5	6	7	8	9
	Total	Land	Water	1965	1980[b]	2000[b]	1965	1980	2000
United States[a]	3,615,202	3,546,227	68,975	194,592	236,797	320,780	54.8	66.7	90.5
				%	%	%			
Northeast:									
New England	66,608	62,995	3,613	5.8	5.5	5.4	177.6	208.1	274.3
Middle Atlantic	102,745	100,496	2,249	18.8	18.0	16.9	364.4	423.4	541.1
Total	169,353	163,491	5,862	24.6	23.5	22.3	292.5	340.4	438.3
North Central:									
East North Central	248,282	244,359	3,923	19.7	18.9	18.7	157.1	183.4	246.3
West North Central	517,237	508,606	8,631	8.2	7.4	6.9	31.3	34.3	43.3
Total	765,519	752,965	12,554	27.9	26.3	25.6	72.1	82.7	109.1
South:									
South Atlantic	278,902	267,535	11,367	14.8	15.6	16.0	107.9	137.7	192.1
East South Central	181,966	179,427	2,539	6.6	6.2	5.8	71.7	82.6	102.8
West South Central	438,885	429,284	9,601	9.6	9.6	9.3	43.4	53.1	69.6
Total	899,753	876,246	23,507	31.0	31.4	31.1	68.9	84.9	113.7
West:									
Mountain	863,887	856,636	7,251	4.0	4.4	4.6	9.0	12.0	17.2
Pacific	916,690	896,889	19,801	12.5	14.4	16.4	27.2	38.1	58.6
Total	1,780,577	1,753,525	27,052	16.5	18.8	21.0	18.3	25.3	38.4

[a]Includes the 50 States and the District of Columbia.
[b]U.S. Bureau of the Census, projection Series I-B; for year 2000, includes Armed Forces abroad.

Table B-5.—Public Recreation Lands and Water by Census Region

Scenario II

Public recreation acreage of land, wetlands, and water, 1965, and hypothetical acreage (in thousands of acres) for 1980 and 2000 based on extension of present regional distribution.

Region	Total	Land	Wetlands	Water	Number of swimming pools[a] (thousands)
United States:					
1965	346,169	322,452	11,330	12,387	34.3
1980	348,172	324,413	11,330	12,429	57.7
2000	350,828	327,012	11,330	12,486	127.1
Northeast:					
1965	10,052	9,484	174	394	6.6
1980	10,112	9,543	174	395	10.4
2000	10,191	9,621	174	396	20.9
North Central:					
1965	38,835	30,925	4,580	3,330	6.0
1980	39,213	31,295	4,580	3,338	12.8
2000	39,715	31,785	4,580	3,350	22.8
South:					
1965	34,859	28,225	2,957	3,677	9.9
1980	35,218	28,575	2,957	3,686	16.7
2000	35,694	29,040	2,957	3,697	35.9
West:					
1965	262,423	253,818	3,619	4,986	11.8
1980	263,629	255,000	3,619	5,010	21.2
2000	265,228	256,566	3,619	5,043	50.9

Assume: Pollution proportions in 1980 and 2000 remain the same as the 1965 proportions of water type A, B and C.
[a]This is the same under Scenario III.

Table B-6.—Public Recreation Lands by Type and Census Region

Scenario II

Public recreation acreage by the Bureau of Outdoor Recreation land classification, 1965, and hypothetical acreage (in thousands of acres) for 1980 and 2000 based on extension of present regional distribution.

Region	Total	Class						Number of golf courses[a] (thousands)
		I	II	III	IV	V	VI	
United States:								
1965	338,619	728	26,858	255,459	8,415	46,641	519	10.5
1980	340,623	759	27,435	256,816	8,451	46,641	520	16.8
2000	343,278	800	28,201	258,615	8,499	46,641	522	26.0
Northeast:								
1965	6,392	64	396	5,536	180	198	18	3.1
1980	6,452	66	404	5,584	181	198	18	4.8
2000	6,531	70	416	5,647	182	198	18	9.7
North Central:								
1965	36,889	110	5,468	29,585	401	1,304	21	4.1
1980	37,267	114	5,586	29,840	402	1,304	21	6.3
2000	37,769	121	5,742	30,177	405	1,304	21	13.1
South:								
1965	34,091	212	6,078	25,079	793	1,863	66	1.6
1980	34,450	221	6,208	25,295	796	1,863	66	2.6
2000	34,926	233	6,382	25,581	801	1,863	67	5.6
West:								
1965	261,247	343	14,916	195,258	7,041	43,276	414	1.7
1980	262,454	357	15,237	196,097	7,072	43,276	415	3.1
2000	264,052	377	15,662	197,210	7,112	43,276	416	8.6

Assume: Index of growth in amusement, and private commercial recreation increases by a factor of 1.25 from 1965 to 1980 and a factor of 1.73 from 1965 to 2000.

[a]This is the same under Scenario III.

Table B-7.—Distribution of Recreation Land and Water

Scenario III

Public recreation acreage of land, wetlands, and water, 1965, and hypothetical acreage (in thousands of acres) for 1980 and 2000 based on estimated needs by Census Division.

Region	Total	Land	Wetlands	Water
United States:				
1965	346,169	322,451	11,331	12,387
1980	356,785	325,955	11,331	19,499
2000	362,911	327,977	11,331	23,604
New England:				
1965	2,171	2,050	48	73
1980	2,559	2,178	48	333
2000	2,840	2,271	48	522
Middle Atlantic:				
1965	7,881	7,433	126	321
1980	8,236	7,551	126	559
2000	8,551	7,654	126	770
East North Central:				
1965	15,363	11,911	2,501	951
1980	17,014	12,456	2,501	2,057
2000	18,210	12,851	2,501	2,858
West North Central:				
1965	23,472	19,014	2,080	2,378
1980	23,472	19,014	2,080	2,378
2000	23,472	19,014	2,080	2,378
South Atlantic:				
1965	16,260	12,291	2,317	1,651
1980	16,353	12,322	2,317	1,714
2000	16,929	12,512	2,317	2,100
East South Central:				
1965	7,237	6,250	63	924
1980	7,670	6,393	63	1,214
2000	8,409	6,637	63	1,709
West South Central:				
1965	11,363	9,684	577	1,102
1980	12,066	9,916	577	1,573
2000	13,372	10,347	577	2,448
Mountain:				
1965	153,604	151,269	225	2,110
1980	153,704	151,303	225	2,177
2000	154,106	151,435	225	2,446
Pacific:				
1965	108,819	102,548	3,394	2,876
1980	115,710	104,822	3,394	7,493
2000	117,022	105,255	3,394	8,373

Table B-8.—Distribution of Different Quality Recreation Land

Scenario III

Public recreation acreage by the Bureau of Outdoor Recreation land classification, 1965, and hypothetical acreage (in thousands of acres) for 1980 and 2000 based on estimated needs by Census Division.

Region	Total	Class					
		I	II	III	IV	V	VI
United States:							
1965	338,619	728	26,858	255,459	8,415	46,641	519
1980	349,412	1,130	36,818	255,459	8,415	46,641	519
2000	355,550	1,990	42,276	255,459	8,415	46,641	519
New England:							
1965	2,172	29	142	1,661	157	182	2
1980	2,593	55	537	1,661	157	182	2
2000	2,890	94	796	1,661	157	182	2
Middle Atlantic:							
1965	4,220	34	254	3,875	23	17	16
1980	4,558	112	514	3,875	23	17	16
2000	4,853	187	734	3,875	23	17	16
East North Central:							
1965	13,523	72	529	12,620	58	240	5
1980	15,113	101	2,089	12,620	58	240	5
2000	16,247	175	3,149	12,620	58	240	5
West North Central:							
1965	23,365	38	4,939	16,965	343	1,064	16
1980	23,365	38	4,939	16,965	343	1,064	16
2000	23,365	38	4,939	16,965	343	1,064	16
South Atlantic:							
1965	15,603	55	2,884	10,686	663	1,266	50
1980	15,697	149	2,884	10,686	663	1,266	50
2000	16,278	268	3,345	10,686	663	1,266	50
East South Central:							
1965	7,216	23	1,436	5,642	64	41	10
1980	7,646	23	1,436	5,642	64	41	10
2000	8,385	23	2,604	5,642	64	41	10
West South Central:							
1965	11,272	134	1,758	8,752	66	556	6
1980	12,010	134	2,496	8,752	66	556	6
2000	13,392	222	3,657	8,752	66	556	6
Mountain:							
1965	153,093	275	10,960	119,558	3,552	18,462	286
1980	153,209	391	10,960	119,558	3,552	18,462	286
2000	153,664	730	10,960	119,558	3,552	18,462	286
Pacific:							
1965	108,154	67	3,956	75,700	3,490	24,814	127
1980	115,220	127	10,962	75,700	3,490	24,814	127
2000	116,476	254	12,091	75,700	3,490	24,814	127

Chapter 7

Agriculture, Population and the Environment

by
A. Barry Carr and
David W. Culver
Economic Research Service
U.S. Department of Agriculture

ACKNOWLEDGMENT:

This chapter was prepared for Resources for the Future under the terms of a contract with the Economic Research Service, U.S. Department of Agriculture. Assumptions with respect to the rate of growth of population and GNP as well as the subject matter emphasis were specified by the terms of that contract.

The authors wish to gratefully acknowledge the cooperation of many people who provided information for this report. Many colleagues of the authors within the Farm Production Economics Division, the Economic and Statistical Analysis Division, and the Natural Resource Economics Division assisted in the planning, data collection, analysis, and review of these materials.

COMMISSION ON POPULATION GROWTH AND THE AMERICAN FUTURE, *RESEARCH REPORTS, VOLUME III, POPULATION RESOURCES AND THE ENVIRONMENT,* EDITED BY RONALD G. RIDKER

CONTENTS

Agriculture, Population and the Environment

A major concern today is the fear of ecological disaster resulting from man-made disturbances to the environment.[1] These disturbances include the fertilizers, pesticides, and wastes associated with agriculture. Yet another fear is the possible reduction of a man's productive capacity to mere subsistence, or worse.[2]

This chapter projects to the year 2000 the nation's food and fiber needs, along with the resources required to produce them, with alternative assumptions about population growth rates, economic growth rates, and production technologies. In the process, it examines the effects on output and production costs of environmental protection regimes designed to reduce or offset some of the important ecological consequences of this agricultural growth. More generally, by examining agriculture's likely responses to alternative levels of demand and production restraints, the chapter attempts to clarify possible food and environment issues to be faced in the next two or three decades.

AGRICULTURE AND ECOLOGICAL CHANGE

Man's success in learning and applying new techniques has given him increasing influence over his surroundings. While the food gathering activities of early cultures had some impact on nature, the change to an agricultural system with domesticated plants and animals gave man an important advance in harnessing and directing natural events. Similarly, the technical and agricultural revolutions of recent decades have brought rapidly increasing ability to modify the system and increase production.

In recent years, rising farm production has been increasingly the result of new technology. Plant and animal varieties have been genetically improved and new hybrid varieties created. The results for crops have included higher per-acre yields, higher quality products, and improved resistance to diseases and pests. In the livestock sector, product quality has been improved along with feed conversion efficiency and production per animal.

Mechanization of farm production and use of pesticides have been major factors in the drop in farm labor use at an annual rate of nearly six percent over the last 30 years. They have also done away with many strenuous or disagreeable jobs and have allowed increased crop yields. Applications of mechanical power have now been made in varying degrees to most phases of agricultural production and harvesting with the exception of some specialty crops.

Modern technology has been primarily directed toward modifying natural processes, but it has also begun to include direct chemical synthesis of agricultural products. Synthetic fibers have taken over half of the total fiber market, while the synthetic production of food for humans and feed for animals has only barely begun. A substantial shift to synthetically produced foods, while probably not likely over the next two or three decades, could radically alter agricultural resource use.

Any change in the system of production can be expected to alter the environment. However, recent technological advances have brought increasing potential for overloading the natural system of recycling leading to a buildup of unwanted residues in soil, water, and air. Historically, the major agricultural sources of air pollution have been wind erosion of the soil (dust storms) and burning of crop and forest waste. In addition, the concentrated handling of livestock has created localized problems of odor and ammonia pollution of air from manure.

The main agricultural concerns with soil have been to keep the soil in place and to maintain its fertility. And success in these efforts is important in preventing air and water pollution. While soil conservation practices are now widely used in agriculture, sedimentation of streams and lakes from both agricultural and nonagricultural sources remains an important concern. The modern system of soil fertility maintenance—use of chemical fertilizers rather than livestock manures—has increased potential water pollution in two ways. Nutrients from chemical fertilizers may enter surface or ground water. And livestock manure—no longer competitive in most cases with chemical fertilizers—has become a serious disposal problem.

FIGURE 7-1
SIMPLIFIED MODEL OF AGRICULTURE

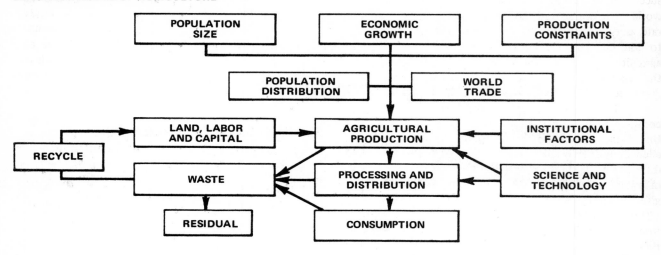

Because of the regional specialization in agriculture, the distribution of these residues varies widely. In addition, the cumulative environmental effect may be substantially greater than what is observed on a short-term basis.

A MODEL OF AGRICULTURE

As a result of previous learning, man is now entering a new era in understanding and control of his surroundings. Because of this vastly increased ability to influence nature, the sustenance and control processes must be viewed as an integrated, rationalized system. Agriculture, because of its emphasis on biological processes, is an important part of more general models which illustrate ecological dynamics. The agricultural model should be interpreted as a moving, growing, adaptive force in more general environmental models. Figure 1 makes agriculture a focal point for available physical resources, for key economic forces, and for the rest of our culture including science and technology. Wastes are included as one of the end products of the agricultural process and are noted separately here because of current concern with pollution problems.

METHODOLOGY

The central objective of this study was to evaluate the resource requirements and environmental consequences for agriculture of alternative levels of population, income, and technology. In order to do this, we first developed alternative estimates of demand for major agricultural commodities and then derived estimates of resource use.

The scenario and the alternative future were used as a method for synthesizing great detail into a few key variables.[3] Scenarios are hypothetical sets of events constructed to focus attention on causal processes and decision points. Alternative futures systematically compare selected combinations of assumptions and objectives. The value of the synthetic conditions expressed as scenarios is in isolating a small number of forces so that the impact of these different forces can be more easily compared.

In this study, three operating variables were specified and the impact of each was evaluated. They are (1) population growth, (2) economic growth, and (3) technology. Two alternative levels were considered for each. For population and the economy, these alternatives are the same as those specified in Chapter 1. For technology, the "high" alternative assumes applications of foreseeable new technologies so that crop yields and livestock output per unit of input continue progressing more or less as they have in the recent past. No dramatic technological breakthroughs are assumed, however. The "low" alternative assumes that institutional restraints slow the rate of increase in yields for the purpose of creating a "cleaner" environment. Further details about the relation between agricultural technology and the environment are given in Appendix A.

Several other assumptions were necessary in the course of the study. They include the following:

1. The next several decades are assumed to be relatively surprise-free in the sense that no dramatic changes in life style of international relations are expected.

2. The rest of the world will be moderately successful in feeding itself over the next 30 years, but world agricultural trade will expand at about the same rate as economic growth. The United States is assumed to continue to increase both exports and imports of agricultural products. The background and rationale for the assumption on government-assisted exports are discussed in Appendix C.

3. The basic conditions for domestic demand continue to be similar to recent past years. This means that domestic demand for agricultural products can be adequately projected using trend data modified for different population and income levels. Procedures used in projecting alternative levels of domestic demand are given in Appendix B.

4. Development and use of synthetics and substitutes for agricultural products will generally follow trends of recent years. No radical shift in the form or source of food and fiber is assumed.

With alternative assumptions about each of three operating variables, there are eight possible combinations. This array of alternatives contains some rather uninteresting combinations and is rather large for analysis. A more manageable set of five combinations was chosen to maximize the relevant range of outcomes, yet isolate the effect of specific assumptions. Those five alternative scenarios are presented in Table 1.

The first scenario, with high growth rates for population and income and minimal restraint on production technology, would result in the maximum level of agricultural output. Scenario 2 provides an examination of agriculture's capacity to meet high demand levels with restricted technology. Scenario 3, through comparison with number 2, provides an opportunity to evaluate the impact of different levels of income growth. The fourth scenario, by comparison with the first, shows the impact of different population levels, while the fifth scenario provides a picture of the minimum level of agricultural output possible with these alternative assumptions.

These five conditional futures were then analyzed in terms of the response of agriculture to alternative levels of the operating variables. More specifically, we sought to identify the effects of varying population, income, and technology. The emphasis of the analysis is on whether agricultural resources can meet the demands of rising population and income with restrictions on technology by an ecologically conscious society.

COMPONENTS OF THE ANALYSIS

Population and Economic Growth

As indicated, the population and economic growth assumptions are the same as those indicated in Chapter 1. For convenience, their numerical implications are summarized in Tables 2 and 3.

Population Distribution

Analysis of population distribution projections suggests that likely urban land use patterns will not materially affect the total area available to agriculture during the next three decades. This is not to say that some local, specific problems of urban sprawl such as the notable instances in California will not continue to be important. But from the standpoint of overall productive capacity, urbanization by present trends does not reduce the cropland base even by as much as new or reclaimed areas are adding to the base. Accordingly, although urban land use was included in the calculation of land available to agriculture, a direct comparison of high and low urban demand for land is not presented as part of the results of this investigation.

Technology

Two alternative assumptions are made in this study with respect to the nature of production technology employed in agriculture. The concern here is chiefly, but not entirely, with the level of fertilizer and pesticide (insecticide, herbicide, fungicide) usage, the level of

Table 1.—Construction of Five Alternative Scenarios

Assumption	Scenario				
	1	2	3	4	5
Population growth	High	High	High	Low	Low
Economic growth	High	High	Low	High	Low
Production technology	Unrestricted	Restricted	Restricted	Unrestricted	Restricted

Table 2.—Components of Population Assumptions

Component	1968	1980 Series B	1980 Series E	2000 Series B	2000 Series E
		Million			
Total population	200.6	237	226	321	266
Population 16 and over	137.7	167	167	220	202
Total labor force	82.3	101	103	136	127

[a]Note that the Series E labor force is larger initially and through 1980 than Series B. This is because the lower birth rate allows greater participation in the labor force by women.

Source: Data for 1968 from U.S. Bureau of the Census, Current Population Reports, Series P-25, No. 456, Feb. 1971; Projections to 1980 and 2000 from Series P-25, No. 448, Aug. 1970.

Table 3.—Components of Economic Growth Assumptions (in 1967 dollars)[a]

Component	Unit	1968	1980 Series B	1980 Series E	2000 Series B	2000 Series E
			High economic growth rate			
GNP	Bil. dol.	831.0	1,351	1,374	2,991	2,774
Personal income	Bil. dol.	676.3	1,051	1,069	2,328	2,159
Disposable income	Bil. dol.	570.8	920	936	2,037	1,889
Per capita disposable income	Dol.	2,845	3,886	4,149	6,351	7,096
			Low economic growth rate			
GNP	Bil. dol.	831.0	1,260	1,282	2,414	2,239
Personal income	Bil. dol.	676.3	980	997	1,879	1,742
Disposable income	Bil. dol.	570.8	858	873	1,644	1,525
Per capita disposable income	Dol.	2,845	3,623	3,870	5,126	5,727

[a]Figures differ from those of Tables 1 and 2, Chapter 2, because those of Chapter 2 are derived from the model which, as explained in that chapter, excludes certain portions of officially defined GNP. Growth rates, however, are approximately the same.

hormones and medications in animal feed, and the methods of animal waste disposal from concentrated feeding operations.

The first alternative assumes a continuation of recent trends toward greater use of inputs such as chemical fertilizers and pesticides and greater concentration of animals in confined feeding areas. The second alternative assumes a high degree of institutional constraint imposed on the use of production inputs, as well as the type of waste treatment required for livestock. A comprehensive discussion of animal wastes, chemical fertilizers, pesticides, and feed additives is contained in Appendix A.

One of the most difficult of agriculture's problems with pollution appears to be the disposal of livestock wastes. The main alternatives for disposing of manure from confined livestock operations are biological treatment involving the use of one or more lagoons and spreading it on land even though manure is not economically competitive with chemical fertilizer as a plant food. State and Federal pollution control regulations vary widely among areas and apply primarily to either very large operations or more severe cases of air and water pollution. New regulations are increasingly concerned with noise levels and underground leakage from manure storage areas and lagoons.

Population, Resources, and the Environment

Under the low constraint assumption, only limited regulation including restrictions on drainage and odor is projected for most livestock operations. Such regulations would primarily affect very large operations and those in areas of high population density, or where runoff, odors, or noise are particularly offensive to humans. The high constraint assumption includes regulation of all livestock operations, including disposal of waste by spreading and covering on the land or by using biological and chemo-mechanical treatment. Drainage from manure storage areas into surface or ground water would be prohibited for all operators. Odor, noise, and fly control would be required where these nuisances crossed property boundaries.

Another potentially serious environmental problem in the entry of plant nutrients into water. Farmers use an estimated 85 percent of the total fertilizer consumed in the United States. Corn accounts for about 45 percent of the farm use of fertilizer, and wheat and soybeans another 10 percent.[4] Efficiency of fertilizer use which is related to the potential for pollution is affected by numerous factors—timing and placement, water level, soil physical properties, and type of fertilizer product used. The closer fertilizer can be applied to the time of maximum crop demand, the more efficient it is in producing a given yield. For example, on corn, fall applications of nitrogen allow more leaching and are not as efficient as several summer applications. However, most changes in fertilizer use which might be adopted for the protection of the environment would be more costly to producers. These costs would include more complex fertilizer formulations to effect controlled release of nutrients, frequent small applications of fertilizer during the growing season, and restrictions on the total amount of nitrogen used per acre per year. If the use of fertilizer is restricted to protect the environment, the most obvious substitute input is additional cropland.

Under the low constraint assumption, fertilizer use by farmers would continue to be limited only by profitability criteria. The high constraint alternative assumes restrictions imposed by governmental authority. Farmers would be permitted to use varying amounts of nitrogen fertilizer based on the crop, plant population, soil characteristics, type of fertilizer material, timing of application, and the climatic characteristics of the area. Specifically, nitrogen use on crops that are now heavily fertilized would be restricted to about one-half the current level, while use on crops fertilized lightly at present would, in most cases, be allowed to increase. The effect of these constraints would be to change the temporal and spatial distribution of fertilizer use as well as the total quantity used.

Pesticides, a generic term referring to all kinds of chemicals used to control organisms inimical to human purposes, can be classified by chemical composition, kind of target organism (insects, weeds, disease), or other characteristics such as persistence or toxicity.[5] Depending on the case, pesticides may raise yields, reduce year-to-year fluctuations in yields, or substitute for other inputs including land, labor, and machinery. Agriculture is estimated to account for about one-half of the total chemical pesticide use in the United States.[6] In 1966, pesticides were used by 85 percent of all farmers.[7] While many benefits have accrued to society from the widespread use of pesticides, some aspects of pesticide use have been detrimental to the environment.

With low constraints, continued use of pesticides subject to the present form of regulation is assumed. In general, persistent chemicals would be severely limited as to type and amount. Toxic but nonpersistent chemicals would carry the chief burden of pest control. Consumer protection efforts would rely, as now, on use of tolerance limits on foodstuffs. High constraints are considered to mean a very sparing use of chemicals with the stress on cultural practices, resistant varieties, and biological and mechanical control.

Medications, such as antibiotics and synthetic hormones such as diethylstilbestrol (DES), are added to livestock feeds to stimulate the rate of gain and increase the efficiency of feed conversion. At present, almost all animal protein consumed by humans comes from animals that have received some medicated or hormone-added feed. The elimination of feed additives would cause livestock production to become more costly. In the low constraint assumption, feed additives are permitted so long as their use does not contaminate the livestock product which reaches the consumer. In the high constraint assumption, the regular and continuous use of medications and hormones is prohibited.

Yields for major crops were projected to 1980 and 2000 at two different levels so as to reflect the two levels of technology outlined above. With the assumption of low constraints on technology, yields were projected to increase to 1980 about in line with recent trends, but the rates of increase from 1980 to 2000 were assumed to approximate the much slower rates typical of longer term trends. Projected yields under the high constraint assumption were adjusted downward from the low constraint forecast based on available experimental evidence on the effects of these technological changes.

Foreign Demand for United States Agricultural Products

Projections of United States agricultural trade to the year 2000 are based on two central judgments. The first is that United States agricultural exports will continue to increase with the major increases in feedstuffs. The second is that the rest of the world will be moderately successful in feeding itself over the next 30 years, so government-assisted exports will not need to be greatly increased from recent levels.

These judgments follow from the types of trade developments that have occurred in the past and from the following assumptions about the next three decades:

1. There will be no major wars.

2. Expansion of international trade will continue.

3. The industrialized countries will continue to support economic development of the poorer countries.

4. Long-term assistance to the poorer countries will be primarily in the form of technical help rather than in direct shipments of food.

The United States is in a strong competitive position to export most major field crops, especially the grains and soybeans where mechanization and large, productive, land resources continue to be important in production. In addition, as incomes in foreign countries rise, consumers generally want to increase consumption of livestock products; this in turn generates an increased world demand for feeds (feed grains and oilmeals). This change is exemplified by the demand shift over recent years in Europe and Japan toward feedstuffs in order to support an expanding livestock industry.[8] Thus, commercial exports of United States feed grains and oilseeds (soybeans) seem likely to increase over the foreseeable future. The United States is in a sufficiently strong position in food grain production to perhaps allow a modest increase in commercial wheat exports. Imports into the United States are projected to rise further for those commodities in which the United States is at a relative competitive disadvantage—those with high labor requirements where mechanization is occurring slowly.

The level of government-assisted exports will depend in part on the agricultural progress of the developing countries. The adoption of new seeds and other improved technology (the "Green Revolution") may well reduce the need for government food aid programs in most developing countries. But the rate of progress is likely to be uneven; and with rapid population growth expected to continue in many areas of the world, the overall need for such programs may not decline much, if any, over the foreseeable future.

Experience of recent years suggests that few countries will be willing, unless absolutely necessary, to remain for a long period in a position of dependence for basic food needs on gifts or subsidies from the United States. However, the United States is likely to keep sizeable stocks of food crops and supply them on a temporary basis to various poor countries. A more detailed examination of long-term prospects for the world population-food balance is given in Appendix C.

RESULTS

The five alternative sets of results, while far from exhaustive, provide enough variation to allow some judgments about important outcomes such as overall levels of production and consumption, relative farm prices, and use of agricultural chemicals. The kinds of tools and the amount of time available for analysis required the use of relatively simple assumptions and techniques. Nevertheless, the results obtained appear to be reasonable outcomes for the conditions assumed in each alternative.

The absolute levels of estimates for agricultural production, prices, and resource use should be viewed with considerable caution. Since the methods of analysis relied rather heavily on trend data, there is a possibility that major technological events could occur to substantially alter either the demand conditions or resource requirements. But the comparisons among alternative futures may be sufficiently accurate for use in making tentative policy decisions about the future. A summary of the five alternative futures is given in Table 4.

Comparison of Alternative Futures

Future 1 would result in the highest output of food and fiber among the five considered. Population growth and economic growth are at the highest assumed levels and technology is unrestrained. The combination of high domestic demand and low cost of production would evoke a high production response. Because of low constraints on production practices, yields would be high and cropland requirements would be relatively low due to the continuing substitution of pesticides and fertilizer for agricultural land and labor.

Future 2 couples a high demand for food and fiber with a series of constraints on production technology. These constraints on technology would, by restricting use of farm chemicals such as fertilizers and pesticides, tend to reduce yields and require greater use of other inputs such as land and labor in the production process. A reduction in fertilizer and pesticide use would be achieved, but land and labor usage would be at the highest levels of any alternative. Harvested cropland would increase by around 90 million acres over 1970, about 60 million from currently idle cropland and about 30 million from new cropland. The restricted technology assumption under this alternative would increase the cost of production which reduces domestic and foreign demand for agricultural commodities from the level of future 1.

Table 4.—Comparison of Alternative Futures in the Year 2000[a]

Item	Unit	1970	Year 2000 alternative I	II	III	IV	V
...arvested cropland[b]	Mil. acres	344	391	438	436	359	390
...opland not harvested[c]	Mil. acres	96	31	33	32	51	32
...otal cropland	Mil. acres	440	422	471	468	410	422
...sture and range[d]	Mil. acres	636	617	580	580	613	617
...ther agricultural land	Mil. acres	29	27	27	27	27	27
...otal agricultural land	Mil. acres	1,105	1,066	1,078	1,075	1,050	1,066
...emental nitrogen	Mil. tons	6.3	14.8	9.4	9.2	12.9	8.2
...sticides	Mil. lbs.	410	662	137	134	608	122
...abor	Bil. man-hours	6.5	2.5	4.0	3.9	2.3	3.5
...oduction Index	(1967=100)						
Crops		101	175	165	164	157	149
Livestock		104	166	150	154	139	129
All commodities		102	171	161	159	149	139
...ice Index[e]	(1967=100)						
Crops		91	101	117	113	85	93
Livestock		107	109	123	113	97	100
All farm products		100	105	120	113	92	97

[a]Greater detail is given in Appendix D.
[b]Includes pasture on cropland.
[c]Includes about 30 million acres required for failure, summer fallow, the remainder being unused cropland.
[d]Includes pasture on and off farms except cropland pasture.

[e]Indexes of Prices Received by Farmers in constant (1967) dollars.

In future 3, although population is high and ...ricultural technology is restricted, the lower economic ...owth rate would reduce consumer demand for food ...d fiber. This would mean less pressure on land and ...her production resources and would result in lower ...ices.

In future 4, low population would result in a low ...vel of overall demand. With demand at a low level and ...th low production constraints, this alternative would ...e the smallest amounts of land and labor. As a result, ...harvested cropland would total about 50 million ...res—about 20 million above the minimum acreage ...eded for cultivated summer fallow and crop failure. ...arm prices would be at the lowest level among the ...ternatives examined.

Future 5 combines low population and economic ...owth with constraints on technology so that the ...roduction of food and fiber would be at the lowest ...vel. Due to the restrictions assumed, fertilizer and ...esticide use would be lower than for any other ...ternative. More land and labor would be required than ... future 4; thus, commodity prices would be slightly ...gher.

It is important to note that the supply of cropland available for agricultural purposes is flexible and is influenced by the level of agricultural prices and the profitability of competing uses of land. Nonharvested cropland, beyond a requirement of about 30 million acres for crop failure and summer fallow, is unnecessary. Thus, low levels of unharvested cropland shown in Table 4 do not imply that additional land from pasture, forest, or other uses is unavailable for conversion to crop production.

Supporting details for the years 1970, 1980, and 2000 are contained in Appendix D.

Effects of Assumptions

Population Size

A comparison of alternatives 1 and 4 shows the effect of the population growth rate on agriculture, since these two futures are alike with respect to other assumptions. Alternative 1 with a population about 55 million greater than alternative 4 would require 32 million more acres of harvested cropland, two million more tons of nitrogen fertilizer, 50 million more pounds of pesticides, and 0.2 billion more man-hours of labor. Total agricultural production and the index of commodity prices would be about 15 percent higher for alternative 1.

A comparison of alternative 1 with the 1970 column of Table 4 indicates that United States agriculture would have the capacity to feed and clothe 321 million people in the year 2000. Due to the increased use of fertilizer and pesticides by about 130 and 60 percent respectively, the labor use and total cropland acreage in 2000 would be less than that of 1970 when production of crops and livestock was little more than one-half the projected year 2000 level.

Alternative future 4 would seem to be a clear environmental improvement over alternative 1—less cropland would be harvested, less animal waste would be produced, less fertilizer and pesticides would be used, and food would be less expensive. On the other hand, returns to owners of land and other agricultural production resources would be lower under alternative 4. Even though there would be in this alternative a net reduction in total cropland of 30 million acres since 1970, there would remain about 20 million acres of excess cropland above the 30 million acres usually not harvested because of summer fallow and crop failure.

Economic Growth Rate

A comparison of alternative future 2 with alternative 3 makes possible an examination of the effect of different rates of economic growth. A lower rate of economic growth operating through a reduction in per capita incomes of $1,225 would result in a slightly lower total demand for agricultural products and a shift away from livestock products in favor of food crops. This lessened demand would cause lower prices for agricultural products and some reduction in total agricultural output.

The reduction in the use of production inputs—land, labor, fertilizer, and pesticides—that would be experienced with alternative 3 is hardly significant in terms of absolute quantities or percentages. Thus, any improvement in environmental quality would seem slight. The lower quality and quantity of foodstuffs in the national diet would seem, however, to be an important adverse effect of lower per capita disposable incomes.

Technology Constraints

The effect of constraints on agricultural production technology to improve environmental quality can be analyzed by means of a comparison of alternative futures 1 and 2. Alternative 2 would substitute additional land and labor inputs for nitrogen fertilizer and pesticides. Additional aspects of the high constraint

alternative, such as animal waste disposal, would also increase the cost of production. With a more expensive combination of inputs, production of agricultural commodities would be reduced and prices would increase.

The total amount of nitrogen fertilizer used per acre of harvested cropland in the year 2000 would be reduced from about 75 pounds in alternative 1 to less than 45 pounds in alternative 2. Total fertilizer use would not be reduced proportionally, however, due to the larger number of harvested acres that would be required in the second alternative. Total active ingredient pesticide use per acre of harvested cropland in the year 2000 would be reduced from more than one and one-half pounds to less than one-half pound.

The waste residuals from fertilizer, pesticides, and livestock would be substantially reduced under the technology constraints of alternative 2. On the other hand, the cultivation of nearly 50 million additional acres of cropland would likely have some inherent deleterious effects on environmental quality particularly from soil erosion. When the increase in the commodity price index of 15 percent is also considered, the net benefit, if any, to society from technological constraints is difficult to assess.

Comparison of Assumptions

If the lowest level of agricultural output, coupled with the lowest use of fertilizer and pesticides is desired, alternative future 5 would be the answer. It combines all factors which would minimize the use of land intensive technology. Fewer people would be fed at a lower level of per capita food consumption. On the other hand agriculture in the year 2000 seems able to meet even the most difficult challenge, that posed by alternative 2.

The effects of different operating variable assumptions on the inputs with greatest environmental impact are shown in Table 5. If a reduction in harvested cropland is desired, a slower rate of population growth would be an effective measure. If a reduction in use of nitrogen fertilizer is sought, either a reduction in population growth rate or the use of technological constraints appears effective. Pesticide use appears to be most effectively reduced by technology constraints. The slower rate of economic growth seems to have a relatively small effect on harvested cropland acreage or use of nitrogen fertilizer and pesticides, although it could be used to enhance the effect of other measures.

A relevant question remains unanswered. What is the effect on environmental quality of alternative combinations of inputs? Until environmental quality can be quantified with some index or scale, interinput comparisons of environmental effects cannot be satisfactorily made.

190

Table 5.—Effect of Assumptions On Use of Selected Inputs in 2000[a]

Assumption	Input		
	Harvested cropland	Nitrogen	Pesticide
	(Percentage reduction in level of use)		
Low population growth rate Alternative 4 vs. 1	8	13	8
Low economic growth rate Alternative 3 vs. 2	1	2	2
Restricted technology Alternative 2 vs. 1	-12[b]	36	79

[a]Computations are based on unrounded data.
[b]Increase.

POLICY IMPLICATIONS

Agriculture employs biological processes to achieve selected outcomes. In market-oriented countries like the United States, strong incentives have encouraged the production of goods such as crops and livestock. Science, experience, and husbandry have been extremely successful in developing the means for producing these commodities. Until this nation became aware of some of the negative effects of food and fiber production on the environment, particularly on water supplies and some wildlife species, the unqualified success of this culture—agriculture—remained unchallenged.

Agriculture is now challenged with achieving a new "selected outcome"—a wholesome, attractive environment—in addition to abundant supplies of food and fiber. Agriculture is being asked to be beautiful and clean. Agriculture is being asked to conserve land and water, to protect wildlife, and to landscape the countryside. As yet, the traditional market forces which provided signals for agriculture have not been mobilized toward the new selected outcomes. Some doubt whether the market can provide the needed incentives for agriculture to produce these new selected outcomes. Others, seeing an improved environment as a fundamental right of all persons, demand that agriculture donate productive resources to these new desired ends. It is within such a cultural, economic, and political circumstance that policy is to be reshaped.

Where the food and fiber objective and the environmental objective compete, some mechanism should provide agriculture with the appropriate guidance. The chance of success will be greater if the same mechanism—the traditional market place—is employed to accomplish both objectives. This does not imply that environmental "products" will be raised, processed, packaged, and sold in the supermarket like pork chops or cheese. For the present at least, the environmental "products" are too loosely defined, and the customers are too widely diffused to make effective use of traditional market procedures. Nevertheless, the rapid growth in health foods, the availability of vacation farms, the expansion of sport and commercial fish farming, and the second home development are evidence that some of the environmental products are entering the market. Economical means for handling some agricultural wastes are also being designed.

Yet the costs and benefits of alternative outcomes, environmental products, or food and fiber, have not been clearly arrayed before decision makers—farmers, suppliers, processors, marketers, and consumers. Researchers and educators are still seeking to sort out and express desired ends and the precise means to bring about these ends.

The question is how does society design guides or incentives for decision makers who affect the environment. At present, these decision makers are unable to appropriate the benefits, and are able to avoid the costs, associated with actions affecting the environment. These benefit-cost incentives are external to the decisions of the individual. If the decision makers are to be induced to provide the right combination of food, fiber, and environmental products, they must feel the benefit of doing the right thing and the cost of doing the wrong thing. In short, these benefits and costs must be internalized. How can this be done?

For purposes of explication, the policy instruments available to governments have been summarized into three broad categories. All three methods are presently used in a variety of situations and continue to be suggested for further application. These three categories of public policy are: (1) regulations and standards; (2) subsidies, payments, and credits; and (3) taxes, charges, and fees.

Regulation

Regulation is most obvious to the consumer at the food inspection level. At present, a system of tolerances for pesticide residues is in existence to safeguard the public from harm. These tolerances impose certain restrictions upon the producers of these products. Additional regulations extend directly back to the producer specifying which materials may be used, crops or animals on which they may be used, and the frequency and method of application. Other regulations have been proposed that would license material handlers so as to keep toxic substances out of the hands of those not qualified to use them. Restrictions on animal and other waste effluent discharged into surface and ground water have been used in some jurisdictions to obtain efficient, effective waste management systems in feed lots and other agricultural operations. Some have suggested that some maximum level of fertilizer use per acre be set to reduce the possibility of surface and ground water contamination. Location of agricultural production may also be regulated through land use restrictions.

Subsidization

Subsidies are payments made to firms or expenses assumed from firms for the purpose of inducing them to modify their conduct in a socially desirable manner. For example, a proposal has been advanced to pay livestock producers a set amount for each unit of animal waste returned to the land. Tax credits have been advocated for construction of waste treatment facilities. Biological methods of pest control have been developed and made available by the government at reduced costs to individual producers. In general, government-supported research coupled with government-financed educational programs have been used to influence the agricultural technology in use. Subsidies frequently lead to lower direct costs to the consumer and tend to increase consumption of the product. Should this occur, the level of pollution could be higher than that which existed prior to the subsidy.

Taxation

For many years, the environment, particularly air and water, were considered by most users to be "free" goods. The time has now come when these formerly "free" goods have become scarce. There is an optimal level of use of scarce goods, generally achieved in our society by charging those who seek to use the good. This concept is the basis for user charges or taxes. One application is a charge per unit of effluent discharge. The use of such charges has been suggested to encourage the reduction of effluent discharge to some predetermined acceptable level. An economic incentive then exists for the polluter to reduce the extent of damage he creates. Higher costs of production require higher prices and reduce the quantity of product demanded; this in turn reduces waste production. Likewise, taxes can be used to internalize the externalities associated with fertilizer and pesticide use. Producers can be expected to maximize profits by using fertilizer and pesticides on each crop up to the level where the additional value of the crop is just equal to the additional cost of the input. And since a tax added to the price of an input would raise the marginal

cost of production, it can be applied to reduce the use of an input such as fertilizer or pesticides.

Other Government Programs

In addition to direct action programs to deal with pollution, there are a number of indirect government programs which have had or could have an effect on agriculture's environmental impact.

Insurance

A government-subsidized program of insurance to protect from unusual losses due to insects, disease, or weeds would lessen farmers dependence upon pesticides. Such a form of compensation would allow decisions about the profitability and desirability of controlling some very destructive, but localized, economic pests to be made on an aggregate basis rather than placing the sole responsibility on individuals. When a localized pest outbreak occurs, it might be cheaper to sacrifice part of the crop than to upset the ecological balance of the area.[9]

Production Control

Production control programs of the Federal government include feed grains, wheat, rice, peanuts, cotton, and tobacco. For the most part, the control mechanism has been brought to bear on land as a factor of production, ignoring labor, capital, and other inputs (fertilizer, pesticides, etc.). Previous per acre yields are often the basis for computing future program payment rates. This has provided an incentive for farmers to offset producing acreage restrictions by higher yields per acre than would economically optimize input use in the absence of programs. In many farm operations, chemicals (fertilizer and pesticides) have been used partly as a substitute for land in an effort to offset program restrictions on eligible cropland.

Marketing quotas, which control and subsidize the number of units sold rather than the acreage used to produce them, have been suggested as a method which would improve resource allocation over present programs. Some have questioned why income maintenance payments to farmers should be tied at all to the production of a specific commodity. A flat income maintenance payment per farm family could be adopted. Volume of production and resource allocation would then be controlled by free market forces.

What differences in concern for the environment exist between large corporate farms and small farmers who live on their land? Are individual farmers any less careless with nature? Must the small farmer be protected from the conglomerate? Would public policy to limit the size of agricultural operations in terms of acres, animal units or dollar sales have a beneficial effect on environmental quality? Additional study is needed on the broader impact of alternative supply control programs.

Land Use

Related to the nation's concern for a wholesome environment is the emerging discussion about land use policy. Such a policy would insure the maintenance of sufficient prime agricultural land as well as forests and open spaces. All land—public and private—and all uses, including related water resources, should be included.[10]

State and Federal cooperation in the planning and regulation of land use has been proposed. The amount and location of land for agricultural, urban, and industrial uses would be allocated under such a program. Programs providing for land use are most effective when coordinated with other related governmental programs including land taxation based on use; transportation facilities to provide for the needs of people, agriculture, and industry; and management of public lands.

Research

Research necessary to develop alternative technologies, which could reduce the agricultural impact on the environment, can often be done more efficiently on a public rather than a private basis. Generally, the total benefits to society are often far in excess of total costs in this type of research. This, of course, is the rationale for publicly financed agricultural research.

Entomology and agronomy research directed to biological or highly specific chemical control of pests fits the above criterion. Recycling of agricultural wastes, particularly animal, into useful channels is another area where potential benefits appear to be high. Genetic improvement of plants and animals for increased efficiency of nutrient use would save scarce resources and minimize losses through waste. In light of projected increases in fertilizer use, expanded research to improve the formulation and application of fertilizer materials to reduce field losses is essential. Better statistical data series are needed to gauge the quantities of chemicals used, the quantities of residuals entering the environment, and the effects of accumulation in the ecosystem.

Resource Improvement and Development[11]

Agricultural resources appear to be generally adequate at least to 2000. Nevertheless, steadily increasing demand and likely environmental constraints on technology raise the question of resource adequacy over the very long run. Natural resources such as soil, water, minerals, and ores are, for the most part, either nonrenewable or replenishable only at some fixed rate

by nature. Resources can be used at exhaustive rates and eventually depleted, or their use can be regulated. Resources also may be developed to improve their quality and availability over time.

Resource improvement and development by the public are alternatives and also complement public research expenditures to promote general technology. Improvements in natural resources can have an effect similar to general technology—allowing output to be produced with less input. Thus, resource development can be an alternative to increasing use of other inputs such as chemical fertilizer and pesticides. In agriculture, such practices as land drainage, leveling, terracing, and irrigation are typical.

The implication is that positive action should be continued to insure that resource barriers do not become critical. Further research and analyses on the potential gains and losses of alternative public actions for alleviating resource problems are needed.

Nonagricultural Policy

Government policy in such broad areas as labor and foreign trade also can have implications for agriculture and the environment. Labor legislation with respect to wages, benefits, and unionization may increase the cost of this input to farmers. The environmental result is mixed. In some cases, chemicals such as herbicides are used to substitute for labor. In other cases, production of labor-intensive crops such as strawberries and some fresh vegetables has moved outside the nation's boundaries. On the other hand, import tariffs and quotas when applied by the United States, will tend to increase domestic production of some commodities such as livestock and thereby add to the domestic generation of waste residuals.

CONCLUSIONS

American agriculture appears capable, in terms of resource adequacy, technology, and structural flexibility, of meeting the challenges of the year 2000. Even under the most demanding assumptions about population and constraints on technology, food and fiber needs could be met without great difficulty, but would require some increase in prices. Under less stringent requirements on technology and lower demands on food, total agricultural land use is lower, and food prices in constant dollars are generally comparable with present levels.

The four operating variables studied in this analysis vary widely in their effect on the use of various production inputs and, therefore, on their contribution to environmental quality. The rate of population growth has a direct, but not necessarily linear, effect on resource use. For example, fertilizer use would increase more rapidly than acreage of harvested cropland as land of lower quality is brought into production. Alternative rates of growth in per capita income, at least of the size studied here, would have a rather modest effect on total agricultural output, land use, and the use of other production inputs. The alternative assumptions about population distribution result in some differences in land used for purposes of human habitation, but the changes in overall land use are not large enough to have any substantial effect on agricultural production. Constraints on production technology of the nature assumed here would result in substantial changes in cultural practices, cropping patterns, and a substantial reduction in fertilizer and pesticide use at the expense of some additional acreage of harvested cropland.

Assumptions made about trends over the next three decades in crop yields and the mix between traditional versus synthetic or substitute products result in a higher acreage of harvested cropland under all five alternatives. In three cases (alternatives 1, 4, and 5), the increase in harvested cropland would largely come from the 60 million acres of presently idle excess cropland. In the case of the other two alternatives (2 and 3), where high population is teamed with high constraints on technology, some addition to the present cropland base would be required. The U.S. Department of Agriculture has classified some 637 million acres of privately owned land in capability classes I-III as suitable for cultivation.[12] The necessity to develop this new cropland from land presently in pasture and range, timberland, or idle nonagricultural land would require higher prices for farm commodities under these two alternatives.

Fertilizer usage would increase by the year 2000 under each of the five alternatives. For the three alternatives involving high constraints on technology, this increase is on the order of 50 percent from present levels. When low constraints on technology are assumed, the level of use would likely be about double that of recent years. For both economic and environmental reasons, farmers are expected to improve fertilizer application techniques in ways that will reduce losses through surface drainage and into groundwater. As a consequence, the detrimental effect on the environment should in no case be any greater than at present.

Pesticide usage is projected to increase in the low constraint futures. However, the environmental impact should be no greater than in recent years because of expected changes in methods of application and in persistence of the formulations. The level of pesticides which would result with the high constraint alternatives would reduce the environmental exposure far below present levels.

One of the effects of technological development in United States agriculture has been the reduction in labor requirements per unit of output. This reduced labor requirement has led to a migration of nearly six million farm workers from agriculture in the last 20 years. With low constraints on technology this analysis shows that less than half of the four million presently remaining would be needed in the year 2000. High constraints on technology would slow this trend somewhat and would require nearly one million more farm workers than the low constraint futures.

Although this analysis has been confined to prospects up to the year 2000, there are implications which relate to the much longer run. For example, if this analysis were continued out to the year 2020, the cost of bringing additional farmland into production could possibly increase food prices substantially, and thus significantly increase the difficulty of achieving the restricted technology case. However, over such a long time period, the range of possibilities becomes so broad that analysis grows increasingly difficult. The capabilities of science in 50 years or more are difficult to imagine. If we begin to face scarcity of resources and high resource prices, for example, use of substitute and synthetic products could be sharply increased.

Conclusions of resource adequacy in the year 2000 should not lead to complacency about potential problems in the decades to follow. Water for irrigation of agricultural lands is likely to be severely restricted in some regions of the country. As other land requirements, such as suburban and transportation uses, continue to expand, increases in cropland acreage will become more difficult to achieve. Thus, the question of resource adequacy and cumulative environmental damage will continue to command our attention. The choices being made now in areas such as public policy and technological development will determine mankind's inheritance.

REFERENCES

1. Sterling Brubaker, *To Live on Earth: Environmental Problems in Perspective* (Baltimore: Johns Hopkins Press for Resources for the Future, 1972); Daniel H. Kohl and Barry Commoner, "A Study of Certain Ecological, Public Health and Economic Consequences of the Use of Inorganic Nitrogen Fertilizer" (research proposal submitted to the National Science Foundation, 1970); and David R. Zwick and Mary Benstock, *Water Wasteland* (Washington: Center for Study of Responsive Law, 1971).

2. Robert White-Stevens, "Farm Chemicals and Water Pollution" (paper presented to the 22nd Annual Midwest Fertilizer Conference, The Fertilizer Institute, Chicago, Illinois, Feb. 16-17, 1970); and W. C. Shaw, "How Agricultural Chemicals Contribute to our Current Food Supplies"(paper presented to

Agricultural Chemicals Symposium, University of California, Sacramento, California, Feb. 16-17, 1971).

3. Herman Kahn and Anthony Wiener, *The Year 2000* (New York: The Macmillan Co., 1968), p. 6.

4. Velmar W. Davis, "Economics of Fertilizer Use by United States Farmers" (paper presented at a Symposium on Chemical and Toxicological Aspects of Environmental Quality, Institute for Ecological Chemistry, Munich, Germany, May 27-28, 1971).

5. Brubaker, *op. cit.,* p. 47.

6. U.S. Department of Agriculture, *Qualities of Pesticides Used by Farmers in 1966,* by Theodore Eichers *et al.,* Agricultural Economic Report No. 179, 1970, p. 6.

7. U.S. Congress, House, Committee on Agriculture, testimony by Velmar Davis on *Federal Pesticide Control Act of 1971, Hearings,* 92nd Cong., 1st sess., February 23, 1971.

8. Arthur B. Mackie, "Patterns of World Agricultural Trade" (paper presented at Conference on U.S. Trade Policy and Agricultural Exports at the Center for Agricultural and Economic Development, Iowa State University, Ames, Iowa, June 1-3, 1971).

9. Robert Jenkins, "A Systems Appraisal to Pest Control" (paper presented at Economic Research on Pesticides for Policy Decision Making Seminar, Washington, April 27-29, 1970), p. 105.

10. Ned Bayley, "Policies and Regulations on Environmental Quality" (paper presented at a Conference on Agriculture and the Environment, University of Florida, Gainesville, Florida, March 3, 1971), p. 3.

11. For a comprehensive discussion of these points, see Melvin L. Cotner, "A Policy for Public Investments in Natural Resources," *American Journal of Agricultural Economics,* 1969, Vol. 51.

12. U.S. Department of Agriculture, *Basic Statistics—National Inventory of Soil and Water Conservation Needs,* Stat. Bulletin No. 461, Jan. 1971.

APPENDIX A
AGRICULTURE AND POLLUTION

The relationship between agriculture and the environment has been stated by Brubaker as follows: Modern agriculture employs the soil as a medium to hold roots, water and nutrients and to expose plants to the sun. In every other respect, it departs from the natural cycle. The three technical bases of modern agriculture are the use of fertilizer to provide nutrients, improved seed to maximize the special qualities sought in a plant, and the use of pesticide to control enemies or competition.[1] Agricultural production processes are polluting when they introduce into man's environment—air, food, water, soil—a deleterious substance, living or inanimate, in sufficient quantity as to constitute a danger, hazard, or inconvenience to the health and well-being of man and his favored plants and animals, wild or domestic.[2]

Livestock Waste

Of all of the agriculture's problems with pollution, one of the most costly to overcome appears to be the disposal of solid wastes. These account for over one-half of the total solid wastes produced in the United States. Every day, 3.5 million tons of raw manure are produced, accompanied by a million tons of liquid waste.[3] This quantity of waste—the equivalent of the waste from a human population of 1.9 billion—has created problems of odor, dust, flies, groundwater contamination by nitrates, and surface water contamination by bacteria, nitrogen, phosphates, and oxygen-removing organic matter.

Most livestock feeding systems result in manure being stored for some time in an untreated or partially treated form. Stored manure frequently creates the problem of gas and odor. The principal gaseous products of manure are ammonia, carbon dioxide, hydrogen sulfide, and methane. Their presence is offensive and dangerous to men and animals because ammonia is an irritant, carbon dioxide is an asphyxiant, hydrogen sulfide is a poison, and methane is an explosive.[4] However, these gases are seldom present in sufficient concentrations or quantities to have a physiological effect. Odors can interfere with the enjoyment of life and property and thus are more likely to be considered a public nuisance than a health hazard.

Bacteria, which are considered pollutants when found in water, are of course present in abundant quantities in raw animal waste. Some of these bacteria can be human pathogens. Generally, only surface water is affected by bacteria of animal origin. This can occur when feedlots drain into streams or when large quantities of manure are spread on soil surfaces and enter the runoff of rain or melting snow. Groundwater is protected by the filtering action of soil as water percolates to the aquifer.[5]

Probably the most serious pollution threat from animal wastes lies in the pollution of water from nitrates, phosphates, and organic matter. Groundwater supplies in areas of heavy cattle feeding can receive sufficient quantities of nitrates from leaching to make their consumption dangerous for humans, particularly infants. Surface waters can be sufficiently enriched in nitrogen and phosphorus to cause excessive algae growth making it unpotable for humans and deadly for fish.

It should be clear from the preceding discussion that animal waste disposal has become a serious problem where intensive livestock operations have developed. Methods of disposal include heavy spreading or plow down, lagooning, feeding fish and livestock, burning, pyrolysis, fermenting, and drying and selling.

Before the advent of inexpensive inorganic fertilizer, a large proportion of manure produced was spread on cropland and pastures. At this time, most cattle, swine, and poultry feeders also produced grain and forage crops. Therefore, most livestock producers had land on which manure could be used beneficially and economically. Today, inorganic fertilizers are available in a variety of labor saving forms at low costs per unit of nutrient content. Today, increasing specialization in animal agriculture has led to feeders with no cropland of their own.

What is the competitive position between manure and inorganic fertilizer as inputs for crop production? Cattle manure contains approximately 10 pounds of nitrogen, two pounds of phosphorous, and 10 pounds of potassium per ton. When these three plant macro-nutrients are valued at their replacement cost from inorganic fertilizer, their total value is about $1.40 per ton. Not included in this total is the value of minor elements and organic matter. Poultry manure is more concentrated than bovine. On a per ton basis, it contains 25 pounds of nitrogen, 11 pounds of phosphorus, and 10 pounds of potassium with a total value of $3.35. Since manure is less concentrated than commercial fertilizer, the cost of loading, hauling and spreading in the field is more expensive per unit of nutrient. Studies have shown the cost of hauling and spreading manure varied from $1.92 to $3.18 per ton.[6] On a pure cost basis then, the cost of spreading a ton of manure is approximately the equal of its fertilizer value. For this reason, farmers frequently purchase their fertilizer on a custom spread basis, eliminating the need for extra equipment and labor. Also, most workers would rather, on a purely aesthetic basis, load and spread fertilizer than manure.

Although spreading manure on land is an obvious means of disposal, farmers may not spread animal waste for the following reasons:

1. The ground may be covered with snow or frozen so that manure can not be incorporated into the soil surface.

2. Excessive applications of manure on pasture may kill the grass or poison grazing cattle.

3. Other means of manure disposal may be less costly per ton.

4. The livestock operation may not be located near land suitable for spreading.

A small specialty market exists for dried and packaged animal wastes for use as a lawn, garden, and house plant fertilizer. The cost of drying and packaging is high if the plant is equipped to avoid air pollution. Competition from commercial inorganic fertilizers restricts the quantity of processed animal manure that can be sold in the nonagricultural market.

Coprophage (the feeding of manure) is another method of livestock manure utilization. For many years, hogs have been used as scavengers after cattle. Poultry manure has also proven successful in limited trials as an animal feed. Livestock are able to reutilize the feed value in manure with a reduction in the cost of other feed. Meat products have shown no off-flavors. The practice does have public health implications, however; the processing methods, status of pathogenic organisms, pesticide, drug, and heavy metal residues must all be known and controlled.[7] Widespread adoption of this practice awaits development of technology which would be economically feasible on a mass scale.

A decided trend toward biological treatment of animal wastes has emerged in conjunction with confined livestock feeding operations. The common system involves the use of one or more lagoons where the waste components are broken down by microorganisms. The first treatment is usually anaerobic, where the organic matter is digested into sludge. Secondary treatment is aerobic with a further reduction of the volume of sludge. The sludge remaining, a small fraction of the original quantity, can be returned to the land at a lesser cost than the original waste.

Lagoons are an economical method of disposal in many situations. The manure can be flushed by water into the lagoon, with a reduction in hand labor of 80 percent. Odors and nutrient runoff into streams can be controlled with properly designed systems. Cold weather does reduce the biological activity in the lagoon. In areas of heavy rainfall, the disposal of excess liquid can be a major problem. But if the system is properly designed and has sufficient capacity, lagoons can be used year around in most areas of the country.

Increasingly, livestock producers are coming under the provisions of state and Federal pollution control acts. It would seem that the economic and institutional pressures associated with protecting the environment will fall hardest on the larger specialized livestock feeders. On the other hand, the farmer-feeder, with a lower concentration of livestock per unit of land and, therefore, land on which manure can be applied, may escape inclusion in the regulations and enjoy an advantage in cost of production.

Fertilizer

Of the 16 known plant nutrients, three are derived from air or water—carbon, hydrogen, and oxygen. The remaining 13 nutrients can be supplied in varying degrees of sufficiency by the soil. Although nitrogen and potassium are often more abundant than the other soil-derived nutrients, crops generally require more of these two elements.[8]

It became readily apparent hundreds of years ago to tillers of the soil that plants would respond to supplemental applications of nutrients. Indians, for example, placed dead fish alongside of growing corn. Manure from farm animals was taken from barns and spread on cropland. Later, a more abundant and concentrated source of manure was exploited for agricultural use—guano, the manure of sea birds from islands off the coast of Peru. More recently, man discovered that plant nutrients can be chemically extracted from such sources as rocks, natural gas, and air.

With the knowledge that plants respond to supplemental fertilizer, the farmer's task ultimately became one of determining how much fertilizer he could use before the cost of fertilizer equaled the value of the added crop production. The agronomist's task became one of determining what cultural practices utilized supplemental fertilizer most efficiently. The plant breeder's task became one of developing plant varieties that maximized the response to supplemental fertilizer. The chemical industry's task became one of providing fertilizers in a form convenient to use at the lowest possible cost per unit of nutrient. All parties diligently applied themselves to their respective responsibilities. In the last 15 years, total use of fertilizer (in terms of principal plant nutrients) in the United States increased from 4.5 million tons to 12.7 million tons. During this period, the use of supplemental nitrogen rose from less than two million tons to 7.4 million tons partly as the result of a decline in price from 10 cents per pound to less than five cents.[9] However, since 1969, prices paid by farmers for fertilizer have been increasing.

The heavy use of nitrogen fertilizer in recent years has led some environmentalists to place the blame on agricultural use of fertilizer for nitrate polluted water. Yet nitrogen makes up 78 percent of the atmosphere and is present in all living tissue. The burning of fossil fuels, the life processes, and the decay of organic matter all release concentrated forms of nitrogen into the ecosystem. In Connecticut, it was found that industrial smoke and auto exhausts contributed 52 percent of the nitrogen injected into the environment, and that 40 percent of this ultimately returned to land and water surfaces.[10] A Wisconsin study showed 30 percent of the nitrogen and 58 percent of the phosphorus entering surface waters originated in municipal and private sewage.[11] A study of the Potomac River watershed showed forest land as the source of 16 percent of the nitrates in the water.[12]

The entry of fertilizer nutrients into water can cause two very different, but equally serious, types of problems. Even very low concentration of nitrogen or phosphorus can stimulate a very profuse growth of algae and other aquatic plants. These plants produce large quantities of organic matter which ultimately decompose. Fish are killed from the removal of dissolved oxygen in the water. The aesthetic quality of the water for human consumption is reduced. Humans and livestock consuming water contaminated by nitrates can be affected more directly. Infants and ruminant livestock are particularly sensitive and may develop methemoglobinemia (oxidation of blood hemoglobin) when the nitrogen content of drinking water exceeds 10 ppm nitrate.

Has the nitrate content of the nation's surface and groundwater increased in recent years? If so, has fertilizer use caused this increased nitrate content? The evidence is conflicting and seems to indicate different conclusions for different regions. In three irrigated areas along the upper Rio Grande, fertilizer use increased 100-fold in the 1934-1963 period, yet the nitrate content of return drains to the river has not increased measurably.[13] Nitrate content of the Wabash River near Lafayette is no higher now than in 1906, although use of commercial fertilizer in the watershed has increase; substantially.[14] On the other hand, it has been estimated that at least 60 percent of the nitrate entering Lake Decatur (Illinois) during the January-July period in 1970 originated from inorganic nitrate fertilizer applied in the watershed.[15]

Phosphorus, in contrast to nitrogen, when added to the soil, is rapidly immobilized through absorption in clays or becomes a precipitate with iron or aluminum. Very little phosphate is lost by leaching and none by volatilization. Phosphorus additions to water bodies from agricultural lands are almost wholly the result of soil erosion. Thus, erosion control practices, which include good plant cover, will tend to control water pollution from phosphorus.[16]

Stanford, and others, conclude that current levels of fertilizer use, when applied according to accepted principles, are normally not a threat to water quality except in isolated instances.[17]

In many cases, the efficiency with which crops utilize the fertilizer applied may be as important as the amount applied.

Efficiency of fertilizer use is defined simply as the percentage of applied nutrient recovered by the crop. Only rarely have tests shown nitrogen recoveries greater than 95 percent; values of 70 percent to 90 percent are fairly common. Nitrogen recovery under field conditions may be no greater than 50 percent to 60 percent of the nitrogen applied.[18] Data from Nebraska experiments on corn gave efficiencies of 55 percent to 69 percent for applications of 100 to 160 pounds of nitrogen. Iowa data showed an efficiency of 76 percent from an average application of 66 pounds of nitrogen per acre.[19]

Efficiency of use of an applied nutrient is affected by numerous factors—timing and placement, adequacy of other nutrients, water level in soil, soil physical properties, and the type of product used. Timing of application includes consideration of temperature and the plant growth stage. The longer fertilizer remains unused in the soil, the greater the probability of loss. If less fertilizer is required to produce the same yield, it can be applied closer to the time of maximum demand by the crop. Fall application of nitrogen causes especially heavy nutrient losses on sandy soils, or poorly drained soils, or on soils subject to erosion. Many times, however, timing of fertilizer application is determined as much by considerations involving convenience to the farmer or the sales organization as by principles of efficient use.

If the use of fertilizer in agriculture is restricted in order to protect the environment, the most obvious substitute is additional cropland. Estimates of the additional agricultural land required to sustain the present United States population on a continuous basis without the use of any fertilizer range up to 200 million acres.[20]

It is not yet clear what benefits, if any, society would gain by a total or partial substitution of land for fertilizer. Severe restrictions on fertilizer could increase the level of environmental pollution. High yields produce heavier crop residues which contribute to improved physical condition of the soil. In addition, the increased yields from fertilizer use have allowed formerly eroded agricultural land to be returned to forest, pasture or recreational use.

Restrictions on fertilizer will raise food costs. Corn production budgets for the corn belt states in 1970 show an average use of 110 pounds of fertilizer nitrogen per acre, an average yield of 94 bushels per acre, and an average production cost of $1.00 per bushel. These same budgets show the cost of corn production rising to $1.13 per bushel when only 50 pounds of fertilizer nitrogen are used and $1.39 per bushel when no fertilizer is used.[21] Mayer and Hargrove studied the effect of a nationwide restriction on fertilizer use. Their data show that limiting farmers to 50 pounds of nitrogen per acre would have resulted in an increase in food costs of 4.4 percent in 1970; by 1980, the increase in food costs from such a limitation would be more than 20 percent. A complete prohibition on fertilizer use would have increased food costs 11.2 percent in 1970 and nearly 40 percent by 1980.[22]

Most changes in the technology of fertilizer application which might be adopted for the protection of the environment would be cost-increasing for the farmer. These could include more complex and expensive fertilizer formulations to effect controlled release of nutrients, and more frequent, smaller applications of fertilizer. Farmers, being rational businessmen, would not willingly convert to such practices, unless there was a financial incentive for their adoption or unless they were required to do so by regulation. If fertilizer materials become more costly, a likely forecast for the years ahead, the market system itself will provide some economic incentives to improve the efficiency of fertilizer use.

Pesticides

Man has found himself in competition with various other forms of life. In the agricultural sphere alone, it has been estimated there are 1,500 diseases caused by fungi, 1,800 species of weeds which cause serious economic loss, 1,500 species of nematodes which attack plants, and 10,000 species of insects which cause serious losses. Annual losses in potential United States agricultural production, crops and livestock, during the decade 1951-1960, were nine percent due to weeds, 10 percent due to disease, one percent due to nematodes, and 13 percent due to insects—a total loss of potential production of 33 percent.[23]

Man's attempts to control such pests have taken four different forms: (1) mechanical methods such as cultivation, barriers, and trapping; (2) cultural methods such as timing of planting and crop rotations; (3) biological methods such as diseases or insects, resistant varieties, predators, and parasites; and (4) chemical pesticides. Although most farmers employ all four methods of pest control, the primary environmental concern is with chemicals.

Many changes have occurred during the last two decades in the amounts and types of pesticides used. For example, 15 years ago, Mississippi Delta farmers used one chemical application along with six to 10 mechanical cultivations and 25 hours of hand weeding to control grass and weeds in cotton. Today, they used three to six chemicals in six or more applications along with four to six mechanical cultivations and four to eight hours of hand weed control.[24]

Table A-1 details changes in the production of common chemical pesticides. Currently, farmers account for a little over one-half of all pesticides used in the United States. In addition some United States production is exported. This table makes clear the switch in technology from compounds of arsenic to the organic insecticides. Recent data show a substitution of organophosphates and carbamates for organochlorines.

There is considerable variation between crops in the amounts and types of pesticides used. Cotton and corn are the leading pesticide users. In 1966, cotton accounted for 47 percent of all insecticides used on crops, while corn accounted for 41 percent of the total herbicides in agriculture.[25] Eighty percent of the total acreage of fruits and nuts are treated with insecticides—2.3 million acres at an average rate of seven pounds per acre annually. Likewise, about 80 percent of cotton acreage in areas where the boll weevil is a problem is normally treated with insecticide.[26] In the Dakotas, where weed control is a major problem, about 80 percent of the hard red spring wheat acreage is treated with herbicide annually.

The widespread adoption and increased use of pesticides are caused by three types of effects upon the farmer's profit and loss statement. Pesticides raise yields and thus gross receipts from crops or livestock above levels which could be obtained by other practical means. Pesticides may reduce year-to-year fluctuations in yields and gross receipts. In some cases, pesticides may substitute for more costly inputs, such as labor or land.

Benefits to society from widespread use of pesticides include increased productivity and improved control of human diseases. Human nutrition is improved when food of better quality and wholesomeness is produced at lower costs. Man's fiber needs are also better provided at lower cost. Land and labor are freed from agricultural usage for the other needs of man. In addition, many insect-borne diseases, such as malaria, yellow fever, and encephalitis, have been reduced.

But, unfortunately, there are also costs to society. There are occupational hazards inherent in the formulation and application of pesticides. The public also may be accidentally exposed during the storage, application, or disposal of pesticides. During 1959 in California alone, there were 1,100 cases of occupational disease attributed to agricultural chemicals (not all of these agricultural chemicals were pesticides). Deaths attributed to parathion, a widely used insecticide, numbered 100 in the United States during the period 1947-1960. Residues in plants or animals, although controlled by law, may find their way into the human diet. It is difficult to be certain about the long-run effects of high pesticide usage, but some warn of possible serious damage. One major concern is that the entire ecosystem—soil, wildlife, the sea—may become polluted by pesticides.[27]

Much criticism of pesticides is, on the basis of present information, rather speculative. While improper handling of pesticides has resulted in death, no human deaths have been clearly linked to residuals in the environment. Nor are there any known cases of consumers being poisoned from residues of pesticides applied in accordance with approved practices (as to application rate, delay between application and harvest, and crop clearance for particular chemicals). Although pesticide residues have been found in the body tissues of the general population, in food and in potable water supplies, apparently, the level of concentration has not been increasing in recent years.[28]

Immediate elimination of pesticides would work a massive hardship on society as a whole. Crop yields would be importantly affected. Insecticides applied to small grains have increased yields from 24 percent to

Table A-1.—Total Production of Selected Pesticides in the United States

Chemical	1934	1960	1969
	Thousands of pounds		
Calcium arsenate	41,349	6,590	2,000
Lead arsenate	59,569	10,062	7,000
White arsenate	44,686	0	0
Copper sulfate	134,032	116,000	42,072
Aldrin-toxaphene	0	90,671	107,311
Benzene hexachloride	0	37,444	(a)
DDT	0	164,180	123,103
Methyl bromide	0	12,659	20,033
Methyl parathion	0	11,794	50,572

[a]Data not available for 1969.

Source: J.C. Headly and J. N. Lewis, *The Pesticide Problem* (Washington: Resources for the Future, 1967).

1,900 percent above yields on untreated plots. Corn treated with insecticides has out-yielded untreated plots by 13 to 27 percent.[29]

A complete ban on use of DDT would, according to one estimate, raise insect control costs for cotton producers by $55 million annually.[30] Since the recently implemented restrictions on DDT, certain forest insects such as the gypsy moth and insect-borne diseases such as malaria and encephalitis have again appeared as serious problems in parts of the world.[31] Elimination of phenoxy herbicides would add an estimated $290 million a year to the production cost of food and fiber.[32] Yields of many food and feed grains are reduced about 10 percent when herbicides are excluded from use. Vegetable crops are more adversely affected—yield increases in test trials have ranged between 12 percent and over 500 percent from use of herbicide. Fungicides used in production of fruits and vegetables have also accounted for yield increases of 16 percent to 700 percent.[33]

There can be no question that present agricultural production technology is geared to widespread use of a variety of pesticides. Given time and the proper economic and institutional incentives, farmers could adopt a production technology which stressed alternative methods of pest control. Such a technology changeover, while possible, would tend to raise costs for agricultural products.

One alternative is the substitution of less persistent chemicals for those creating persistent residue problems. The substitution of organic phosphates for chlorinated hydrocarbons is a recent example of this concept. While this reduces the problem of residue accumulation in the environment, it frequently necessitates the more frequent use of a more toxic chemical to achieve the same degree of control. At this point, it appears that the substitution ratio between persistent and biodegradable chemicals which would maintain equal control is not linear but more likely a hyperbolic function; it becomes progressively more difficult to substitute one for the other. The reduction in the use of persistent but effective chemicals seems a more reasonable goal than their complete elimination.[34]

Another alternative to chemical pest control is different quality standards for food products. What is marketable depends on state regulations, USDA grades and standards, and consumer preferences. Elimination of insecticide on California apples and pears resulted in 21 percent to 23 percent wormy fruit compared with 0.5 percent wormy fruit from sprayed trees. Wormy ears of sweet corn increased from nine percent to 42 percent without spray.[35] Fewer pesticides could be used if consumers were willing to accept changes in quality standards, particularly those related to aesthetic considerations.

Crop rotations can be successfully used to reduce the building of disease and insect infestation. For example, insect damage in corn is reduced when soybeans are grown in alternate years. However, farmers' incomes are reduced when they are forced to include crops of lesser profitability in the rotation.

A variety of management tools, used along with pesticides, can reduce the total quantity of pesticide used while still achieving a satisfactory level of control. Traps have been used to indicate when certain fruit tree pests have emerged so that spray applications can be timed exactly. Many farmers could replace routine treatment schedules with treatment-when-necessary schedules if public information services were provided to predict crop losses. Herbicide use can be reduced by the use of narrow band applications directly over the crop row coupled with mechanical cultivation between the rows. In some cases, the material saved will compensate for the additional machinery costs.

Land is a partial substitute for pesticides as an input in the food and fiber production function. One study has estimated that insecticide usage could be reduced by 70 to 80 percent without any reduction in the present level of output if 40 million acres diverted under present government farm programs were returned to production.[36]

Additional labor and machinery would be required to operate additional acres. Farm production costs would increase. Cultivation of added acres could increase pollution from soil erosion and water runoff.

Varieties of plants and animals resistant to insects and diseases have been a favored method of control for years. Development of resistant varieties that possess all the other desirable attributes for agricultural purposes can be a lengthy and expensive process. An increased emphasis in this direction might well require greater public financial support.

A promising new approach is the use of integrated pest control programs where chemical agents are used sparingly with biological controls. The idea is to attack insect or other pests in a number of different ways at once. Included are use of predators, pathogens or diseases, cultivation practices, crop diversity, sterile males (insects), and chemical attractants (insects). Chemicals are used only in minimal effective dosages when needed to forestall imminent destruction of the crop.[37] Stronger quarantine regulations can reduce pesticide usage because many insects and diseases causing major damage to agriculture in the United States have been introduced from other areas of the world.

Feed Additives

While feed additives are only partially metabolized by the animal's system, residues in manure do not normally pollute the soil, air, or water. Feed additives may, at times, enter the human diet as residues in animal products, primarily meat and milk.

An estimated 80 percent of all animal protein for human food comes from animals that have received medicated feeds during part or all of their lives. One possible danger comes from the fact that bacteria tend to develop resistance when exposed to drugs over extended periods. These drug-resistant bacteria in animals may in turn transfer their drug resistance to human pathogenic bacteria.[38] A second danger lies in the ingestion of drug residues by humans with acute allergies to these substances.

Diethylstilbestrol (DES) and other synthetically produced hormones are widely used as additives in cattle feeding. Only minute quantities of these hormones can stimulate the rate of body growth (gain per unit of time) and increase the efficiency of feed conversion by as much as 10 percent.[39] DES is considered a dangerous carcinogen by some scientists and was banned from use in broiler production by the FDA in 1961 and from cattle feed by several European countries about the same time.[40]

Hormones and medications, along with other substances, are used in animal production because they reduce the cost of production. Neither of these substances, when used according to regulation, reach the consumer as residues in food. If their use is discontinued, the result will be higher costs to consumers. The cost to consumers of eliminating DES alone has been estimated between $300 million and $460 million annually.[41]

APPENDIX A
REFERENCES

1. Sterling Brubaker, *To Live on Earth: Environmental Problems in Perspective* (Baltimore: Johns Hopkins Press for Resources for the Future, 1972), p. 45.

2. Robert White-Stevens, "Farm Chemicals and Water Pollution" (paper presented to the 22nd Annual Midwest Fertilizer Conference, The Fertilizer Institute, Chicago, Illinois, Feb. 16-17, 1970), p. 2.

3. U.S. Department of Agriculture, "Environment: Who Pays for What," *The Farm Index,* May 1971, pp. 7-8.

4. Clyde Barth, "Engineering Research on Farm Animal Manure," *Proceedings of Farm Animal Waste and By-Product Conference* (Madison, Wisc.: University of Wisconsin, 1969), p. 76.

5. Elizabeth McCoy, "Health Problems," *Proceedings of Farm Animal Waste and By-Product Conference* (Madison, Wisc.: University of Wisconsin, 1969), p. 24.

6. C. R. Frink, "Plant Nutrients and Water Quality," *Agricultural Science Review,* 1971, Vol. XI, second quarter, p. 19.

7. Barth, *op. cit.*

8. U.S. Department of Agriculture, *Fertilizer Use and Water Quality,* by G. Stanford, *et al.,* ARS 41-168, 1970, p. 4.

9. U.S. Department of Agriculture, *Fertilizer Situation,* FS-1, March 1971, pp. 40-42.

10. White-Stevens, *op. cit.,* p. 10.

11. Frink, *op. cit.,* p. 21.

12. *Ibid.,* p. 17.

13. *Ibid.,* p. 19.

14. White-Stevens, *op. cit.,* p. 25.

15. Daniel H. Kohl and Barry Commoner, "A Study of Certain Ecological Public Health and Economic Consequences of the Use of Inorganic Nitrogen Fertilizer" (research proposal submitted to the National Science Foundation, 1970), pp. 8-19.

16. U. S. Department of Agriculture, *Fertilizer Use and Water Quality, op. cit.*

17. *Ibid.* and Barth, *op. cit.*

18. Frink, *op. cit.,* pp. 15-16.

19. U. S. Department of Agriculture, *Fertilizer Use and Water Quality, op. cit.*

20. White-Stevens, *op. cit.,* p. 13.

21. Velmar W. Davis, "Economics of Fertilizer Use by United States Farmers" (paper presented at a symposium on Chemical and Toxicological Aspects of Environmental Quality, Institute for Ecological Chemistry, Munich, Germany, May 27-28, 1971), pp. 22-23.

22. Leo V. Mayer and Stanley H. Hargrove, *Food Costs, Farm Incomes and Crop Yields,* CAED Report No. 38 (Ames, Iowa: Iowa State University, 1971).

23. W. C. Shaw, "How Agricultural Chemicals Contribute to our Current Food Supplies" (paper presented at a Symposium on Agricultural Chemicals, University of California, Sacramento, California, Feb. 16-17, 1971).

24. Fred T. Cooke, Jr., "The Effect of Restricting DDT or Chlorinated Hydrocarbons on Commercial Cotton Farms in the Mississippi Delta" (paper given at a symposium on Economic Research on Pesticides for Policy Decision Making, Economic Research Service, U.S. Dept. of Agriculture, Washington, April 27-29, 1970), p. 123.

25. U.S. Congress, House, Committee on Agriculture, testimony by Velmar Davis on *Federal Pesticide Control Act of 1971, Hearings,* 92nd Cong., 1st sess., Feb. 23, 1971.

26. J. C. Headly and J. N. Lewis, *The Pesticide Problem* (Washington: Resources for the Future, 1967), pp. 9-63.

27. *Ibid.,* pp. 78-87.

28. White-Stevens, *op. cit.,* p. 38.

29. Headly and Lewis, *op. cit.,* pp. 63-64.

30. U.S. Congress, House, *op. cit.*

31. Claire Sterling, "Pest Control: Finding a Substitute for DDT," *The Washington Post,* June 12, 1971.

32. U.S. Department of Agriculture, "If 2,4,5-T were Banned," *The Farm Index,* May 1971.

33. Davis, "Economics of Fertilizer Use by United States Farmers," *op. cit.,* pp. 66-71.

34. W. F. Edwards and M. R. Langham, "Pesticides, Public Welfare and Policy" (unpublished manuscript, University of Florida, Gainesville, Florida, 1970), p. 54.

35. Headly and Lewis, *op. cit.,* p. 67.

36. M. R. Langham, J. Headly, and W. F. Edwards, "Agricultural Pesticides: Productivity and Externalities" (paper presented to Resources for the Future Conference, Research on Environmental Quality, Washington, June 16-18, 1970), p. 20.

37. Brubaker, *op. cit.,* pp. 61-62.

38. J. A. Rohlf, "What You Must Do to Keep your Feed Additives," *Farm Journal,* June 1971.

39. U.S. Congress, House, Committee on Government Operations, *Regulation of Food Additives and Medicated Animal Feeds, Hearings,* before a subcommittee of the Committee on Government Operations, 92nd Cong., 1st sess., March 16-30, 1971.

40. David R. Zwick and Mary Benstock, *Water Wasteland* (Washington: Center for Study of Responsive Law, 1971).

41. U.S. Congress, House, Committee on Government Operations, *op. cit.*

APPENDIX B
METHODOLOGY FOR PROJECTING DOMESTIC DEMAND

Population and income are the primary forces influencing domestic demand for farm products. The two alternative assumptions for these two variables are specified elsewhere in this report. In addition, the level of technological restraints was assumed to influence the amount demanded through an impact on prices.

A detailed set of use tables was developed for each of the major commodities. This procedure allowed an examination of the prospects for each commodity group and allowed maximum use of the available commodity oriented research as well as the in-house expertise of various specialists.

Estimates were developed for each of the major use categories: food, feed, seed (for major crops), and industrial and other uses. Previous projection studies by the Economic Research Service were drawn upon. These included recent projections to 1980,[1] ERS-OBE projections to 2000 and 2020 done for the Water Resources Council,[2] and various unpublished studies done in recent years. However, each of the major items was re-examined for this project.

Two distinct steps were used in developing the demand projections. First, a base solution was developed; then, demand for the various alternatives was estimated by computing the impact of differences in population, income, and level of environmental restraint which affects prices.

The alternative levels of demand for major livestock commodities and for feed were estimated by two different methods. One method used a model while the other used a series of partial adjustments. The formal livestock-feed model used is a recursive system of equations which, given values for a set of exogenous variables including population, income, and feed prices, generates annual estimates of livestock production and consumption, livestock prices, and feed use.[3]

The model was not designed to generate estimates over a long enough period to allow direct estimation of values for the year 2000. So the system was adjusted to incorporate the differences among alternatives over a recent 12-year period. The model generated estimates for the five alternatives, and the results were then converted to year 2000 values. Appropriate values of the exogenous variables were derived by first defining the exogenous variables of the base solution as equal to actual data and then adjusting the data for other alternatives in the proper proportion. For example, per capita income in 2000 for the base solution was $5,006 while it was $4,481 and $6,203 for the lowest and highest levels respectively; so the income levels for these two alternatives were computed as 90 percent and 124 percent, respectively, of the base level.

In estimating food use by the partial adjustment method, per capita consumption of each item is viewed as a function of its own price, prices of other foods, per capita disposable personal income, and changes in tastes and preferences. The demand coefficients used for these projections were synthesized from published and unpublished studies.[4] It is generally accepted that income coefficients tend to decline over time as consumers in aggregate become more affluent.[5] Thus, the value of most coefficients were trended downward for application to the year 2000 in order to account for the higher assumed per capita income levels.

A base set of per capita food use data was projected for the year 2000, taking account of the composite effects of changing tastes, income, and other factors. Then, estimates of the five alternatives were made by applying the projected income and price coefficients to income and price differences.

Feed requirements for each of the alternatives were estimated by computing livestock production units and feeding rates per unit. Livestock production units were computed from production requirements for each type of livestock by applying appropriate conversion factors. The livestock production units and projected concentrates fed per livestock unit give the total concentrates fed.

High protein feed was projected in the usual proportion of total feed. After computing the amounts of byproduct feeds likely to be available from animal sources, grain protein feeds, and fish meal, the remainder was projected to come from the oilseed meals. The estimated production of cottonseed meal, produced as a byproduct of cotton lint, and minor oilseed meals were then subtracted with the residual representing projected use of soybean meal.

Price-weighted indexes were computed from the projected per capita consumption data. These indexes for all food and for livestock and crop subtotals were then compared with historical trends as a check on the overall food consumption projections. Total food use was combined with estimated use of feed, seed, and other uses to give total use estimates except for fiber. Demand for cotton lint was projected separately within the Economic Research Service; the alternative assumptions used for cotton demand projections were the same as used for other commodities.

The prospective impacts of synthetics and substitutes for agricultural products were not projected explicitly. They are, however, implicitly included in the base projections to the extent that synthetics and substitutes appear in the trend data and through judgments about future demand conditions.

Recent research suggests a wide interest in developing new, nontraditional products;[6] however, to date, major impacts have occurred in only a relatively few commodity areas such as cotton and wool fibers, and dairy products. The prospective rate of new product developments will depend on the amount of research effort as well as on price levels of traditional products.[7]

If substantial developments of new synthetics and substitutes do occur by 2000, the demands for traditional products might be below projections used in this report.

APPENDIX B
REFERENCES

1. D. W. Culver and J. C. Chai, "A View of Food and Agriculture in 1980," *Agricultural Economics Research,* July 1970, Vol. 22, No. 3, pp. 61-68; U.S. Department of Agriculture, "Beef Cattle: The Next 10 Years," by Donald Seaborg, in *Livestock and Meat Situation,* LMS-173, May 1970, pp. 32-35; U.S. Department of Agriculture, "Changes in the Poultry Meat Industry and Projections for the Decade," by W. E. Cathcart, in *Poultry and Egg Situation,* PES-261, April 1970, pp. 10-19; U.S. Department of Agriculture, "Dairying in the 1970's," by A. G. Mathis, in *Dairy Situation,* DS-329, March 1970, pp. 30-34; U.S. Department of Agriculture, "Feed Grains in the Seventies," by Malcolm Clough, in *Feed Situation,* Fda-235, August 1970, pp. 24-31; U.S. Department of Agriculture, "The Vegetable Industry—A Review of Progress and Prospects," by C. W. Porter, in *Vegetable Situation,* TVS-177, August 1970, pp. 15-23; U.S. Department of Agriculture, "Trends and Prospects in the U.S. Fruit Industry," by Ben W. Huang, in *Fruit Situation,* TFS-176, September 1970, pp. 11-21; and U.S. Department of Agriculture, "The Cotton Fiber-Textile-Apparel Complex: Structure and Outlook for the 1970's," R. G. Barlowe and J. R. Donald, in *Cotton Situation,* CS-246, May 1970, pp. 10-23.

2. U.S. Department of Commerce, Office of Business Economics, and U.S. Department of Agriculture, Economic Research Service, for United States Water Resources Council, *Economic Activity in the United States by Water Resources Regions and Subareas: Historical and Projected: 1929-2020,* Vol. 1 (in press).

3. A. C. Egbert and S. Reutlinger, "A Dynamic Model of the Live-Stock Feed Sector," *Journal of Farm Economics,* December 1965, Vol. 47, pp. 1288-1305; and J. D. Ahalt and A. C. Egbert, "The Demand for Feed Concentrates: A Statistical Analysis," *Agricultural and Economics Research,* April 1965, Vol. 17, pp. 41-49.

4. G. E. Brandow, *Interrelations Among Demands for Farm Products and Implications for Control of Market Supply,* Pennsylvania Agricultural Experiment Station, Bulletin 680, 1961; P. S. George and G. A. King, *Consumer Demand for Food Commodities in the U.S. with Projections for 1980,* Giannini Foundation Monograph No. 26, California Agricultural Experiment Station, 1971; and J. C. Chai, "Estimating Income Coefficients from Cross-Section Data," Economic Research Service, U.S. Dept. of Agriculture, (unpublished).

5. Brandow, *op. cit.*

6. William S. Hoofnagle *et al., Synthetics and Substitutes for Agricultural Products—A Compendium,* Misc. Pub. 1141, U.S. Dept. of Agriculture, April 1969.

7. U.S. Department of Agriculture, Economic Research Service, Marketing Economics Division, *Synthetics and Substitutes for Agricultural Products—Projections to 1980,* in press.

APPENDIX C

LONG-TERM PROSPECTS FOR THE WORLD POPULATION-FOOD BALANCE

In recent years, a wide range of opinion has been expressed about world food prospects. A number of writers have suggested the likelihood of widespread famine within a few years.[1] A nearly opposite view is presented by others,[2] while several studies, including some considerable analysis of world agricultural data,[3] offer a hopeful but more cautious assessment.

A Long-Term Perspective on Food versus Population

Prevailing views on food supply prospects have apparently tended to follow directly from near-term changes in the situation. Thus, Abercrombie has described these changing views as moving from the acceptance of recurrent famine as inevitable to a belief in the power of efficient administration to avert it, from Malthusian pessimism to Victorian optimism, from fears of soil erosion to confidence in technology and international cooperation, and now from a pessimistic view of the ability of developing countries to raise food production to somewhat greater optimism on this score.[4]

It seems clear that, in the very long view, the number of people has been limited to a large extent by available food supplies. This very long view has been described in terms of two major historical turning points.[5] The first was when man changed from a food gathering to an agricultural economy. The changed system, including domestication of plants for food use, apparently allowed a more rapid increase in population; but recurrent famines due to periodic crop failures still operated to severely limit the population growth rate, at least until recent history.

The other profound change was the onset of the scientific and industrial revolution in the seventeenth century. The technical and agricultural revolution brought rising productivity, encouraged more land cultivation, and provided a greater ability to transfer food from surplus to deficit regions. These changes did encourage the accelerating increase in population over the past 300 years. In addition, over the last several decades, an increasing number of people have been able to live at a dietary standard substantially above hunger levels. Nevertheless, a perceptible part of the world's inhabitants continue to be undernourished, to face hunger; and another sizeable number live on diets which are inadequate in nutritional quality.

Recent Years

The period since World War II has seen rapid technological advances both in human health measures and in agricultural production. An obvious result has been the further acceleration of population growth. Agricultural production has generally increased a little faster than population in both the developed and the less-developed countries (Table C-1). But food production has been somewhat erratic, largely due to weather variations, leading to occasional severe food shortages in some areas. For example, unusually severe drought was a major cause of food shortages in Asia during the mid-sixties.

In several industrialized countries, agricultural production capacity has grown considerably faster than demand requiring limits to be placed on crop output in several countries. This situation, along with periodic food needs by various developing countries, has encouraged a substantial program of United States government-assisted exports of agricultural products, especially food grains.

However, food aid to the less-developed countries may create a variety of problems. One problem is that a large supply of food grains (or any other commodity) from outside tends to depress both local farm prices and the farm economy.[6] It could also mask the basic conditions in the agriculture of less-developed countries and consequently worsen the long-term population-food imbalance.[7] The more lasting solution to food supply problems is generally to be found in increasing agricultural productivity within the developing nations themselves.[8] However, United States food aid to developing countries may well continue for the next few decades. Thus, government-assisted exports of basic food crops (wheat and rice) were projected at levels which are about the same percentage of our total production as in 1967-69.

Technological Potentials

A report by Abel and Rojko projects a world surplus grain production capacity in 1980 that would likely exceed 30 million metric tons a year, but most of the excess capacity would probably be in the developed countries.[9] Their analysis suggests that such a surplus capacity would be likely to continue at least for several years beyond 1980. However, actual production in the major developed countries can be expected to continue, as in recent years, to be adjusted to a market demand. The prospects for production gains in the less-developed countries appear more uncertain.

With the high rates of population growth in many countries, the conclusion has sometimes been reached

Table C-1.—Annual Rate of Change in Per Capita Agricultural Production by Regions and Selected Countries, 1954 to 1970

Region or country	Rate of change
	Percent
Western Hemisphere, excluding U.S.	
Latin America, 22 countries	.1
Mexico	.7
Canada	.6
Western Europe	1.4
Eastern Europe and USSR	2.2
Africa	
Africa, excluding UAR and S. Africa	.1
United Arab Republic	−.3
Republic of South Africa	.6
Asia	
South Asia[a]	.2
East Asia, excluding Japan[b]	.6
Japan	1.6
West Asia[c]	.4
Greece	3.2
Oceania	
(Australia and New Zealand)	1.2
World[d]	.7
Less-developed countries[e]	.3
Developed countries	
All[f]	1.4
United States	.3
Others[g]	1.8

[a]Includes Ceylon, India, and Pakistan.
[b]Includes Burma, Cambodia, Indonesia, Republic of Korea, West Malaysia, Philippines, Taiwan, Thailand, and Republic of Vietnam.
[c]Includes Cyprus, Iran, Iraq, Israel, Jordan, Lebanon, Syria, and Turkey.
[d]Excludes Communist Asia.
[e]Less-developed countries: Latin America, Asia (except Japan and Communist Asia), and Africa (except Republic of South Africa).
[f]Includes North America, Europe, USSR, Japan, Republic of South Africa, Australia and New Zealand.
[g]Includes Canada, Europe, USSR, Japan, Republic of South Africa, Australia, and New Zealand.
Source: Computed using least squares fit of annual indexes compiled by U.S. Department of Agriculture, Economic Research Service, Regional Analysis Division.

Table C-2.—Past and Projected Per Capita Gross Agricultural Production[a]

Region	Annual compound rates of growth	
	1959 to 1969	1970 to 1980
	Actual	Projected
	Percent	
World[b]	0.5	0.4
High-income countries[c] . .	1.3	1.1
Developed market economies . . .	1.2	1.0
USSR and Eastern Europe	2.0	1.2
Developing countries . . .	.3	.6
Latin America . . .	.4	.4
Africa	.1	.6
Near East	.2	.6
Asia and Far East .	.3	.6
Asian centrally planned economies[d]	. . .	.5

[a]Food and feed, fish, beverages, tobacco and agricultural raw materials other than forestry products.
[b]Excludes Asian centrally planned economies.
[c]The lower projected rates of growth for high-income countries reflect the expectation of deliberate restrictions on agricultural production in these countries.
[d]Projections for the Asian centrally planned economies do not have an adequate basis.
Source: U.N. Food and Agricultural Organization, *Agricultural Commodity Projections, 1970-80,* 1971, Vol. I.

that available land and other resources will be quickly exhausted and starvation will be inevitable within a decade or two.[10] However, there are a variety of ways of achieving increased agricultural production. In the developing countries, increased production since 1950 has come nearly equally from higher yields and area harvested.[11]

The increase in area harvested includes both new lands and multiple cropping of land already in use. The level of output per unit of area (yield) can also be increased in two ways: raising the yield of traditional crops, and changing to higher yield crops. Rising crop yields have resulted from the application of modern technology including improved seeds, increased use of fertilizers and pesticides, irrigation, and better management.

The supply of good cropland is quite limited in many areas of the world. Crop area can be expanded substantially by irrigation of arid lands and by clearing and drainage operations. Nevertheless, over any long period of time, it appears that the greater increase in production will need to come from more efficient use of land already being cultivated.

There is reason to think that the rate of increase in yields can be improved substantially in the developing countries. Over the past several years, the production increase of 2.9 percent per year in developed countries was due entirely to increasing yields.[12] Also, yields have increased quite rapidly in a number of developing countries where agricultural technology has received emphasis. For example, in Mexico, production rose over the period 1940-65 at an annual rate of 4.6 percent, with land use increasing at a 2.0 percent rate and yields rising at a 2.6 percent rate.[13]

Prospects

Recent projections by FAO suggest a rate of growth in world per capita agricultural production of 0.4 percent per year from 1970 to 1980, which is slightly less than occurred over the past decade (Table C-2). This includes a lower projected growth rate for high-income countries and a higher rate for developing countries than over the past decade.[14] The lower projected rates of growth for high-income countries reflects the expectation of deliberate restrictions on agricultural production in these countries.

It seems reasonable to think that per capita agricultural production may well continue to rise gradually over the period 1980-2000. In fact, a case can be made that the expanded emphasis on agriculture in recent years might well result in accelerating growth of production over the next 10 to 20 years.

The substantial application of modern technology to agriculture is quite new in most developing countries, so the potential increase in productivity has only begun to appear. On the other hand the application of new medical technology, beginning more than two decades ago, has brought sharply increased population growth in many areas of the world. Thus, it can be argued that growth in agricultural production may be accelerating while population growth rates peak and begin to decline over the next several years. However, the heavy demands of continued population and income growth and the substantial difficulties involved in transforming traditional agriculture suggest that a continued modest improvement in output per person may be optimistic enough to project over the next 30 years.

APPENDIX C

REFERENCES

1. R. Dumont and B. Rosier, *The Hungry Future* (New York: Methuen, 1970); W. Paddock and P. Paddock, *Famine 1975* (Boston: Little Brown, 1968); and Paul R. Ehrlich, *The Population Bomb* (New York: Ballantine Books, 1968).

2. L. R. Brown, *Seeds of Change—The Green Revolution and Development in the 1970's* (New York: Praeger Publishers for the Overseas Development Council, 1970); and C. Clark, *Starvation or Plenty?* (New York: Taplinger Publishing Co., 1970).

3. U.S. Department of Agriculture, Economic Research Service, *World Food Situation—Prospects for World Grain Production, Consumption and Trade*, by M. E. Abel and A. Rojko, Foreign Agricultural Report No. 35, Sept. 1967; W. W. Cochrane, *The World Food Problem, A Guardedly Optimistic View* (New York: Thomas Y. Crowell Co., Inc., 1969); and Food and Agricultural Organization (FAO), *Agricultural Commodity Projections, 1970-1980* (Rome, 1970), Vol. I.

4. K. C. Abercrombie, "Changing Views on the Man-Food Relationship," *Ceres*, March-April 1971, Vol. 4, No. 2.

5. H. Brown *et al.*, *The Next Hundred Years* (New York: The Viking Press, 1957).

6. L. P. Schertz, "The Green Revolution: Production and World Trade," *Columbia Journal of World Business*, March-April 1970, Vol. V, No. 2.

7. M. Clawson, *Policy Directions for U.S. Agriculture—Long-Range Choices in Farming and Rural Living* (Baltimore: Johns Hopkins Press, 1968).

8. Q. M. West, "World Food Needs: Who Will Produce—Who Will Pay?" (paper presented at the Governor's Conference on Nebraska and the World Food Needs, Lincoln, Nebraska, Jan. 4, 1968).

9. U.S. Department of Agriculture, *op. cit.*

10. Paul R. Ehrlich and Anne H. Ehrlich, *Population, Resources, Environment: Issues in Human Ecology* (San Francisco: W. H. Freeman and Co., 1970).

11. U.S. Department of Agriculture, Economic Research Service, "Agriculture's Performance in the Developing Countries," by John R. Schaub, in *Economic Progress of Agriculture in Developing Nations, 1950-68,* Foreign Agricultural Economic Report No. 59, May 1970.

12. *Ibid.*

13. U.S. Department of Agriculture, Economic Research Service, "Mexico: Its Sources of Increased Agricultural Output," by Reed Hertford, in *Economic Progress of Agriculture in Developing Nations, 1950-68,* Foreign Agricultural Economic Report No. 59, May 1970.

14. FAO, *op. cit.*

Table D-1.—Yields per Harvested Acre for Specified Crops, Historic and Projected

Crop	Unit	1970[a]	Production technology			
			Restricted		Unrestricted	
			1980	2000	1980	2000
Oats	Bu.	49	52	60	62	70
Barley	do.	43	43	50	55	55
Corn[b]	do.	72	92	100	105	125
Grain sorghum	do.	51	59	60	67	70
Wheat	do.	31	31	35	35	40
Rice	Cwt.	46	46	57	56	67
Soybeans	Bu.	27	27	35	31	40
Peanuts	lb.	2,031	2,050	2,300	2,510	2,700
Cotton	do.	437	450	540	530	600
Tobacco	do.	2,122	2,100	2,300	2,300	2,600
Cropland hay	Feed unit	1,440	1,990	2,200	2,200	2,600
Cropland pasture	Feed unit	1,230	1,280	1,500	2,200	2,500
Other pasture	Feed unit	220	260	300	1,600	2,000
					260	300

[a]U.S. Department of Agriculture, Statistical Reporting Service, *Crop Production,* 1971 Annual Summary, Jan. 1972.

[b]In 1970, corn yields were affected by corn blight epidemic. In 1969, corn yield was 84 bushels per acre.

Table D-2.—Projected Demand for Key Agricultural Commodities

Commodity	Domestic use			Net exports	Domestic production	Domestic use			Net exports	Domestic production
	Food	Feed & other	Total			Food	Feed & other	Total		
	Million									
Feed grains (tons)										
1967-69 average	7	142	149	21	169					
			1980					**2000**		
Alternatives										
I	8	197	205	35	240	11	286	297	55	352
II	7	182	189	32	221	11	274	285	47	332
III	7	174	181	32	213	11	269	280	49	329
IV	8	197	205	35	240	9	242	250	64	314
V	7	181	188	32	220	9	227	236	60	296
Food grains (tons)										
1967-69 average	16.9	6.8	23.6	21.9	45.5					
			1980					**2000**		
Alternatives										
I	19.0	5.8	24.8	25.3	50.1	24.6	10.6	35.2	30.6	65.8
II	17.5	5.4	22.9	23.3	46.1	25.4	10.6	36.0	28.6	64.6
III	16.8	5.2	22.0	23.2	45.2	25.9	10.5	36.4	29.1	65.5
IV	19.0	5.8	24.8	25.3	50.1	20.2	9.0	29.2	32.6	61.8
V	17.5	5.9	23.4	23.3	46.6	20.8	9.0	29.8	31.5	61.3
Oilseeds (tons)										
1967-69 average	1	25	26	10	36					
			1980					**2000**		
Alternatives										
I	1	32	33	19	52	2	47	49	26	75
II	1	29	30	17	48	1	46	47	22	69
III	1	28	29	17	47	1	45	46	23	69
IV	1	32	33	19	52	1	40	41	30	71
V	1	30	31	17	48	1	38	39	27	66
Cotton (bales)										
1967-69 average	0	8.4	8.4	3.2	11.6					
			1980					**2000**		
Alternatives										
I	0	8.5	8.5	4.0	12.5	0	9.4	9.4	3.5	12.9
II	0	7.8	7.8	3.7	11.5	0	9.2	9.2	2.8	12.0
III	0	7.5	7.5	3.7	11.2	0	8.9	8.9	2.8	11.7
IV	0	8.5	8.5	4.0	12.5	0	7.8	7.8	3.5	11.3
V	0	7.8	7.8	3.7	11.5	0	7.4	7.4	2.8	10.2
Tobacco (pounds)										
1967-69 average	0	1,644	1,644	369	2,013					
			1980					**2000**		

Table D-2.—Continued

Commodity	Domestic use			Net exports	Domestic production	Domestic use			Net exports	Domestic production
	Food	Feed & other	Total			Food	Feed & other	Total		
	Million									
Alternatives										
I	0	1,200	1,200	200	1,400	0	1,165	1,165	160	1,325
II	0	1,200	1,200	200	1,400	0	1,165	1,165	160	1,325
III	0	1,200	1,200	200	1,400	0	1,165	1,165	160	1,325
IV	0	1,200	1,200	200	1,400	0	1,100	1,100	180	1,280
V	0	1,200	1,200	200	1,400	0	1,100	1,100	180	1,280
Red meats (cwt., carcass)										
1967-69 average	367	0	367	−18	349					
			1980					2000		
Alternatives										
I	469	0	469	−20	448	700	0	700	−31	668
II	431	0	431	−20	411	653	0	653	−35	619
III	414	0	414	−19	395	634	0	634	−32	601
IV	469	0	469	−20	448	589	0	589	−29	560
V	431	0	431	−24	408	534	0	534	−29	505
Poultry (cwt., ready to cook)										
1967-69 average	93	0	93	2	95					
			1980					2000		
Alternatives										
I	138	0	138	2	140	215	0	215	4	219
II	127	0	127	2	129	215	0	215	4	219
III	122	0	122	2	124	215	0	215	4	219
IV	138	0	138	2	140	179	0	179	4	183
V	127	0	127	1	129	179	0	179	4	183
Eggs (dozen)										
1967-69 average	5,372	373	5,746	41	5,787					
			1980					2000		
Alternatives										
I	5,900	550	6,450	50	6,500	7,131	839	7,970	50	8,020
II	5,428	506	5,934	46	5,980	7,192	864	8,056	36	8,092
III	5,211	486	5,697	46	5,743	7,233	865	8,098	46	8,144
IV	5,900	550	6,450	50	6,500	5,919	699	6,618	60	6,678
V	5,428	506	5,934	44	5,978	5,987	719	6,706	58	6,764
Dairy (cwt., milk equiv.)										
1967-69 average	1,162	18	1,181	−8	1,173					
			1980					2000		
Alternatives										
I	1,070	5	1,075	−5	1,070	1,290	5	1,295	−15	1,280
II	984	5	989	−5	984	1,213	5	1,218	−18	1,200
III	945	5	950	−5	945	1,200	5	1,205	−16	1,189
IV	1,070	5	1,075	−5	1,070	1,078	5	1,083	−13	1,070
V	984	8	992	−5	987	1,001	5	1,006	−13	993

Table D-3.—Land Use, Historic and Projected

Crop or use	1970	1980 I	1980 II	1980 III	1980 IV	1980 V	2000 I	2000 II	2000 III	2000 IV	2000 V
						Million					
Feed grains	100	104	119	115	104	118	136	164	163	119	141
Oats	19	19	28	27	19	28	24	39	39	21	34
Barley	10	10	13	13	10	13	14	18	18	12	15
Corn	57	60	61	59	60	60	79	84	83	69	72
Grain sorghum	14	15	17	16	15	17	19	23	23	17	20
Wheat	44	43	44	44	43	45	47	55	56	42	51
Rice	2	2	2	2	2	2	2	2	2	2	2
Soybeans	42	48	51	50	48	51	57	58	59	53	55
Peanuts	1	1	2	2	1	2	2	2	2	1	2
Cotton	11	11	12	12	11	12	10	11	10	9	9
Vegetables, fruit, sugar	14	10	13	13	10	12	11	12	12	10	11
Cropland for hay and pasture	124	115	117	115	114	113	122	129	128	120	115
Miscellaneous	6	4	5	4	4	4	4	5	4	3	4
Total harvested cropland[a]	344	338	365	357	337	359	391	438	436	359	390
Cropland not harvested[b]	96	91	64	72	91	70	31	33	32	51	32
Total cropland	440	429	429	429	428	429	422	471	468	410	422
Other pasture and range	636	620	625	625	620	625	617	580	580	613	617
Other agricultural land	29	28	28	28	28	28	27	27	27	27	27

[a]Total includes pasture on cropland.
[b]Includes failure, summer fallow, and unused cropland.

Table D-4.—Use of Nonland Inputs, Historic and Projected

Year and alternative	Labor (billion man-hours)	Fertilizer (million tons, elemental N)	Pesticide (million pounds, active ingredient)
1970	6.5	6.3	410
1980			
I	5.0	9.0	572
II	8.4	6.7	137
III	8.2	6.7	134
IV	4.9	8.9	570
V	8.2	6.6	134
2000			
I	2.5	14.8	662
II	4.0	9.4	137
III	3.9	9.2	134
IV	2.3	12.9	608
V	3.5	8.2	122

Chapter 8

Future Water Needs and Supplies, with a Note on Land Use

by
Ronald G. Ridker
Resources for the Future Inc.

COMMISSION ON POPULATION GROWTH AND THE AMERICAN FUTURE, *RESEARCH REPORTS, VOLUME III, POPULATION RESOURCES AND THE ENVIRONMENT,* EDITED BY RONALD G. RIDKER

CONTENTS

FIGURES

TABLES

Future Water Needs
and Supplies, with a Note on Land Use

This chapter highlights the main conclusions derived from our assessment of future water problems as they relate to population and economic growth. It is based on a model developed by Wollman and Bonem which we were able to run against our assumptions with the help of staff members of the National Water Commission.[1] The model is particularly useful for present purposes since it projects regional as well as total water requirements out to the year 2020 by major user under alternative assumptions about treatment levels, quality standards, and storage capacity.

The quickest way to obtain an overview is to look at national aggregates, although a warning should be attached that most water problems are regional in scope. Figure 1 indicates national requirements necessary to meet specified quality standards for four basic

FIGURE 8-1
U.S. WATER REQUIREMENTS, MINIMUM FLOW PROGRAM

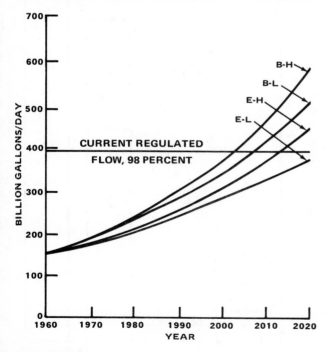

Source: Table 1

scenarios.[2] Note that current supply (current regulated flow) is far above requirements today and is likely to remain so out to the year 2000. Thereafter, the date at which current supplies become inadequate depends on the scenarios we are looking at. Clearly, for this resource, population does make a significant difference: In the year 2000, the savings in water requirements under Series E rather than Series B population projections (for the high economic series) is 17 percent; in 2020, the comparable figure is 27 percent.

The line at the top of the figure indicating maximum regulated flow represents a potential only; it indicates the flow that could be achieved (98 percent of the time) if all possible storage facilities were built throughout the country. Given the magnitude of the costs involved, plus increasing concerns about environmental impacts, it will not be easy to bring about a significant move towards this potential. Fortunately, however, at least at this aggregate level, there appears to be considerable time before such a move becomes necessary.

Figure 2 indicates the principal users of water and how their needs are likely to change over time. Note the dramatic increase in withdrawals of water for electricity generation. This is due to the need to dissipate heat. Very little water is consumed in this process, but the added heat does increase total requirements for dilution purposes to keep water temperature from rising above specified limits. There are, of course, means of transferring heat to the atmosphere rather than to water sources, which could reduce dilution requirements significantly; but, the model assumes no appreciable change in technology from 1960 practices in this regard. Agriculture will remain the largest consumer, but municipal uses will increase significantly.

Figure 3 portrays the principal sources of waste loads requiring dissolved oxygen to degrade into less harmful substances.[3] If minimum oxygen standards in the water are to be maintained, biochemical oxygen demand (BOD) must be met either through treatment prior to emission into the waterways or through additional streamflow for dilution purposes. The estimates of water requirements here assume that treatment has been pushed to relatively high levels (tertiary treatment which removes over 97 percent of BOD) so as to minimize required streamflow for dilution purposes. This is the meaning of the phrase "minimum flow program" that appears in some of the titles to figures and tables. Note in Figure 3 the extent to which BOD from chemical processing will come to dominate the picture in the future. Municipal requirements also increase significantly, in absolute terms, even though its share of total decreases.

A different way of looking at future prospects is presented in Figure 4, which portrays annualized costs of meeting water requirements for the United States. These costs include the capital and operating expenditures for storage facilities as well as treatment plants. We have chosen to portray the least cost combination of the expenditures on these two items, one that will just meet the specified standards in the years concerned. This accounts for the designation, "minimum cost program" in Figure 4 and Table 2, rather than "minimum flow program," used in other tables and figures.

Comparing both 2020 and 2000 with 1960, costs appear to increase at increasing rates over time: It becomes increasingly expensive to meet requirements and standards as we press closer and closer to capacity in some regions.[4] As a percentage of GNP, however, these costs decline slightly, since GNP increases over time at even more rapid rates. The savings due to lower population growth rates are quite sizeable. In 2000, substituting the Series E for the Series B population would save 23 percent; by 2020, this savings would mount to 32 percent over what would have to be spent in that year. In contrast, savings due to lower rates of growth in income, holding population constant, are less. In 2000, such savings would amount to 11 percent; in 2020, the comparable figure is 17 percent.

We must hasten to add, however, that aggregate figures of this sort have limited value in assessing the

FIGURE 8-2
PRINCIPAL USES OF WATER, TOTAL U.S.

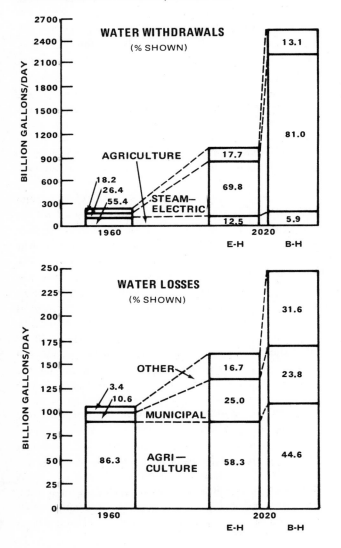

FIGURE 8-3
PRINCIPAL SOURCES OF BOD WASTE LOADS

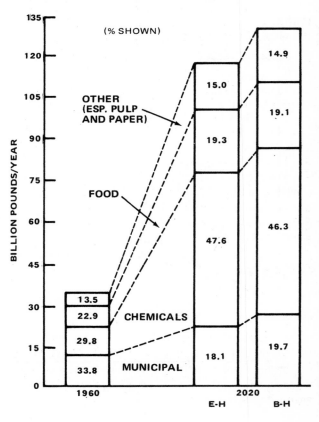

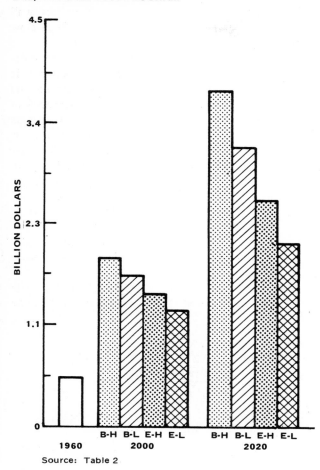

FIGURE 8-4

ANNUALIZED COST OF WATER REQUIREMENTS FOR U.S., MINIMUM COST PROGRAM

BILLION DOLLARS

4.5
3.4
2.3
1.1
0

1960

B-H B-L E-H E-L
2000

B-H B-L E-H E-L
2020

Source: Table 2

region. In the Colorado and Rio Grande-Pecos regions, deficits are met by reduced use of water on a per unit basis; some users are simply not getting as much water as similar users in other parts of the country. In some areas, groundwater, which is not easily replenished, is being mined. And in most areas, quality standards specified by the model are simply not being met since dilution flows are inadequate.

2. As of 1980, nine regions will require more flow than is currently available under all scenarios; and two additional regions—the Upper Arkansas and the Western Gulf—will join this category if the Series B rather than Series E population projection prevails. Many of these deficits can be made up by investments in added storage facilities. The potential to do this is reflected in the figures in the first column of Table 1 for maximum regulated flow.

3. For some areas, however, no additional storage facilities can be added. These are the Colorado and the South Pacific regions, where complete regulation of available flows has already been achieved.

4. The number of regions where required flow surpasses maximum regulated flow increases with time depending on the scenario investigated. Figures 6, 7, and 8 use data from Table 1 to indicate which regions these are and when such absolute deficits are likely to occur. As can be seen, such deficit regions tend to creep across the country over time, faster for the Series B than for the Series E projection.[5]

How can such deficits be dealt with? There is little scope to reduce them by adding additional treatment facilities over and above what the model already assumes since, as indicated above, treatment has been specified at quite high levels in calculating flow requirements. The other possibilities are interregional transfers of water, people, or economic activities; mining of groundwater; and augmentation of water flows through such means as weather modification, desalinization, and reduction in water use through rationing or technical change.

Redistribution possibilities vary greatly from region to region and, among other things, depend on terrain, the type of economic activities for which the region is suited, and the availability of alternative sites for these activities. As examples, which also illustrate the great diversity to be found in regional needs and prospects, consider the Delaware-Hudson, Upper Arkansas, and South Pacific regions, referred to in Figures 9, 10, and 11.

The problems of the Delaware-Hudson region are mainly qualitative. If watercourses in this region ceased to be treated as free waste disposal media, and if high

adequacy of water supplies: They only indicate possibilities assuming that population, economic activities, or water can be moved from region to region in order to eliminate local deficits. This is not a completely unrealistic assumption when projecting ahead for a half century. But if regional deficits are present now, or are likely to arise in the near future, the situation may still be serious despite supplies that are adequate on an aggregate basis.

Table 1, therefore, is of more interest. From it and Figures 5, 6, 7, and 8 which follow, four important conclusions can be drawn.

1. As of 1960, requirements specified by the model were less than available flow in five regions. These deficits are resolved in a number of ways, depending on the region. In the South Pacific region, substantial quantities of water are imported from outside the

Table 1.—Required Flows, Minimum Flow Program (billion gallons per day)

Region	(98%) Maximum regulated flow	1960	1980				2000				2020				(98%) Present regulated flow
			B-H	E-H	B-L	E-L	B-H	E-H	B-L	E-L	B-H	E-H	B-L	E-L	
Northeast															
New England	61.0	1.8	3.4	3.2	3.4	3.2	5.2	4.5	4.9	4.3	7.8	5.8	7.2	5.3	22.4
Delaware and Hudson	28.6	4.0	7.1	6.6	7.0	6.5	11.3	9.3	10.7	8.7	18.3	12.4	16.5	11.0	7.5
Chesapeake Bay	46.7	2.9	6.7	6.5	6.4	6.2	12.5	10.7	11.1	9.6	23.8	17.4	19.3	13.9	3.4
Ohio River	99.5	2.6	4.8	4.1	4.7	4.0	10.4	7.0	9.7	6.3	19.9	11.1	17.9	9.7	10.0
Eastern Great Lakes	33.3	3.5	5.3	4.9	5.1	4.7	9.9	7.8	8.9	6.9	18.9	12.2	15.9	9.9	3.5
Western Great Lakes	30.3	6.2	12.7	12.1	12.2	11.5	24.4	21.0	21.3	17.8	47.2	34.3	37.5	26.7	8.8
Upper Mississippi River	46.1	2.1	4.0	3.1	3.9	3.0	7.4	5.0	6.9	4.6	13.1	7.7	11.7	6.6	15.8
Lower Missouri River	16.2	0.4	0.8	0.8	0.8	0.7	1.5	1.2	1.3	1.1	2.7	1.9	2.2	1.6	5.4
Southeast															
Southeast	186.0	13.1	29.9	27.5	28.7	26.4	59.3	49.7	52.2	43.2	112.7	82.3	89.9	64.6	95.0
Cumberland River	14.6	0.1	1.9	1.9	1.7	1.8	4.7	4.3	3.9	3.6	10.3	8.5	7.6	6.3	11.1
Tennessee River	40.4	2.1	4.3	4.2	4.1	4.0	9.3	7.9	8.1	6.7	18.6	13.9	14.6	10.7	20.8
Lower Mississippi River	35.2	1.6	3.6	2.2	3.5	2.1	6.5	4.0	6.1	3.7	10.7	6.4	9.5	5.5	1.5
Lower Arkansas River	57.7	2.4	3.4	2.8	3.4	3.8	5.0	3.9	4.7	3.7	7.2	5.1	6.5	4.5	23.9
Mid-Continent															
Upper Missouri	25.6	13.0	17.4	15.0	17.2	14.9	23.2	18.6	22.3	17.6	34.5	25.9	30.8	22.1	25.6
Upper Arkansas River	7.1	6.2	6.9	5.6	6.9	5.6	8.1	6.3	8.0	6.2	10.2	7.2	9.8	6.9	6.7
Western Gulf	25.9	10.9	17.8	14.9	17.4	14.5	30.8	23.9	27.9	21.2	56.8	39.7	46.2	31.3	15.4
Southwest															
Upper Rio Grande-Pecos Rivers	3.0	6.3	6.4	5.8	6.4	5.8	6.8	6.0	6.7	5.9	8.1	6.8	7.8	6.5	3.0
Colorado River	11.4	14.3	19.1	16.6	19.0	16.5	25.3	22.6	24.5	21.8	35.3	28.6	31.9	25.9	11.4
Great Basin	6.9	6.0	7.2	6.1	7.1	6.0	7.9	6.5	7.5	6.1	10.5	8.0	9.3	7.0	5.4
South Pacific	0.8	4.9	7.1	6.7	7.1	6.6	11.5	9.7	11.2	9.4	18.9	13.5	18.1	12.8	0.7
North Pacific															
Central Pacific	45.5	25.3	28.0	26.3	27.9	26.2	31.7	28.4	30.9	27.7	40.8	32.7	38.1	30.6	26.2
Pacific Northwest	134.6	18.2	34.3	29.0	33.6	28.2	49.2	4.17	45.2	38.2	75.1	58.8	63.5	49.7	62.8
United States, total	956.2	147.1	231.9	205.7	227.7	201.2	362.1	299.7	334.3	274.3	601.6	439.3	512.1	369.0	386.3

FIGURE 8-5
WATER REGIONS

FIGURE 8-6
WATER DEFICIT REGIONS, SCENARIOS B-H AND B-L *†

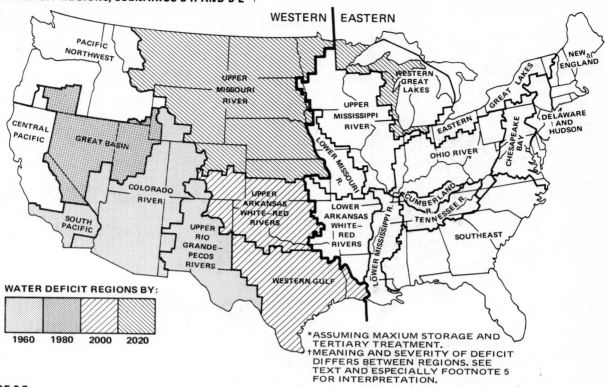

WESTERN | EASTERN

PACIFIC NORTHWEST

UPPER MISSOURI RIVER

WESTERN GREAT LAKES

NEW ENGLAND

CENTRAL PACIFIC

GREAT BASIN

UPPER MISSISSIPPI RIVER

GREAT LAKES

DELAWARE AND HUDSON

LOWER MISSOURI R.

EASTERN

OHIO RIVER

CHESAPEAKE BAY

COLORADO RIVER

UPPER ARKANSAS WHITE-RED RIVERS

CUMBERLAND R.

TENNESSEE R.

SOUTH PACIFIC

UPPER RIO GRANDE-PECOS RIVERS

LOWER ARKANSAS WHITE-RED RIVERS

LOWER MISSISSIPPI R.

SOUTHEAST

WESTERN GULF

WATER DEFICIT REGIONS BY:

| 1960 | 1980 | 2000 | 2020 |

*ASSUMING MAXIUM STORAGE AND TERTIARY TREATMENT.
†MEANING AND SEVERITY OF DEFICIT DIFFERS BETWEEN REGIONS. SEE TEXT AND ESPECIALLY FOOTNOTE 5 FOR INTERPRETATION.

FIGURE 8-7
WATER DEFICIT REGIONS, SCENARIO E-H *†

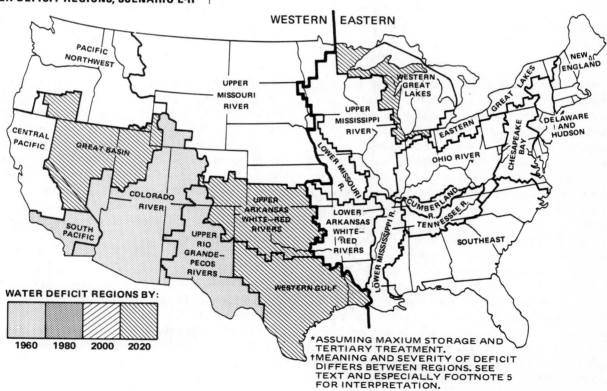

WESTERN | EASTERN

PACIFIC NORTHWEST

UPPER MISSOURI RIVER

WESTERN GREAT LAKES

NEW ENGLAND

CENTRAL PACIFIC

GREAT BASIN

UPPER MISSISSIPPI RIVER

GREAT LAKES

DELAWARE AND HUDSON

LOWER MISSOURI R.

EASTERN

OHIO RIVER

CHESAPEAKE BAY

COLORADO RIVER

UPPER ARKANSAS WHITE-RED RIVERS

CUMBERLAND R.

TENNESSEE R.

SOUTH PACIFIC

UPPER RIO GRANDE-PECOS RIVERS

LOWER ARKANSAS WHITE-RED RIVERS

LOWER MISSISSIPPI R.

SOUTHEAST

WESTERN GULF

WATER DEFICIT REGIONS BY:

| 1960 | 1980 | 2000 | 2020 |

*ASSUMING MAXIUM STORAGE AND TERTIARY TREATMENT.
†MEANING AND SEVERITY OF DEFICIT DIFFERS BETWEEN REGIONS. SEE TEXT AND ESPECIALLY FOOTNOTE 5 FOR INTERPRETATION.

Future Water Needs and Supplies, with a Note on Land Use

219

FIGURE 8-8
WATER DEFICIT REGIONS, SCENARIO E-L *†

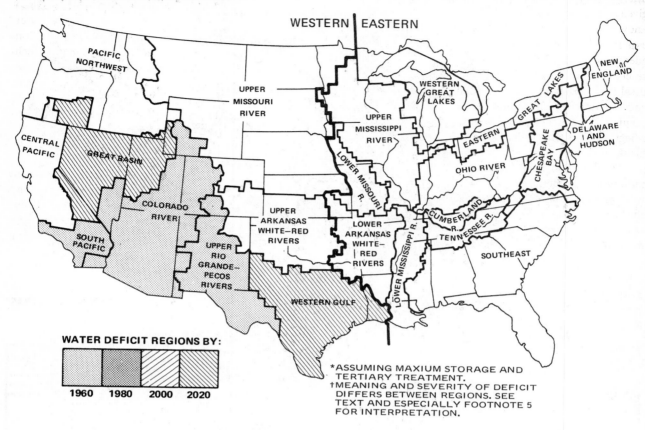

WATER DEFICIT REGIONS BY:

1960   1980   2000   2020

*ASSUMING MAXIUM STORAGE AND
 TERTIARY TREATMENT.
†MEANING AND SEVERITY OF DEFICIT
 DIFFERS BETWEEN REGIONS. SEE
 TEXT AND ESPECIALLY FOOTNOTE 5
 FOR INTERPRETATION.

levels of treatment were achieved, there would be abundant water supplies for at least the next 50 years, despite high concentrations of population and manufacturing. Interregional transfers (of water in, or people and economic activities out) would be an excessively costly way to solve these qualitative problems. As can be seen from Table 2, total annualized costs of meeting requirements for both streamflow and treatment increase much less rapidly for this region than for the nation as a whole.

In the Upper Arkansas region, if high levels of streamflow regulation and treatment were achieved, deficits could be avoided until 1990 or so. Whether they will appear thereafter depends on national population and economic assumptions: If the Series B projection for the nation prevails, deficits would appear in 2000; if the Series E projection occurs, deficits would not appear until 2020 under the high economic growth assumptions and until perhaps 2025-2030 under the low economic growth assumption. In this region as well, costs mount

more slowly than for the nation as a whole; here it is due to the fact that there is a limit to the ability to augment flow, beyond which additional expenditures in this direction are of no avail. Importation of water would not be a viable economic proposition for this area; and since agriculture rather than population and manufacturing is the dominant water user, there is little scope for outmigration as a means of alleviating these deficits. In the absence of other possibilities, the best that can be done is to slow future growth of agricultural and other activities in this region.

In contrast, population growth in the South Pacific region appears to be the major contributor to this region's deficit. Outmigration or a slowdown in in-migration could have a major impact on future water requirements here. Current policy, however, appears to favor importation despite its cost. The cost figures in Table 2 for this region do not include cost of importation; despite this, they mount more rapidly than for the nation as a whole.

The scope for augmenting water supplies in different regions also appears to be fairly limited, at least given currently available technology. While little is known about the extent of groundwater reserves, most experts do not consider the mining of such reserves an adequate alternative. For regions along the western seacoast and the Gulf of Mexico, a cheap procedure for desalting water could significantly change the outlook; and weather modification might be developed to the point where it could provide relief for some localities on a regular basis. But both methods require technological breakthroughs that are not on the immediate horizon.

On the other hand, reduction in water use through rationing and technological change are quite feasible and will certainly be the main method utilized to alleviate shortages. Most water consumption is not priced or is vastly underpriced; free use of water bodies as waste dumping grounds is more the rule than the exception. If

the cost of utilizing water for these purposes were raised to more appropriate levels, over time households would adjust by reducing the extent of lawns and shrubbery requiring irrigation, and factories would install water-saving rather than water-using techniques of production. Even farmers could and would find agricultural techniques requiring far less water than they currently use.

In summary, then, growth in population and economic activities during the next half century will force upon us significant expenditures for treatment and storage facilities; moreover, for a growing number of regions, such investments will eventually prove inadequate. When one takes a region-by-region look at the situation, it becomes clear that the scope for redistribution of water, activities, and people is more limited and difficult to achieve than it might appear at first glance. But there is considerable scope for inducing reductions in demand for water. Short of significant technological

FIGURE 8-9
WATER LOSSES AND WITHDRAWALS, DELAWARE AND HUDSON REGION

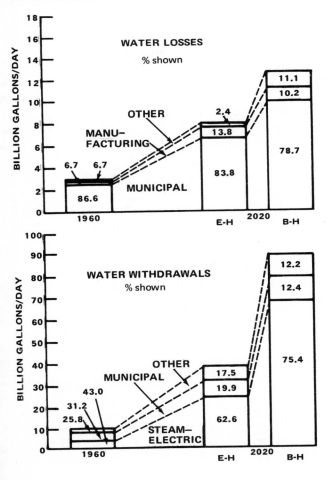

FIGURE 8-10
WATER LOSSES AND WITHDRAWALS, UPPER ARKANSAS REGION

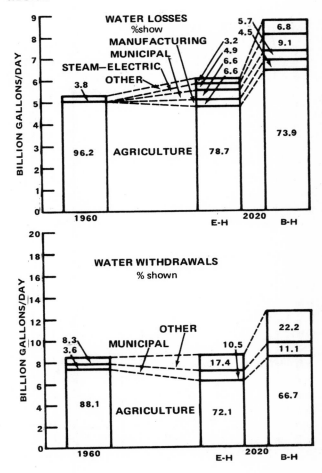

Future Water Needs and Supplies, with a Note on Land Use

breakthroughs in water augmenting procedures, this is the method that will have to be relied upon to hold expenditures on treatment and storage facilities to reasonable levels and to avoid difficult and painful redistributions. Population growth has a large role to play in determining how rapidly we must accomplish all these changes.

A NOTE ON LAND USE IN THE UNITED STATES

There is limited value in an assessment of aggregate demand and supply for land in a country. Local problems, which tend to be covered up in such an analysis, are typically more important. But given recent concerns about (1) the amount of good agricultural, scenic, and recreational land that we are covering over with asphalt or concrete, and (2) whether we will have enough such lands to meet future needs, some overall

evaluation is in order. Also, the farther out in the future we project—the more time we allow for interregional disparities to iron themselves out—the more relevant an aggregate view becomes.

If all the land in the United States were divided equally amongst its citizens, each American would have 11 acres at his disposal (nine acres excluding Alaska and Hawaii). Of this amount, approximately two acres are used to grow crops and half an acre is used in conjunction with man-made structures (houses, businesses, roads, public installations, etc.). The remainder is tricky to classify since much of it is subject to multiple use. Three acres per capita is classified as pasture and range, but contains much commercially exploitable timber as well as land used for recreational purposes. Similarly, about four-tenths of an acre is devoted to national and state parks, monuments, nonurban reservoirs, designated wilderness areas, and state and Federal wildlife refuges. But these lands do not include recreation lands in urban areas or lands under the jurisdiction of the National Forest Service; because they are potentially useful for commercial purposes, these lands are classified as commercial forest and woodland. If such areas as recreation land were included, we would have about one and three-quarters acres per person available for recreational purposes.

Compared to most developed countries of the world, these figures are very large. In 1967, the United States had a population of 55 persons per square mile. The corresponding figure for France was 237; for West Germany, 624; for the United Kingdom, 588; and for Europe as a whole, 239. Even when one takes account of differences in terrain, fertility of the soil, and international trade, these are dramatic differences.

But what about the future. Are we destined to live at densities comparable to those experienced in Europe? Are we paving over large amounts of good agricultural and recreational land? Thirty years from now, will we still have sufficient agricultural and recreational land to maintain an economy and way of life comparable to what we know today?

One way to shed some light on these questions is to make fairly generous assumptions about future land requirements and compare them with aggregate supplies of land. Suppose, for example, we assume that land associated with human habitation, business, and transportation expands more or less in proportion to the increase in population. Suppose, moreover, we take estimates of future recreational land requirements per capita from Chapter 6 on outdoor recreation, and hold this per capita figure constant as we vary population assumptions for the year 2000. For future agricultural land requirements, we can use the estimates presented in

FIGURE 8-11
WATER LOSSES AND WITHDRAWALS, SOUTH PACIFIC REGION

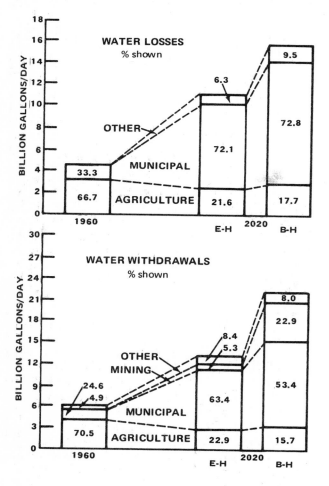

Population, Resources, and the Environment

Table 2.—Annualized Cost of Water Requirements for United States Minimum Cost Program[a]
(million 1960 $)

Region	1960 Cost of flow	1960 Total cost	1980 Cost of flow	1980 Total cost	2000 Cost of flow	2000 Total cost	2020 Cost of flow	2020 Total cost
SCENARIO B-H								
Northeast								
New England	0	21.6	0.1	31.9	0	53.1	0	88.5
Delaware and Hudson	0	58.9	0	108.1	28.9	189.3	81.3	335.9
Chesapeake Bay	3.5	26.2	5.2	55.7	12.0	95.7	14.0	194.9
Ohio River	0	34.2	16.5	67.9	64.0	143.8	0	297.5
East Great Lakes	0.6	33.0	5.9	60.9	14.9	98.5	19.4	173.7
West Great Lakes	4.4	44.2	7.3	82.9	43.5	162.7	173.6	293.7
Upper Mississippi River	1.0	26.7	3.8	47.4	15.4	92.6	0	216.5
Lower Missouri River	0	3.8	.02	4.0	0.4	9.7	4.7	24.7
Southeast								
Southeast	0	45.5	3.6	113.6	9.9	243.2	17.7	558.3
Cumberland River	0	1.4	0	8.0	1.4	18.9	0	40.8
Tennessee River	0	6.3	0	17.1	0	33.9	0	77.1
Lower Mississippi River	1.8	10.1	6.1	20.1	5.6	43.0	16.0	88.2
Lower Arkansas River	0	7.2	0	10.4	0	20.0	2.1	41.8
Mid Continent								
Upper Missouri	0	10.4	0	17.9	0	29.7	0	48.4
Upper Arkansas	3.3	9.9	3.2	12.9	3.2	18.9	3.2	27.9
Western Gulf	0	39.4	6.1	85.3	69.5	139.4	69.5	194.0
Southwest								
Upper Rio Grande-Pecos Rivers	0	2.8	0	4.1	0	7.8	0	12.5
Colorado River	0	3.1	0	6.9	0	14.5	0	24.3
Great Basin	1.8	3.8	13.1	16.3	13.1	19.7	13.1	23.2
South Pacific	8.8	25.0	8.8	37.8	8.8	59.6	8.8	93.4
North Pacific								
Central Pacific	3.4	21.0	7.1	52.4	19.9	103.0	74.5	205.2
Pacific Northwest	0	10.6	0	58.7	17.7	116.2	19.1	264.9
United States								
Total	28.5	445.2	87.0	920.3	328.2	1713.3	517.2	3325.7
SCENARIO B-L								
Northeast								
New England	0	21.6	0	31.2	3.1	49.0	3.9	76.1
Delaware and Hudson	0	58.9	0	105.8	24.4	172.4	68.1	286.0
Chesapeake Bay	3.5	26.2	4.9	54.1	10.1	86.2	29.7	152.9
Ohio River	0	34.2	15.5	70.4	50.2	123.6	0	253.2
East Great Lakes	0.6	33.0	5.5	59.4	12.6	90.3	15.8	149.5
West Great Lakes	4.4	44.2	6.4	80.0	28.0	136.7	173.6	277.1
Upper Mississippi River	1.0	26.7	3.3	45.9	11.3	82.2	27.4	169.8
Lower Missouri River	0	3.8	0	3.8	0	8.0	2.2	17.7
Southeast								
Southeast	0	45.5	0	106.6	0	210.5	0	446.6
Cumberland River	0	1.4	0	7.6	0	15.1	0	31.6
Tennessee River	0	6.3	0	16.5	0	30.1	14.3	61.8

Table 2.—Continued

Region	1960 Cost of flow	1960 Total cost	1980 Cost of flow	1980 Total cost	2000 Cost of flow	2000 Total cost	2020 Cost of flow	2020 Total cost
SCENARIO B-L (Continued)								
Lower Mississippi River	1.8	10.1	5.8	19.4	7.9	37.4	10.4	67.5
Lower Arkansas River	0	7.2	0	10.1	0	15.4	0	32.2
Mid Continent								
Upper Missouri	0	10.4	0	17.7	0	28.2	0	42.8
Upper Arkansas	3.3	9.9	3.3	12.8	3.3	17.9	3.3	24.9
Western Gulf	0	39.4	4.9	82.3	69.5	134.0	69.5	175.3
Southwest								
Upper Rio Grande-Pecos Rivers	0	2.8	0	4.1	0	7.5	0	11.6
Colorado River	0	3.1	0	6.9	0	14.2	0	22.5
Great Basin	1.8	3.8	13.1	16.3	13.1	19.2	13.1	21.8
South Pacific	8.8	25.0	8.8	37.6	8.8	58.3	8.8	88.6
North Pacific								
Central Pacific	3.4	21.0	6.8	51.4	17.0	95.9	48.4	165.4
Pacific Northwest	0	10.6	0	55.9	5.5	90.4	1.1	189.8
United States								
Total	28.5	445.2	78.1	895.9	253.6	1522.5	420.3	2764.7
SCENARIO E-H								
Northeast								
New England	0	21.6	0	30.7	2.5	46.8	0.9	63.6
Delaware and Hudson	0	58.9	0	105.2	13.3	154.6	37.3	227.5
Chesapeake Bay	3.5	26.2	5.1	55.0	10.2	84.9	25.9	135.8
Ohio River	0	34.2	15.7	65.8	52.1	125.4	103.2	219.3
East Great Lakes	0.6	33.0	5.4	59.1	11.6	84.6	22.8	119.4
West Great Lakes	4.4	44.2	6.0	80.1	24.1	129.7	117.3	262.9
Upper Mississippi River	1.0	26.7	3.1	45.5	7.7	76.0	38.2	132.2
Lower Missouri River	0	3.8	0	3.8	0	8.2	1.9	17.2
Southeast								
Southeast	0	45.5	1.6	109.4	0	202.9	0	399.9
Cumberland River	0	1.4	0	8.0	0	15.8	0	31.6
Tennessee River	0	6.3	0	16.9	0	29.9	8.0	52.9
Lower Mississippi River	1.8	10.1	5.3	19.1	7.3	37.4	7.8	64.1
Lower Arkansas	0	7.2	0	10.1	0	14.6	4.8	29.3
Mid Continent								
Upper Missouri	0	10.4	0	17.2	0	25.7	0	35.5
Upper Arkansas River	3.3	9.9	3.3	12.6	3.3	17.1	3.3	22.3
Western Gulf	0	39.4	0	77.5	69.5	13.2	69.5	16.5
Southwest								
Upper Rio Grande-Pecos Rivers	0	2.8	0	4.0	0	6.7	0	9.0
Colorado River	0	3.1	0	6.6	0	12.2	0	17.6
Great Basin	1.8	3.8	1.9	7.1	13.1	19.0	13.1	21.0
South Pacific	8.8	25.0	8.8	36.7	8.8	52.1	8.8	70.2
North Pacific								
Central Pacific	3.4	21.0	1.4	45.0	8.7	80.3	23.2	119.8
Pacific Northwest	0	10.6	0	58.4	2.0	90.0	49.2	188.1

Table 2.—Continued

Region	1960 Cost of flow	1960 Total cost	1980 Cost of flow	1980 Total cost	2000 Cost of flow	2000 Total cost	2020 Cost of flow	2020 Total cost
SCENARIO E-H (Continued)								
United States								
Total	28.5	445.2	57.6	873.7	234.1	1327.1	535.3	2255.8
SCENARIO E-L								
Northeast								
New England	0	21.6	0	30.1	0.8	42.1	0	54.8
Delaware and Hudson	0	58.9	0	102.9	9.1	138.7	26.7	187.4
Chesapeake Bay	3.5	26.2	4.8	53.3	8.8	77.6	14.0	105.1
Ohio River	0	34.2	13.3	62.2	39.4	106.7	62.8	159.6
East Great Lakes	0.6	33.0	5.0	57.6	9.5	77.0	15.4	98.4
West Great Lakes	4.4	44.2	5.1	77.2	16.7	112.5	60.4	185.0
Upper Mississippi River	1.0	26.7	2.6	44.1	13.2	65.6	15.7	94.6
Lower Missouri River	0	3.8	0	3.7	0.7	6.6	1.7	11.8
Southeast								
Southeast	0	45.5	0	104.5	0	182.4	29.6	275.9
Cumberland River	0	1.4	0	7.6	0	13.6	0	24.4
Tennessee River	0	6.3	0	16.3	0	22.4	0	35.9
Lower Mississippi River	1.8	10.1	5.1	18.5	6.1	32.6	5.9	50.2
Lower Arkansas	0	7.2	0	9.9	0	12.3	0	19.6
Mid Continent								
Upper Missouri	0	10.4	0	17.0	0	24.2	0	31.0
Upper Arkansas	3.3	9.9	3.3	12.5	3.3	16.2	3.3	19.6
Western Gulf	0	30.4	0	75.6	69.5	126.5	69.5	149.3
Southwest								
Upper Rio Grande-Pecos Rivers	0	2.8	0	3.9	0	6.4	0	8.2
Colorado River	0	3.1	0	6.5	0	11.9	0	16.1
Great Basin	1.8	3.8	1.7	6.8	2.2	13.0	13.1	19.9
South Pacific	8.8	25.0	8.8	36.5	8.8	50.8	8.8	66.1
North Pacific								
Central Pacific	3.4	21.0	0.9	44.0	6.0	73.8	15.9	101.7
Pacific Northwest	0	10.6	4.8	52.0	0	75.7	21.3	128.3
United States								
Total	28.5	445.2	55.3	842.7	194.1	1174.6	364.3	1843.1

[a]Total cost equals cost of flow plus treatment costs. Cost of flow does not include cost of importation, where relevant. Figure 4 uses United States total cost figures from this table converted to the 1967 price level.

Chapter 7 on the agricultural sector, assuming first, that there is no restriction on the use of chemical fertilizers and pesticides and then, that there is such a restriction so that additional land must be used to obtain the same output. Resulting estimates based on these assumptions are presented in Table 3.

The first and most obvious result is that, even under the high population growth assumption, the United States will still be classified as a relatively land-rich country. Per capita acres would drop from 11 to seven by the year 2000; but even this latter figure is higher than what most European countries have at their disposal today. On the other hand, compared to what Americans are accustomed, this is a sizeable irreversible reduction that will require some adjustments.

Second, we do not appear to be "paving over" large quantities of land, at least not in the aggregate. Land devoted to human habitation, transport, industry, ports, etc.—which includes urban parks and many other areas that are not covered by man-made structures—increases from 2.9 percent in 1970 to somewhere between 3.9 percent (for population Series E) and 4.7 percent (for population Series B) under assumptions. Of course, within specific geographic areas, a much higher percentage of the land may become covered. But in the aggregate, the change between 1970 and 2000 does not seem very dramatic.

Third, the need for harvested cropland will continue to fall up to 1980; but thereafter it will begin to rise again. Indeed, by the year 2000 under these assump-

Table 3.—Land Use Without and With Constraint on Fertilizer and Pesticide Use

	1964	1970	1980 B	1980 E	2000 B	2000 E
A. MILLION ACRES						
Land associated with man-made structures	97	100	105	102	153	135
Areas of human habitation[a]	29	31	36	34	46	40
Public installations (outside towns)[b]	33	34	30	30	46	46
Other (transportation, industry, ports, etc.)[c] ..	35	35	39	37	60	48
Agriculture and forest land	1595	1595	1522	1521-1522	1522-1609	1545-1561
Cropland harvested[d]	354	345	338-365	337-359	391-437	359-390
Cropland not harvested[e]	90	95	91-64	91-70	31-33	51-32
Pasture and range[f]	640	632	620	620	580-617	613-617
Commercial forest and woodland[g]	511	523	473	473	522	522
Pure recreation land (outside towns)[h]	76	81	107	102	177	146
Residual (wasteland and other)[i]	498	490	532	541-540	414-327	440-424
Total land[j]	2266	2266	2266	2266	2266	2266
of which contiguous U.S.	1904	1904	1904	1904	1904	1904
Total recreation land[k]	339	342	366	349	430	356
B. ACRES PER CAPITA						
Land associated with man-made structures	.50	.49	.44	.45	.48	.51
Areas of human habitation[a]	.15	.15	.15	.16	.15	.16
Public installations (outside towns)[b]	.17	.17	.13	.13	.14	.17
Other (transportation, industry, ports, etc.)[c] ..	.18	.17	.16	.16	.19	.18
Agriculture and forest land	8.30	7.77	6.43	6.75	4.74-5.02	5.80-5.86
Cropland harvested[d]	1.84	1.68	1.43-1.54	1.50-1.59	1.22-1.36	1.35-1.46
Cropland not harvested[e]	.47	.46	.38-.27	.40-.31	.10	.19-.12
Pasture and range[f]	3.33	3.08	2.62	2.75	1.80-1.92	2.30-2.32
Commercial forest and woodland[g]	2.66	2.55	2.00	2.10	1.63	1.96
Pure recreation land (outside towns)[h]	.40	.39	.45	.45	.55	.55
Residual (wasteland and other)[i]	2.59	2.38	2.25	2.40-2.39	1.29-1.02	1.65-1.59
Total land[j]	11.80	11.03	9.57	10.05	7.06	8.51
of which contiguous U.S.	9.91	9.27	8.04	8.44	5.94	7.15
Total recreation land[k]	1.76	1.66	1.55	1.55	1.34	1.34
C. PERCENT OF TOTAL						
Land associated with man-made structures	4.3	4.4	4.6	4.5	6.8	6.0
Areas of human habitation[a]	(1.3)	(1.4)	(1.6)	(1.5)	(2.1)	(1.8)
Public installations (outside towns)[b]	(1.5)	(1.5)	(1.3)	(1.3)	(2.0)	(2.0)
Other (transportation, industry, ports, etc.)[c] ..	(1.5)	(1.5)	(1.7)	(1.6)	(2.6)	(2.1)

Table 3.—Continued

	1964	1970	1980 B	1980 E	2000 B	2000 E
C. PERCENT OF TOTAL—Continued						
Agriculture and forest land	70.4	70.4	67.2	67.1-67.2	67.2-71.0	68.2-68.9
Cropland harvested[d]	(15.6)	(15.2)	(14.9)-(16.1)	(14.9)-(15.8)	(17.3)-(19.3)	(11.4)-(17.2)
Cropland not harvested[e]	(4.0)	(4.2)	(4.0)-(2.8)	(4.0)-(3.1)	(1.4)-(1.5)	(2.2)-(1.4)
Pasture and range[f]	(28.2)	(27.9)	(27.4)	(27.4)	(25.5)-(27.2)	(27.1)-(27.2)
Commercial forest and woodland[g]	(22.5)	(23.1)	(20.9)	(20.9)	(23.0)	(23.0)
Pure recreation land (outside towns)[h]	3.3	3.6	4.7	4.5	7.8	6.4
Residual (wasteland and other)[i]	22.0	21.6	23.5	23.9-23.8	18.3-14.4	19.4-18.7
Total land[j]	100.0	100.0	100.0	100.0	100.0	100.0
of which contiguous U.S.	84.0	84.0	84.0	84.0	84.0	84.0
Total recreation land[k]	15.0	15.1	16.2	15.4	19.0	15.7

[a]Data includes incorporated and unincorporated towns with a population of 1,000 and over. Projections by U.S. Department of Agriculture, adjusted to include Alaska and Hawaii. Projections assume a growth factor of .13 acres per capita on both B and E population series.

[b]Includes primarily national defense areas outside towns. Also includes flood control land, Federal industrial land and state institutional areas. Projections reflect an assumed low level of armed forces as well as a declining percentage in forces maintained overseas.

[c]Includes highways (interurban), railroads, airports, etc.; farm roads and farmsteads; urban parks; industrial sites (outside towns); and ports.

[d]Includes harvested cropland used for crops and for pasture.

[e]Includes idle cropland under government programs, summer fallow, and crop failure—21-22 million acres is summer fallow while 10-11 million acres is crop failure. Nonharvested cropland acreage above 31 million acres would thus be available as surplus.

[f]Includes permanent pasture in farmland and public grazing outside farms.

[g]Includes forests either commercially exploited or capable of exploitation and forests and woodland grazed if also commercially exploited or exploitable for wood and timber.

[h]Includes national and state parks, monuments, nonurban reservoirs, designated wilderness areas, and federal and state wildlife refuges. Does not include recreation land in urban areas or lands under the jurisdiction of the National Forest Service which are potentially available for either recreation or commercial exploitation.

[i]Consists of largely unusable land such as swamp, tundra, mountaintop, etc. Some would be potentially usable as wildlife preserves.

[j]Includes Alaska and Hawaii.

[k]Base year is 1965 rather than 1964. Data includes pure recreation land (see above, footnote c) as well as urban recreation areas (footnote c) plus areas owned by the National Forest Service, which are classified as commercial forest and woodland because of their potential for this use but which are also available as recreation land. Projections are by Charles Cicchetti. Demand for total recreation land for the E population was projected on the basis of income, age distribution, and other factors explained in his paper; demand for total recreation land for the B population was increased in proportion to the increase in population.

Note: Wherever two figures appear in a column, lefthand figure represents projection assuming current policy, and righthand figure represents projection assuming constraint on use of fertilizers and pesticides.

Source: U.S. Department of Agriculture, *Major Uses of Land and Water in the United States—Summary for 1964,* Agricultural Economic Report No. 149, November 1968; *Agricultural Statistics, 1970,* Table 619, p. 428; and *Changes in Farm Production and Efficiency, A Summary Report, 1970,* Statistical Bulletin No. 233, June 1970. Projections, unless otherwise stated, are by Economic Associates, Inc., Washington, D.C.

tions, we will have put back into production most if not all of the land classified as surplus cropland (cropland not harvested over and above the 31 or 32 million acres for summer fallow and crop failure). With the Series E population, this will be the case if we also restrict the use of chemical fertilizers and pesticides; with the Series B population, this will be the case even without such restrictions.

Fourth, for convenience, we have assumed in the table that the additional cropland in these cases will come from lands classified as pasture and range, plus the residual category; in reality, all categories of land would adjust. The main point to be made is that they all could adjust without serious welfare losses. There is considerable "fat" included in each use. Thus, we have generously estimated the amount of land required for recreation use in 2000; if we held the per capita figure constant at its 1970 level instead of permitting it to increase, even under the high population assumption some 50 million acres of recreation land could be released from this use in 2000. Moreover, we have said nothing about the category classified as public installations, which includes at least as much land as do areas of human habitation. A large fraction of such land consists of government land set aside for military use; surely some of this could be released for other uses without loss to the national welfare. Finally, if needed, additional cropland could be obtained from the vast areas classified as pasture, range, or forest, as well as from lands which had been used for agriculture in the past.

Of course, the figures do also suggest a definite, progressive elimination of such comfortable margins over time, more rapid under the Series B than under the Series E population growth assumption. Our land-rich status cannot continue for many decades beyond 2000 if the population continues to grow. By 2020, per capita acres would have dropped to five for the Series B and 7.5 for the Series E population assumptions. In the latter case, this would be virtually the end of the decline; in the former case, this irreversible decline continues.

But the picture provided by Table 3 is inadequate in several respects. First, as suggested above, these aggregate figures may cover up serious local problems, problems that may only be solvable by oftentimes painful institutional changes or migration. Similarly, they ignore special categories of land, especially for recreation—beaches, unique scenic or wilderness areas— that are not in ample supply.

Second, this picture ignores the fact that landownership and the bargaining power necessary to acquire it is unequally distributed in this country, as it is in most. Such inequalities have never caused serious conflicts in this country largely because, traditionally, there have been new lands and jobs for the discontented to move to. But as the country continues to fill up over time, this safety valve is slowly but progressively tightened. We must anticipate increasing difficulty and conflict involved in bringing about appropriate changes in land use in the future. Obviously, a lower rate of population growth would be helpful in reducing the magnitude of such problems.

Third, the fall in agricultural yields, and hence the increase in cropland, when pesticides and chemical fertilizers are restricted, assumes that no biochemical techniques of pest control are devised as alternatives. If such techniques come along in the next 30 years, demand for agricultural land will not rise as rapidly as assumed under a clean environment policy.

A shift towards a closed agricultural system, discussed briefly in Chapter 10, could also alter this picture during the next half century. The logical extreme of this shift would be hydroponic production of food: the growth of plants with chemicals and artificial lights in enclosed areas. Protection from pests would be accomplished mechanically rather than chemically, no nutrients or water would be lost to land or air, and use of land would be minimal. For special crops, where water, land, or distribution costs are especially high, this method of production is proving to be commercially viable even now. If the price of good agricultural land increases very greatly, as the projections to the year 2020 imply, this method of production may become sufficiently important to release substantial quantities of cropland for other purposes.

REFERENCES

1. Nathaniel Wollman and Gilbert W. Bonem, *The Outlook for Water: Quality, Quantity, and National Growth* (Baltimore: The Johns Hopkins Press for Resources for the Future, 1971). We are grateful to James MacFarland and Leon Hyatt for running the model for us.

2. These standards are: minimum of 4 mg of dissolved oxygen per liter of water, phosphorus not to exceed 0.1 ppm of water; nitrogen not to exceed 1 ppm of water; and instream temperature not to rise by more than $5.4°F$. Pollution from bacteria, viruses, chemicals, dissolved solids is assumed to be reduced to acceptable levels by the dilution flows necessary to meet the dissolved oxygen standard after waste treatment.

3. Measurements here are in terms of annual biochemical oxygen demand (BOD). Since it was estimated in a different way from that used in the overall model—e.g., non-sewered population (mostly animals many of which are in feed lots) has not been included here—the figures in Chapter 2 and those provided here are not strictly comparable.

4. An exception must be made for earlier decades when there is a need for higher rates of investment, especially in treatment facilities, to meet water quality standards. As a consequence, between 1960 and 1980, the rate of growth in expenditures is much higher than it is in later decades.

5. In judging the meaning and severity of these deficits several points should be borne in mind. First, some regions are too aggregated to be used as a basis for detailed regional planning. This is the case wherever there are significant dry and wet areas within a single region. Second, the model takes account only of stream flow in the United States; groundwater and lake water are assumed not to be mined. For some regions these assumptions give a misleading picture. The Western Great Lakes, for example, is fed primarily by water from Canada; to this extent at least, the model understates the supply picture for this region.

Chapter 9

Urban Scale and Environmental Quality

by
Irving Hoch
Resources for the Future, Inc.

ACKNOWLEDGMENTS

Hyder Lakhani served as research assistant on this project, and performed capably in a literature search and in organizing data. Dina Labourdette typed the draft manuscripts of this report. Useful information was obtained from Thomas McMullen and Ronald Venezia, Environmental Protection Agency; Eric Zausner, Council on Environmental Quality; Daniel P. Loucks, Cornell University; the National League of Cities and the library files of the Conservation Foundation. A first statement of the second section of this chapter was discussed at the University of Chicago Workshop in Urban Economics, directed by George Tolley, and the interchange with the workshop participants was helpful. I have also benefitted from information and review comments given by members of the Population Commission staff and by my colleagues at Resources for the Future.

COMMISSION ON POPULATION GROWTH AND THE AMERICAN FUTURE, *RESEARCH REPORTS, VOLUME III, POPULATION RESOURCES AND THE ENVIRONMENT,* EDITED BY RONALD G. RIDKER

CONTENTS

Urban Scale and Environmental Quality

INTRODUCTION

It is generally the case that, in large urban areas, there is degradation of environmental quality; and, the larger the area, the lower the quality. This has led to many proposals to dismantle the urban complex and to redirect growth to smaller, more pleasant places. But such arguments neglect the existence of compensations that occur with larger size. These include both the availability of specialized production and amenities that are viable only with large scale, and higher pay for the same work as urban size increases. Higher pay more than covers the increased cost of living that occurs with increases in urban size, primarily reflecting rent increases; the amount left over seems best interpreted as compensation for a net decline in the quality of life, interpreted to cover both amenities and disamenities that are a function of size, and viewed in terms of majority preferences. (The evidence indicates that disamenities outweigh amenities, in terms of majority preferences, which, for simplicity, tend to be treated here as universal.)

Sample surveys show that the expression of dissatisfaction with their locale is more common for people in large urban areas than for people in smaller areas. And, they show that a majority of people in large areas expresses a preference for location in rural areas or small towns. It is possible to interpret such results as evidence of massive market failure. It is more plausible, however, to see this as a consequence of a tradeoff that has occurred. Other things equal, people in large places prefer smaller places. But other things are not equal, and income in large urban areas is enough higher than that in the smaller places to attract and keep people in those larger places.

Because economists can generally explain existing situations as if they were equilibria attained through effective market mechanisms, there is the possibility that the explanation will slide over into the proposition that this is the best of all possible worlds. That slide is resisted here. In particular, it appears possible that improvement can be had through institutional rearrangements, especially through better pricing of components of environmental quality by effluent charges or tolls.

But if such improvement occurs, the likely consequence is that an urban area making the improvement will grow larger. The area will become more attractive, on net, and more people will migrate into it until an equilibrium is again attained. (It is recognized that attempted improvements may sometimes cost more than they are worth, leading to real losses in income in the system.) It is possible that effluent charges and tolls have not been introduced because of negative impact on rather massive vested interests, involving implicit property rights in "free goods"; the vested interests may well be those of the majority.

The remainder of this paper is devoted to documentation of the argument sketched above, with sections on population and income, environmental quality, and policy issues. (Data have been drawn from a number of sources. Where money magnitudes are presented, they are generally referenced by date; where a date is not given, the interpretation is that the data are "current," that is, specific to the recent past.)

The next section considers the distribution of urban population, both within and between cities, and develops evidence on cost-of-living and wage differentials by city size. (A city or urban area is defined here as economic unit, rather than as political unit, and corresponds to the urbanized area of the Census Bureau. However, available data series generally use the Standard Metropolitan Statistical Area as base, and for most purposes, the SMSA is quite close to the urbanized area. Most of the data employed here are on the SMSA base, but some cover central cities of SMSA's, or individual cities defined as political jurisdictions.) Cities are viewed as analogous to firms in production theory, and it is argued that each city has its own optimum size, with large cities having become large because of some comparative advantage.

Increased size leads to corresponding increases in population density, other things equal; urban population size and density are catalogued under the general heading of urban scale.

The wage comparisons made are for homogeneous populations, and the difficulty that might arise from disequilibrium appears to be minor.

Money wages were deflated by cost of living indexes as a function of city size for each of the four major United States regions. The results, which can be interpreted as indicating net compensatory payment, showed considerable consistency between regions, making possible the estimation of values for the United States, overall. These rough orders of magnitude emerge:

SMSA population in 000	Relative level, deflated wages
100	1.00
2000	1.12
10,000	1.18

Analysis of data within regions led to the conclusion that, for an SMSA of two million, the money wage differential relative to smaller places consisted of about 35 percent as a cost of living effect and about 65 percent as a compensatory payment.

Within urban areas, level of environmental quality is seen as affecting density, land value, and rent, with changes in the first leading to changes of the same sign in the last three variables.

The third section of this paper is central, and involves a detailed examination of the relation of environmental quality to urban scale, with major focus on the physical environment: air quality, water quality, solid waste disposal and noise. There is also a brief review of effects in the social environment, including traffic congestion, crime, and health and welfare effects. The basic hypothesis, of course, is that environmental quality declines with scale. The decline in quality may occur in terms of level, in the sense of lower levels of psychic income (less open space) or higher levels of psychic cost (more air pollution), or it may occur in terms of dollar cost, in the sense of higher outlays needed to achieve a given environmental standard. (Higher quality can always be obtained at a price; one can conceive of an upward sloping supply curve relating quality levels to money cost, with an upward shift of the curve as urban scale increases.)

The basic hypothesis was clearly supported by evidence for air pollution, solid waste disposal, and noise, with these rough orders of magnitude emerging:

| SMSA population in 000 | Air pollution levels | | | Solid waste disposal, relative cost per ton |
	Particulates	Sulfur dioxide	Nitrogen dioxide	
100	1.0	1.0	1.0	1.0
2,000	1.4	2.3	1.3	1.6
10,000	1.6	3.2	1.5	1.8

Outdoor noise levels in central sections of large cities are on the order of twice the perceived level in the residential areas of those cities, in turn twice the perceived level in suburban areas or small towns. (A doubling of perceived level corresponds to an increase of 10 dBA or decibles on the A scale.)

Congestion cost, expressed as journey-to-work time, was also clearly a function of urban scale. Crime rates, too, show some positive relation to population size and density; however, this is much less than is indicated by the raw data, because of confounding of scale effect with racial composition and other explanatory variables.

In the case of water quality, the basic hypothesis is open to some doubt, because there is engineering evidence of scale economies for both sewers and waste treatment. However, some scattered empirical evidence suggests that per capita costs are U-shaped with urban size, first decreasing and then increasing. This conclusion becomes much stronger if low levels of water pollution are specified as stream standards that must hold at all points. In this event, it is likely that large cities will have to engage in high cost tertiary treatment of their sewage. Some rough orders of magnitude are:

Urban population in 000	Sewer and water treatment costs (relative levels)
10	1.7
100	1.0
2,000	0.9 (engineering data)
2,000	1.1 (rates charged)
2,000	1.5 (investment "requirements")

Sources: Inferred from data in Figure 9, Tables 24 and 26.

Urbanization has hydrological and climate effects. The former includes increased risk of flooding, presumably handled by urban site selection and flood control investment. The latter includes less sunshine and higher temperatures; the last may be a net benefit because it is primarily a night-time effect.

Finally, though there is widespread belief that increasing urban scale has negative impact on a number of indices of health and welfare, the evidence is sketchy, at best.

In sum, it can be concluded there is general support for the basic hypothesis.

The fourth and concluding section of this paper discusses policy issues involved in environmental quality and urban population distribution, focusing on issues common to the two topics. The argument that people ought to be redirected away from large cities is considered and rejected. The locus of quality-of-life problems is seen as a matter of institutional arrangements, rather than population distribution. It seems more sensible to work on the causes of the problems—the institutional arrangements—and let population

Population, Resources, and the Environment

distribution emerge as one of the effects of the solutions. Effluent charges and tolls for some common property resources are advocated as solutions to some specific environmental problems.

There is some examination of the impact of existing environmental and urban policies on cities and on the distribution of urban population. One tentative conclusion emerging here is that middle-sized cities are likely to be subsidizing those at the size extremes. Finally, it is recognized that a case can be made for subsidized experimentation with new towns, growth centers, and a variety of forms of housing and urban development. We shall gain knowledge that might otherwise be unavailable, and if the experiment works, the positive externalities can be considerable. Given what seem to be strong preferences (yearnings?) for the psychic income of small scale, as well as the reluctance to give up the extra money income of large scale, perhaps successful experiments will enable us to do better at having our cake and eating it, too.

ON THE DISTRIBUTION OF URBAN POPULATION

Some Hypotheses Applying Production Theory

The distribution of urban population, both between and within cities, can be explained by some highly simplified but useful hypotheses. The hypotheses seem particularly useful in interpreting the impact of urban size and density on environmental quality.

Let us view cities as analogous to firms. The existence of new towns as single-owner corporate enterprises indicates that the analogy is not terribly strained. Each city has its own production function, employing the services of labor, capital goods, and urban land in the production of a single product, common to all cities. For simplicity, labor quantity is treated as a constant proportion of population; for example, one worker corresponds to three residents. A further key specification is that cities differ in their production functions, so that, for given levels of input, some cities obtain more output than others. These differences can be related to the natural resource base, broadly defined to include both locational advantages and the supply of "natural" goods valuable in production. The former includes access to various transportation networks and to market centers on those networks, yielding comparative advantage in regional, national, and world trade. The latter includes water quality and quantity, climate, soil characteristics affecting the cost of urban structures, and risk of natural disasters (earthquake, flood, hurricane, etc.). Rivers and harbors can be classified under both headings.

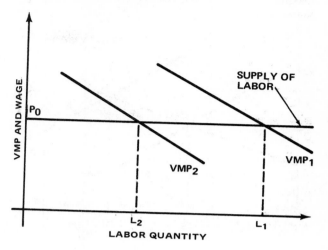

FIGURE 9-1

LABOR MARKET EQUILIBRIUM FOR TWO CITIES, WITH PERFECTLY ELASTIC SUPPLY

Production function differences are represented in Figure 1 as differences in value of marginal product curves (VMP's) for labor; city 1 is more efficient than city 2, with VMP_1 above VMP_2 at any level of labor input.

If we assume a perfectly elastic, long-run supply of labor, at wage P_0, then the equilibrium labor quantities L_1 and L_2 hold for the respective cities, with corresponding levels of population. An immediate insight is that there is no universal "optimum city size"; each city has its own optimum (defined as the equilibrium level); and, of course, the optimum will change over time, with changes in the underlying demand and supply relations.

The area under the VMP curve equals total value of product; the net after payments to labor and capital is the payment to the residual claimant, urban land. This can be viewed as the value of the stream of services from the natural resource base. In less than the longest run, there will also be rent (or quasi-rent) payments to city infrastructure—city streets, sewer and water systems, school buildings, etc.

Cities will vary in utility furnished consumers, as well as in production functions. A harsh climate or higher risk of natural disaster may shift the VMP curve down; it should certainly shift the labor supply curve up, with the latter becoming P_0 plus a risk or disamenity component. In this situation, city size will be reduced and money wage increased.

Of more interest here, as city population increases there is reason to expect (1) cost-of-living increases, in terms of a conventional cost-of-living index, and (2) greater net disamenity, at least in terms of majority

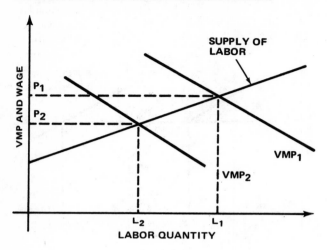

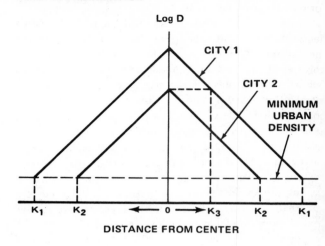

preferences. The consequence is that Figure 1 needs refinement, with the introduction of an upward sloping long-run labor supply function, as shown in Figure 2. Money wages in city 1 will be above those in city 2, so that real wages are equivalent. The increment $P_1 - P_2$ just compensates for the increased cost of living and disamenity associated with living and working in the larger city.

Within the city, the center will tend to be the focus of economic activity, since it will be the point minimizing intra-urban transport costs. Because transport costs increase with distance from the center, building rent and land values will decline with distance, given that transport costs are subtracted from gross product prices and/or wages via shipment of product or commuting of workers to a central market. Land will be used less intensively with increasing distance from the center, and floor space and population density will decline in similar fashion. There is good evidence that population tends to be distributed according to the function $D = Ae^{-bK}$, where D is population density, K is distance from the center, and A and b are parameters; A is density at the center, and b is the density gradient measuring the relative rate of decline in density.[1]

Figure 3 plots the log form of the density function for two cities, with city 1 larger than city 2. As a first approximation, it is assumed that the density gradient, b, is the same for both cities.

Note that the area under the respective density functions equals the respective city populations, which correspond (by assumption) to the total labor quantities of Figure 2. A similar density function could be drawn

for land value; the area under that curve, between the city limits, will equal the aggregate urban land value implicit in Figure 2: the residual derived by subtracting total wages and payment to capital from the total value of product.

It is intuitively obvious that building rent plus transport cost is everywhere higher in city 1 than in city 2. At the center, there is a bidding up of rental values, corresponding to the increase from A_2 to A_1. And it is an equilibrium condition that, in each city, land values have adjusted so that rent plus transport costs are everywhere the same. The minimum urban land rents occur at K_2 and K_1, respectively; here urban land value just equals its opportunity cost in nonurban use— generally in agriculture.[2] Clearly, the person at K_1 pays more transport cost than does the person at K_2.

Because housing rent plus transport costs are higher, workers to be attracted into the larger city must be compensated for this differential. Hence, we have one explanation for the upward sloping supply curve of Figure 3.

From Figure 3, it is also plausible that average density of city 1 is above that of city 2. The city 1 function from K_3 to K_1 parallels the city 2 function; the geometric average of density for the city 1 segment will equal the average density for city 2. The addition of the segment from 0 to K_3 should then raise the city 1 average above that of city 2.[3] In any event, city 1 people living in the segment 0 to K_3 will live at densities above any prevailing in city 2.

Figure 3 is a first approximation plotted on the assumption that the percentage increase in density between city 2 and city 1 is the same at every distance. (Multiplying the original density function by a constant corresponds to adding the log of the constant to the log form of Figure 3.)

But there is evidence that, with both increasing density and population size, there are negative effects on the "quality of life": for example, traffic congestion, noise, and air pollution probably increase with both factors. In particular, a number of such disamenities will increase with movement toward the center. This consideration allows for refinement of the first approximation of Figure 3. Consider Figure 3 in a somewhat new light, now assuming that the VMP of city

2 has shifted upward and that city 2 is in process of growing toward the population level of city 1. Assume that increased rent with city size is built into the labor supply curve of Figure 2, but that increased disamenity is not. As increased disamenity comes into play, we get the inhibited density pattern shown in Figure 4: City 1′ rather than city 1 emerges. There is less growth than would occur if underlying conditions had not changed through the process of growth itself. (The area under the city 1′ density function is less than that for city 1.) The city 1′ pattern might be viewed as only the first stage of a movement to an ultimate equilibrium; because population growth has been inhibited, total labor is less than the initially aimed-for equilibrium level (L_1 in Figure 2). This raises the labor wage and attracts more labor, and so on, until an ultimate equilibrium is attained—shown as city 1* in Figure 5. Figure 2 can now be reinterpreted as presenting a labor supply function with both rent and disamenity compensation built in, so that its slope is greater than under the original interpretation.

In Figure 5, city 1* has a lower density gradient, b, than city 2; its intercept, A^*_1, has increased less than proportionately with population growth; and more land has been converted from rural to urban use than under the city 1 pattern; that is, there is more suburban sprawl. There have been effects on both income and rent—an increase in money income (relative to the city 1 level), and a decline in rent near the city center, and an increase in rent in outlying portions of the city. (The population density function is treated as perfectly correlated with building rent.)

FIGURE 9-4
POPULATION DENSITY FUNCTIONS, REFLECTING QUALITY EFFECTS OF SIZE

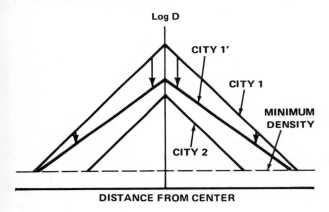

FIGURE 9-5
POPULATION DENSITY FUNCTIONS, REFLECTING QUALITY EFFECTS OF SIZE

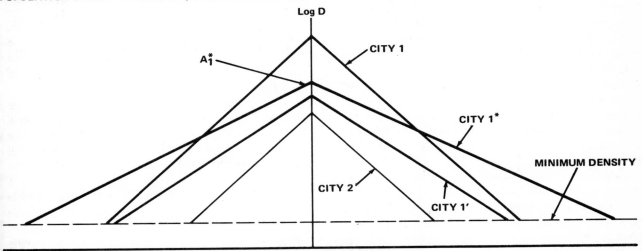

As a final refinement, note that there are likely to be multiplier effects associated with compensatory payments. George Tolley has recently developed a model of the urban economy in which goods are classified as exports, imports, and nontraded goods produced locally for local consumption. He obtains a multiplier of $1/(1-b_3 E_3)$, where E_3 is the share of total expenditures devoted to nontraded goods, and b_3 is the share of wages in nontraded goods production. "If wages in city A are higher than elsewhere, the cost of producing nontraded products will be raised which in turn will increase the wage that must be paid in city A to make real returns the same as elsewhere."[4]

Empirical Documentation

A fair amount of casual evidence is available to support the hypothesis that money income increases with city size. However, much of this data is subject to the critiques that the populations covered may not be homogeneous, that disequilibrium may be involved, and that there has been no accounting for cost-of-living differences. Some information is available, however, which appears to avoid many, and perhaps all, of the difficulties noted.

A study by Victor Fuchs is a good source, because Fuchs standardized for race, sex, age, and years of school, and accounted for regional differences.[5]

Fuchs had a 1/100th sample from the 1960 Census of Population for all persons employed in nonagricultural industries in April 1960, with some earnings in 1959. The observations were classified by region and city size as well as demographic characteristics. The total of 56,247 observations for the United States as a whole were grouped into 168 cells by color, sex, age, and years of school completed. (The number of classes for each characteristic was 2, 2, 7, and 6, respectively.) Annual hours worked were estimated for each worker and aggregated across each grouping. Aggregate earnings for each group were then divided by the aggregate of hours worked. This yielded a United States average wage per hour for each cell. These averages were used as weights to obtain an "expected" hourly wage for a given region or city size, given the distribution for the groupings in a particular locale. The ratio of actual to expected earnings was then derived and presented as a measure of differentials in money income for a standardized population.

Table 1 presents Fuchs' results for city size classes by region—Northeast, North Central, South, and West.[6]

Cost-of-living adjustments in Fuchs' results can be based on data published by the Bureau of Labor Statistics covering 39 selected metropolitan areas and nonmetropolitan areas for the four major regions of the

Table 1.—Money Income Differential by City Size and Region, 1959

Locale, and population in 000	Actual/expected wage rate by region			
	North-east	North Central	South	West
Urban place:				
<10	.92	.85	.76	.89
10-<100	.95	.93	.83	.95
SMSA:				
<250	.96	1.03	.89	1.01
250-<500	.96	1.03	.94	1.00
500-<1000	.99	1.11	.96	1.05
1000+	1.10	1.16	1.06	1.14

Source: Victor R. Fuchs, *Differentials in Hourly Earnings by Region and City Size, 1959* (New York: National Bureau of Economic Research, 1967), Occasional Paper 101, Table 8, p. 16.

Table 2.—Cost of Living Index, 1966 by Population Size and Region

Population size in 000	Region			
	North-east	North Central	South	West
5	.935	.923	.875	.930
50	.970	.954	.894	.960
125	.987	.968	.903	.978
250	.999	.979	.910	.990
375	1.007	.986	.914	.997
750	1.021	.999	.921	1.011
1000	1.027	1.004	.925	1.016
2000	1.042	1.018	.933	1.031
5000	1.064	1.037	.945	1.052

Source: Regression equation using BLS data. Observations are for 38 SMSA's and for nonmetropolitan areas. Nonmetropolitan area populations were set at 25,000.

country.[7] Excluding Honolulu, whose very high cost of living presumably reflected ocean transport costs, cost of living was regressed on SMSA size and region for 1966 as base year. The regression equation obtained was:

$$\log (C - 80) = 1.0538 + .0938^* \log P + .0208 \ (NE)$$
$$- .0254 \ (NC) - .2390^*(S)$$

where C is cost of living, P is population in thousands, and NE, NC, and S are dummy variables for Northeast,

Table 3.—Deflated Money Income Levels for Standardized Population

Locale and population in 000	Assumed average population size in 000	Deflated wage rate			
		Northeast	North Central	South	West
Urban place:					
<10	5	.984	.921	.869	.957
10-<100	50	.979	.975	.928	.990
SMSA:					
<250	125	.973	1.064	.986	1.033
250-<500	375	.953	1.045	1.028	1.003
500-<1000	750	.970	1.111	1.042	1.039
1000 + ...	2000	1.056	1.119	1.122	1.106
1000 + relative to (<10)		1.073	1.215	1.291	1.156

North Central and Southern regions, respectively. The Western region was set equal to zero to prevent multicollinearity, and an * indicates significance at the five percent level. The R^2 was .660.

Table 2 presents the cost of living index in fraction form for selected levels of population, applying the regression equation. Statistically, population size was significant at the five percent level as was the regional effect for the South. Correspondingly, in Table 2, there is a fair increase in the cost of living index with city size, and the Southern region is substantially below the other three, which have similar magnitudes for given population size. Some of the southern differential may reflect climate differences, and lower heating and clothing costs.

Table 2 was now used to deflate corresponding entries in Table 1,[8] with resulting estimates of deflated wage rates appearing as Table 3.

The general pattern of results in Table 3 fits the hypothesis that there are additional compensatory payments beyond cost of living compensation. The differential between largest size group (over a million) and smallest (less than 10,000) is only seven percent for the Northeast, but ranges from 15 to 30 percent for the other regions. This might be viewed as an upper bound for disamenity compensation; other components could include cost-of-living items not accounted for by the BLS, and disequilibrium.

Data from a separate source and a later time period yield results that square well with those of Table 1, tending to weaken the disequilibrium counter-hypothesis.

Data on wages for four female and three male occupations for 85 SMSA's were obtained from the BLS area wage surveys for 1968-69.[9] The occupations tend to be precisely defined (e.g. keypunch operator, class B) so that population nonhomogeneity should be limited. Hourly wages were deflated by the Monthly Consumer Price Index to a 1957-59 base, because observation dates varied within a year period. The use of the 1957-58 base allowed easy comparison with the Fuchs estimates. Deflated wages were regressed on log of SMSA population, log of central city density, and regional dummy variables. Results are presented as Table 4.

The southern regional effect is statistically significant in all cases, and SMSA population is significant in six of seven cases. The signs of both SMSA population and central city densities are always positive, fitting the hypothesis that money wages increase with both population size and density. The density effect appears less important than the size effect, given the former's lack of statistical significance. This interpretation receives further support when hourly wages are calculated from the regression equations, using extreme values of the variables. In the sample, density ranged from about 1,000 to 25,000 (New York City), while SMSA population ran from 100,000 to 10 million. Table 5 presents the extreme value calculations, using the western region as the base. In moving from lowest to highest level, population accounted for more than three-fourths of the increase in five of the occupations. But the density and population effects were about the same for two of the male occupations.

A comparison to the Fuchs estimates was made by deleting the density variable. Because SMSA population and density were fairly well correlated, as hypothesized (with correlation = 0.67), the population coefficient increased after density was deleted. Table 6 compares

Table 4.—Regression Results for Hourly Wages, 85 SMSA's, 1968-69, On 1957-59 Base

Explanatory variable	Female occupations				Male occupations		
	Keypunch operators, class B	Steno-graphers, general	Switchboard operator-receptionists	Typists, class B	Mechanics, automotive	Laborers, material handling	Janitors, porters, & cleaners
Constant	1.29	1.41	1.20	1.27	2.42	1.97	1.61
Region[a]:							
NE	−0.07	−0.07	−0.02	−0.00	−0.36[c]	−0.35[c]	−0.08
NC	−0.05	−0.08	−0.04	−0.03	−0.18[c]	−0.07	0.16[c]
S	−0.17[c]	−0.14[c]	−0.12[c]	−0.12[c]	−0.51[c]	−0.66[c]	−0.34[c]
Log SMSA population[b]	0.20[c]	0.22[c]	0.21[c]	0.15[c]	0.27[c]	0.13[c]	0.08
Log cc density[b]	0.04	0.02	0.10	0.02	0.10[d]	0.22	0.12
R^2	0.47	0.45	0.65	0.45	0.69	0.73	0.58

[a]Western region set equal to zero.
[b]Both SMSA population and central city density in units of 1,000. Population estimated as of 1969; density was 1960 value.

[c]Significant at 0.05 level.
[d]Significant at 0.10 level.

Table 5.—Estimated Wages from Regression Equations—Western Region

SMSA population in 000	Density in 000	Keypunch operators, class B	Steno's, general	Switchb. operator-recepts.	Typists, class B	Auto. mech.	Laborers, material handling	Janitors, etc.
		Wage rates per hours ($)						
100	1	1.69	1.85	1.62	1.57	2.96	2.23	1.77
100	25	1.75	1.88	1.76	1.60	3.10	2.54	1.94
10,000	25	2.15	2.32	2.18	1.90	3.64	2.80	2.10
		Index, lowest size density group = 1.00						
100	1	1.00	1.00	1.00	1.00	1.00	1.00	1.00
100	25	1.04	1.02	1.09	1.02	1.05	1.14	1.10
10,000	25	1.27	1.25	1.35	1.21	1.23	1.26	1.19

the Fuchs SMSA estimates from Table 1 to the average of five occupations—the three male plus two of the female occupations (keypunch operator and stenographer). All data are in index terms, with lowest size western class set equal to one. Individual occupation wage values were used to test the hypothesis of equality to the Fuchs estimates. This was done by subtracting the former from the latter estimates, for given region and city size, and testing the hypothesis of a zero population mean for the difference variable. The t test statistic obtained was 1.1, so the hypothesis was accepted. This can be interpreted as indicating no significant change in income differential by city size over a decade, more suggestive of compensatory payments than of disequilibrium. (The South was the only region in which the comparative levels seemed to show some disagreement. This occurred because of low wage levels for male occupations, particularly janitor and laborer. A factor here may be low wages for black workers in the South, and high concentration of blacks in those occupations.)

Data on weekly hours of work were available for female occupations, and these were regressed on regional dummy variables, population, and density. Similar patterns appeared in all cases, with these results for hours of work averaged over all occupations:

Constant ....: 40.05
SMSA population (in millions) .... −0.07a
Central city density (in 000) .... −0.07a
Northeast .... −0.54a
North Central 0.11
South .... −0.35a
West 0.00

a—Significant at 0.05 level

Hours of work drop with both population and density increases. Given the respective ranges of the two variables (0.1 million to 10 million for population, and 1,000 to 25,000 for density), and given an increase from the lowest to the highest levels of each, it can be seen that density contributes about two-thirds of the drop in hours. This may reflect the impact of density on traffic congestion. Of incidental interest, the largest population and density class corresponds to the New York SMSA, with an estimated drop of around 2.5 hours relative to the smallest population and density group. For a five day work week, this amounts to a half hour per day. This figure squares well with data on family head work trip time for New York versus other (smaller) metropolitan areas, as shown in Table 7.

Weekly wages were available for female, but not for male occupations. Regressions here yielded the usual kind of results for regions and log of population, but the coefficient for log of density was negative in three of the four cases, with t value extremely low, indicating no effect or even a mildly negative effect. It thus appears that density's impact is limited to hours of work—for female occupations, at any rate. To rationalize this result, perhaps density impacts primarily involve rent adjustments; or perhaps female office workers in large cities typically use mass transit, with mass transit usually subsidized. Such "explanations" are quite speculative, of course.

Table 6.—Comparative Wage Indexes

Region and SMSA size in 000	Fuchs estimate (1959)	Five occupation average (1968-69)
Northeast		
125	0.95	0.94
375	0.95	0.99
750	0.98	1.02
2,000	1.09	1.06
North Central		
125	1.02	1.00
375	1.02	1.04
750	1.10	1.07
2,000	1.15	1.12
South		
125	0.88	0.84
375	0.93	0.89
750	0.95	0.92
2,000	1.05	0.96
West		
125	1.00	1.00
375	0.99	1.05
750	1.04	1.08
2,000	1.13	1.14

Sources: Fuchs estimate from Table 1, all entries divided by 1.01, value of West, lowest population class.

Focusing on density relationships, there is a good deal of empirical evidence that density increases with city size, and further, that the density function tends to shift as shown in Figure 5: The intercept does not increase proportionately with size, and the curve becomes flatter (the density gradient, b, decreases).

Table 7.—Time Spent by Heads of Families in Daily Work Trips, by Location

Time spent in daily trips to and from work (minutes per day)	New York-N.E. New Jersey consolidated area	Within next 12 largest metropolitan areas		Within other metropolitan areas		Outside metropolitan areas	
		Central cities	Suburbs	Central cities	Suburbs	Adjacent	Outlying
Median time	63	53	50	35	41	27	17
Average time	68	59	55	42	43	42	25

Source: James N. Morgan, Ismail A. Sirageldin, Nancy Baerwaldt, *Productive Americans* (Ann Arbor, University of Michigan, Institute for Social Research, Survey Research Center, Monograph 43, 1966), Table S-3, p. 80.

Table 8.—Average Value of A and b (Muth Estimates) by Region and Urban Size, 1950

Urbanized area population in 000	East and South	West and Southwest
	Average value of A	
(1) below 500	25.9	15.7
(2) 500 to below 1000	37.9	19.0
(3) above 1000	46.4	14.0
	Average value of b	
(1) below 500	0.527	0.390
(2) 500 to below 1000	0.383	0.308
(3) above 1000	0.252	0.078

Note: Number of cases: East and South—(1), 17; (2), 8; (3), 9. West and Southwest—(1), 7; (2), 4; (3), 1. The one case in group (3) is Los Angeles. For density relation of form $D = Ae^{-bK}$, where D is density, K is distance from city center, and A and b are parameters.

Source: Richard F. Muth, *Cities and Housing* (Chicago: University of Chicago Press, 1969), Table 1, p. 142.

Some specific evidence here is based on Muth's results, presented as Table 8. (Lower A and b values for western and southwestern cities are explainable by the preponderance of automobile transportation in those newer cities. Urban form—street width and layout, miles of street per square mile of land, size and shape of land parcels, etc.—will have been influenced by dominant transport modes during the city's formative period.)

Using regression analysis, Muth found a significant negative association between urbanized area population and his estimated density gradient. (He had initially expected a positive association, on the presumption that traffic congestion and travel costs would increase with size, making the center more attractive.) He hypothesized that the result might be at least partially explained by an increasing elasticity of housing supply from the city center, causing a faster rate of increase in housing and population with distance.[10] The hypothesis that disamenity associated with increasing density causes shifts in the density function can be viewed as either supplementary or competitive with Muth's hypothesis.

Some recent studies show that disamenity can have substantial impact on land value. Harris, Tolley, and Harrell developed estimates of travel saving and amenity components of value for land clusters in Raleigh, North Carolina. Where travel savings are high, amenity value is strongly negative; one suspects this occurred near the city center, given their definition of travel savings.[11] And a number of studies show a pronounced negative association between pollution and land values.

Implications and Qualifications

Implicit in the argument underlying Figures 2 and 5 is the notion that a number of presumed externalities are, in a sense, internalized by market mechanisms. The externalities are imposed by a city's residents collectively on one another, and they respond by requiring higher wages and/or lower rents.[12]

But this is not to argue that what exists is necessarily optimal. There may be alternative institutional arrangements or pricing policies that could account for externalities in cheaper fashion than compensatory payments. Consider Figure 6. Labor supply slopes upward because of both rent-transportation cost and disamenity compensation with city size. Say an engineering process, or effluent charges, or some form of regulation can be introduced and it eliminates the disamenity—hence, the disamenity payment. Supply shifts from S_1 to S_2, with remaining slope accounting for increases in rent-transportation cost with increases in city size. The new arrangement costs something, and this cost can be treated as an offset to VMP: VMP shifts from VMP_1 to VMP_2. The result is "cheaper" than equilibrium through compensatory payments because more income is generated in the system, as measured by the area under the respective VMP curves. One consequence here is that the city grows larger: Labor increases from L_1 to L_2.

This conclusion could apply to a single city, if the process were a local one. Or it could apply to the economy as a whole, with a general population increase until real income again attained Po. If "standards of living" increased over time, the real income gains could be taken in higher wages and/or population increase.

Figure 7 illustrates the case of an imposed clean-up which costs more than it is worth. Here, total area under the VMP curve falls, and the city shrinks in size. On the macro level, there would be a decline in real income in the short run (assuming labor supply is fixed at L_1 in the short run), and a reduction in population in the long run.

A number of qualifications and clarifications are necessary, given the simplifications employed in the argument.

A major simplification was the aggregation of all products into one product. Given the more realistic case of many products, we can expect that some industries will impose negative externalities on others. The imposition of "proper" effluent charges will cause some industries to expand output, and others to contract. The impact on amount of labor employed presumably will not be obvious, since it will depend on the ratio of output to labor in the various industries. This led George Tolley to conclude that proper internalization of

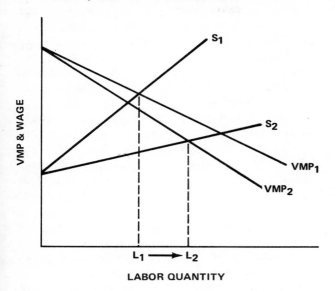

FIGURE 9-6
EFFECTS OF INSTITUTIONAL CHANGE ON LABOR DEMAND, SUPPLY AND EQUILIBRIUM

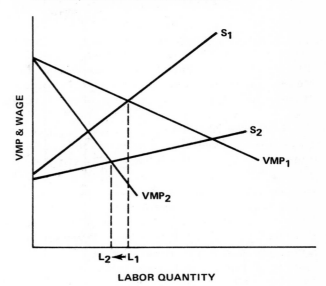

FIGURE 9-7
EFFECTS OF INSTITUTIONAL CHANGE ON LABOR DEMAND, SUPPLY AND EQUILIBRIUM

externalities might make a city either expand or contract in size.[13]

But further discussion is of help. If there are a large number of industries involved, it seems plausible that a "weighted average" ratio of labor to output will be about the same for the set of victims of externalities as for the set of sources; there is no a priori reason to expect more labor relative to output in one set of industries than in the other. Further, one would expect that an effective system of effluent charges would increase total output; combined with the previous argument, this yields the intuition that labor will also expand.

The labor-output argument receives support from the results of an input-output study carried out for the Chicago region.[14] Using a 50 sector model with households endogenous, the impact on households of a dollar change in final demand was obtained for each industry, in turn. Treating households as endogenous in effect allowed for in-migration and outmigration of labor. Over all industries, the average expansion in expenditures on household labor was $3.34 per dollar expansion in final demand—an expansion of one dollar in production by an industry caused expansion in its expenditure on labor, in its suppliers' expenditure on labor, in that of the suppliers of the suppliers, etc., culminating in a $3.34 increase in labor expenditures, on average. The range of these interdependence coefficients ran from a low of $2.82 to a high of $3.65, with 31 of 46 endogenous sectors having values between $3.20 and $3.50. It can be concluded that if the imposition of effluent charges

caused a contraction of a dollar of output in some industries, with a corresponding expansion in other industries, the total change in labor would not be very pronounced.

Of more importance, perhaps, the supply side (of Figures 6 and 7) has been neglected so far, in this attempted generalization to more than one product.

Consider this simple case: Say a subset of noxious industries generates effluents that have negative consequences only for consumers, but affect all consumers and hence, all labor supplied. Say an effluent charge is now placed on the noxious industries to obtain removal of the effluents; further assume that only a small charge is necessary to effect some far-reaching reorganization which removes most or all of the effluents.[15] Aggregate VMP now falls a little, reflecting both the increased cost to the noxious industries, and administrative costs of imposing effluent charges. Assume that supply shifts downward a good deal, for consumers are substantially better off. The message of Figure 6 again emerges.

There has been aggregation on the supply side, too, and in reality there will be supply curves for a number of subcategories of labor. It is conceivable that proper internalization of externalities will lead to more output with more of some types of labor, and less of others, perhaps with a net reduction in labor overall. (Applying this to the labor-output argument above, it may be that the ratio of wages to labor hours is not constant between industries.)

Nonetheless, the argument to this point seems to make the expansion of city size, rather than its contraction, the more plausible case.

Let us consider some additional qualifications and clarifications.

It is plausible that there are some non-money compensations that increase with city size. These include the benefits of increased specialization and the availability of products that have a minimum threshold of demand before production can occur. Large cities may generate psychic income for those who like the opera or major league sports, or who want the services of big city medical centers.

It is argued here, however, that the net effect for disamenities plus amenities is negative, at least for a rather large majority. This is based on the evidence for deflated wages. It is also supported by surveys of metropolitan residents which show strong expressed preference for smaller places and, within the area, for location away from the center. Thus, in 1970 the Gallup Poll found that for a sample of adults in metropolitan centers, the location preferences were: city, 18 percent; suburbs, 26 percent; small town, 31 percent; and farm, 24 percent; with one percent undecided. A 1965 survey of metropolitan residents by the Survey Research Center found these intra-urban location preferences, relative to actual location:[16]

Closer to the center of the city	9%
Just where we are	66%
Farther from the center of the city	25%

with these attitudes on location attributes:

Like the excitement of living close to the center	15%
Indifferent or ambivalent	8%
Don't like the hustle and bustle	77%

A strong preference by urban residents for smaller and less dense places can be interpreted as market failure, or—as argued here—as indicative of the existence of payments compensating for the unimplemented preferences.

Admittedly, majority preferences have been treated as universal, and a more realistic formulation would yield some modifications. If certain groups (professional and executive?) preferred location in large cities, their compensatory payments would be reduced or perhaps even go the other way. Again, the sloping supply of labor used here corresponds to a constant level of real income. Given differences in location preferences, each locale might well have an upward sloping supply of labor as a function of real income.

The discussion throughout has assumed the longest of runs, with all factors mobile. A shorter length of run yields another reason for a less than perfectly elastic supply of labor in real terms. Further, there may well be short-run uncompensated losses from negative externalities which reflect absence of perfect mobility or information.

More generally, people may be ignorant of some negative consequences of city size and density. One policy response would be to make such information—insofar as it exists—available. But we do get a great many messages of the form: "Warning—Big Cities May Be Dangerous To Your Health" so that people must perform some assessing of risks.

It may be that some people have restricted choice in reacting to such risks, for example, if segregation limits the location choices of inner-city blacks. However, available evidence indicates that inner-city blacks attach much less weight to possible pollution damage than do higher income groups: Concern with pollution exhibits high income elasticity.

If people attach less risk to possible pollution damage than outside observers think is warranted, we get into the value-loaded question of whether people are to be treated as if they know their own best interests. A negative answer can lead to the enforced consumption of "merit goods."[17]

Of course, it seems clear that there is majority approval of the general proposition that government ought to take action to improve the environment. Because the issues are complex and demand special knowledge, reliance on government can be viewed as a form of soliciting and applying expert opinion, particularly in matters of health and welfare.

In practice, environmental externalities will range from the extreme of the ubiquitous, collective "bad" to that of clearly identifiable disparate sources and victims of negative externalities. Insofar as abatement is a collective good, a case can be made for regulation as a substitute for compensatory income. In a city where everyone drives an automobile, everyone may be better off if forced to use lead-free gasoline. With the identification of a specific villain that is generating negative externalities, a case emerges for effluent charges or tolls to improve allocation; the use of those charges to compensate the victim may be defended on distributive grounds. (Coase makes the important point that villain and victim can often be interchanged;[18] this suggests the possibility of effluent charges or tolls on both competing interests.)

Negative externalities may be imposed on persons outside the city, causing divergence between private and social cost. This is likely to be the case for water pollution, with cities upstream damaging those downstream. (Of course, a body of water usable for waste disposal is one of the natural resources contributing to urban growth.) Similar effects may occur for air pollution, with damage to forests or vegetation or inhabitants of other locales. Effluent charges on an upstream city should cause some decline in its size, but this is likely to be more than balanced by a size increase for a downstream city. However, insofar as cities damage the surrounding countryside, effluent charges may cause some reduction in city size.

In sum, the locus of quality-of-life problems is seen here as a matter of institutional arrangment, rather than population distribution. It seems sensible to work on the causes of the problems—the institutional arrangements—and let population distribution emerge as one of the effects of the solution. This seems a good deal more reasonable than identifying large size with the problems, neglecting the existence of compensatory payments, and arbitrarily restricting city size.

It must be added that some problems may be inherent in scale, for example, a certain amount of crowding and congestion, with no improvement possible beyond compensatory payments. And some institutional changes could lead to the situation of Figure 7, rather than that of Figure 6: Empirical tests of hoped-for improvements are necessary.

Finally, despite the existence of a number of qualifications, the metaphor of Figure 6 suggests that, more often than not, improved accounting for externalities will generate increases in city size.

URBAN ENVIRONMENTAL QUALITY

This section is a survey of the impact of urban scale (size and density) on environmental quality, viewed primarily in terms of the physical environment. Topics covered are air quality, water quality, solid waste disposal, noise, and the social environment. Air quality encompasses air pollution and climate effects, while water quality covers water supply, waste disposal, and flooding. The treatment of the social environment is quite brief, in line with the focus on the physical environment.

For most of the topics covered, there are data problems, with sparse coverage and often questionable estimates; and there is usually a good deal of controversy about the meaning of the often limited results. Withal, the cumulative impact of the evidence lends strong support to the widespread intuition that environmental quality declines as urban scale increases.

Air Quality

Air Pollution

Air pollutants are classified into the basic categories of gases and particulates (or particles). The five most common pollutants, in terms of tons emitted annually, are the particulates (as a group) and four groups of gases: carbon monoxide, hydrocarbons, sulfur oxides and nitrogen oxides, with sulfur dioxide and nitrogen dioxide the most important members of the latter categories.

The Environmental Protection Agency has established air quality standards for these five pollutants plus photochemical oxidants. The last are produced by reactions of hydrocarbons and nitrogen oxides when exposed to sunlight, with ozone one of the major forms. Known more commonly as Los Angeles smog, the pollutant occurs in most major metropolitan areas. The National Air Surveillance Network records levels of a great many individual pollutants, with most of these likely to have some health and welfare effects.[19] These include lead, asbestos, chlorine, arsenic, and vanadium.

Table 9 exhibits estimated emissions of the five most common pollutants by source.[20] There are

Table.9.—Estimated Emissions of Air Pollutants, United States, 1969

Source of emission	Carbon monoxide	Partic-ulates	Sulfur oxides	Hydro-carbons	Nitrogen oxides	Total
	Millions of tons per year					
Transportation (primarily automobiles and trucks)	111.5	0.8	1.1	19.8	11.2	144.4
Fuel combustion in stationary sources (space heating, power plants)	1.8	7.2	24.4	0.9	10.0	44.3
Industrial processes	12.0	14.4	7.5	5.5	0.2	39.6
Solid waste disposal	7.9	1.4	0.2	2.0	0.4	11.9
Miscellaneous	18.2	11.4	0.2	9.2	2.0	41.0
Total	151.4	35.2	33.4	37.4	23.8	281.2

Source: U.S. Council on Environmental Quality, *Second Annual Report*, 1971, p. 212.

Table 10.—Selected Particulate Constituents as Percentages of Gross Suspended Particulates (1966-67)

	Urban (217 stations)		Nonurban Proximate (5)		Intermediate (15)		Remote (10)	
	µg/m³ [a]	%	µg/m³ [a]	%	µg/m³ [a]	%	µg/m³ [a]	%
Suspended particulates	102.0		45.0		40.0		21.0	
Benzene soluble org.	6.7	6.6	2.5	5.6	2.2	5.4	1.1	5.1
Ammonium ion	0.9	0.9	1.22	2.7	0.28	0.7	0.15	0.7
Nitrate ion	2.4	2.4	1.40	3.1	0.85	2.1	0.46	2.2
Sulfate ion	10.1	9.9	10.0	22.2	5.29	13.1	2.51	1.8
Copper	0.16	0.15	0.16	0.36	0.078	0.19	0.060	0.28
Iron	1.43	1.38	0.56	1.24	0.27	0.67	0.15	0.71
Manganese	0.073	0.07	0.026	0.06	0.012	0.03	0.005	0.02
Nickel	0.017	0.02	0.008	0.02	0.004	0.01	0.002	0.01
Lead	1.11	1.07	0.21	0.47	0.096	0.24	0.022	0.10

[a]Unit of measure: µg/m³ = micrograms per cubic meter.
Source: Thomas B. McMullen, *Comparison of Urban and Nonurban Air Quality,* presented at 9th Annual Indiana Air Pollution Control Conference, Purdue University, Oct 13-14, 1970, Table 4, p. 7.

Table 11.—Distribution of Annual Mean Levels of Pollutants, by City Size, 1968

Population	Suspended particulates (µg/m³)[a]											
	0-19	20-39	40-59	60-79	80-99	100-119	120-139	140-159	160-179	180-199	200	Total
	Urban											
>3,000,000						2						2
1,000,000 to 3,000,000						1	2					3
700,000 to 1,000,000			1	2	3		3					9
400,000 to 700,000			1	4	9	1	1	1	1			18
100,000 to 400,000			6	25	16	17	5	1	2	1	1	74
50,000 to 100,000			5	18	19	12	4	3			1	62
25,000 to 50,000		4	13	16	7	2	2				2	46
10,000 to 25,000		3	12	15	7	5		1				43
<10,000		7	8	18	11	1	1		1			47
Total		14	46	98	72	41	18	6	4	1	4	304
	Nonurban											
	10	16	4									

regional differences in the distribution of pollutants, reflecting differences in the distribution of sources; weather and topography, affecting ventilation; and local regulation. Despite these sources of variability, however, there is generally a pronounced urban scale effect for major pollutants.

Urban Scale Effect

Thomas McMullen has made some general urban-nonurban comparisons for particulates and a number of particulate constituents.[21] Table 10 reproduces some of his results. McMullen concludes that some nonurban sites may be receiving significant influence from urban

Table 11.—Continued

Population	Sulfur dioxide ($\mu g/m^3$)[a]											
	0-9	10-19	20-29	30-39	40-49	50-59	60-69	70-79	80-89	90-99	>100	Total
Urban												
>3,000,000											2	2
1,000,000 to 3,000,000							1			1		2
700,000 to 1,000,000	1	3		1			1		3	1		10
400,000 to 700,000	2	5	5	3		1		1			1	18
100,000 to 400,000	7	5	11	2	5	4	2	2	2		2	42
50,000 to 100,000	1	4	2	2			2	1	1			13
25,000 to 50,000	1	1			1							3
10,000 to 25,000	1	2	1									3
<10,000	13	1	2			1						5
Total		21	21	8	6	6	6	4	6	2	5	98
Nonurban												
	2	3										

Population	Nitrogen dioxide ($\mu g/m^3$)[a]														
	40-59	60-79	80-99	100-119	120-139	140-159	160-179	180-199	200-219	220-239	240-259	260-279	280-299	≥300	Total
Urban															
>3,000,000												1	1		2
1,000,000 to 3,000,000							1				1				2
700,000 to 1,000,000					1		2	1	5	1					10
400,000 to 700,000				2		4	1	6	2	1	2				18
100,000 to 400,000		2		3	7	5	8	7	4	3	1		1	1	42
50,000 to 100,000			1		1	2	1	4	3		1				13
25,000 to 50,000	1				1		1								3
10,000 to 25,000				1	1	1									3
<10,000	1		2	1		1									5
Total	2	2	3	7	11	13	14	18	14	5	5	1	2	1	98
Nonurban															
	3	1	1												

Sources: Particulates and SO2 from George B. Morgan, Guntis Ozolins, and Elbert C. Tabor, "Air Pollution Surveillance Systems," *Science,* Oct. 16, 1970, pp. 294-295. Nitrogen dioxide from Thomas B. McMullen, *Comparison of Urban and Nonurban Air Quality,* 9th Annual Indiana Air Pollution Control Conference, Purdue University, 1970, p. 6. Particulates—geometric mean; sulfur dioxide and nitrogen dioxide—arithmetic mean.

[a] Unit of measure: $\mu g/m^3$ = micrograms per cubic meter.

sources. This is generally supported by the values in Table 10, with nonurban pollution levels declining with distance from urban areas, suggesting that urban areas do impose some negative externalities on nonurban areas. However, there may also be fewer rural people to cause pollution with increasing distance from urban areas.

It is worthy of note that particulates in Table 10 include sulfates and nitrates. There is some expectation that these will be correlated with the corresponding gaseous sulfur oxides and nitrogen oxides.[22] Inspection of some limited observations across cities, however, indicates that such holds for sulfates but not for nitrates.

Table 12.—Values for Pollutant Concentration Versus Population Class (1969-70)

Class number and population class	Concentration TSP[a]	Concentration SO²	Concentration NO²	Number of sites
1. Nonurban	25	10	33	5
2. Urban <10,000	57	35	116	2
3. 10,000	81	18	64	2
4. 25,000	87	14	63	2
5. 50,000	118	29	127	9
6. 100,000	95	26	114	37
7. 400,000	100	28	127	17
8. 700,000	101	29	146	9
9. 1,000,000	134	69	163	2
10. 3,000,000	120	85	153	2
Slope	9.152	6.103	12.109	
Intercept	41.467	0.733	44.000	
r^2	0.748	0.590	0.719	
t statistic	4.874	3.392	4.526	

[a]TSP: Total suspended particulates.

Source: The Mitre Corp., MTR-6013, p. 70. Time span—second half of 1969, first half of 1970. Cited in Council on Environmental Quality, *Environmental Quality, Second Annual Report,* 1971, pp. 215 and 243.

Regressions: Pollutant concentration on population class number (1 through 10).

Table 13.—Regression Results for Mean Pollutant Levels Related to Size of Metropolitan Area

Dependent variable (geometric mean)	Constant	Coefficient	t Value	R^2
Particulates	30.61	25.06	3.58[a]	0.15
Nitrates	−0.42	1.07	3.49[a]	0.14
Sulfates	−1.19	4.02	3.75[a]	0.16

[a]Significant at 0.05 level. Size of metropolitan area measured as log of 1966 population.

Sources: Regression equations estimated for this study. Pollution data obtained from U.S. Public Health Service, National Air Pollution Control Administration, *Air Quality from the National Air Surveillance Network-1966 edition,* Durham, N.C., 1968. Measures on pollutants were obtained as follows: Particulates for 1966, Table 7, pp. 34-40; Nitrates for 1965, Table 18, pp. 62-66; Sulfates for 1965, Table 20, pp. 69-73. The 76 cities employed had observations for all three pollutants. Central city density as of 1960 from U.S. Bureau of Census, *1960 Census of Population.* SMSA population for 1966 estimated as 0.4 (1960 population) +0.6 (1970 population). 1960 population from *1960 Census of Population.* 1970 population from U.S. Bureau of Census, Advance Population Reports. Manufacturing Production workers from U.S. Bureau of Census, *1963 Census of Manufactures, Vol. III Area Statistics,* Washington, 1966. Central City Gasoline Sales from *County and City Data Book, 1967.*

Table 14.—Regression Results for Mean Pollutant Levels Related to Set of Explanatory Variables

Dependent variable (geometric mean of pollutant listed) and explanatory variable	Coefficient	t value	R^2
Particulates			
Constant	51.55	. . .	0.26
Log SMSA population	22.94	3.10[a]	
January temperature	−0.54	1.67[b]	
Iron and steel production workers in 000	0.66	2.41[a]	
Nitrates			
Constant	0.664		0.34
Log SMSA population	0.816	1.93[b]	
Central city density (000)	−0.127	3.44[a]	
Total central city gasoline sales, in million dollars	0.011	3.38[a]	
Sulfates			
Constant	5.84		
Central city density (000)	0.53	5.01[a]	0.48
Nonferrous metals production workers in 000	0.81	3.26[a]	

[a]Significant at 0.05 level.
[b]Significant at 0.10 level.
Sources: See sources, Table 13.

Table 11 exhibits cross-classifications of average levels of particulates, sulfur dioxide, and nitrogen dioxide with city size, for 1968. An urban scale effect seems apparent in all three cases, with the effect most pronounced for nitrogen dioxide.

Table 12 presents the same sort of information in the form of average levels of pollutants by population size for 1969-70. Results are also shown for the regression of concentration level on population class number (shown as 1 through 10 in Table 12).

Some additional evidence was developed here using total particulates, nitrates and sulfates for 1965-66 as dependent variables in a series of regressions. Table 13 presents results when urban size is the only independent variable, measuring size by log of SMSA population. In all three cases, size is significant, though R^2 is only about 0.15. A number of additional explanatory variables were then introduced, with Table 14 presenting results in terms of significant coefficients. In the case of particulates and sulfates, the additional explanatories included January temperature, to measure space heating effects, and indexes of industrial output, measured as number of production workers, for those industries expected to be major sources of pollution.[23] For nitrates, total gasoline sales (of the central city) were included. In all three cases, central city density was included.

January temperature was negative and significant only for particulates; the index of production was positive and significant for iron and steel in the case of particulates, and for nonferrous metals in the case of sulfates. For particulates, the industry measures not yielding significant results were grain handling and milling, and kraft (sulfate) pulp, while petroleum refining was not significant for sulfates. Gasoline sales were positive and significant for nitrates.

The population coefficient was always positive; but, with the introduction of density, it was no longer significant in the sulfates equation. Density was not significant in the case of particulates, and had the wrong sign; density had a wrong (negative) sign and significant coefficient in the case of nitrates. Because Los Angeles and San Diego had high nitrate levels and low densities, the regression was rerun with observations for those cities omitted, but this did not help make the results much more plausible: Density remained negative, though no longer significant; but gasoline sales became negative and significant. As noted earlier, nitrates do not appear to correlate well with nitrogen dioxide, indicating a plausible explanation for these results: Nitrates (as particulates) and nitrogen dioxide have different sources.

Reviewing the evidence across cities, it seems clear that city size is generally associated with increasing levels of air pollution. The limited results for density are much less convincing; this may reflect high correlations between density and population size. However, there is strong within-city evidence that increasing levels of density are associated with increasing levels of pollution.

Within urban areas, density is a factor in the distribution of most pollutants. Pollutants having the automobile as their primary source will usually decline in level with distance from the center. This is illustrated by Figure 8, which exhibits the spatial pattern of carbon monoxide emission in Washington, D.C., in 1964, with the White House selected as central point. There is a regular and pronounced decline in emissions from the center outward.

Data for New York City show a pronounced between population density and air pollution for a number of pollutants. Table 15 exhibits the relation in terms of 1962-64 readings at five sites at increasing distance from the city center. Table 16 shows correlations between pollution level and density using 1969-70 data.

Many pollutants are associated with both density and specific point sources of emissions. This can be seen rather quickly by inspection of intra-urban maps.[24] A plot of particulate levels against distance from the central business district (CBD) for 20 stations in Chicago showed a rather regular decline in level with distance, save for two far, south-side stations which had fairly high levels, clearly the effect of the South Chicago and Gary-Hammond-East Chicago complex of heavy industry. Similar patterns were apparent for sulfur dioxide levels.[25]

Regression of the Chicago particulate data on distance from the CBD yielded $Y = 176.09 - 6.033X$ ($R^2 = 0.70$; $t = 6.2$) where Y is average particulate level, 1964-67, in $\mu g/m^3$; and X is distance in miles. Employing density as explanatory variable gave: $Y = 104.46 + 1.485D$, ($R^2 = 0.692$, $t = 6.0$), where D is density, measured as population per unit of land.[26]

Because blacks are concentrated in the inner city of most metropolitan areas, they are generally exposed to higher pollution levels than whites. Freeman has developed pollution indexes by housing tenure and by race for Kansas City, St. Louis and Washington, D.C., which are presented here as Table 17. Both rental housing and percentage nonwhite will tend to increase with density, so Table 17 affords additional indirect evidence on the latter variable.

There is some evidence indicating a drop in pollution levels for cities over time. To some extent, this probably involves the secular decline in urban density functions given the impact of urban freeways and increased car ownership. The resultant "suburban

FIGURE 9-8
ESTIMATED CARBON MONOXIDE ISOLINES, WASHINGTON, D.C., 1964

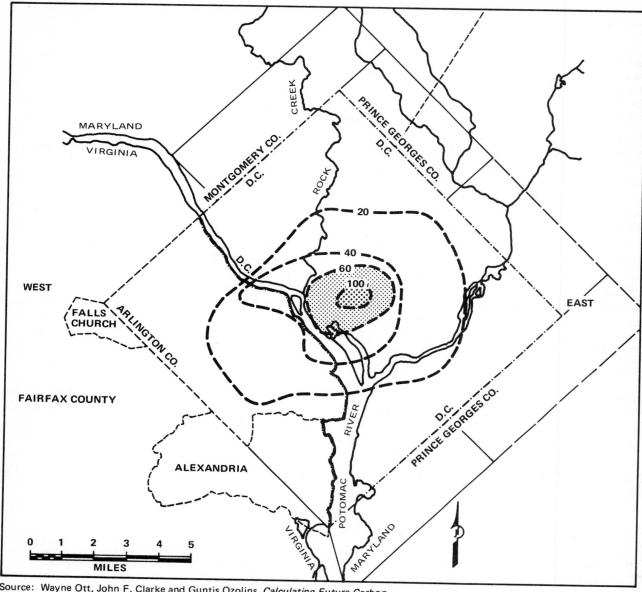

Source: Wayne Ott, John F. Clarke and Guntis Ozolins, *Calculating Future Carbon Monoxide Emissions and Concentrations from Urban Traffic Data,* Public Health Service, Durham, North Carolina, 1967, Figure 3, p. 10.

sprawl" means less concentration at the CBD, and some decline in monitored levels at that locale. To some extent, the decline may reflect emission controls in automobiles, with considerable further improvement to come.

Spirtas and Levin examined trends in particulates for 60 central cities and 20 nonurban sites by comparing 1962-66 average levels to 1957-61 averages. Almost half of the cities showed a significant downward trend, as exhibited in Table 18. Nonurban sites show some upward movement. Spirtas and Levin also qualify the urban results by noting that most of the sites with highly significant decreases had high levels of emissions initially.[27]

There also appears to be a downward trend for sulfur dioxide over the period 1962-69, based on data for 21 cities, and a marked reduction in carbon monoxide since 1965, though this is based on only six

Table 15.—Annual Average Pollutant Concentrations, New York City Area, 1962-1964

Site	CO, ppm	Lead	Vanadium	Sulfate	Tar	BaP[a]	BaA[b]
		$\mu g/m^3$ [c]					$\mu g/10^3\,m^3$ [c]	
Herald Square	10.3	8.3	1.06	56	59	3.9	5.6
Columbus Circle	6.8	5.1	1.20	67	29	1.3	2.5
Queens Expressway Interchange	4.0	4.1	0.83	36	23	1.3	2.5
Queens residential	3.3	2.7	0.23	26	19	0.6	1.2
Scarsdale, Westchester County	2.1	1.7	0.17	25	7	0.3	0.6

[a] BaP is Benzo(a)pyrene, a strong carcinogen.
[b] BaA is Benz(a)anthracene, a weak carcinogen.
[c] Units of measure: $\mu g/m^3$ = micrograms per cubic meter, and $\mu g/10^3\,m^3$ = micrograms per 1,000 cubic meters.

Source: Joseph M. Colucci and Charles R. Begeman, "Carcinogenic Air Pollutants in Relation to Automotive Traffic in New York," *Environmental Science & Technology*, Feb. 1971, p. 146.

Table 16.—Pollution and Density Correlations, New York City Area, 1969-70

Air pollution measures	Correlation coefficient
SO$_2$	+0.430
Dustfall	+0.599
Smokeshade	+0.394
Suspended particulates	+0.602

Source: Unpublished memorandum, Jeffrey M. Zupan, "Environmental Quality Study-Progress Report," Regional Plan Association, July 1971, p. 5. Pollution data from 38 monitoring stations in New York City.

Table 18.—Long Term Trends in Suspended Particles

Long term trends	Significance level[a]	Number of center-city urban sites	Number of nonurban sites
Highly significant downward . . .	0.01 level	21	1
Significant downward . . .	0.1 level	4	0
No change	(Not significant at 0.1 level)	33	13
Significant upward	0.1 level	2	4
Highly significant upward	0.01 level	0	2

[a] Trend categories defined in terms of listed significance levels.
Source: U.S. Public Health Service, *Characteristics of Particulate Patterns 1957-1966*, by Robert Spirtas and Howard J. Levin (Raleigh, N.C., 1970), p. 13.

Table 17.—Air Pollution Exposure Indexes by Housing Tenure and Race

	Suspended particulates	Sulfation	Mean
Kansas city			
Housing tenure:			
Owner-occupied	63.9	0.16	0.91
Rented	78.0	0.24	1.23
Race:			
White	64.3	0.17	0.94
Nonwhite	83.3	0.24	1.26
St. Louis			
Housing tenure:			
Owner-occupied	n.a.	n.a.	n.a.
Rented	n.a.	n.a.	n.a.
Race:			
White	78.2	0.80	1.00
Nonwhite	102.6	1.22	1.42
Washington, D.C.			
Housing tenure:			
Owner-occupied	48.4	0.63	0.90
Rented	57.5	0.79	1.10
Race:			
White	42.8	0.66	0.87
Nonwhite	78.4	0.95	1.42

n.a.—Data not available.
Source: A. Myrick Freeman, III, "The Distribution of Environmental Quality," in *Research on Environmental Quality*, Allen Kneese and Blair Bower, eds. (Baltimore: Johns Hopkins Press for Resources for the Future, 1972), Table 3.

cities.[28] This might reflect freeway construction directly, because carbon monoxide is substantially reduced at increased vehicle speeds, as are hydrocarbons. However, there is a trade-off for increased nitrogen oxides, which increase with fuel consumption, which in turn increases with speed.[29]

The Impact of Pollution on Land Values and Density Functions

There are some studies supporting the analysis embodied in Figures 4 and 5, either on a theoretical level, or empirically, through examination of pollution impact on property values.

For a very simple model of an urban area (containing 13 zones), Rydell derived spatial distribution impacts. He employed quadratic programming to minimize the sum of access costs (distance to the center), density cost (assuming a preference for low density living, per se), and pollution damage. The effect of inclusion of pollution damage paralleled the shift shown as occurring (for the same reason) in Figure 5.[30]

Strotz and Wright appear to reach a conclusion similar to the point of Figures 4 and 5, though this is for a special case within a sophisticated mathematical treatment of more involved cases: "In a one factory town with a nationally mobile population, the external diseconomies of industrial pollution imposed on residents would be properly internalized . . . [by the use of transportation as a pollution control device]," that is, through changes in residential location.[31]

Relevant empirical results include studies by Ronald G. Ridker and John Henning; Robert J. Anderson, Jr. and Thomas D. Crocker; and John Jaksch.[32]

Ridker and Henning related property values in the St. Louis metropolitan area to pollution and a number of socioeconomic variables. Major classifications for the latter explanatories were property, location, and neighborhood characteristics. Property variables included median number of rooms, percent recently built, and houses per mile. Location variables were time zones, measuring express bus travel time to the CBD during rush hour; and a set of three dummy variables for access to highways, shopping areas, and industrial areas. Neighborhood variables included school quality, crime rates, persons per unit, and occupation ratio. Other explanatories included percent nonwhite, median family income, and a dummy for state (Missouri or Illinois). Property values were obtained from 1960 census data; pollution was measured by sulfation levels. Particulates were initially included but were dropped both because of measurement problems and unsatisfactory results, that is, some contrary results did occur. However, the results for sulfation were in line with expectations, and

so were the coefficients for most of the explanatory variables. On the basis of the equation judged best, Ridker and Henning estimated that, if sulfation level per family unit dropped by 0.25 mg/100cm^2 per day, property value would rise by about $100 to $250—with the upper value most likely.

Anderson and Crocker related both property values and rents to pollution and other explanatories for Washington, D.C., Kansas City, and St. Louis, again using 1960 Census data for the dependent variables. Property values were for owned, single-family housing, and rents for tenant-occupied housing. There were two pollutants, sulfation and particulates, both in terms of annual average. Other explanatory variables included income, percent dilipidated housing, percent old housing, percent nonwhite, and distance from the CBD. In all cases, the coefficient of at least one of the pollution variables was negative and statistically significant. For 12 equations estimated, only one pollution coefficient was positive, and it was nonsignificant.

Since log values of variables were employed, elasticities emerged directly. The elasticity of housing price with respect to pollution was between 0.1 and 0.2, that is, a 10 percent increase in pollution yields a one to two percent decrease in price. At the mean, this amounts to a marginal reduction of $2 to $4 per month for rented housing, and a capitalized loss ranging from about $300 to $700 per owned property.

Jaksch carried out his study for the small town of Toledo, Oregon, which has a population of 3,000, and a Kraft pulp mill which employs 1,000 persons. Its 50 square blocks contain mostly single-family residences. The market price of property sales over the period 1961 to 1967 was the dependent variable, which was regressed on size of house, lot size, assessor estimate of housing quality, and pollution level. Pollution was measured as particulate fallout or dustfall in tons per square mile per month, for the average over the month of sale and two months prior to the sale date. Locational variations in dustfall were estimated by isopleth lines. All signs in the regression were as expected, with the implication that a unit of pollution caused a $29 drop in property value. Mean dustfall was 30 tons, and the "normal" background level was estimated as 10 tons; hence, the increment of 20 tons per square mile per month implied an average drop in property value of $580.

Freeman notes that in both the Ridker-Henning and the Anderson-Crocker studies, median property value, rather than unit land value, was the dependent variable. "Property value captures size of lot effects and the value of improvements as well as differential site values."[33] But it seems plausible that income and the other socioeconomic variables will account for most or all of these effects. Further, because pollution may be correlated with distance to the CBD, effects attributed to the former might really stem from the latter. However, both Ridker-Henning and Anderson-Crocker investigated and accounted for this potential difficulty through inclusion of a CBD access variable. Ridker-Henning expected the measure of access (the express bus time zone) to have a negative coefficient. It turned out that a quadratic term worked best, with the impact on property value first negative and then positive. However, both the linear and quadratic form of the variable showed little correlation with pollution. In the Crocker and Anderson studies, when distance to the CBD was significant, it was always negative. (However, some non-significant cases were positive.) Their results suggested that the "rent gradient was less in outlying areas," which fit the hypothesis that amenities available only outside the central city could be offsets to increased travel costs. This hypothesis squares with the results Ridker-Henning obtained, and, at least to some extent, with the discussion of the intra-urban distribution of population presented alone. In particular, noise levels and amount of greenery and open space may be some of the amenities involved. Future work might introduce measures of these variables. A further factor that might explain the statistical results is the existence of suburban employment opportunities.

Damage Functions

The matter of declines in rent as an offset to pollution damage deserves some stress; the neglect of the point can lead to double counting of cost, and an overestimate of the benefits of abatement. The problem corresponds to likely double counting that occurred when highway planners counted both savings to drivers (time, operating cost, accidents) and increase in land value as benefits of new highways.

The Council on Environmental Quality[34] has presented a set of estimates on the annual cost of pollution in the United States:

Item	Estimated cost (in billions of dollars)
(1) Mortality and morbidity	6.0
(2) Materials and vegetation	4.9
(3) Lowered property values	5.2
Total cost	16.1

The Council staff was aware of the possible problem of double counting with item (3), but felt that reduced property values probably covered other costs than those covered in items (1) and (2)—that is, aesthetic costs, lowered visibility, physical damage to structures. (There was the additional intuition that health effects might be understated.)[35]

Anderson and Crocker take a position at considerable variance with that of the Council report. They note the argument that buyers rarely think about pollution with the exception of odors and obvious irritants. But "buyers need only know that they prefer some properties to others, and other things being equal, are willing to pay more for the preferred properties." It is hypothesized that relative absence of the effects of air pollution is a cause of difference in preferences, irrespective of whether or not the cause of the effects is known. They conclude that even odorless, tasteless, and invisible pollutants exert a substantial negative influence on residential property values.[36]

It seems likely that the true situation empirically is between these extreme interpretations: People are aware of, and react to, some but not all of the risks of pollution. Hence, it is likely that some, but not all, of the Council's property value figure involves double counting. Also, note the implication of Figure 5 that some property away from the center should increase in value, in response to pollution. This will be at least a partial offset to the decline in property value near the center. Finally, in a full-knowledge, perfectly rational and mobile world, income increases should account for the remaining costs of pollution. But recall that such is not necessarily the best possible way of so accounting, via Figure 6.

Lave and Seskin have carried out extensive research relating mortality rate to pollution levels and other socioeconomic variables, using data on 117 SMSA's for their observations. The following equation for 1960 is an example of their results:[37]

$$MR = 19.607 + 0.041 \text{ Mean } P + 0.071 \text{ Min } S + 0.001 \text{ P/M}^2$$
$$(2.53)) \qquad (3.18) \qquad (1.67)$$

$$+ 0.041 \text{ \%NW} + 0.687 \text{ \%} \geqslant 65 \ (R^2 = 0.827$$
$$(5.81) \qquad (18.94)$$

where "MR" is the total mortality rate in the area, "Mean P" is the arithmetic mean of 26 biweekly suspended particulate readings, "Min S" is the smallest of 26 biweekly sulfate readings, "P/M^2" is the population density in the area, "%NW" is the percentage of the SMSA population who are nonwhite, and "% 65" is the percentage of the SMSA population who are 65 and older. Numbers in parentheses are t test values; all are significant at the five percent level, save density. But density is significant in many of the equations they have estimated for other years or for specific disease mortality rates, etc. Lave and Seskin appear to devote little attention to possible causal mechanisms behind the density effect. Some of the factors at work with higher density may be (1) the easier transmission of diseases spread through proximity; (2) the occurrence of buildings of more than a single story (this is likely to lead to more falls, which can be a direct or contributing cause of death, and heart patients can be affected by walking up steps); (3) higher auto accident rates, for auto accidents tend to increase with density; and (4) the greater pressures of big city living—though, here, density is a surrogate for city size. Apparently on the basis of a great many regression equation results, plus an extensive review of the medical literature on pollution, they estimate direct costs and indirect costs of air-pollution-connected disease.[38] Direct costs include hospital and nursing home care, and services of physicians and other health professionals. Indirect costs are earnings foregone by those who are sick, disabled, or prematurely dead.

They argue that the following reductions would occur if air pollution in major urban areas were lowered by 50 percent:

Disease	Decline in incidence (percent)	Cost saving per year millions of dollars
Bronchitis	25-50	$250-500
Lung cancer	25	33
All respiratory diseases	25	1,222
Cardiovascular disease	10-20	468
All cancer	15	390

The total would be about $2.080 billion, or 4.5 percent of all costs of mortality and morbidity.

Some aspects of the Lave and Seskin results are relevant to the concerns of this paper. Consider the regression equations and health estimates, in turn.

In this regression work, basic explanatory variables appear to be particulates, sulfates, density, nonwhite, over age 65, and poor—with the last three variables in percentage terms. (Percent poor appears to be significant only for infant death rate, which may be why it was omitted in the total death rate equation listed above.)

If their results are accepted, note that a decline in pollution should have some positive impact on population density; in other words, there should be some reversal of "urban sprawl," with a reverse shift from Figure 5 to 4. But then, increased density may lead to higher death rates.

Lave and Seskin may understate pollution impact because:

1. Only two pollutants are included. This reflects limited information available at the time of their study, but data on other pollutants are now becoming available.

2. Nothing is done about possible synergistic effects. This might be handled by introducing the cross product of the pollutants as another explanatory variable. In the fitted equation each pollutant can be treated as a parameter, in turn, noting the effect on the other.

Lave and Seskin may overstate pollution impact because:

1. Sulfur dioxide and particulates are high in large, northern industrial cities. One might expect that weather effects could be involved; in particular, severe winters may increase respiratory disease. But the force of this criticism is limited because Lave and Seskin did introduce both climate variables and home heating types (the latter to account for pollutants within the residence) and found that neither caused the air pollution variables to lose significance.[39] Fourteen climate variables were employed, with good coverage of winter effects. But there may be other factors specific to large industrial cities which have some impact on mortality.

2. Persons over age 65 may have higher mortality rates in high pollution areas for reasons other than pollution. Perhaps there is some selectivity in SMSA location by type of retired persons.

3. "Percent poor" is defined as percentage of families with incomes under $3,000. This is probably a poor measure because of the problem of distinguishing between permanent and transitory income. It is also inadequate because money income is not real income, as developed at some length earlier. A money income of $3,000 in a small SMSA is the equivalent of $2,500, say, in a large SMSA. Hence, the poor in large cities will be understated. Because large cities tend to have high pollution levels, there could be some confounding of pollution and income effects.

It is of some interest that a study by Julius Goldberg found the same problem intra-city. Goldberg thought he had separated out socioeconomic class from pollution level, but found results fitting expectations only for his middle class; mortality increased with pollution only for the middle class group. He re-examined his data and discovered he had not fully winnowed out income. Within the middle class, lower-income persons lived in higher pollution areas.[40]

In their review of the medical literature, Lave and Seskin find "extremely good" evidence for an association of pollution with bronchitis and lung cancer, and only "suggestive" evidence for an association with cardiovascular disease and nonrespiratory tract cancers.[41] Yet in their regression results, pollutants have little impact on bronchitis, pneumonia, and influenza; have more impact on digestive than on respiratory cancer; and are generally a significant factor in cardiovascular disease.[42]

256

The differences here cast some doubt on some of the health cost savings estimates based on decline in incidence. There are some more serious questions about these estimates. First, the "direct cost of disease" component appears to assume that such costs will be removed, never to reappear. But it seems more reasonable that such costs will be deferred; that is, as people age, they tend to become ill with something or other. The proper saving might be the interest on the deferred amount, perhaps as a surrogate for the utility of a longer illness-free period. Finally, a major theme is reasserted: Some (if not all) of the health cost could be a component of compensatory payments with larger city size.

Climate

Cities affect their local climate in a number of ways, and the impact tends to increase with city size. Some general notion of the effects for a typical city is given by Table 19, using estimates presented by Helmut E. Landsberg.

Landsberg sees two major impacts of urbanization: (1) reduction in wind speed near the surface because of increases in surface roughness, and (2) generation of an urban heat island, with temperatures above the surrounding countryside, because of local man-made heat, faster runoff of precipitation, reducing evaporation, and high heat absorption by the impermeable surface of the urban area.[43]

The urban heat island is most pronounced in the evening.[44] Some recent studies show the mean annual minimum temperatures for large cities are about $4°F$ higher in downtown areas than in outlying regions. The differential often may be as great as $10°F$, and sometimes as great as $20°F$. The degree of warming diminishes slowly with distance from the center, but then drops sharply at the urban periphery. Daytime heat effects are much less pronounced, with the typical differential for large cities around $2°F$.

In general, the heat effect correlates well with building density. It increases with city size, but at a decreasing rate. Sizeable nocturnal temperature contrasts have been measured even in relatively small cities.

The possible urban heat island of the future has been viewed with some alarm. J. Coulomb has argued that doubling energy consumption every 10 years would lead to "unbearable temperatures."[45] Using an energy consumption growth rate of four percent, corresponding to the current growth rate, R. T. Jaske et al. estimated that, by the year 2000, the Boston-Washington megalopolis would release man-made energy equivalent to 30 percent of the annual solar energy,[46] part of a trend "toward concentration of energy releases in metropoli-

Table 19.—Climatic Changes Produced by Cities

Element	Compared to rural environs
Radiation:	
Total on horizontal surface	15 to 20% less
Ultraviolet, winter	30% less
Ultraviolet, summer	5% less
Cloudiness:	
Clouds	5 to 10% more
Fog, winter	100% more
Fog, summer	30% more
Precipitation:	
Amounts	5 to 10% more
Days with <0.2 in.	10% more
Temperature:	
Annual mean	1 to 1.5°F more
Winter minima	2 to 3°F more
Relative humidity:	
Annual mean	6% less
Winter	2% less
Summer	8% less
Wind speed:	
Annual mean	20 to 30% less
Extreme gusts	10 to 20% less
Calms	5 to 20% more

Source: Helmut E. Landsberg "City Air—Better or Worse," in *Symposium: Air Over Cities,* U.S. Public Health Service, Taft Sanitary Eng. Center, Cincinnati, Tech. Rept. A62-5, Table I.

tan areas beyond the capacity of the physical environment to absorb."[47]

But man-made heat in Berlin, Vienna, and Sheffield, England is now about one-third that from solar radiation; in Manhattan, the heat from combustion alone is 2.5 times solar radiation during the winter (it drops to one-sixth in the summer).[48] This suggests that concern about the year 2000 heat island is overdrawn. Such concern also neglects population redistribution from central city to suburbs, which would be accelerated if heat islands were really to become a source of considerable discomfort, let alone danger.

The heat island phenomena may cause more discomfort or air-conditioning expenditure in the summer, and less discomfort or heating expenditure in the winter. Because it is predominantly a nighttime effect, the winter savings may well outweigh the summer losses. Landsberg notes these beneficial effects of increased minimum temperatures: an earlier cessation of freezes in spring, and later initiation of the freezing season in autumn; a reduction in seasonal snowfall; and a reduction in heating degree-day values (a measure of fuel requirements).[49]

Air pollution in the form of particulates reduces solar radiation at ground level, lowering the total duration of sunlight and ultraviolet radiation. Apparently, there is no reduction in heat from solar radiation because the temperature of the atmosphere is increased through absorption of radiation by the particles. This may even be a minor factor in the heat island effect.[50] A study of Rotterdam showed that the city center received about five percent less radiation than the urban fringe, and about 15 percent less than the country. London annually receives about 270 hours less of bright sunshine than the surrounding countryside.[51]

Air pollution by particulates also causes lowered visibility and more frequent fog, which occurs because water vapor condenses on particulates to form small water droplets, the ingredients of fog.[52]

Landsberg hypothesizes that cities increase precipitation, and that this is on the order of 10 percent (Table 19). Peterson agrees that an urban complex might be expected to increase precipitation, because of increased water vapor, higher temperatures, and greater concentrations of ice nuclei; but, the greatest impact may well occur downwind of the city center.[53] Significant, though obscure, externalities may occur. There is the case of La Porte, Indiana, for example, which is 30 miles east of the large complex of industries in Chicago. Since 1925, there has been a notable increase in total precipitation, number of rainy days, thunderstorms, and hail at La Porte, probably as a consequence of heat, nuclei, and vapor emitted by the distant steel plants and related industry.[54]

It was noted earlier that increases in surface roughness (from replacement of fields and forests by streets and buildings) causes reductions in wind speeds near the surface. This can intensify air pollution problems, by reduced dissipation of pollutants. Landsberg suggests measures to counteract this tendency: the creation of open spaces, parklands, avoidance of buildings arrayed in solid walls, and irregular building height.[55]

The net of benefits versus costs for urban climate effects is anything but obvious. Heat island effects may well be positive, at present; perhaps they will become negative in the future, though not likely to the extent forecast by some gloomy prophets. Increased fog and rainfall, and decreased sunshine, are probably negative effects for most people. Hence, it is likely that the net impact of urban climate effects is negative. In the longest run, the city's residents, presumably aware of these effects, would have to be compensated for the corresponding reduction in utility. Further, some negative externalities may fall on people who live outside of the cities causing them. Perhaps a case could be made for counters to such effects, on both allocative and distributive grounds, for example, an effluent charge on Chicago's steel industry turned over to La Porte landowners.

Water Quality

The discussion of urban water quality will cover (1) water supply, (2) waste disposal, and (3) runoff and flooding. The topics are interrelated but are covered in turn for the sake of convenience. Water pollution is, of course, a central issue; it is a consequence of waste disposal, is exacerbated by increased runoff associated with urbanization, and is a source of concern as it affects municipal water supply. Water pollution can have negative impact on public health, swimming and other forms of water recreation, shellfish beds, fishing and wildlife preservation. The Committee on Pollution of the National Academy of Sciences classifies water pollutants into eight categories:

1. Domestic sewage and other oxygen-demanding wastes.

2. Infectious agents.

3. Plant nutrients, particularly nitrogen and phosphorus.

4. Organic chemical exotics, particularly insecticides, pesticides and detergents.

5. Other mineral and chemical substances from industrial, mining and agricultural operations.

6. Sediments from land erosion.

7. Radioactive substances.

8. Heat.

It is then argued that "all these are the results of man's activities and, with the possible exception of the fifth and sixth on the list, are being produced largely within the large metropolitan complexes that generally are located along the coasts or the main stems of the rivers."[56] The emphasis here may be open to question—Abel Wolman argues that man runs a poor second to nature as a polluter of water[57]—but it does suggest an important connection between cities and water pollution. Let us explore some aspects of the connection.

Water Supply

Water-borne disease from municipal drinking water appears to be a relatively minor problem, despite some occasional gloomy forebodings. Wolman argues "water borne and water-associated diseases are at a low ebb and have been near the vanishing point for some years."[58] Other experts support the general conclusion, but often add that viruses can be a problem. Occasional outbreaks

Table 20.—Number of Cities with Water Supply Problem, March, 1970 (Of cities serving interstate carriers)

1970 population in 000	Water supply problem			Estimated total of U.S. cities in class[b]
	I	II	III	
	Number of cities with problem[a]			
<25	20	12	12	5,000+
25-<100	8	12	4	600
100-<500	5	3	3	110
500+	1	1	0	25

Water supply problems are listed in order of increasing severity:

I. Inadequate monitoring program *or* failure to send sampling reports to Public Health Service and/or failure to meet PHS chemical standards *or* provide adequate data. Note that group I includes reporting failure.

II. Low pressure in distribution system and/or inadequate cross-connection code or inspection.

III. Samples do not meet PHS bacteriological requirements and/or inadequate disinfection.

[a]Coverage here limited to 678 municipal water supplies serving interstate carriers, with total population of 81 million. Cities with problems received only "provisional approval."

[b]Estimated number in each class based on 1960 distribution. In 1960, the Census listed 4,680 urban places as having populations of 2,500 to 25,000; and 596 urban places with populations under 2,500. In the sample of cities with problems, the "under 25,000" category includes 30 cities above 2,500 and 14 below 2,500.

Sources: Water problem data from U.S. Environmental Protection Agency, Bureau of Water Hygiene, reported in Sally Lindsay "How Safe is the Nation's Drinking Water?" *Saturday Review,* May 2, 1970, pp. 54-55. City size distribution based on U.S. Bureau of the Census, *U.S. Census of Population: 1960,* Vol. 1, Part A, Table 7, pp. 1-13.

of gastroenteritis (intestinal flu) and hepatitis may be caused by water-borne viruses. Such viruses can also cause polio, meningitis, rashes, and the grippe. Viruses commonly get into water through inadequate treatment of sewage. Testing procedures for viruses are difficult to carry out, and knowledge of effects of the relatively small numbers of viruses in water supplies is limited.[59]

The U.S. Environmental Protection Agency, Bureau of Water Hygiene, classifies municipal water supplies serving interstate carriers—trains, planes, buses, and ships in interstate commerce. In March 1970, classification occurred for 678 cities serving 81 million persons. Three classifications are used: approved, provisionally approved, and prohibited. No supply was prohibited, but 81 cities were classified as provisionally approved, indicating the existence of some water-supply problem.

Table 20 exhibits the distribution of these 81 cities by population size, and by three types of supply problem. Problem III may be the only serious problem, since it consists of not meeting bacteriological or disinfection standards. The other problems can involve inadequate reporting or inspection.

The occurrence of only 19 cities under Problem III, with 12 of those having a population less than 25,000, lends support to the argument that health problems are relatively minor. It is difficult to infer much about quality as a function of city size, but it seems reasonable to argue that trouble occurs more frequently for small cities, with little in the way of scale effects above a population of 25,000.[60] This is based on the assumption that the 678-city sample includes all cities over 100,000 in population (135); half the cities over 25,000 (300); and the remainder from the below 25,000 category (243).

That there is often a price for progress is illustrated by municipal water quality improvement. The elimination of typhoid fever meant that young children were no longer immunized to polio through exposure to its virus in sewage contaminated water, and hence, they became susceptible to the paralytic form of the disease.[61]

Waste Disposal

Annual expenditures on sewers and waste treatment systems are now measured in the billions of dollars. Eric F. Johnson estimates that "four hundred times as much money is spent on preparing water for dumping as it is on preparing it for drinking."[62]

Treatment of sewage is classified as primary, secondary, or tertiary. In primary treatment, sewage is stored temporarily in tanks, and heavier suspended solids settle into sludge. The liquid is poured off into waterways and the sludge is carted away. Approximately 50 percent of suspended solids and 35 percent of associated biochemical oxygen demand (BOD) are removed by this process. Secondary treatment is biological: Bacteria feed on the organic wastes in the effluent from the primary treatment. The effluent here is again allowed to settle. About 85 to 90 percent of suspended solids and BOD are removed. Tertiary treatment is a generic term applied to more advanced processes which are used to obtain a still greater percentage of suspended solid and BOD removal, or to obtain improved removal of nutrients (nitrogen and phosphorus), which are not handled well by the standard primary plus secondary treatment. Tertiary treatment is expensive. The addition of tertiary treatment can increase costs to two or three times the standard.

Engineering evidence indicates that sewer-system costs per capita decline with density, and that treatment costs decline rapidly with city size for populations up to 100,000, with modest declines, at best, for increasing city size after that point. The city size conclusion is subject to important empirical qualifications.

First, the engineering data often omit land costs and implicitly assume constant labor costs; both costs can be expected to increase with city size. Second, if stream quality standards are fixed at high enough levels, tertiary treatment at high costs becomes necessary. Impact is most pronounced for larger cities. Finally, where storm sewer and sanitary sewers are combined, raw sewage is discharged into waterways during summer rains. The problem of combined sewers increases in magnitude with city size, though this reflects history, rather than engineering.

In sum, it seems plausible that to attain specified stream standards, the needed expenditures per capita are U-shaped with city size. Documentation for these conclusions follows.

Table 21 exhibits sewer costs per capita as a function of density, drawing on the work of Paul B. Downing.[63] In Table 21, a sewer depth of 10 feet, a pipe life of 50 years, and a five percent interest rate are assumed. Reductions in cost per capita with density occur for two reasons: (1) costs per gallon flow per 100 feet decrease as sewer pipe diameter increases and (2) length of sewer pipe per capita decreases.

Costs in Table 21 include all per capita costs of collecting the sewage of a 160-acre area and transporting it to a point on the edge of the area. An additional cost is that of transporting sewage from this point to the treatment plant. This cost also declines as density increases; and, of course, it increases as the distance to the treatment plant increases. The marginal cost of a septic tank is $13.42 per capita per year. Hence, as density increases, there will be a shift from septic tank to sewer, with the changeover point determined where the sum of sewer and treatment cost falls below septic tank costs. Because septic tank effluent may pollute ground water used as a source for drinking water, an earlier point of changeover to sewers may be warranted.[64]

Downing also develops data on treatment costs as a function of city size, which exhibit declining per capita costs as population increases to 100,000, as shown in Table 22. Trickling filter and activated sludge here refer to alternate forms of secondary treatment. Costs are capital costs on an annual basis plus operating and maintenance costs.

There is general confirmation of Downing's results in data based on estimated municipal waste treatment "needs" prepared by the Conference of State Sanitary Engineers in cooperation with the Public Health Service.

Table 21.—Sanitary Sewer Costs at Various Densities of Development

Density (people/acre)	Total sewer cost for 160-acre area ($)	Total sewer cost ($/capita)	Annual sewer costs ($/capita/yr.)
0.4	36,914	576.00	33.60
1.0	40,064	250.40	14.59
4.0	70,920	110.81	6.46
16.0	213,598	83.40	4.86
64.0	215,267	21.02	1.22
128.0	219,370	10.71	0.62
256.0	193.123	4.71	0.27
512.0	222,874	2.72	0.16

Source: Paul B. Downing, *The Economics of Urban Sewage Disposal* (New York: Praeger, 1969), Table 13, p. 53.

Table 22.—Costs of Sewage Treatment

Type of plant	Capacity (people)	Annual total costs ($/yr.)	Average costs ($/capita)	Marginal costs ($/capita/yr.)
Primary	1,000	7,158	7.16	4.83
	10,000	35,933	3.59	2.57
	100,000	197,238	1.97	1.50
Trickling filter	1,000	10,553	10.55	5.02
	10,000	41,154	4.12	2.69
	100,000	199,859	2.00	1.42
Activated sludge	100	1,923	19.23	11.55
	1,000	8,794	8.79	6.16
	10,000	46,643	4.66	3.47
	100,000	267,759	2.68	2.07

Source: Paul B. Downing, *The Economics of Urban Sewage Disposal* (New York: Praeger, 1969), Table 8, p. 35. Data are for 1964 operations, deflated to 1957-59 dollars.

Table 23 presents these needs in terms of capital costs per capita for (1) communities without sewers and treatment plants, and (2) communities discharging raw sewage—with sewers but without treatment plants. For both sets of communities, there is a decline in per capita costs as city size increases. Sewer costs are estimated here as the difference between group (1) and group (2) costs for a given population. No city-size effect emerges for sewers. Perhaps there is little difference in density among the cities of Table 23. The capital costs of the table square fairly well with Downing's estimates of capital cost.[65]

Table 23.—Capital Cost Estimate Based on Municipal Waste Treatment "Needs," 1963

Community population size in 000	Per capita costs for plant		
	(1) Sewers plus treatment[a]	(2) Treatment only[b]	Cost (1) minus cost (2)
1-<5	$84.4	$79.8	$4.6
5-<10	65.4	58.0	7.4
10-<25	52.1	44.7	7.4
25-<50	41.9	34.3	7.6
50-<100	34.7	21.7	13.0
100+	19.0	14.8	4.2

[a]Treatment needs for unsewered communities requiring both sewage collection system and treatment facilities.

[b]Treatment needs for communities discharging raw sewage.

Source: Estimates prepared by Conference of State Sanitary Engineers in cooperation with the Public Health Service. Data presented in U.S. Congress, House, Committee on Government Operations, *Water Pollution Control and Abatement (Part 1A—National Survey), Hearings,* 88th Cong., 2nd sess., 1964, pp. 132-37, Tables I and III in particular.

Table 24.—Annual Revenue per Capita for Sewer Service for a Sample of Cities, 1962

City size in 000	Annual revenue per capita (average for sample)	Sample size
<10	$9.28	8
10-<40	6.72	30
40-<100	6.08	11
100+	6.31	12

Source: G.C. Szego, *Cost Reducing Condominium Systems for Low Cost Homes,* Institute for Defense Analysis, Study S-325, October 1968, Table B-1, pp. 97-99. (From survey data in *American City Magazine,* 1962.)

The evidence to this point shows declining costs as urban population increases to 100,000. Data on costs beyond that point appear sparse, but there are some intimations that average cost levels off and perhaps turns upward. In particular, if pollution standards are set in terms of a maximum stream load rather than a minimum percentage removal of pollutants, the cost advantage of increasing size is considerably diminished. Downing points out that the pollution produced by a 100,000 person plant with a 97 percent removal rate is much larger than that of a 1,000 person plant treating at 35 percent; that is, the former is the equivalent of raw

FIGURE 9-9

LONG-RUN MARGINAL COST OF TREATMENT AT CONSTANT POLLUTION LOAD AND CONSTANT REMOVAL PERCENTAGE

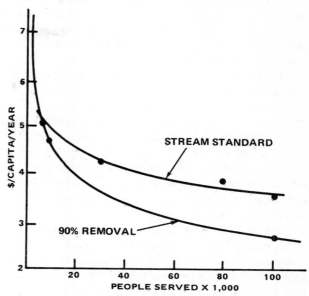

Source: Paul B. Downing, *The Economics of Urban Sewage Disposal,* New York: Praeger, 1969, Figure 12, p. 159.

sewage production by 3,000 persons, while the latter is that of 650 persons. He considers a case where the level of pollutant release is set at 4,500 pounds of BOD per day—in effect, the maximum level. This stream standard is contrasted with a constant removal rate of 90 percent; the cost curves of the two cases are presented as Figure 9.

Under the stream standard, the decline in cost is less pronounced as scale of operation increases. Further, Figure 9 does not show population much above 100,000. If the stream standard were applied to much larger populations, it seems likely that tertiary treatment would be necessary. Data in Downing indicate that the addition of tertiary treatment for a city of 500,000 would raise capital costs to about three times their former level (for primary plus secondary treatment only), while operating costs would double.[66] These estimates are roughly in line with values obtained for an experimental plant in the Washington, D.C. area, which added tertiary treatment. Capital investment was twice that for conventional facilities, while the operating cost was three times as great.[67] The consequence most likely would be an upturn in cost per capita as population increased. (However, tertiary treatment costs also decline with increasing population.)

One item of evidence suggests that there may be a cost upturn even for conventional treatment. G. C. Szego presents data on sewer service charges for 61 United States cities, in the form of revenue per capita per month. The data were used to develop annual averages by city size, presented in Table 24. Revenue first declines with size, but then increases, suggesting that a U-shaped function may hold; of course, this assumes revenues are pegged to costs.

Other items of evidence yield inferences on per capita costs needed to attain specified standards.

A publication of the U.S. Geological Survey summarized water data for United States metropolitan areas as of 1965.[68] It contained a discussion of water problems for each area, including water pollution where this was a problem. Counting the number of instances of a water pollution problem and classifying by population size indicates that the problem becomes more serious with size, as shown in Table 25.

In 1970, the National League of Cities and the Conference of Mayors conducted a survey of sewage treatment facility "needs" in 1,105 cities. On the basis of the survey, total urban needs of $33 billion to $37 billion were projected to 1976.[69] (This contrasts with a Council on Environmental Quality estimate of $11 billion for projects eligible for Federal grants.[70] Of course, perceived "needs" are likely to be above what cities would pay for on their own account.) Data on individual cities[71] were classified by regions and city size, and per capita averages were obtained. Two subsets of data were excluded because of coverage problems: (1) data for metropolitan areas, because the population covered by metropolitan sanitary districts generally does not equal the Census population figure and (2) estimates prepared by the Association of Metropolitan Sewerage Agencies, because internal evidence suggested differences in defining needs.

Table 26 presents needs per capita in terms of primary and secondary treatment, tertiary treatment, interceptor and storm sewer improvements, and the total of the three subcategories.

Total needs per capita appear to be U-shaped with city size for the South, Northeast, and North Central regions, first decreasing and then increasing as city size increases. The western pattern is that of a general increase in costs with size. There are pronounced differences between regions, perhaps explained in part by regional differences in the combined sewer problem, showing up in the needs for interceptor and storm sewer improvements.

Historically, sewers in cities were first employed to carry storm water runoff. With the growth of urban density in the 19th century, the need for domestic

Table 25.—The Incidence of Water Pollution Problems for Metropolitan Areas, 1965

Metropolitan area population size in 000	Total number of areas in group	Areas with pollution problem	Fraction with pollution problem
<100	21	8	0.381
100-<250	78	46	0.590
250-<500	56	35	0.625
500-<1000	35	25	0.714
1000-<2500	22	17	0.773
>2500	7	6	0.857

Source: U.S. Geological Survey, *Water Data for Metropolitan Areas,* by William J. Schneider, Paper 1871, 1968. A metropolitan area was counted as having a pollution problem whenever the source stated there was a problem with municipal-industrial waste disposal, or that waters were polluted.

sewage transportation was met by joining domestic house drains to the existing system of storm drains. Most of the sewer systems built before 1950 were combined sewers.

The general practice was to provide for a treatment capacity equal to two or three times the average dry weather flow, and to bypass directly to the watercourse all flows above this rate. Such overflows begin after only a few hundredths of an inch of rain falls. In many areas, overflows may be expected five or six times a month during the summer. Although only three percent of the system sewage is discharged during the overflow, this discharge can carry with it as much as 20 to 30 percent of the organic matter in the sewage. This results from the scouring of deposited solid matter in the pipes during the runoff period. The negative consequences of storm runoff include the flooding of basements with a mixture of sewage and storm water during very heavy storms, and the large pollution loads imposed on waterways. Newly installed sewer systems and extensions of old systems at the urban fringe now usually separate storm and sanitary sewers.[72]

Estimated costs for handling the combined sewer problem range from $15 billion for partial separation to anywhere from $30 billion to $100 billion for complete separation.[73] As shown in Table 27, the combined sewer problem becomes more prevalent as city size increases, no doubt reflecting greater age with size. (This factor may explain some of the results in Table 26, though it seems unlikely to hold for the western region).

On the other hand, places without sewer facilities tend to have small populations, and in sewered places, the percent of population connected to sewers increases

Table 26.—Sewage Treatment Needs per Capita, by Region and City Size, 1971-1976

Region and city size	Number of cities in sample	Per capita costs (average)			
		Primary and secondary	Tertiary treatment	Interceptor and storm sewer improvements	Total
South					
10-<50	19	$76.01	$40.29	$128.56	$244.86
50-<100	15	45.34	38.44	57.83	141.61
100-<250	14	65.91	28.44	35.60	129.95
250-<1000	9	58.26	22.87	60.06	141.19
Northeast					
10-<50	29	209.86	29.67	167.72	407.25
50-<100	22	124.36	23.68	122.24	270.28
100-<250	9	230.19	52.23	170.03	452.45
250-<1000	2	167.33	201.58	296.44	665.35
New York City	1	165.23	241.49	38.13	444.85
North Central					
10-<50	36	98.02	42.54	170.82	311.38
50-<100	16	97.40	32.52	174.50	304.42
100-<250	17	55.22	16.76	171.40	243.38
250-<1000	3	161.17	15.58	255.34	432.09
West					
10-<50	23	79.94	10.82	14.30	105.06
50-<100	20	45.10	58.56	83.21	186.87
100-<250	8	28.64	25.06	94.26	147.96
250-<1000	2	95.87	6.18	205.44	307.49

Source: Calculated from data appearing in: National League of Cities, "Statement of Donald G. Alexander before the House Appropriations Committee, May 5, 1971," Appendix A, 1971.

with size of place. (It is worth noting that in 1960, places having some sewers encompassed 98 percent of the United States population, with more than 90 percent of the persons in those places connected to sewers. Connected population in small places—below 25,000 persons—equaled about 80 to 90 percent of total population, while large places—over 100,000 persons—had essentially their entire populations connected.[74])

Given the evidence to this point, some conclusions can be essayed.

It is plausible that sewer and treatment costs per capita decline as population increases to 100,000. This could be a factor tending to increase a city's population to that point; one city of 100,000 would have lower costs than two cities of 50,000 each. But the conclusion holds only if other costs and benefits are constant. For example, two cities of 50,000 might be economic if savings in transport cost outweighed increased sewer costs.

As population increases beyond 100,000, sewer and treatment costs per capita are likely to be relatively stable in engineering terms. But empirical evidence indicates that per capita costs, in fact, turn up as size increases. This may reflect the impact of assumed stream standards or of an assumed decision to mitigate the combined sewer problem.

Runoff and Flooding

The hydrological effects of urbanization can be considered by drawing on a comprehensive survey by Luna Leopold.[75] Urbanization increases both the volume of runoff from precipitation and its rate of flow

Table 27.—Percent of Each Type of Sewer Within Population Groups

Population size groups	Percent of reported cases of communities with:		
	Separate sewers	Combined sewers	Both separate and combined sewers
Under 500	95.5%	3.5%	1.0%
500-1,000	90.2	7.6	2.2
1,000-5,000	85.5	10.3	4.3
5,000-10,000	81.0	10.4	8.6
10,000-25,000	78.3	13.2	8.5
25,000-50,000	71.3	13.9	14.8
50,000-100,000 . . .	65.8	22.4	11.7
100,000-250,000 . . .	52.4	22.6	25.0
250,000-500,000 . . .	58.3	19.4	19.4
Over 500,000	27.3	31.8	40.9
Total	85.2%	9.7%	5.1%

Source: U.S. Federal Water Quality Administration, *Municipal Waste Facilities, Statistical Summary, 1968 Inventory*, Table 20, p. 35.

into streams. With an increase in the proportion of an area made impervious to water by pavement and roofs, a higher percentage of the water runs off into streams, rather than infiltrating into the ground. The percent of area that is impervious increases with density, as these data show:

Lot size of residential area (in square feet)	Approximate percent of surface area made impervious
<6,000	80
6,000 to 15,000	40
>15,000	25

Water runs off faster from streets and roofs than from natural vegetated areas. Further, the construction of artificial channels, especially storm sewers, also increases the rate of runoff. As a consequence, urbanization increases the peak discharge—the maximum runoff of water per unit of time for a given amount of rainfall.

Leopold estimated the increased flood potential for various levels of urbanization, measured in terms of area sewered and made impervious. This was presented in the form of an estimated ratio of overbank flows (flooding) of urbanized relative to rural land, shown here as Figure 10. With an area 50 percent sewered and 50 percent impervious, the expected number of floods would increase four-fold.

Leopold's evidence suggests that the risk of flood damage increases with density and, presumably, with city size. Historically, however, such risk may have been greatly reduced or eliminated by (1) flood control investment, often with Federal subsidy and/or (2) selection processes; it is likely that low flood risk was a factor in site selection and growth for many cities.

A comprehensive study of flood insurance, carried out by the Department of Housing and Urban Development in 1966, concluded that the flood damage hazard in the United States is highly concentrated—some cities have higher risk of flooding than others, and there are marked variations in risk within cities. As few as two percent of all dwellings can expect to have more than half the annual flood damage; less than 10 percent of all dwellings have any significant flood hazard; and the other 90 percent are free from any serious or measurable flood hazard.

Some survey data in the study suggested that flood risk was U-shaped with city size, but the data are too limited to draw any firm conclusions. There is some evidence that market mechanisms are at work in the high risk zones. In about a third of the study cities, there was essentially no use of the highest risk zone. Further, in a substantial number of cities, the average value per dwelling was much lower in the high risk zones than in the other zones; and in some cases, there was a fairly regular decline in dwelling value as risk increased.[76] This suggests that a corresponding decline in land value has occurred.

Solid Waste Disposal

An average of 5.32 pounds of solid waste is collected per person per day, or roughly one ton per person per year. The amount collected per day is 3.93 pounds for the average rural resident, 5.72 pounds for the average urban resident.[77] These figures refer to refuse—solid wastes collected routinely. The composition of municipal refuse is indicated by this sample distribution:[78]

Paper	46
Garbage	12
Grass and dirt	10
Glass, ceramics, stones	10
Metallics	8
Wood	7
Textiles, plastics, leather, rubber	7
	100%

George Tolley estimates that approximately three-fourths of all solid wastes are collected by private contractors. About 50 percent of the total is generated by commercial, industrial and Federal government agencies, and is handled almost exclusively by private contractors. The remaining 50 percent is household

FIGURE 9-10
RATIO OF URBAN TO RURAL OVERBANK FLOWS (FLOODING)

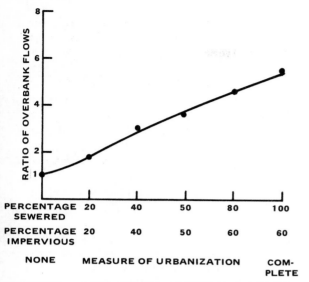

Source: Figure 16.5 in Luna Leopold "The Hydrologic Effects of Urban Land Use" in Thomas R. Detwyler *Man's Impact on Environment*, N.Y. McGraw Hill, 1971, p 211.

wastes, with perhaps half of this amount handled by private contractors, on the basis of trade surveys.[79] (Patricia Conway George estimates the distribution of all collection services as 50 percent public, 50 percent private.)[80]

Refuse production per capita is increasing at a rate of four percent a year; projected to 1980, this yields a per capita total of eight pounds per day.[81]

It is estimated that solid waste is presently disposed as follows:[82]

On land	90
Open dumps	85
Sanitary landfill	5
Burned in municipal incinerators	8
Other	2

The last category includes composted, dumped at sea, fed to hogs, and burned in on-site incinerators (apartment buildings, conical burners at dumps, etc.).

In a sanitary landfill,[83] refuse is spread in thin layers, each compacted by a bulldozer before the next is spread. The landfill is sealed with a layer of compacted earth at the end of each working day, and the complete fill is sealed with two or three feet of earth. The sanitary landfill eliminates a number of negative externalities associated with open dumps, which can serve as breeding grounds for flies, rats, and mosquitoes, and which may well pollute ground water. Of course, there is a cost involved in substituting sanitary landfill for open dumps.

Available data indicate that substitution increases cost per ton of refuse handled by 33 to 50 percent. The estimated total cost of upgrading open dumps to acceptable sanitary levels is $4.2 billion.

When completed, sanitary landfills can be used for parking, some types of construction, and recreation facilities—parks, golf courses, even ski slopes. Use for buildings is constrained because of land subsidence and possible emission of methane gases due to anaerobic decomposition; buildings can trap methane, creating an explosion hazard. Despite these constraints, about 11 percent of the present land area of New York City (for example) was created by solid waste fill, including some of the most valuable recreational and commercial sites. Positive externalities can occur in the filling of ravines and gullies, for such can stabilize surrounding terrain.

Solid waste disposal operations can be classified as collection, including transportation, versus disposal at the final site. Most of waste disposal cost is attributable to collection, which is estimated to run from 75 to 90 percent of total cost.[84] Further, most of collection cost (about 80 percent) is spent for labor.[85]

Disposal at the site shows some scale economies for both landfill and incineration. Collection costs within an urban area may be U-shaped with density; however, as city size increases, it seems clear that collection costs increase, both because of increased wage rates with city size, and because of likely greater congestion, a greater distance to landfill sites, or (alternatively) a higher cost of land at any given distance from the city. Given the share of collection costs in the total, and the labor intensive nature of the operation, total cost can be expected to increase with city size.

The Council on Environmental Quality estimates that site disposal costs can range from $1 to $3 per ton for sanitary landfill, and from $3 to $10 per ton for incineration. Collection costs average roughly $15 per ton, though there is marked variation. In particular, collection costs in large urban areas can go substantially higher; New York City costs were $32 per ton in 1969, not including many employee benefits and depreciation.[86]

There appear to be scale economies in site disposal costs for both landfill and incinerator operations. George lists the following costs per ton for landfill operations as a function of scale, measured in terms of tons of refuse deposited per year:[87]

	Cost per ton	
	11,000 tons	27,000 tons
Sanitary landfill	$1.27	$1.05
Open dump	0.96	0.70

Tolley finds that average unit operating costs for small, medium, and large incinerators are $5.00, $4.72, and $4.56 per ton, respectively. Categories were defined by rated capacity, with small less than 200 tons per day, medium at 200 to 499 tons per day, and large at 500 tons or more, per day.[88] A trend toward large regional incinerators, rather than small local units, is in line with these results.[89]

Some evidence on intra-urban collection cost may be noted. Werner Hirsch developed regression equations relating St. Louis area municipal refuse service to a number of explanatory variables.[90] He concluded that no significant economies of scale occurred, measuring scale by number of pickup units. Density of pickup was measured as number of residential pickups per square mile, and it had a negative and significant coefficient, indicating declining cost as density increased. However, Blair Bower suggests that collection costs per ton are a U-shaped function of tons of refuse generated per acre, first declining and then increasing.[91]

A number of items of evidence support the conclusion that collection cost increases with city size. Thus, in practice, when length of haul to the landfill is over six miles, refuse is transferred from collection trucks to larger vehicles; otherwise, collection vehicles would be out of service too long.[92] The transfer process can be viewed as an additional cost borne by larger cities.

In a contract study for the Bureau of Solid Waste Management, a sample of 166 cities reported solid waste tonnage and collection costs.[93] Average collection cost per ton was found for three city-size categories: below 100,000; 100,000-500,000; and above 500,000. Because a few large cities had exceptionally high costs per ton, median values were obtained as well. These average and median values are presented here as Table 28.

Table 28 supports the conclusion that there are increasing collection costs with city size. To some extent, these increases may be offset by economies of scale in landfill or incineration, but magnitudes shown suggest that the offset is likely to be minor, at best. Further, savings in landfill and incinerator operations may be offset, in turn, by increasing land costs with increasing city size. It is noteworthy that Philadelphia substituted incineration for landfill because "the city long ago ran out of nearby land for dumping"[94] and that New York is expected to exhaust its refuse disposal sites by the mid-1970's;[95] a long term forecast is that "increasingly restrictive land use patterns will continue to limit landfill availability, and much of the slack will be taken up by incinerators."[96] Restated in terms of costs, these arguments indicate that increasing city size increases land costs and/or length of haul to the point where incineration becomes competitive with landfill.

Table 28.—Annual Solid Waste Tonnage and Collection Costs (166 Cities)

Population (1,000's)	Tons (per annum)	Collection cost ($ per annum)	Average cost per ton ($)	Cost per ton for median city ($)
10-100 . . .	2,813,819	26,757,188	9.50	9.90
100-500 . .	2,803,700	28,605,200	10.20	10.64
500 and over . . .	6,734,800	161,677,900	24.05	12.78
Total	12,352,319	217,040,288	17.66	

Source: U.S. Bureau of Solid Waste Management, *A Study of Solid Waste Collection Systems Comparing One-Man with Multi-Man Crews, Final Report,* by Ralph Stone and Co., Engineers, Los Angeles, Calif. (Contract No. PH86-67-248), 1969, Table XVIII, p. 61.

Table 29.—Estimated Costs for Plants Salvaging Materials from Incinerator Residue

Estimated city population in 000	Tons of dry incinerator residue per day	Operating cost per ton	Capital cost per ton	Total cost per ton
500	250	$4.06	$1.08	$5.14
800	400	3.28	0.92	4.20
1,340	670	2.32	0.40	2.72
2,000	1,000	1.80	0.32	2.12

Source: U.S. Department of the Interior, *Economics of Recycling Metals and Minerals from Urban Refuse,* by P.M. Sullivan and M.H. Stanczyk (Bureau of Mines Solid Waste Research Program, Technical Report 33), April 1971, pp. 9, 13-16.

The equilibrium point should occur where the higher incinerator disposal cost plus its associated lower hauling costs just equals the lower landfill disposal cost plus its associated higher hauling cost. Thus, Detroit pays $10 per ton for incineration and $6 per ton for sanitary landfill, implying that hauling costs to the incinerator are $4 below those to the landfill.

Incinerators discharge pollutants, pollution control measures for incinerators are costly, and the need to meet air quality standards increases with city size. Because air pollution control measures double the cost of smaller incinerators but add "only" 30 percent to the cost of larger units—processing over 500 tons per

Population, Resources, and the Environment

day[97]—there may be some mitigation of this additional disadvantage of increasing city size.

The conclusion that waste disposal costs increase with city size is reinforced by some parallel results for snow removal. In Canada, the cost of snow removal in small urban areas ranges from five to 30 cents a ton, while that in large urban areas ranges from 30 cents to one dollar a ton.[98]

A number of potential innovations in waste disposal appear to be favorable to larger cities. (Interest in the possibility of such innovations may well reflect higher costs with city size.)

The Bureau of Mines is carrying out research in the development of low-cost methods to reclaim and recycle metal and mineral values contained in municipal incinerator residues and raw refuse. An experimental plant is in operation to develop engineering data for the design of plants that can salvage materials from 250 to 1,000 tons of incinerator residue per day; these residue levels correspond to population levels of 500,000 to two million. Cost per ton processed decreases with scale (and city size).[99] Data on costs appear as Table 29.

High-density living affords opportunities for innovations in waste disposal. Merril Eisenbud argues that large apartment buildings have available to them a whole spectrum of efficient alternatives for handling refuse. He notes a demonstration project underway, consisting of a vacuum system for handling solid refuse within a large housing complex. "The housewife will drop her refuse into a conveniently located hopper from which the garbage will be transported pneumatically to a central location where it can be compacted and mechanically loaded for removal." He further suggests that all buildings along a subway route might drop their refuse to compactors below street grade with provision for transfer to special subway cars that would haul containerized wastes at night.[100]

A similar transportation proposal has been made by Paul H. Banner of the Southern Railway System. He has suggested that subways could haul containerized refuse at night to rail yards for transfer to rail cars, with estimated substantial savings over present transport of refuse (on the order of 25 percent). City planning officials, however, have not been very receptive to Banner's suggestion.[101]

A number of agencies have been investigating the use of pneumatic tubes, pipelines, sewers, and rapid transit facilities in the hauling of refuse.[102] Such facilities are most likely to be economic in large cities.

If some of these innovations are successful, it is possible that the cost of solid waste disposal in large cities would fall below that of smaller cities. Intuitively, however, it seems more plausible that such success would narrow the cost differential that now appears to exist.

Noise

A standard measure for noise loudness is decibels on the A scale (dBA) which weighs sound intensity according to the presumed pattern of human hearing. Studies of noise perception indicate that an increase of 10 decibels, for a given tone, is perceived as a doubling of noise level; that is, 100 decibels seems twice as loud as 90 decibels. More generally, the perceived difference in relative level of D_i and D_j can be written as $2^{(D_i-D_j)/10}$.

In decibel measurement, the zero decibel level is set at the threshold of audibility for the normal ear. The threshold of hearing at zero dBA is very low indeed, for if man's ears were any keener they would respond to the molecular motions of air particles. The sound of a whisper is around 25 dBA, ordinary conversation is 60 dBA, and a shout around 80 dBA. Automobile traffic ranges from 50 to 80 dBA, a subway train from 90 to 100 dBA, and a jet plane at 1000 feet is over 100 dBA. Construction noise often reaches 110 dBA, the proverbial boiler factory can reach 125 dBA, and the decks of aircraft carriers reach 155 dBA. The threshold of noise-induced pain for humans has been estimated variously at 120 to 140 dBA. Prolonged exposure to levels above 90 dBA induces permanent loss of hearing, and some see the danger level for hearing loss at even lower levels. Dougherty and Walsh, for example, develop evidence that some workers experience hearing loss at a sustained level of 80 dBA.[103] That noise tends to increase with city size and density is obvious, but not easily documented. Some corroboration emerges from the indirect evidence of the location of major noise sources, regulatory standards, and some limited collection of data.

The sources of loudest ambient noise occur in large cities: jet airports, heavy traffic, building construction, and demolition. A New York City Task Force on Noise Control observed: "The New Yorker's day is filled with the nerve-wracking shriek and clank of the subway, the deafening cacophony of pneumatic hammers, traffic, jet planes..."[104] Regulatory standards are indicative of land-use (and density) effects. Swiss standards, for example, are shown in Table 30.

The most useful data bearing on noise by locale are presented by the Environmental Protection Agency in a report to the President and Congress.[105] A series of 24-hour outdoor noise recordings was made at each of 18 sites; major emphasis was on suburban and urban residential areas, but the coverage was quite broad, and represents a preliminary cross-section of the United States noise environment. The range of daytime outdoor

Table 30.—Swiss Standards for Outdoor Noise Levels in dBA

Locale	Basic noise level		Frequent peaks		Infrequent peaks	
	Night	Day	Night	Day	Night	Day
Hospital	35	45	45	50	55	55
Quiet residential . . .	45	55	55	65	65	70
Mixed use	45	60	55	70	65	75
Commercial	50	60	60	70	65	75
Industrial	55	65	60	75	70	80
Main road	65	70	70	80	80	90

Source: Cited by Walter W. Soroka, "Community Noise Survey," American Speech and Hearing Association, Proceedings of the Conference: *Noise as a Public Health Hazard,* Washington, 1969, p. 177.

Table 31.—Qualitative Descriptors of Urban and Suburban Detached Housing Residential Areas and Approximate Daytime Residual Noise Level (L_{90})

Description	Typical range dB(A)	Average dB(A)
Quiet suburban residential . . .	36 to 40 inclusive	38
Normal suburban residential . .	41 to 45 inclusive	43
Urban residential	46 to 50 inclusive	48
Noisy urban residential	51 to 55 inclusive	53
Very noisy urban residential . .	56 to 60 inclusive	58

Source: U.S. Environmental Protection Agency, *Report to the President and Congress on Noise,* Dec. 31, 1971, Table 2-2.

noise levels at each of the 18 locations is presented here as Figure 11. The locations are arrayed in descending order of their daytime "residual noise levels", defined as that reading below which 10 percent of the observations fell, and labeled the L_{90} level. These median noise levels were observed for city versus detached housing residential areas:[106]

	Average daytime	Average nighttime
City (4 locations)	73.0	65.5
Detached residential (11 locations)	50.9	44.2

The evidence was employed to estimate typical L_{90} readings for residential areas, by locale, as shown in Table 31.

The EPA report also investigated the question of trends in noise level over time. The literature on noise contains many references to a presumed increase of one dBA per year in urban environments.[107] A review of five surveys conducted over a 34-year period indicated that, for unchanged land use, little increase has occurred in mean and residual noise levels—perhaps one dBA per decade, given unchanged land use. However, changing land use involving increased density, and the impact of new sources—particularly new freeways and airports—implies that many areas have grown noisier over time.[108]

Whatever the ultimate consequences of noise, it is clear that enough people dislike high noise levels to affect property values. In the long run, a selection process might sort out the population so that only those unperturbed by noise are located near major noise sources. However, because the unperturbed group is a minority, and because all members of a given family are unlikely to be in that minority, long-term price reductions can be expected for land and rental space near major noise sources. This is supported by two statistical studies of the impact of noise on property values. Both dealt with aircraft noise.

Inja Kim Paik regressed median value of single family dwelling units for a given block on a set of explanatory variables, including a measure of aircraft noise exposure.[109] There were 162 observations on city blocks in the proximity of John F. Kennedy Airport in New York. An initial equation and three variants were estimated. In all four cases, the coefficient of noise was negative and statistically significant. (As a qualification, Paik notes that "noise" may be a composite of multiple disutility from planes, including air pollution, visual intrusion and potential hazard.)

Paul Dygert and David Sanders used regression analysis to assess the impact of airplane noise in the vicinity of San Francisco International Airport.[110] Observations covered a subset of San Mateo County census tracts. Assessed property values were obtained for a random sample of 25 to 30 residential properties in each tract. Data were available on mean land values.

Twenty independent variables were employed, and were categorized as expressing (1) the character of the neighborhood, (2) accessibility to a variety of centers, and (3) site characteristics. Aircraft noise level was classified under the third category and was measured in terms of "composite noise rating," which accounts for measured amount of noise, frequency of repetitions, and time of day. Eighteen alternative equation forms were

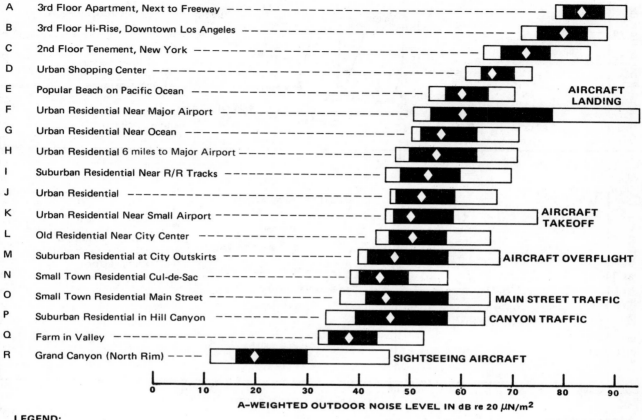

FIGURE 9-11

THE RANGE OF DAYTIME OUTDOOR NOISE READINGS FOR 18 LOCALES

LOCATION

A 3rd Floor Apartment, Next to Freeway
B 3rd Floor Hi-Rise, Downtown Los Angeles
C 2nd Floor Tenement, New York
D Urban Shopping Center
E Popular Beach on Pacific Ocean
F Urban Residential Near Major Airport
G Urban Residential Near Ocean
H Urban Residential 6 miles to Major Airport
I Suburban Residential Near R/R Tracks
J Urban Residential
K Urban Residential Near Small Airport
L Old Residential Near City Center
M Suburban Residential at City Outskirts
N Small Town Residential Cul-de-Sac
O Small Town Residential Main Street
P Suburban Residential in Hill Canyon
Q Farm in Valley
R Grand Canyon (North Rim)

AIRCRAFT LANDING
AIRCRAFT TAKEOFF
AIRCRAFT OVERFLIGHT
MAIN STREET TRAFFIC
CANYON TRAFFIC
SIGHTSEEING AIRCRAFT

A-WEIGHTED OUTDOOR NOISE LEVEL IN dB re 20 μN/m^2

LEGEND:

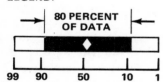

80 PERCENT OF DATA

Source: *EPA Report to the President and Congress on Noise,*
December 21, 1971, Figure 2-5, p. 2-12.

estimated, using land value per square foot as dependent variable; for these variants, R^2's were generally of like magnitude (0.7 to 0.8). The noise level coefficient was negative and significant in 12 of the cases. In a linear equation, average land value was $0.512 per square foot; the mean aircraft noise level was 92.3 with a standard deviation of 10.4; and the aircraft noise level regression coefficient was −0.78. Hence, at one standard deviation above the mean noise level, aircraft noise generated a loss of 0.081 in land value (−0.78 × 10.4), yielding an estimate of 0.431 per square foot (0.512−0.081). This is a 16-percent drop, which seems an appreciable amount.

The Social Environment

This report has focused on physical aspects of the environment. However, other effects of urban scale may generate compensatory payments, and will be briefly surveyed here under the heading of the social environment. Specific topics considered are traffic congestion, crime, and health and welfare effects.

Traffic Congestion

There is a fair amount of empirical evidence to support the obvious proposition that average distance to work and travel time increase with city size; the tradeoff

FIGURE 9-12

AVERAGE AUTO DRIVER WORK TRIP LENGTH, DURATION, AND POPULATION (TWENTY THREE CITIES)

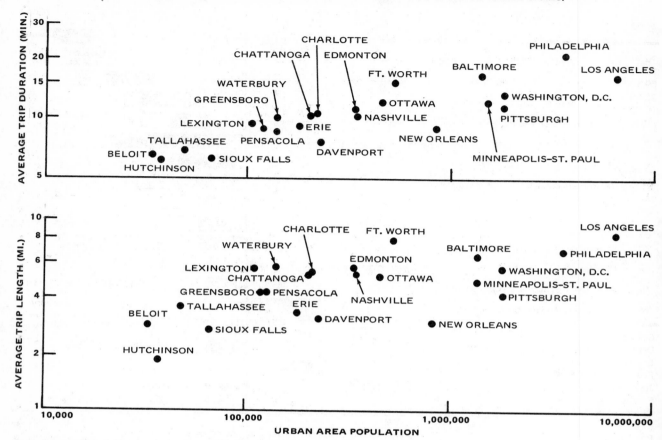

Auto driver average trip times and distance excludes terminal time effects.

Source: Alan M. Voorhees et. al., "Factors in Worktrip Lengths", *Highway Research Record*, 141, 1966, 24-26. Also cited *Highway Research Record*, 229, 1968.

of rent for travel time, and increasing rent with scale, insures a concomitant increase in travel time. Figure 12 and Table 7 (above) are examples of such evidence.

Inter-urban comparisons of time costs of journey to work must impute a value of time to differences such as those shown in Table 7. Evidence developed by Beesley,[111] and outside supporting evidence, indicates work trip time is valued at about one-third the wage rate; given increasing wages with size of city, the price per unit, as well as the quantity, will increase with city size. (Rough calculations with the data of Table 7 yielded an equilibrium differential of about one percent of income between succeeding SMSA's in the set of four.)

Rees and Schultz argue that compensation for the time and money costs of intra-area commuting occurs in the form of higher wages or lower rents, depending on

the distribution of employment and residences. They see both adjustments as occurring in the Chicago area, with large establishments having to pay wage premiums to attract workers from outside the neighborhood. Rees and Schultz examined wage rates for a sample covering a dozen occupations. Distance was included as an independent variable in regressions explaining wage rates; it had a positive coefficient in 11 cases, with five cases significant at the 0.05 level.

For a one-way work trip of 10 miles per day, estimated travel compensation ranged from two percent of mean earnings for janitors to 13.5 percent of mean earnings for accountants.[112]

An alternative form of compensation is reduction in hours of work for unchanged weekly pay. (Admittedly, this involves an increase in hourly wages.) As noted in the earlier discussion in connection with Table 7, hours

Table 32.—Crime Rates by City Size, 1967, per 100,000 Inhabitants

City population in 000	Homicide	Rape	Robbery	Assault	Burglary	Larceny	Auto theft
>250	11.8	14.8	95.1	130.0	229.1	376.7	122.3
100-250	7.2	8.2	36.5	77.6	180.4	418.6	102.0
50-100	3.5	5.6	25.9	56.4	152.7	385.3	83.1
25-50	2.9	4.9	18.0	49.7	135.2	362.9	69.9
10-25	2.8	4.4	12.5	45.9	122.9	314.3	58.4
<10	2.1	3.8	7.3	47.6	114.6	253.4	52.0
Suburban areas	3.2	6.1	18.4	44.1	132.6	245.1	61.1
Rural areas	4.3	6.5	9.1	33.9	110.8	116.0	37.0

Source: U.S. Federal Bureau of Investigation. *Crime in the United States—Uniform Crime Reports, 1967,* 1968, pp. 116-117.

Table 33.—Regression Results for Violent Crimes, 56 Large Cities, 1967 (Significant Coefficients Only)

Independent variable	Homicide	Rape	Assault	Robbery
Constant	−14.14	21.02	−463.12	108.75
Density (D)	. . .	. . .	8.22[a]	14.78[a]
Log city population (log P)	. . .	12.43[a]	. . .	. . .
Fraction Negro (N)	33.84[a]	208.03[a]	335.27[a]	562.35[a]
July temperature (T)	0.24[a]	. . .	7.14[a]	. . .
Fraction white collar (W)	. . .	79.32[b]	. . .	. . .
City in confederacy (C)	. . .	−7.76[b]	. . .	. . .
Median income (Y)	. . .	−9.32[a]	. . .	−37.07[a]
Precipitation (R)	. . .	−3.19[a]	. . .	. . .
<5 year schooling (E)	. . .	−102.37[a]	. . .	. . .
Interactions				
NZ	. . .	. . .	. . .	307.28
NW	. . .	−377.59[a]	. . .	. . .
R²	0.72	0.51	0.38	0.61

[a]Significant at 0.05 level.

[b]Significant at 0.01 level.

Note: C is significant if NW and W do not enter. Z = Population class—for population > 500,000, Z = 1; for population < 500,000, Z = 0.

of work for female occupations tend to drop with both population and density increases. The amount of the drop seems to correspond fairly well to the increase in travel time shown in Table 7.

Crime and the City

Crime rates increase with city size. Black crime rates appear well above white, with 1967 arrest rates about 12 times that of whites for the violent crimes of homicide, aggravated assault, forcible rape, and robbery.[113] Because blacks are not uniformly distributed by city size, but tend to locate in large cities, there is apt to be confounding of city size and racial effect. This is an obvious point, yet it tends to be neglected in the literature on crime, with much reference to the impact of increasing urbanization on crime.[114] Data like that of Table 32 are often cited to support this argument.

In an attempt to separate out causation, regression analyses relating 1967 crime rates to a number of explanatory variables were carried out for two sets of data: (1) observations on 56 central cities with populations over 250,000 in 1967, and (2) observations on 99

Table 34.—Regression Results for Crime in California, 99 Cities, 1967
(Primarily Significant Coefficients)

Independent variable	Homicide	Rape	Robbery	Assault	Burglary	Larceny	Auto theft
	Coefficients						
Constant	10.27	9.16	268.80	103.71	−268.52	1809.77	−54.84
Log city population	...	...	39.13^a	...	...	...	116.43^a
Density (in 000)	0.19	...	15.31^a	4.78^b	53.34^a	−1.80	61.83^a
Fraction Negro (N)	23.74^a	55.46^a	634.52^a	1875.93^a	3708.89^a	4621.22^a	5075.42^a
Log SMSA population	...	6.82^a	28.14^a	...	...	...	...
Fraction <18	54.32^a	...	...	...	...	...	...
Fraction >65	...	67.74^a	...	717.20^a	...	...	...
Population per household	−8.50^a	...	−69.51^a	...	...	−5412.46^a	...
Fraction white collar (W)	−16.00^a	−41.39^a	−402.06^a	...	...	−724.08^a	−150.69^a
Fraction single unit housing	−4.08	...	...	−201.12^a	...	...	−648.58^a
July temperature	0.15^a	...	...	...	17.69^b	28.44^a	11.30^a
W.N.	...	...	...	−2741.97^a	...	−9622.07^b	−8531.47^a
R^2	0.57	0.48	0.78	0.71	0.48	0.23	0.77

^{a}Significant at .05 level.

^{b}Significant at .10 level.

California cities of all size classes.[115] Results obtained are presented in Tables 33 and 34 respectively, with listing limited to significant coefficients.

The 56-city study was limited to the four violent crimes of homicide, rape, assault, and robbery. City size was significant only for rape, while density was significant for assault and robbery.

The California study included burglary, larceny, and auto theft, as well as the four violent crimes. Both individual city and SMSA populations were employed as explanatories here, and each was significant in two cases: robbery and auto theft for city size, and robbery and rape for SMSA size. Density was significant at the five percent level for robbery, burglary, and auto theft, and at the 10 percent level for assault. In all cases, significant coefficients had a positive sign.

It can be concluded that population size and density are associated with increasing levels of crime even after accounting for other explanatory variables. However, the degree of association is greatly overstated when the effect of the other explanatories is neglected.

The last point is illustrated by estimating crime rates for cities over 250,000 under the assumption that the black fraction of the population was 11 percent, the 1967 percentage for the country as a whole. Applying regression equations in which population size, density, and fraction black appeared, the violent crime rates were reduced to these fractions of their original levels:

	Crime rate
Homicide	0.66
Rape	0.86
Assault	0.69
Robbery	0.61

Health and Welfare Effects

There is little hard evidence on the effect of city size and density on social problems and social disorganization. Most items of evidence pointing toward one conclusion can be countered by evidence indicating the opposite.

For example, Robert C. Schmitt claimed to have controlled income and education; yet he obtained close associations between density measures and indicators of health problems and social disorganization for the Honolulu SMSA in 1950. Positive partial correlations above 0.5 were obtained for density and death rate, TB rate, VD rate, mental hospital rate, and juvenile delinquency rate; infant death rate, illegitimate birth rate, and prison rate were below 0.5 and positive; suicide rate was negative.[116] But Hallinan H. Winsborough reached conclusions pointing the other way, using 1950 census tract data for Chicago. Simple correlations of density and death rate, infant death rate, TB rate, and public assistance rate were positive; but then Winsborough introduced a dozen other variables and obtained significant negative coefficients for all social problems except infant mortality.[117]

The costs of any health and welfare effects may be direct, in terms of increased risk to the city dweller, or indirect, in terms of increased taxes for public services to ameliorate or prevent such effects. Direct costs may be concentrated among low income groups, while indirect costs may fall primarily on middle or upper income groups, perhaps serving as an incentive for relocation to suburbs or smaller towns.

It also seems likely that, true or not, there is a widespread belief that behavior in large cities relative to small is colder, more impersonal, and less polite, and that life is liable to be more frenetic and irritating. Obviously, some will make positive comparisons: There is more going on, and less social control. It seems likely that, for a majority, the negative aspects outweigh the positive, yielding another source for compensatory payments.

POLICY ISSUES

The concluding section of this report will consider policy issues under several headings. First, the question of limiting city size is taken up, amplifying the earlier discussion of the topic. The compensatory increase in money income with urban scale has implications for prediction and policy, and these are considered next. Then, there is a review of the impact of specific environmental policies on urban areas. Finally, there is some advocacy of the use of tolls in solving urban environmental problems.

On Limiting City Size

It is often proposed that the size of large cities be limited, and/or that settlement in smaller places be encouraged. The proposal is buttressed by noting that the quality of life declines in large cities. Some examples may be noted. In 1970, the National Goals Research Staff called for alternative growth centers and new towns in response to such declines in quality. In similar fashion, the National Committee on Urban Growth Policy called for the creation of new towns with a total population of twenty million. And Athelstan Spilhaus, an early mover in the Minnesota Experimental City Project, wanted to get rid of the pollution, traffic congestion, and other ills of the big city by getting rid of the big city; he had a vision of an optimum city size of around a quarter of a million people.[118]

In discussing the decline in quality of life with urban scale, none of these sources considered a possible balancing through compensatory income, a rather obvious gap in the argument. One wonders, too, if the writers felt that real income in the new towns would be

unchanged: Can we have our cake and eat it, too?

If the proponents of new, small towns felt that they (or someone) could build a better town and the world would beat a path to the new town doors, then why not get on with it and do the building and sell the new good things to the eager customers? (In fact, some new towns have been moderately successful, though others exhibit various degrees of failure. The successful cases have been located in or near existing metropolitan areas. At present, and certainly for some time to come, the number of people in new towns is miniscule, relative to total population.)

But most arguments for a substantial shift of population seem predicated on a substantial Federal subsidy, as well. (Often, the financing question is not dealt with too explicitly, so this is an inference.) One wonders why the people left behind in the low quality cities ought to subsidize the better life for those in the new towns. If the shift occurs only for a few old towns, with most of the subsidy borne by other places, labor in the old towns will be better off because VMP and wages will rise while supply price falls. (In Figure 2, move from L_1 and L_2, retaining VMP_1 and the labor supply curve.) Of course, this is a disequilibrium situation, which will attract new labor unless entry is legally restricted, which may be mitigated somewhat by illegal entry. In any event, the movement away from the initial equilibrium, via the subsidy, implies some loss in real income. More generally, if subsidized redirection occurs for all large cities, there will be a general loss of real income in the system because of redirection from more productive to less productive places.

The redirection of people away from large cities is sometimes defended in more sophisticated fashion by arguing that in-migrants to cities impose increasing marginal costs on city inhabitants—via increased congestion and pollution, in particular—and that policies ought to be developed to redirect such in-migrants to smaller places. Niles M. Hansen and Joseph J. Spengler, for example, have taken this position.[119] But the call for marginal cost pricing here seems equivalent to drawing a marginal curve to the supply curve of Figure 2, and setting that marginal factor cost equal to VMP, yielding a monopsonistic equilibrium. It is not too obvious who the beneficiaries of such monopoly will be; this will depend on whether price of labor is set equal to supply price or VMP. But it seems quite plausible that restriction of entry will reduce real national product. Put another way, it is argued here that the upward sloping supply curve of Figure 2 "properly" accounts for increasing costs of size. (It is assumed here that competitive equilibrium corresponds to optimality; on the product market, this occurs where average revenue equals aggregated marginal cost; on the factor market, this occurs where aggregated VMP equals average factor cost.)

There is a commonly held intuition that cities will decline in size, given effluent charges; this is probably based on the insight that some common property resources are being zero priced through institutional arrangement, and hence, must be overused. Proper pricing would reduce the use, and presumably, the number of users. But there are counters to this conclusion. If the resource is exhaustible, overuse in the short run may imply no use in the long run. It may be that if property in buffalo herds had been legally vested, buffalo husbandry might now exist. Of more importance for the present discussion, presumed common property resources are often a component of private land values and/or incomes. Quality degradation reduces land values, which corresponds to less intensive land use and less people. (See Figure 4, and attendant discussion.) Further, some form of rationing generally occurs for zero-money-priced goods; thus, there is a charge for highway congestion in the form of time costs. It is conceivable that "proper" pricing would lead to more highways and more people.

There is apparent popular support for policies redirecting growth from large to small places. In one survey,[120] respondents were asked whether the Federal government should discourage the growth of large areas and encourage people to move to smaller cities and towns. The response took this form:

	Discourage growth of large metropolitan areas? (percent)	Encourage movement to smaller towns and cities? (percent)
Should	52	58
Should not	33	33
No opinion	15	9

One problem here, of course, is that many big-city people answered with the hope that others would move out, reducing congestion, pollution, etc., and thus increase the real income of those who stayed behind.

In contrast, the position taken here (fairly consistently, it is hoped) is that some environmental problems are inherent in scale and really cannot be helped, beyond the balm of compensatory income; but, others may be susceptible of improvement. The criterion of improvement in both cases is whether benefits exceed costs for proposed solutions. It is further argued that, for problems susceptible of improvement, the cause of the problems is not scale, per se, but rather institutional arrangements, often involving pricing policies. It follows that the "direct solution" of arbitrarily restricting scale is a false solution, either because it does not operate on the real causes of soluble problems, or because it denies that some problems are best handled by market mechanisms which generate compensatory income. If scale is restricted by direct limits on entry to large cities, there will be a gap between VMP and supply price in large cities, yielding a motive for illegal entry; augmented supply in smaller places will drive wages down there. Total product will be reduced because of the malallocation. Redirection by taxes on large places and subsidies to small may reduce the problem of illegal entry, but will yield essentially the same malallocation: a monopolistic solution in the large cities, and too many resources in the small.

There are some possible qualifications.

First, a case can be made for subsidized experimentation with new towns and growth centers, because the benefits of some of the new knowledge obtained cannot be appropriated by its private developers. A condition for public support might be easy public access to the experimental results. Much of United States agricultural development can be traced to the work of the land grant college experiment stations and extension services. Similar activities might be effective in housing and urban development. However, applications of results might be restricted by such existing institutional features as zoning regulations, building codes, and union rules. To turn this around, experiments might be undertaken where such restrictions did not hold.

Again, it is sometimes argued that large cities harm the characters of their inhabitants in some way, which seems a variant of the proposition that people do not know their own best interests, though there may also be externalities if outsiders are affected by the urbanite's bad character. Robert Dahl, for example, worries about the future of democracy in a country of large cities.[121] Since the argument generally reflects rural ethnocentricism, or a set of value judgments that might be labeled pastoral-romantic (as exemplified by Jean Jacques Rousseau through Lewis Mumford), it is subject to dismissal as the disguised expression of self-interest or personal preference. That is the tentative conclusion adopted here.

Finally, large cities may generate more than proportionate economic growth, furnishing a case for extra-market promotion of large cities. The proposition on growth squares with hypotheses of T. W. Schultz and Wilbur Thompson. Schultz sees economic development occurring at urban-industrial centers, and Thompson sees large urban centers as having developed a capacity to innovate through the acquisition and encouragement of growth industries.[122] Allen R. Pred argues that innovation and invention are positively related to both city population size and growth rate, with the rate of information flow increasing with city size. He develops some documentation on the basis of patents per capita by locale.[123] Assuming that economic growth is generally, if not universally, accepted as a good thing, it follows that large cities may well yield positive externalities in the form of growth.

Implications of Compensatory Payments

Acceptance of the existence of compensatory payments, which seems strongly supported by the evidence, leads to some implications for prediction and policy.

1. There is a good deal of current interest in refining national income accounts to include measures of environmental degradation; similarly, there is interest in constructing social indicators, or measures of non-money sources of welfare. The argument and data on compensatory payments, suitably extended, may be useful in such efforts. In particular, change in the distribution of city size will imply corresponding predicted changes in per capita income and measures of environmental quality, which can be compared to actual changes in those measures.

2. Agencies such as the Postal Service, with uniform national pay scales, appear to neglect compensatory payments. If the policy is not circumvented de facto by such devices as quicker promotion, the consequence should be a deterioration in service quality with city size, as real effort matches real pay level. On the other hand, the national minimum wage should be a greater constraint, and possible source of unemployment, in smaller places. Some proposed welfare reforms involve a nationally uniform level of welfare payments; this should be an incentive for the movement of welfare recipients to smaller places.

3. Migrants from smaller to larger places may suffer from money illusion, with imperfect knowledge of compensatory differentials. Waste motion (ex post) may occur, with some migrants returning home. Better information might help.

Economic studies of migration and related topics might benefit by relating migration to "adjusted" wages (adjusted for compensatory payments) rather than money wages; that is, if migrants' information is not perfect, it may nevertheless be good.

Environmental Policy and Urban Impact

This section will review the effects on urban areas of environmental policies (particularly size and density effects), and how urban policy is being shaped by environmental considerations.

Impact of Air Pollution Regulation

EPA air pollution standards may initially reduce the attraction of large cities relative to small, and of the central city relative to the suburb. The long-run effect, however, might well be the reverse, because costs of meeting standards will tend to fall equally on all vehicle operators, nationwide.

In regulations published August 14, 1971, the EPA defined Priority I regions based on measured pollution levels in areas of maximum concentration (presumably the CBD or industrial areas), or—in the absence of measured data to the contrary—any region containing a 1970 urban place population over 200,000.[124] Priority I regions must develop and implement a control strategy within a specified time.[125] (The latest date allowable is May 30, 1977, assuming a possible two-year extension under some circumstances.)[126]

Standards for Priority I regions are somewhat less stringent than standards promulgated on April 1, 1971.[127] For example, some of the annual emission levels compare as follows (in $\mu g/m^3$).

	EPA standards, April, 1971	Priority I standards
Sulfur dioxide	80	100
Particulates	75	95
Nitrogen dioxide	100	110

Applying Table 11 yields the distribution of cities (as of 1968), meeting the Priority I standards; results appear as Table 35. Divergence from Priority I standards is least pronounced for sulfur dioxide, most for nitrogen dioxide, with particulates in between; not surprisingly, large cities will have most difficulty in meeting standards. Let us focus on the nitrogen dioxide problem, and consequently on auto emissions, in large cities.

Auto emissions are expected to be reduced substantially as a consequence of the Clean Air Act Amendment of 1970. The EPA has forecast total emission rates for urban area vehicles, accounting for both increasing numbers of vehicles, as well as emissions per vehicle.[128] The forecast nitrogen oxide emission rate is exhibited as Figure 13; the 1975 rate is approximately equal to that of the 1967 base year, while the 1980 rate will be 50 percent and the 1985 rate will be 25 percent of that base-year level.

Treating 1967 and 1968 as equivalent, and nitrogen oxides as perfectly correlated with nitrogen dioxide implies that at the 25 percent level of 1985 only one city does not meet the Priority I annual standard of 110 $\mu g/m^3$; at the 50 percent level of 1980, 14 cities are above the standard; even if their 1968 level is cut in half, the reduced level is above the standard.

Table 35.—Distribution of Cities Meeting and Not Meeting 1971 Standards, Using 1968 Pollution Levels

City size in 000	Sulfur dioxide			Particulates			Nitrogen dioxide		
	Total	Meeting	Not meeting	Total	Meeting	Not meeting	Total	Meeting	Not meeting
3,000+	2	0	2	2	0	2	2	0	2
1,000-<3,000	2	2	0	3	0	3	2	0	2
700-<1,000	10	10	0	9	6	3	10	0	10
400-<700	18	17	1	18	14	4	18	2	16
100-<400	42	40	2	74	47	27	42	5	37
Below 100	24	24	0	198	163	35	24	7	17

Source: Table 11 and Priority I standards, *Federal Register,* Aug. 14, 1971, Vol. 36, No. 158.

FIGURE 9-13

NITROGEN OXIDES EMISSION RATES FROM URBAN VEHICLES IN UNITED STATES — PROJECTED FROM 1967 BASE OF 1

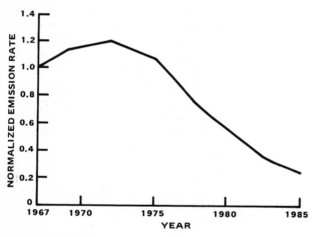

Source: *Federal Register,* Vol. 36, No. 158, Aug. 14, 1971, 15502.

It can be expected, then, that a number of large cities will have to take action in the 1975-1985 period to reduce central city auto traffic. In February 1971, the EPA identified New York, Chicago, Philadelphia, Los Angeles, Denver, and Washington as cities that might have to restrict vehicle use in downtown areas.[129] (The discussion indicates that some other large cities will be faced with the same prospect in the 1975-85 period.) Restrictions on central-city auto traffic during 1975-1985 may well cause some redirection of population growth to the suburbs and smaller cities, if the costs

of access to central cities rise more than the benefits of reduced pollution levels.[130] However, by 1985, reduced air pollution levels should increase the livability of large urban areas relative to small, and of central cities relative to suburbs. Since the costs of emission control will have been imposed on all cars nationwide, there will be no offsetting costs that are specific to large urban areas. Figure 6 applies with no downward shift in VMP: Some long run increase in size and density can be expected for large urban areas as a consequence of air pollution regulation.

It can be argued that costs of emission control ought to be borne only by residents of large urban areas on both distributive and allocative grounds: Residents of smaller places are forced to buy something they don't need, and in effect, subsidize larger places. This argument is used by John Lear in support of a suggested license fee of $500 a year or more to operate a car in the central city. He advocates using the fees collected to improve mass transit.

The license fee could be defended as an effluent charge, though a more refined system of charges would impose greater fees on vehicle discharging greater emissions; these generally would be older vehicles owned by lower-income people, so there would likely be regressive redistributive effects of the more refined system.

Lear's suggested level of fees contrasts with much lower estimated annual costs of emission controls per car on a national basis. Capital cost per car is estimated at $300; assuming a five-year life and 10-percent interest yields an annual cost of about $75. Adding inspection costs of $12 a year, fuel costs of $13 per year via prohibition of lead additives, and operation and maintenance costs of $90 (presumably on an annual basis), yields a total annual cost of around $200.[131]

In contrast to use of the effluent charge as a mass transit subsidy, it might be more reasonable to compensate the victims of air pollution, for example, by reducing central city taxes, and by using some of the funds to pay for urban vehicle emission controls.

The case for nationwide controls is generally put in terms of technical economy: Presumably, emission controls limited to urban vehicles would cost a good deal more than $200 per year; further, vehicles change locales.

As noted earlier, the diffuse nature of air pollution damages and abatement (the collective good argument) may make regulation preferable to effluent charges. Or else, the society (through its government) assesses air pollution damages as so great that the proper effluent charges would be extremely high, making regulation a more economic approach.

Impact of Water Quality Legislation

Early Federal grants for water pollution control and abatement (1958-1963) appear to have favored smaller places, particularly because of size limits on individual grants. Grants per capita by size of place for the 1958-1963 period are shown in Table 36. The pattern apparently prevailed in the 1965-69 period, when small municipalities, of less than 5,000 population, received 74 percent of the Federal sewer grant outlay.[132]

At this writing, emergent legislation has the goal of ending all water pollution by 1985. Expenditures over the next four years may run as high as $27 billion. As much as $20 billion will be allocated to sewage treatment grants, with 75 percent the maximum Federal share. Eventually, all communities and industries are to eliminate all discharges by using "the best available technology."[133]

A number of critiques may be noted. The expressed goal of zero pollution and the devoting of massive expenditures to waste treatment after discharge neglects the possibility of reaching relatively low levels of pollution by effluent charges at the source. Such charges can generate considerable internal reorganization by waste producers and greatly reduce waste discharge, usually at minimum cost.[134] There is disregard of the truisms that movement from low levels to zero levels of pollution can be extremely costly, and that reduction in water pollution can cause increases in air pollution and solid wastes. And one wonders about the foregone alternatives of the anticipated expenditures: What could be bought in the way of air pollution abatement, given a much greater risk to health from air pollution? Or in auto accident reduction, crime control, increased investment in human resources, particularly in the ghetto?

Perhaps this kind of allocation is to be explained as

Table 36.—Federal Grants per Capita for Water Pollution Abatement, 1958-1963, by Size of Place

Population size group in 000	1960 population in size group (millions)	Federal grants 1958-1963 (million dollars)	Grants per capita
<5	18,660	$147.1	$7.88
5-10	9,780	75.8	7.75
10-25	17,568	76.1	4.33
25-50	14,951	43.0	2.88
50-250	25,488	48.5	1.90
250-500	10,766	9.7	0.90
500+	28,595	12.4	0.43

Sources: Federal grants from U.S. Congress, House, Committee on Government Operations, *Water Pollution Control and Abatement, Hearings* Part 1A, 88th Cong., 1st sess., 1963, p. 166. Population from U.S. Bureau of the Census, *Census of Population: 1960,* Vol. 1, Part A, 1961, Table 6, pp. 1-12.

the result of an irresistible combination of noble purpose (enhanced quality of life) and the benefits of pork-barrel legislation, certainly a national tradition.[135] Emergent water quality regulation and subsidy might be viewed as an affirmation of implicit property rights of both recreationists and waste discharges to "free use" of water, though the affirmation may be stronger for the former than for the latter group. The large subsidies involved in waste treatment, however, indicates there is some affirmation for the latter group as well.

The pattern of past expenditures on waste water treatment was that of subsidy to small places. The distribution of water "needs," however, implies subsidy to both very small and very large places at the expense of middle-sized places. (This assumes that the combined sewer problem, and the need for tertiary treatment, are specific to large cities, and that most of the cost involved will be borne by the Federal Government.)

Institutional Aspects of Solid Waste Disposal and Noise Problems

Government itself is often a major source of environmental degradation, either directly as a polluter, or indirectly through the institutional arrangements of our legal and political system.

Public waste disposal, for example, is generally financed by real estate taxes, rather than user charges. As a consequence, there is "no incentive to reduce the amount of refuse that is generated; whether one produces a lot of refuse or a little makes no difference, for it is removed 'free of charge.' "[136]

Proper pricing presumably would improve allocation, as well as reduce the quantity of wastes to be disposed by virtue of increased incentives for salvage and recycling. Public disposal—and financing through general revenue—accounts for 25 to 50 percent of all solid waste disposal, using estimates presented earlier and noting that some municipal disposal is subcontracted to private firms. Hence, a good share of the activity is affected.

Even with proper pricing, if incineration is employed, a case can be made for greater recycling than that generated by the private market. For even with "good" pollution control, some air and water pollutants stem from incinerator residuals.[137] Proper accounting for the external costs generated by these pollutants would imply less waste disposal and more recycling than the private market solution. Walter Spofford presents a good statement of this argument.[138]

Much of the noise problem stems from institutional arrangements. The law greatly limits legal redress for noise caused by public or quasi-public enterprises. Under Federal law, the doctrine of "legalized nuisance" holds that a public or quasi-public agency is not liable for nuisance arising out of its "proper operation." No right of action exists against airports, for example, when noise causes some decline in property value. Recovery has occurred only when damages are total, that is, when the property is abandoned. At the state level, prospects of recovery are somewhat brighter; about half the states have a constitution which will permit broader recovery against the government for nuisance.[139] At the municipal level, most noise ordinances contain no provision for quantitative measurement of noise levels, hence, are difficult to enforce—and generally, are not enforced.[140]

Further, both Federal regulatory agencies and municipal governments often appear more concerned with the effective operation of public and quasi-public enterprises than with the interests of a broader public; put another way, government agencies have not been particularly concerned with internalizing externalities for which they bear some responsibility, such as noise caused by municipal garbage trucks operating in the early hours of the morning. And it is often alleged that the FAA and the CAB are more concerned with the progress of the airline industry than they are with noise externalities.[141]

The National Environmental Policy Act of 1969 (Public Law 91-190) requires all projects undertaken with Federal funds to carry a statement indicating environmental impact.[142] This, in itself, should counter some of the negative externalities imposed by government. Further, it has opened the way for legal redress in such cases.[143]

New Towns and the Environment

The argument for (subsidized) experimentation with new towns has wide currency. For example, in 1966, the National Academy of Science Committee on Pollution argued: "The massiveness and urgency of the [environmental quality] problem justify large-scale experiments, even in new experimental cities or in urban redevelopment plans."[144] Some experiments are now underway, and it is hoped, will yield useful results; of course, reports are often more glowing in prospect than retrospect. The most extensive experimentation with environmental focus appears to be the French new town of Le Vaudreuil, which is designed to be a "showcase of pollution control." Investment and regulations aim at limiting air and water pollution; building materials will be of sound absorbent substances; solid wastes will be conveyed to underground treatment plants and incinerators, with some utilization for the city's heat supply; and elevated walkways will segregate traffic.[145]

Some additional experimentation appears in English new towns and in six United States new towns that have received HUD loan guarantees; for the latter, guidelines on environmental impact are in force.[146] Congress has authorized HUD to provide up to half a billion dollars in loan guarantees which insure repayment of funds borrowed for infrastructure, reducing the cost of borrowing. It has also authorized another half billion dollars of subsidized assistance to private developers; but, as of this writing, it has not yet appropriated those funds.[147]

In retrospect, it is of some interest that air pollution regulation may favor large urban areas, while water quality expenditures appear to favor both very small and very large areas, and that new town subsidies will occur for rather small places. (New town populations are generally on the order of 100,000, though admittedly, most are located on the periphery of large urban areas, and some new town loan guarantees are for "new towns-in-town"—developments within a city.) This evidence suggests that middle-sized urban areas are subsidizing areas at the size extremes.

An Advocacy of Tolls

It is conceivable that many urban environmental problems could be substantially reduced, even solved, if markets were established for the goods at issue. Consider the case of traffic congestion, for example. An urban toll road authority could set prices that would effectively ration road use, eliminating congestion. The road network would be expanded until competitive equilibrium were attained, which would occur where average revenue equaled marginal cost of constructing more roadway; we would not want our authority acting as a monopolist. However, given the peak load problem, different prices might well prevail by time of day. Externalities could be internalized by appropriate payments to affected parties. Damages from noise, fumes, neighborhood disruption, relocation, etc., would be paid to both property owners and residents who were near enough to be affected. Such damages, of course, would be a component of the tolls charged. There might be problems with the physical collection of tolls, though some simple expedients come to mind, such as a special license plate for travel on a restricted set of high speed roads, or toll plazas at major entrance ramps. Advances in electronics and computers might yield more sophisticated procedures.

It is possible that many people, even a large majority, would object to this procedure, although their money costs of travel would be roughly the same as at present, since the tolls could substitute for gasoline and other highway user taxes in urban areas. The opposition might arise because the present system involves rationing by time costs; hence, people with a higher marginal value of time pay higher prices. (This is qualified by the observation that high income persons are more likely to be able to arrange their own travel time.[148] The substitution of money rationing might involve some redistribution in favor of higher income persons, as well as improving allocation. An approach that might reduce resistance would be to charge tolls only on newly constructed high speed highways. For those valuing their time highly, such a system would improve welfare. Certainly, there are interstate toll roads as precedent.

The setting up of markets for the sale of pollution rights has been advocated by J. H. Dales; this would involve the purchase from government of limited rights to use air and water held in common property for waste disposal.[149]

The notion can be amplified. It might be that a river basin pollution authority would have an either-or decision: sell most of a river's services to waste disposers for use as a sewer, or sell most of those services to swimmers, boaters, sports fishermen and commercial fisheries, allowing little or no use of the river for pollution. Implicit here is the notion that some streams, or even stretches of streams, would be reserved for one use, and some for the major alternative.

The decision presumably could turn on which use yielded maximum net revenue. In this situation, property rights to the stream's use would no longer be vested (implicitly) in either waste discharges or recreationists. This might cause considerable antipathy to the idea, for recreationists might feel their use "ought" to be free—that they had vested property rights in such use.

Emergent water quality regulation and subsidy might be viewed as an affirmation of implicit property rights of both recreationists and waste dischargers to "free use" of water, though the affirmation may be stronger for the former than for the latter group. The large subsidies involved in waste treatment, however, indicates there is some affirmation for the latter group as well.

In the case of air pollution, negative externalities are very diffuse. This may be the case to some extent in water pollution, too, if non-recreationists have widespread aversion to dirty water on esthetic grounds. In such situations, perhaps local government could represent the interests of the citizenry in bargaining with the pollution authority. Widespread damage could be compensated by payments reducing local property taxes, for example.

Tolls can be viewed as a form of effluent charges in which there is an attempt to use market mechanisms to achieve proper levels for charges. Of course, as argued throughout this paper, market mechanisms are at work even in the absence of such charges. But there is the intuition that tolls (or effluent charges, generally) may well work better.

It is likely that the imposition of tolls would often conflict with widespread vested interests, perhaps those of the majority. The proper "practical" response might be a mixed system, such as that advocated for urban toll roads; in addition, some missionary work might convince decision makers that this approach was the most pleasant of a number of painful alternatives.

REFERENCES

1. Colin Clark states that the density relationship was discovered by Bleicher in 1892, and rediscovered by Clark in 1951. Clark and Richard Muth have since made detailed empirical studies using the function. Colin Clark, *Population Growth and Land Use* (New York: St. Martin's Press, 1968), Chapter IX, p. 341, in particular; and Richard F. Muth, *Cities and Housing* (Chicago: Univ. of Chicago Press, 1969), Chapter 7 in particular.

2. View building rent as a payment for land plus a payment for construction inputs and maintenance services. At K_1 and K_2 the payment for land equals the value of land in nonurban use, presumably in agriculture. Urban land rent could have been defined as the net value above this opportunity cost, but I have chosen to define it as including that item.

3. Muth, *op. cit.*, p. 75, footnote 5, develops an equation for average population density up to any distance K miles from the city center. As I read his equation, the ratio of average densities for city 1 relative to city 2 will lie between K_2 and K_1 and $C+A_1K_1/C+A_2K_2$, where C is the minimum urban density (occurring at K_1 and K_2), and A_1, A_2, K_1 and K_2 are as shown in Figure 3.

4. George Tolley, "Economic Policy Toward City Bigness," in *Proceedings of Inter-University Committee on Urban Economics* (Conference Papers presented September 11-12, 1969, Cambridge, Mass.), p. 6.

5. Victor R. Fuchs, *Differentials in Hourly Earnings by Region*

and City Size, 1959, Occasional Paper 101 (New York: National Bureau of Economic Research, 1967).

6. *Ibid.,* p. 16.

7. Phyllis Groom, "A New City Worker's Family Budget," *Monthly Labor Review,* November 1967, pp. 1-8.

8. Midpoints of class intervals in Table 3 were used as point estimates of population for the intervals, except for the 10 to 100 class, where 50 rather than 55 was used, any difference here seeming trivial. For the 1000+ entry in Table 3, the corresponding Table 2 entry was the 2000 case. There is a seven year difference between the two tables, which could be a cause of difficulty.

9. U.S. Bureau of Labor Statistics, *Area Wage Survey,* Specific Metropolitan Area, 1968-9, Bulletin 1625-1 to 1625-90, 1970.

10. Muth, *op. cit.*

11. R. N. S. Harris, G. S. Tolley and C. Harrell, "The Residence Site Choice," *The Review of Economics and Statistics,* May 1968, Table 1, p. 244 in particular.

12. Robert M. Solow, "The Economist's Approach to Pollution and Its Control," *Science,* August 6, 1971, p. 499, discusses external effects and argues "each of a million cars contributes its small bit of the Los Angeles Smog, each driver pays in coughs and tears, and perhaps lung disease, for everyone else's exhaust emissions, but his own responsibility is negligibly small." But in the longer run, each driver has chosen to remain in Los Angeles.

13. George Tolley, *op. cit.*

14. Irving Hoch, "A Comparison of Alternative Inter-industry Forecasts for the Chicago Region," *Papers and Proceedings of the Regional Science Association, 1959,* p. 230.

15. This is one of the standard points made by my colleagues at Resources for the Future; for example, see Blair Bower and Associates, *Waste Management: Generation and Disposal of Solid, Liquid and Gaseous Wastes in the New York Region* (New York Regional Plan Association, March 1968), p. 41, in particular; and George O. G. Lof and Allen V. Kneese, *The Economics of Water Utilization in the Beet Sugar Industry* (Washington: Resources for the Future, Inc., 1968).

16. Interarea preferences from Gallup Poll reported in *New York Times,* Feb. 19, 1970, p. 8. The antipathy of metropolitan area residents to their locale appears greater than that of people in smaller places to theirs. This is suggested by a 1,700 person survey carried out for the Commission on Population Growth and the American Future, which found this distribution of preferences relative to actual location:

	Preferred location	Present location
Rural or small town	53%	32%
Small or medium urban area	33	27
Large metropolitan	13	42

17. For examples of the argument that people do not know their own best interests, as applied to pollution abatement, see Harold Wolozin "Environmental Control at the Crossroads," *Journal of Economic Issues,* March 1971, pp. 26-41, in particular p. 36; and Anatol Murad, "Comments on Wolozin," *Ibid.,* pp. 45-46.

18. R. H. Coase, "The Problem of Social Cost," *The Journal of Law and Economics,* Oct. 1960, pp. 1-44. Coase also makes the point that the easier it is to identify the parties at issue, the more practical it is to establish a private market transaction.

19. See U.S. Council on Environmental Quality, *Second Annual Report,* 1971, p. 105, for an extended list classified by kind of economic impact.

20. For similar tables exhibiting values at some variance with those in text, see American Chemical Society, *Cleaning our Environment* (Washington, 1969), Table 2, p. 25; and U.S. Environmental Protection Agency, *Air Quality Data for 1967, Revised 1971,* August 1971, Tables 1-7, p. 10. The variability in estimates is indicative of data problems in the field.

21. Thomas B. McMullen, "Comparison of Urban and Non-Urban Air Quality" (presented at the 9th Annual Indiana Air Pollution Control Conference, Purdue University, Oct. 13-14, 1970).

22. For example, see U.S. Public Health Service, *Air Pollution Measurements of The National Air Sampling Network, Analyses of Suspended Particulates, 1957-1961,* Publication 978 (Cincinnati, Ohio, 1962), p. 3.

23. This drew on industry sources specified in U.S. Congress, Senate, *The Economics of Clean Air,* EPA Report to Congress, S. Doc. 92-6, 92nd Cong., 1st sess., 1971, pp. 3-5, 4-8, 4-18.

24. U.S. Public Health Service, *New York-New Jersey Air Pollution Abatement Activity: Sulfur Compounds and Carbon Monoxide* (Cincinnati, Ohio, 1967), pp. 52-56; *Phase II-Particulate Matter* (Cincinnati, Ohio, 1967), pp. 69, 79-85; *Interstate Air Pollution Study, Phase II Project Report 11. Air Pollutant Emission Inventory,* by R. Venezia and G. Ozolins (Cincinnati, Ohio, 1966), pp. 13-34, 26-27; and *Washington, D.C. Metropolitan Area Air Pollution Abatement Activity* (Cincinnati, Ohio, 1967), pp. 98-108.

25. Data on Chicago particulate levels from Julius Goldberg, "Final Report, Chicago Air Pollution Medical Center, Contract PH-22-68-8" (Loyola University Medical Center, Maywood, Illinois, 1971), contract study for U.S. Public Health Service. A mapping of Chicago area particulate concentrations, based on a computer simulation model, appears as U.S. Council on Environmental Quality, *op. cit.,* Figure 2, p. 194. A similar mapping for sulfur dioxide appears as Figure 1, p. 193. Station readings on sulfur dioxide concentrations appear in Northeastern Illinois Planning Commission, *Managing the Air Resource in Northeastern Illinois,* Technical Report No. 6, August 1967, Table 9, p. 40.

26. Density from Muth, *op. cit.,* equation for Chicago, Table 1, p. 142; the density equation was $D = 60e^{-X_1(0.180)}$. There were 20 observations, reflecting the 20 stations reporting particulate levels.

27. U.S. Environmental Protection Agency, National Air Pollution Control Administration, *Characteristics of Particulate Patterns, 1957-1966,* by R. Spirtas and H. J. Levin, Publication AP-61, March 1970, p. 13.

28. U.S. Council on Environmental Quality, *op. cit.,* p. 214.

29. U.S. Public Health Service, *Calculating Future Carbon Monoxide Emissions and Concentrations from Urban Traffic Data,* by Wayne Ott, John F. Clarke, and G. Ozolins, 1967, p. 3; and C. S. Holling and M. A. Goldberg, "Ecology and Planning," *Journal of the American Institute of Planners,* July 1971, p. 228.

30. C. Peter Rydell, *Air Pollution and Urban Population Distribution* (New York: Urban Research Center, Hunter College, City University of New York, 1968).

Population, Resources, and the Environment

31. Robert H. Strotz and Colin Wright, "Spatial Adaptation to Urban Air Pollution" (paper presented at meeting of Committee on Urban Economics, Chicago, 1970), pp. 2, 15.

32. Ronald G. Ridker, *Economic Costs of Air Pollution* (New York: Praeger, 1967), pp. 121 and 137 in particular; Ronald G. Ridker with J. A. Henning, "The Determinants of Residential Property Values, with Special Reference to Air Pollution," *Review of Economics and Statistics,* May 1967; Robert J. Anderson, Jr. and Thomas D. Crocker, "Air Pollution and Housing," Paper No. 264 (Lafayette, Ind.: Purdue University, Institute for Research in the Behavioral, Economic and Management Sciences, Jan. 1970), p. 12; and John Jaksch, "Air Pollution: Its Effects on Residential Property Values in Toledo, Oregon," *Annals of Regional Science,* Dec. 1970, pp. 43-52, in particular, p. 46.

33. A. Myrick Freeman, III, "The Distribution of Environmental Quality," in *Research on Environmental Quality,* Allen Kneese and Blair Bower, eds. (Baltimore: Johns Hopkins Press for Resources for the Future, 1972).

34. U.S. Council on Environmental Quality, *op. cit.,* pp. 105-7.

35. Based on conversation with Eric Zausner, U.S. Council on Environmental Quality, Aug. 25, 1971.

36. Anderson and Crocker, *op. cit.,* pp. 3, 31.

37. Lester B. Lave and Eugene P. Seskin, *Does Air Pollution Cause Ill Health?* (Pittsburgh: Carnegie-Mellon University, Graduate School of Industrial Administration, processed, June 1971), p. 3.

38. Lester B. Lave and Eugene P. Seskin, "Air Pollution and Human Health," *Science,* Aug. 21, 1970, pp. 723-732, esp. pp. 729-730.

39. Lester B. Lave and Eugene P. Seskin, "Air Pollution, Climate and Home Heating," Working Paper No. 35, 1970, Carnegie-Mellon University, p. 1.

40. Julius Goldberg, *op. cit.*

41. Lave and Seskin, "Air Pollution and Human Health," *op. cit.*

42. Lave and Seskin, "Air Pollution, Climate and Home Heating," *op. cit.,* pp. 14-19, and appendix tables.

43. Helmut E. Landsberg, "Man-Made Climatic Changes," *Science,* Dec. 18, 1970, p. 1270.

44. Discussion of the city heat island primarily draws on U.S. Environmental Protection Agency, *The Climate of Cities: A Survey of Recent Literature,* by James T. Peterson, Oct. 1969, pp. 7-11.

45. Landsberg, *op. cit.,* p. 1271.

46. R. T. Jaske, J. F. Fletcher and K. R. Wise, "Heat Rejection Requirements of the United States," *Chemical Engineering Progress,* Nov. 1970, p. 21.

47. R. T. Jaske, "Thermal Pollution and Its Treatment," Battelle Memorial Institute paper BNWL-SA-3581, 1970, p. 30.

48. U.S. Environmental Protection Agency, *The Climate of Cities, op. cit.,* p. 16.

49. Helmut E. Landsberg, "City Air—Better or Worse," in *Symposium: Air Over Cities* (U.S. Public Health Service, Taft Sanitary Eng. Center, Cincinnati, Tech. Report A62-5, 1962), p. 13.

50. *Ibid,* p. 11.

51. U.S. Environmental Protection Agency, *The Climate of Cities, op. cit.,* p. 25.

52. *Ibid.,* p. 21.

53. *Ibid.,* pp. 31, 33.

54. Stanley A. Changnon, Jr. "The La Porte Weather Anomaly—Fact or Fiction?" in Thomas R. Detwyler, *Man's Impact on Environment* (New York: McGraw-Hill, 1971), pp. 155-164.

55. Landsberg, "City Air—Better or Worse," *op. cit.,* p. 25.

56. National Academy of Sciences, *Waste Management and Control,* Publication 1400 (Washington, 1966), pp. 12-13, 136, 138, 142-144. Quotation from p. 136.

57. Report on presentation by Abel Wolman at Fifth International Water Quality Symposium, *Public Utilities Fortnightly,* Sept. 24, 1970, p. 44.

58. *Ibid,* p. 45.

59. *Washington Post,* July 29, 1971, p. B1, citing six experts and National Academy of Sciences, *op. cit.,* p. 71.

60. Eric F. Johnson, Executive Director, American Water Works Association, makes a similar inference from the same sort of data, in *Nation's Cities,* September 1970, p. 11.

61. National Academy of Sciences, *op. cit.,* p. 60.

62. *Public Utilities Fortnightly, op. cit.,* p. 44.

63. Paul B. Downing, *The Economics of Urban Sewage Disposal* (New York: Praeger, 1969), pp. 49-54.

64. *Ibid.,* pp. 100-106.

65. Downing's data on capital cost appear as his Table 2, *Ibid.,* p. 25. Table 23 in text contains values for capital plant, exclusive of "ancillary works." The latter equals about 80 percent of plant costs, on average (from source to Table 23). Table 23 values times 1.8 square fairly well with Downing's Table 2 values.

66. Based on estimates derived from Downing's Tables 2, 5, 7, and 16. The latter presents tertiary cost estimates developed by Richard J. Frankel.

67. Reported by David G. Stephan, Federal Water Pollution Control Administration, in *Washington Post,* April 3, 1969, p. 38.

68. U.S. Geological Survey, *Water Data for Metropolitan Areas,* by William J. Schneider, Water-Supply Paper 1871, 1968.

69. *Nation's Cities,* August 1970, pp. 6, 8-9.

70. U.S. Council on Environmental Quality, *op. cit.,* p. 145.

71. National League of Cities, "Statement of Donald G. Alexander before the House Appropriations Committee, May 5, 1971," Appendix A, 1971.

72. The material here drew on useful discussions at the National Academy of Sciences, *op. cit.,* pp. 155-157, 169-170; Roger Starr and James Carlson "Pollution and Poverty: The Strategy of Cross-Commitment," *The Public Interest,* Winter 1968, pp. 116-122 in particular; and U.S. Public Health Service, Division of Water Supply and Pollution Control, *Pollutional Effects of Stormwater Overflows from Combined Sewer Systems,* Nov. 1964.

73. U.S. Public Health Service, *ibid.,* p. 28; U.S. Council on Environmental Quality, *op. cit.,* p. 145; and Starr and Carlson, *ibid.,* p. 122.

74. From comparison of data in U.S. Federal Water Quality Administration, *Municipal Waste Facilities in the United*

States–Statistical Summary, 1968 Inventory, 1970, Tables 5 and 14; and U.S. Bureau of the Census, *U.S. Census of Population, 1960*, Volume I, *Characteristics of the Population*, Part A, *Number of Inhabitants*, 1961, Table 6, pp. 1-12.

75. Luna B. Leopold, "The Hydrologic Effects of Urban Land Use" in Thomas R. Detwyler, *op. cit.*, pp. 205-216. The Leopold paper is extracted from U.S. Geological Survey, "Hydrology for Urban Land Planning," Circular 554, 1968.

76. U.S. Congress, Senate, Committee on Banking and Currency, *Insurance and other Programs for Financial Assistance to Flood Victims*, A Report from the Secretary of Housing and Urban Development to the President, 89th Cong., 2nd sess., 1966, pp. 6, 61, 69.

77. American Chemical Society, *op. cit.*, p. 165.

78. *Ibid.*, p. 167.

79. George Tolley, "Decision Making in Solid Waste Disposal," Report to the U.S. Public Health Service, 1971, III-3.

80. Patricia Conway George, "Solid Waste: America's Neglected Pollutant," *Nation's Cities*, June 1970, p. 14.

81. U.S. Public Health Service, "National Solid Wastes Survey: Report Summary and Interpretation," by Richard D. Vaughn, in *1968 National Survey of Community Solid Waste Practices: An Interim Report*, 1968, p. 47; and National Academy of Sciences, *op. cit.*, p. 14.

82. P. C. George, *op. cit.*, p. 15.

83. The discussion of sanitary landfills draws on American Chemical Society, *op. cit.*, pp. 165-170; National Academy of Sciences, *op. cit.*, pp. 84-86; P. C. George, *op. cit.*, pp. 15-16; George Tolley, "Decision Making in Solid Waste Disposal," *op. cit.*, p. III-11; and Merril Eisenbud, "Environmental Protection in the City of New York," *Science*, November 13, 1970. p. 712.

84. American Chemical Society, *op. cit.*, p. 179–75 percent; American Chemical Society, *Supplement to Cleaning Our Environment* (Washington, 1971), p. 16–80 percent; "Special Report on Solid Wastes," *Environmental Science and Technology*, May 1970, p. 386–80 percent: Arsen J. Darnay, "Throwaway Packages–A Mixed Blessing," *Environmental Science and Technology*, April 1969, p. 328–90 percent.

85. Darnay, *op cit.*, p. 238.

86. U.S. Council on Environmental Quality, *op. cit.*, p. 153.

87. P. C. George, *op. cit.*, p. 15.

88. Tolley, "Decision Making in Solid Waste Disposal," *op. cit.*, pp. VI-8, 10.

89. American Chemical Society, *Cleaning Our Environment, op. cit.*, p. 170.

90. Werner Z. Hirsch, "Cost Functions of an Urban Government Service: Refuse Collection," *The Review of Economics and Statistics*, Feb. 1965, pp. 87-92.

91. Blair Bower and Associates, *op. cit.*, Chart II and discussion, p. 41.

92. P. C. George, *op. cit.*, p. 17.

93. U.S. Bureau of Solid Waste Management, *A Study of Solid Waste Collection Systems Comparing One-Man with Multi-Man Crews, Final Report*, by Ralph Stone and Co., Engineers, Los Angeles, Calif., Solid Waste Management Contract No. PH 86-67-248, 1969, pp. 59-63.

94. P. C. George, *op. cit.*, p. 17.

95. Eisenbud, *op. cit.*, p. 712.

96. "Special Report on Solid Wastes," *op. cit.*, p. 386.

97. American Chemical Society, *Cleaning Our Environment, op. cit.*, p. 170.

98. R. F. Leggett and L. W. Gold, *Snow Removal and Ice Control in Canada* (Ottawa, Ontario: National Research Council of Canada, Division of Building Research, 1965).

99. U.S. Bureau of Mines, *Economics of Recycling Metals and Minerals from Urban Refuse*, by P. M. Sullivan and M. H. Stanczyk, Solid Waste Research Program, Technical Progress Report-33, April 1971; and David Mansman, "Urban Ore: An Untapped Natural Resource," *Washington Post*, July 20, 1971, p. C1.

100. Eisenbud, *op. cit.*, p. 711.

101. Paul H. Banner, presentation at Conference on Urban Commodity Flow, Dec. 7, 1970. See Highway Research Board, *Special Report 120: Urban Commodity Flow* (Washington, 1971).

102. See American Chemical Society, *Cleaning Our Environment, op. cit.*, p. 4; and P. C. George, *op. cit.*, p. 16.

103. John D. Dougherty and Oliver R. Walsh, "Environmental Hazards: Community Noise and Hearing Loss," *New England Journal of Medicine* (Vol. 275, no. 14:759-65), October 6, 1966.

Some useful sources on noise are: U.S. Federal Council for Science and Technology, Committee on Environmental Quality, "Noise-Sound Without Value," in T. R. Detwyler, *Man's Impact on Environment, op. cit.*, p. 178 (from committee final report, same title, Washington, 1968); U.S. Department of Commerce, Report of the Panel on Noise Abatement, *The Noise Around Us*, 1970, p. 35; Vern O. Knudson, "Acoustics: Noise in Our Environment" (paper read at meeting of American Association for Engineering Education), in *Congressional Record*, Oct. 3, 1968, pp. 29529-29530; and Frederick W. Parkhurst, Jr., "Noise, Jets and the Sonic Boom," in *Congressional Record*, Nov. 3, 1967, pp. 31102-31112.

104. Mayor's Task Force on Noise Control, *Toward a Quieter City* (New York, 1970), p. 13.

105. U.S. Environmental Protection Agency, *Report to the President and Congress on Noise* (as required under PL 91-604), Dec. 31, 1971.

106. *Ibid.*, Table 2-1.

107. Some examples: Anthony Bailey, "Noise is a Slow Agent of Deaths," *New York Times Magazine*, Nov. 23, 1969, p. 131; "A New Pollutant 'Chronic Noise Syndrome' Predicted," *Journal of the American Medical Association*, May 5, 1967, p. 35; *Christian Science Monitor*, May 1, 1971, p. 7.

108. U.S. Environmental Protection Agency, *Report to the President and Congress on Noise, op. cit.*, pp. 2-33 to 2-39.

109. U.S. Dept. of Commerce, *Impact of Transportation Noise on Urban Residential Property Values with Special Reference to Aircraft Noise*, by Inja Kim Paik, National Technical Information Service, Document PB 194101, 1970.

110. U.S. Dept. of Commerce, *Transportation System Noise Generation, Propagation and Alleviation*, Ch. 4, by Paul K. Dygert and David L. Sanders, National Technical Information Service, Document PB 196391, 1970, pp. 4-1 to 4-36.

111. M. E. Beesley, "The Value of Time Spent in Travelling: New Evidence," *Economica*, May 1965.

112. Albert Rees and George P. Schultz, *Workers and Wages in an Urban Labor Market* (Chicago: University of Chicago Press, 1970), pp. 11, 169-174.

113. U.S. National Commission on the Causes and Prevention of Violence, *Crimes of Violence Vol. II,* by Donald J. Mulvihill and Melvin M. Tumin, 1969, p. 182.

114. For example, see the President's Commission on Law Enforcement and Administration of Justice, *Task Force Report: Crime and Its Impact—An Assessment* (Washington, 1967), p. 25; Marvin E. Wolfgang, "Urban Crime," in *The Metropolitan Enigma,* James Q. Wilson, ed. (Chamber of Commerce of the U.S., 1967), p. 237; and *ibid.,* pp. 61-63, and Appendix 2. The latter draws on the work of Theodore Ferdinand, stated to be forthcoming in the *British Journal of Criminology.*

115. Crime data from U.S. Federal Bureau of Investigation, *Crime in the United States: Uniform Crime Reports for the United States—1967, 1968.*

116. Robert C. Schmitt, "Density, Health and Social Disorganization," *Journal of the American Institute of Planners,* January 1966, pp. 38-40.

117. Hallinan H. Winsborough, "The Social Consequences of High Population Density," in *Social Demography,* Thomas R. Ford and Gordon F. DeJong, eds. (Englewood Cliffs, N.J.: Prentice-Hall, 1970), pp. 84-90.

118. National Goals Research Staff, *Toward Balanced Growth: Quantity With Quality* (Washington, 1970), pp. 57-60; The National Committee on Urban Growth Policy, "Report of the National Committee," in *The New City,* Donald Canty, ed. (New York: Praeger, for Urban America, Inc., 1969); and Athelstan Spilhaus, "The Experimental City," *Science,* February 1968, pp. 710-11, and *Daedalus,* Fall 1967, pp. 1129-41.

119. A short statement of the Hansen position appears in Niles M. Hansen, "Urban Alternatives for Eliminating Poverty," *Monthly Labor Review,* August 1969, p. 46. Also see Niles M. Hansen, *Rural Poverty and the Urban Crisis; A Strategy for National Development* (Bloomington: Indiana University Press, 1970). Joseph J. Spengler makes the same argument in "Megalopolis: Resource Conserver or Resource Waster?" *Natural Resources Journal,* July 1967, pp. 376-395; pp. 386 and 395, in particular. He advocates taxes on cities at progressively higher rates when a "stipulated size" is exceeded. The article contains a great many citations supporting arguments used in the present paper, e.g., that density increases with urban size, and that increases with money income that occur with size correspond to declines in quality of life. Yet Spengler discerns no equilibrating process at work, and views large urban areas with antipathy as "resource wasters."

120. Dianne Wolman, *op. cit.*

121. Robert A. Dahl, "The City in the Future of Democracy" (Presidential Address, the American Political Science Association), *The American Political Science Review,* Dec. 1967.

122. T. W. Schultz, *The Economic Organization of Agriculture* (New York: McGraw-Hill Book Co., 1953), p. 147; and Wilbur Thompson, "Internal and External Factors in the Development of Urban Economies," in *Issues in Urban Economics,* Harvey S. Perloff and Lowdon Wingo, eds. (Baltimore: Johns Hopkins Press, 1968), pp. 52-57.

123. Allen R. Pred, *The Spatial Dynamics of U.S. Industrial Growth, 1800-1914* (Cambridge: MIT Press, 1966), Chapter 3, pp. 86-142.

124. *Federal Register,* Aug. 14, 1971, Vol. 36, No. 158, p. 15488.

125. *Ibid.,* p. 15490.

126. *Ibid.,* p. 15486.

127. *Federal Register,* April 30, 1971, Vol. 36, No. 84, p. 8187. An initial, somewhat more stringent set of regulations appeared in *Federal Register,* Jan. 30, 1971, Vol. 36, No. 21.

128. *Federal Register,* Aug. 14, 1971, pp. 15501-15502.

129. *Wall Street Journal,* Feb. 1, 1971, p. 2.

130. A number of alternative methods for restricting traffic are discussed in U.S. Environmental Protection Agency, *A Guide for Reducing Automotive Air Pollution,* by Alan M. Voorhees and Assoc., Inc., and Ryckman, Edgerley, Tomlinson, and Assoc., 1971.

131. John Lear, "The Skeleton in the Garage," *Saturday Review,* June 5, 1971, pp. 47-48.

132. From statement by James R. Ellis, cited in *Environmental Science and Technology,* April 1970, p. 278.

133. The Senate water pollution bill passed 86-0 on Nov. 2, 1971, and the House Public Works Committee supported the timing features of the Senate bill in closed hearings in December, 1971. Newspaper accounts of the legislation and related topics appear in: *Washington Post,* 11/3/71, p. A1; 11/20/71, p. A2; 12/8/71, p. A6; 12/10/71, p. A3; and 12/11/71, p. A17; *Wall Street Journal,* 7/6/71, p. 5; 11/10/71, p. 38; 12/17/71, p. 7; and *New York Times,* editorial 11/12/71, p. 44; 11/18/71, p. 22; and 11/23/71, p. 24.

For a critique of the water quality legislation see Ad Hoc Panel to Advise on National Water Quality Problems, "Report to Dr. Edward E. David, Jr." submitted to House Public Works Committee by Office of Science and Technology, Dec. 10, 1971.

134. This point, and some relevant citations, also appear in Ref. 15.

135. The pork barrel tradition of subsidy for local infrastructure is illustrated by an interchange in U.S. Congress, House, Committee on Government Operations, *Water Pollution Control and Abatement, Hearings,* Part 1A—National Survey, 88th Cong., 1st sess., May 1963, pp. 130, 131.

136. E. S. Sayas, "Mass Transfer and Urban Problems," *Science,* Oct. 23, 1971, p. 365.

137. Bower and Associates, *op. cit.,* p. 15.

138. Walter Spofford, "Closing the Gap in Waste Management," *Environmental Science and Technology,* Dec. 1970, pp. 1108-14.

139. James J. Kaufman, "The Legal Aspects of Noise Control," *Congressional Record,* Oct. 29, 1969, pp. 32178 and 32182.

140. U.S. Dept. of Commerce, Panel on Noise Abatement, *op. cit.,* p. 4; and James J. Kaufman, *op. cit.,* p. 32180.

141. Compare Frederick W. Parkhurst, Jr., *op. cit.,* pp. 31106 and 31111; U.S. Congress, House, statement by Congressman Ottinger, 90th Cong., 1st sess., Sept. 27, 1967, *Congressional Record,* pp. 27020; and *New York Times,* Feb. 25, 1970.

142. Section 102 (2) (c) of PL 91-190 calls for preparation of the impact statement. The Council on Environmental Quality has developed guidelines on the preparation of such statements, and a number of Federal agencies have set forth procedures in response. See *Federal Register,* April 23, 1971, and December 11, 1971.

143. Some noise damage awards have been obtained under the act. *New York Times,* Oct. 3, 1971, p. 66.

144. National Academy of Sciences, *op. cit.,* p. 5.

145. Constance Holden, "Le Vaudreuil: French Experiment in Urbanism Without Tears," *Science,* Oct. 1, 1971.

146. U.S. Dept. of Housing and Urban Development, News Release, 7/1/70 and 6/29/71; *Washington Post,* 1/2/72, p. A8.

147. A review of new towns policy and current developments appears in "New Towns U.S.A.," *Resources* (Washington, D.C.: Resources for the Future, January 1972), pp. 19-20.

148. J. Meyer, J. Kain, and M. Wohl, *The Urban Transportation Problem* (Cambridge: Harvard University Press, 1965), p. 340.

149. J. H. Dales, *Population, Property and Prices* (Toronto: University of Toronto Press, 1968).

Chapter 10

Ecological Perspectives

by
Frederick J. Smith
Harvard University

COMMISSION ON POPULATION GROWTH AND
THE AMERICAN FUTURE, *RESEARCH
REPORTS, VOLUME III, POPULATION
RESOURCES AND THE ENVIRONMENT,*
EDITED BY RONALD G. RIDKER

CONTENTS

TABLES

Ecological Perspectives

INTRODUCTION

This paper is speculative and general, being applied to broad, long-term aspects of human ecology. Interrelationships between people and their environments change over time, and change greatly over long periods of time. They will certainly continue to change in the future.

Thirty years of human history, however, is as short for ecology as it appears to be long for economics. In the United States, it is only three years more than the average time between one generation and the next, and it is less than half the life expectancy. Between now and the year 2000, changes in people and in the environment will be relatively small. Under these circumstances, an ecological crisis would be a surprise, unless it already exists, because incremental change can be met with incremental response.

A better perspective can be gained if a longer period is reviewed. The history of population growth in the United States since 1790 (Table 1) is long enough to span several major periods of development and change. A first period of extension was dominated by the spread of our culture over the landscape. The settling of virgin lands, increases in acreage of cropland, and establishment of additional towns accompanied a more or less exponential growth in population. This began well before independence and continued until late in the nineteenth century.

Growth by extension declined rapidly after 1880, and has been a very minor process since 1910. This first "filling up" of the land ended with the first national programs in conservation.

A second period of growth is dominated by intensification—an increase in population density and in demands per unit area of used land. This process was minor before 1850, but has increased to become the only significant process of growth in this century. Growth within a system of fixed size is not the same as growth by extension. Ordinarily, growth becomes increasingly difficult as the constraints of the system tighten. Under any one system of operation, growth against these constraints produces a decrease in individual welfare: Returns to the individual per unit of effort decline as more people share the same resources.

The dual problems of growth by intensification and the maintenance of individual welfare can be solved only by change in the system. In 1900, the land of this country supported 76 million people. It is through profound technological, institutional, and social change that this same land today is able to support 205 million people. By contrast, the effects of inadequate change (or, rather, of population growth without adequate compensatory change) are evident in the deterioration of human welfare that plagued China before 1945, and India before 1965.

Intensification in the United States shows two phases. The first, which lasted until about 1940, was based on a continuation of the same kinds of adjustments that had begun on a much smaller scale in the preceding century. The management of renewable resources was pushed toward higher and higher yields as population demands mounted. This led to over-utilization and a loss of environmental "capital," much as in the ancient civilizations of the Middle East. Overgrazing, overcropping, and the plowing of marginal lands produced extensive soil erosion and culminated in the era of the dustbowl (1931-1938).

Since 1940, the process of change has been much more profound. Increased yields have been coupled with better inputs, and alternative resources have been developed to supplement living resources. The result has been not only a considerable improvement in individual

Table 1.—Population Growth in the United States over Successive 30-Year Periods

Year	Population (millions)	People added (millions)
1790	4	
1820	10	6
1850	23	13
1880	50	27
1910	92	42
1940	132	40
1970	205	73

Source: U.S. Bureau of the Census.

welfare, but the ability to support an additional 73 million people (Table 1).

Although modern technology may have "solved" the problems caused by population growth before 1940, the unprecedented addition of people in the last 30 years has lifted another set of problems to prominence. Among these, urban deterioration and environmental pollution seriously threaten material welfare. These problems are recognized but not solved. Accommodations among life styles, living standards, and population size remain to be worked out.

Under these conditions it is difficult to evaluate expectations of the next 30 years. Increases in population size and in human activity (Table 2) are projected to be nearly as great as those of the last 30 years, or very much greater. They are certain to produce another new set of problems, above and beyond those recognized now.

Recent and projected growth in the world population (Table 3) shows this difficulty to be general. Some areas of the world ran out of new land a long time ago, and only trivial additions have occurred since 1950.[1] Thus, all recent and projected growth must be accommodated primarily by intensification. Modern techniques of industrialized production are developed to very different levels in different countries, with the result that problems of over-utilization of renewable resources are paramount in some countries, and problems of industrial pollution are more urgent in others. Continuing population growth makes all of these problems more serious. It is no surprise that ecologists identify population growth as the major ecological problem.[2] Since 1950, the numbers of people added per decade have been more than twice as large as ever before, and the projected increase for the present decade is even greater.

POPULATION GROWTH, ECONOMIC GROWTH, AND INDIVIDUAL WELFARE

Material welfare has benefited profoundly from the industrial revolution. In their simplest form, these benefits can be estimated in the rising ratio of goods produced per unit of labor input, or man-hour productivity. The use of power driven machinery as a substitute for muscular effort is an unquestioned improvement in life style.

Sometimes, however, the apparent gains from new technology prevent or offset a loss in welfare, rather than offering a real increase. A simple case is the depletion of a nonrenewable resource, for example copper. Technological gains have permitted the use of ores of lower and lower grades without significant changes in the price of the product. These gains have allowed the flow of copper to continue, but have not

Table 2.—Comparisons of Projections for the Next 30 Years with Additions During the Last 30 Years

Comparison	1940 level	Last 30 years 1940-1970	Next thirty years	
			B-H	E-L
People (millions)	132	+73	+116	+61
Farm output (1967=100)	59	+43	+69	+37
Industrial production (1967 index = 100) .	29	+75	+205	+126
Energy output (10^{15}BTU)	24	+45	+151	+96

Data, when available, from Chapters 2, 5, and 7 of this report; additional 1940 estimates from U.S. Bureau of the Census, *Statistical Abstract of the United States.*

Table 3.—Additions to the World Population in Each Decade Since 1900

Decade	People added (millions)
Ending:	
1910	120
1920	132
1930	208
1940	225
1950	222
1960	488
1970	604
1980 (projected)	848

Source: Workshop on Global Ecological Problems, *Man in the Living Environment* (Madison, Wisc.: The Institute of Ecology, 1971).

added a benefit to man that was not there before. Indeed, such changes usually include a larger throughput of energy and/or material, which may have deleterious side effects. In some cases, newer technologies may increase productivity, allowing a decrease in the price of the product, which then gradually reverts to its former level as the average mineral content of ore declines. This is a form of running to stay in place, an important change that allows life to continue unchanged.

A second kind of technological "progress" that offers no increase to individual welfare takes place with population growth by intensification. Since more people .

in the same space doing the same things would suffer a welfare loss, a certain amount of "progress" must be used to offset that loss. The two processes usually go on simultaneously and the relationship is difficult to quantify. The complexities of human systems are such that all kinds of technological change are involved, the same kinds that would improve individual welfare if population growth did not occur. Thus, a better transportation system may shorten commuting time, improving commuter welfare. Increased congestion may erase this gain, translating the increase in individual welfare into the support of more people. Here again, the through-put per capita of materials and energy is generally increased as part of the process.

A third kind is also related to population growth. Some of the most spectacular technological gains in this country are associated with an increased ability to synthesize goods directly from the non-living environment, kinds of goods that used to be available only from living resources. Synthetic fibers in textiles, plastics in furniture and construction, and industrially produced fertilizers are examples of modern supplements to plant and animal products.

The problem here is that the population then outgrows the capacity of living systems to produce the desired volume of products at reasonable costs. Natural supplies are not depleted they become insufficient. Under these conditions, supplementation by industrial synthesis prevents a welfare loss. This permits the support of more people, but their welfare is little different from that of earlier and smaller populations. Certainly, the basis for preferring a nylon sweater and a plastic chair to a woolen sweater and a wooden chair is small, compared with severe shortages of supply.

A distinction between the industrial revolution and the current chemical revolution can be made. By and large, progress in the use of energy and machinery, to the degree that it has increased man-hour productivity, has allowed improvements in human welfare. Progress in the substitution of synthetic materials for natural products, to the degree that it has little effect on productivity, allows the support of more people. It develops a welfare component only in the sense of avoiding a loss because the population outgrew the capacity of natural sources. Admittedly, the distinction is not clean, since these two kinds of processes interact with each other, and exceptions are not difficult to find. Nonetheless, this kind of separation of the gains from technology into additions to individual welfare and support for more people is useful.

Social change also accompanies growth by intensification. At the time our nation was established, life styles were adapted firmly to the pioneering spirit, appropriate for exponential population growth and extension across the land. Self-sufficiency, self-employment, and individual free enterprise offered much of the security and opportunity that shaped individual welfare. The concept of minimal government was practiced. Most people worked for themselves or for relatives in a family business, whether it was a farm, a grocery store, or a skilled craft. This mode of life survived well into the 20th century, and the value placed upon it is still strong.

Among the changes that have followed, and which became necessary if losses in welfare were to be prevented, the most universal and continuing processes include increases in job specialization and increased interdependence among individuals, changes that increase the general complexity of living. The pioneering life style is not adapted to these changes. Most workers are now employed outside their families. Free enterprise is much less available to the individual, becoming primarily a corporate activity. Individualism is practiced less, and collectivism is practiced more.

With these changes, the individual is much less able to provide for his security, and opportunity exists primarily to the extent that training and education meet the demands of alternative careers. Provisions for individual security and opportunity have become societal obligations, institutionalized in many programs of social security and in greatly expanded educational systems. These institutions are expensive; to the extent that they substitute for earlier mechanisms, and prevent losses in welfare, they are part of the cost of population growth.

Advances in medicine have increased individual welfare greatly, especially with respect to such attributes as physical health and life expectancy. Increasingly, however, medical gains offer only potential benefits to individuals. The delivery of health services has become increasingly difficult, and often fails to provide all of the benefits that should be available. Sharply rising costs indicate a welfare loss, a failure of the system to cope with problems arising from increased population densities. The radical changes of recent years have not yet solved this problem.

If all of these changes are considered together, it appears that many of the increases per capita in services and industrial output are related to population growth; only a portion results in a higher standard of living. The substitutions forced by population growth are those that have greater capacities, in the sense of being able to support more individuals at the same average level of welfare. The replacement of individual responsibility with social responsibility, and of natural products with synthetic products, are examples in which earlier sources of satisfaction become insufficient, even though human behavior and living resources have not themselves deteriorated.

Expectation that the total resource demand will increase more rapidly than the population, even if individual welfare is held constant, has been noted earlier.[3] The same applies to such aggregate measures as GNP. Some basis for allocating increases in GNP per capita between the cost of population growth and additions to individual welfare would be instructive. Between 1940 and 1970, GNP per capita in the United States increased 2.4 percent per year, while the population increased 1.5 percent per year. (See Chapter 5.) Since the most rapidly growing sectors of the economy include major substitutions of the kinds discussed above, the portion of the 2.4 percent that was absorbed by population growth cannot be small.

The present ability to produce consumer goods directly from non-living resources has developed primarily in this century, and amounts to a revolution in human ecology. Its significance is as great as that of the industrial revolution, which has been based primarily on the development of non-living resources for energy consumption. The two together will continue to produce high rates of industrial production as part of the process of supporting moderate rates of population growth. Increasing interdependence will continue to force a rapid growth in services. Thus, economic growth and population growth are closely coupled processes.

MAN-MADE WORLD AND NATURE

Primitive man, like any other species, was enmeshed completely in his living environment. Much of human progress is the struggle to break some of those bonds, with many setbacks along the way. Early agriculture assured larger and more dependable supplies of living resources, but problems of soil management and water supply became overwhelming to many civilizations. Early towns and cities offered protection from enemies and encouraged the development of new skills, but exposed people mercilessly to pestilence and disease. The breaking of each bond revealed more bonds, more constraints to population growth. Yet, the cumulative achievements of man have been effective. Modern civilization is a large, growing, self-differentiating system.

The man-made world is managed as an open system intermingled with surrounding natural systems. The advantages of the self-maintaining, self-repairing capacities of natural systems for aesthetics, habitat maintenance, resource renewal, and waste removal have been enormous. But problems have arisen from the free exchange of materials between systems. Local overloads of waste have disturbed natural systems, and various pests and diseases have invaded the man-made world to exploit man, his crops, and his animals. When human populations were small, and the material goods used by man were largely of natural origin, these problems of open systems were small compared with the advantages.

With the very large population increase in this century, the built environment has been vastly expanded. The majority of people now live in places where the man-made world dominates nature. Material inputs and outputs have grown to levels well beyond the self-renewing capacities of nature. Thus, the per capita advantages derived from nature have declined.

At the same time, problems of exchange between the man-made world and nature have increased. The pollution of nature is more general. Problems of waste overload are aggravated by larger inclusions of toxic materials. Totally new compounds become new forces in natural systems, and nondegradable materials accumulate. Whereas pollution formerly led to local losses of amenities and local health hazards, it now adds to these effects a regional and possibly global deterioration of nature.

Problems of pests and diseases have also increased. The list of crop pests now runs to several thousand species, and more are continually appearing. As agricultural industry intensifies, differing more and more from natural systems, more species find in agriculture an escape from the complex bonds of their natural habitats.

The man-made environment deteriorates. Buildings, roads, and most other structures decay or corrode. Lawns, parks, and farmlands revert spontaneously toward the natural condition. No inherent process of recycling removes dirt and debris. Without human intervention, natural systems would gradually invade and replace the man-made world. The per capita burden of effort needed to maintain and repair the man-made world has become very large. It has for many years exceeded actual effort in many urban areas.

Thus, as people become free from natural bonds, and also become more numerous, they acquire greater problems of environmental maintenance. These now extend throughout the man-made and natural worlds. One view of the environmental crisis is that man has taken on more problems than he can manage.[4] Although the magnitude and severity of present problems are difficult to assess, it is certain that further population growth will add to the burden.

With all of its faults, the man-made world is essential to the maintenance of human welfare, and increasingly so as the population grows. Highly industrialized, socialized societies offer material wealth, a diversity of occupation, and an excitement of interaction that are accepted eagerly wherever they become available. Continued development of the man-made world is definitely part of the future.

Natural systems are also essential to human welfare, providing man with many benefits.[5] They maintain the habitability of the planet, especially with respect to the composition of the atmosphere. They produce most of the fish yields that now average, globally, about 40 pounds of fish per person per year.[6] They provide biological control for most of the potential pests of forests and grasslands. They modify regional climate; the air-conditioning accomplished by vegetation is several orders of magnitude greater than human efforts. They prevent flash floods and erosion, create a more continuous flow of water in rivers, and produce the highest quality of water for domestic use.

Natural systems offer aesthetic benefits. As a source of beauty, fascination, relaxation, and recreation, nature is unexcelled. Nature has inspired many of the best creations in poetry, music, and art. The value placed upon contact with nature increases as more and more of human life is surrounded by the man-made world. The continued ability of natural systems to provide these various benefits is intended to be part of the future.

Continuing development of man-made systems and continuing function of natural systems have become more difficult to achieve. As the former changes qualitatively and quantitatively, differing more and more from nature, exchanges between them become more disrupting. The time will arrive when the man-made world can no longer be managed as an open system. Enclosing portions will be a simpler solution. As discussed in the next section, some aspects of agriculture may already be at this point; isolating them in vast greenhouses may offer better solutions to pest control and pollution abatement. The domed city is another example of a closed system that may soon be needed.

A mixed pattern of closed systems for intensely industrialized activities and open systems for more relaxed activities may permit large populations to enjoy the best of both worlds, just as small populations are able to do without using closed systems. The larger the population, the fewer the activities that can safely be allowed "outdoors."

If changes of these kinds are not accomplished, population growth will lead to the progressive deterioration and elimination of nature. This has long been happening on a local scale. As pavement spreads in cities, the trees become weakened, diseased, ugly, and are finally removed. New trees fail to survive, and soon the area is treeless—better looking without broken, dead limbs. Ponds and streams attract development, which eventually fouls the water. But many suburban ponds have been filled, and many streams covered over to become sewers. Natural systems rapidly lose attractive-

ness as they deteriorate, often becoming noisome sources of pests. The final stage of elimination is often not mourned.

So far, severe environmental deterioration has been local, and disturbance of the vast ecological systems that dominate the planet has been slight.[7] Should large-scale deterioration become severe, however, the entire planet will take on the unwanted characteristics of the man-made world: It will deteriorate in all of its aspects unless prevented by human effort. This would be an inevitable result if the population succeeded in growing large enough.

At population levels far short of such global saturation, nature can remain vigorous and useful if changes such as the development of closed systems are made. The effect is not an improvement to human welfare, but the prevention of a loss due to population crowding. The advantages will not even prevent a loss in welfare if they are used instead to support more people—unless more changes are made, such as restricting more activities to closed systems. This cycle of growth and change, as in the previous section of the chapter, can be continued for a long time.

IMPLICATIONS OF GROWTH PROJECTIONS

In the preceding sections, perspectives were developed in which population growth influences the style of living, and continues to do so no matter how many adjustments have been made to accommodate earlier population growth. To the degree that change is endless, it is difficult to imagine a "maximum population size" unless it is conditional upon a defined life style. It is simpler, and perhaps more useful, to identify the sequence of constraints to human activity that is forced by population growth, beginning at population levels lower than the present (history) and continuing into levels that are considerably higher (projection). Such a task is well beyond the capacities of an individual, but would be feasible for a working group of appropriate specialists.

Speculations that a portion of per capita economic growth is required to support population growth, and that only the remainder can contribute to a net increase in individual welfare, lead to further interpretations of the model output presented in Chapter 2. It is still assumed that per capita gains in GNP, disposable income, and other aggregates are useful measures of potential contributions to human welfare, but it has not previously been assumed that population growth with a constant per capita GNP diminishes individual welfare. The portion of per capita gains absorbed by population growth is unknown. It must have been very small in the

19th century, when population growth was accompanied by extension, rising more rapidly with the shift toward growth by intensification. Concepts of environmental resistance, and the equivalent concept of diminishing returns, suggest that a larger and larger and larger allocation is needed as population growth continues.

Let us suppose, as an arbitrary decision, that the present population level is one that requires a rate of increase in GNP per capita that is two-thirds the population growth rate, if losses in welfare are to be prevented. Table 4 shows the resulting estimates of potential gains to individual welfare under the four projections of the study. The difference between the Series B and E projections becomes large, so much so that the welfare components of B-H (high rates of population and per capita economic growth) and of E-L (low rates of population and per capita economic growth) are alike.

Since this relationship may be significant, a major study to define it more clearly and quantitatively would greatly improve our perceptions of the relations between population growth and economic growth.

Modern Agriculture

Since 1940, agriculture has become a rapidly evolving system. The industrial production of fertilizers and synthetic pesticides, the mechanization of husbandry, and new achievements in breeding (such as the development of hybrid varieties) have been combined in an integrated technology whose potential for agricultural production is well ahead of demand. The historical effect is profound. Between 1920 and 1940, crop output

per acre changed very little. Since 1940, it has increased with an average annual growth rate of 1.9 percent.[8] The yields of meat and other livestock products per unit of livestock (including poultry) have also increased.

With these changes the production process has become more like that in other industries, in which output is dependent primarily on input, and less like a system in which output depends strongly upon self-renewing resources. Before this century, very little went into the land (except sunlight, carbon dioxide, and water) that did not previously come from that land (namely, seed, manure, mulch, horsepower, and human labor). Today, much less of the input (seed, fertilizer, pesticides, mechanized power, etc.) comes from a previous harvest. To a considerable degree, the biological processes of production are cogs in an industrial machine, managed for much higher rates of production than were possible when they were managed as renewable resources.

Greater yields can be achieved with further increases in the various inputs, and feeding the population of the United States through the year 2000 is not a critical issue under any of the projections. Several problems that exist now, or that may arise in the near future, can be alleviated with changes in management practice and in the mix of inputs, as discussed in the section on policy implications in Chapter 7.

There remain, however, some issues of major concern in relation to the long-term development of industrialized agriculture. It is still managed as an open system, it occupies very large acreages, and it is increasingly different from the interspersed and surrounding natural systems. Two areas emerge in which problems may become very difficult to control: pollution and pest control.

The use of fertilizers has increased very rapidly. Agricultural inputs of primary nutrients (N, P_2O_5, K_2O) in the United States rose from four million tons in 1950 to seven in 1960 and 14 in 1970.[9] The use of nitrogen fertilizers increased from one to more than six million tons within this period. Thus, in most places the history of heavy use is not only relative short, but one of continuing rapid increase. The side effects of intense fertilization are poorly known. For a variety of physical and biological reasons, nitrogen fertilizers pose the greatest pollution threat.[10]

In some areas, but not others, pollution of waterways has been observed. (See Chapter 7.) The direct loss of nitrates by leaching from the soil to surface water or groundwater can be monitored; but in fact, the number of such efforts over a series of years at the same sites has been small. A variety of such programs are now in progress.

Table 4.—Allocation of Rates of Increase in GNP Per Capita to the Prevention of Losses in Welfare Due to Population Growth, and to Net Increases in Individual Welfare. (Allocation assumes arbitrarily that the former is equal to two-thirds the population growth rate.)

Annual percentage growth rate	B-H	E-H	B-L	E-L
Gross National Product	3.9%	3.7%	3.1%	2.9%
Population	1.5	0.9	1.5	0.9
GNP/Capita	2.4	2.8	1.6	2.0
Offset losses from population growth	1.0	0.6	1.0	0.6
Net potential gains to individual welfare	1.4	2.2	0.6	1.4

Source: Chapter 2.

Population, Resources, and the Environment

The longer-term effects of high fertilizer levels on the microflora of the soil, soil organic matter, and the future ability of soil to hold fertilizers, are also poorly known. In Britain, which has one of the most intensive farming systems in the world, evidence is appearing that increased production no longer follows increased inputs; and, for some products, the yields have begun to decline. Soil structure appears to be deteriorating.[11] Some of the most desirable characteristics of soil (ability to hold water and to bind ions, loosely enough to prevent loss and yet allow roots to take them up) are biological products of decomposition, a process likely to be affected by chemical fertilizers.

For these reasons, judgment on the side effects of present levels of fertilizer use is impossible. Soil deterioration and regional water contamination are possibilities, and their probabilities will increase with increased levels of fertilizer use.

Pest control has a greater probability of becoming a serious problem. The first pesticides used in large amounts were general poisons, compounds of lead, arsenic, copper, etc. These were harmful to people and other life as well as to the pest, and had to be used carefully. They were followed after World War II by a rapidly growing list of synthetic organic compounds, much more powerful and specific in their action, in the sense that they are more toxic to the target and less toxic to many other organisms than their predecessors. A third generation of pesticides based on the target's biochemical idiosyncracies, and still more specific in action than their predecessors, is now being developed.

The use of more specific pesticides, however, has brought with it a new problem: pest resistance. By hindsight, it is easy to predict: Since all organisms operate with much the same biochemical machinery, resistance should develop more easily to a chemical that is much less toxic to other organisms, than to a chemical that is strongly toxic to everything. Only 10 cases of pesticide resistance were recognized before 1940. There were 60 in 1958 and over 200 in 1967.[12] These arise from genetic change (evolution) in the pest populations. It is impossible to achieve a 100 percent kill, and among the survivors are those happening to have more resistance. The use of pesticides selectively breeds strains of pests that are resistant, if the genetic potential for resistance is present.

The usual response to resistance is to change pesticides. The use of DDT in this country is declining primarily because an increasing number of target species have become immune. Thousands of pesticides are available for use, but choosing another one has a complication. Many pesticides are chemically similar, so much so that resistance to one commonly confers

resistance (sometimes less, sometimes more) to others.[13]

Among the modern insecticides, four chemical families can be recognized: (1) DDT and its relatives, (2) dieldrin and its relatives, (3) organophosphorus compounds, and (4) carbamates.[14] Cross-resistance is common within members of each family, much less common between families. Multiple resistance has also appeared; and, in the laboratory, a strain of boll weevils has become immune to all four chemical groups.[15]

The effect of this is that new families of pesticides will be needed periodically as the utility of the old ones fails. Here a squeeze is developing: New pesticides harmful to a broad spectrum of organisms will not be approved for use, and those with a narrow target are not likely to be useful for very long (a short useful life of third generation pesticides can be predicted). The problem becomes critical when choices have to be made between pesticides that are not safe and pesticides that are not adequate.

The general problem of pesticide pollution will not be reviewed here. Environmental consequences of using persistent pesticides are familiar to all. To these effects, resistant pests add another. Loaded up with the pesticide to which they are resistant, they can become a lethal food for their natural enemies.[16]

The movement of potential pests into agricultural systems, and the movement of nutrients and pesticides out, are problems that result from the open boundaries between agricultural and natural systems. A quantum jump in agricultural technology would be to close these boundaries.[17] Nutrients would no longer be able to leak out and pollute natural waters. Pests would no longer be able to wander in and out. High doses of strong pesticides could be used inside to achieve complete control (100 percent kill), preventing the development of resistance. The ecological balance of natural systems, including biological control of potential pest species, would be unimpaired.

Other benefits could be realized. Most, perhaps 80 percent of the phosphate fertilizers presently being used is lost in place, bound in insoluble salts of iron and aluminum.[18] Unless more is added each growing season, the levels of available phosphate decline rapidly to maximal "natural" levels, well below those needed for present levels of production. Since phosphate ores are limited, and phosphate is essential to life, this ecological waste of a resource will not be appreciated by future generations. If sand or water were used instead of soil, the problem of phosphate binding could be reduced greatly. Erosional loss would be eliminated.

Water requirements would be reduced. Not only does wind exclusion reduce evaporation, but water that is transpired (through the plants) or evaporated could be condensed and recycled. Closed systems could be located in more arid regions where more sunshine is found, freeing the more humid regions for other uses. If enclosed systems were heated, several crops a year could be grown in temperate regions.

Altogether, benefits from the development of closed agricultural systems would be very great. Large acreages of greenhouse agriculture already exist, especially to produce vegetables in the southwest where water conservation is critical. Many of the technological components of hydroponic agriculture have been developed, but large-scale implementation appears to be well in the future because of currently very high costs. Other variants may also be useful, such as isolating the below-ground area to prevent water loss and nutrient leaching, or recycling the stream outflow, where these are the only serious problems.

In addition to support for research on the improvement of present-day agriculture, a well-supported long-term program to develop closed-system agriculture would be a profoundly significant investment in the future.

Forestry

For the last 15 years, forest production has increased slowly (Table 5), both in the United States and in the world. Within the United States, the volume of manufacture of lumber has changed little since 1953, when the production of pulp has more than doubled.[19] Net imports for the period 1963-68 changed little.[20]

Any large increase in the demand for forest products will force major changes in forest practice. Fischman and Landsberg have noted this problem; they recommended a number of measures that could be taken to match demand with supply. (See Chapter 4.)

To an ecologist, a major issue concerns whether forestry adopts the intensive practices of agriculture, complete with fertilizers and pesticides. Intensive forestry already exists on relatively small acreages, and a sharp increase in demand would tend to increase this trend. Large acreages of forests will be managed more like agriculture. Forests contain hundreds of thousands of potential pest insect species whose gradual release from biological control would create problems considerably greater than those in agriculture.[21] Most forest management is directed toward sustained yields from a renewable resource, with minimal inputs. These are the forests that require the least amount of pesticide, best conserve the soil, and produce the highest quality of water.

A burst of "catch-up" construction in this century could be accommodated with a sufficient amount of

Table 5.—Annual Percentage Increases in Yield from Agriculture, Forestry, and Fisheries, Compared with Population Growth. (Data for the period 1953-1968.)

	Population	Agriculture	Forestry	Fisheries
United States . . .	1.5%	1.7%	1.3%	−0.6%
World	1.8	2.7	1.6	6.0

Source: United Nations, *Statistical Yearbook,* 1969.

product substitution. More plywood and particle boards would use more of the tree; plastics, aluminum, and other materials can be substituted; and more forest products can be recycled. If population growth follows the Series E projection, most of the forests could continue to be managed as renewable resources. If population growth follows the Series B projection, either we will substitute plastics and metals on a larger scale than the model contemplates, or demands for forest products will eventually exceed the capacity of this form of management.

The industrialization of forestry is presently encouraged, when it should be deterred. The existence of forests as agents of climatic modification, creators of aesthetic pleasures, and producers of clean water is more valuable to society than the value of its products.[22] These roles are best served if forests are managed as renewable resources, from which the yield is not inconsiderable.

Fisheries

The harvest of fish has declined slowly in the United States (Table 5), but increased rapidly for the world as a whole. Although United States production is down, net imports are up.[23] The United States is the largest importer of fish meal, and also imports a variety of other fish products. Total consumption, expressed as the original fresh weight of the fish, is about 70 lbs. per person per year. This is 75 percent higher than the world average. The larger part is used as a feed supplement (substituting for more than two million acres of soybeans); direct human consumption accounts for less than a third of the total.

World catches have increased from 29 million tons in 1953 to 70 million tons in 1968.[24] Much of the increase is due to the development of new fisheries (growth by extension). Increases in catch from the developed fisheries have been accomplished with large increases in gear and equipment (growth by intensification).[25] From an analysis of potential fisheries that remain to be developed, and those that are already maximally harvested, world catches of as high as 110 million tons may be possible on a sustained yield basis.[26] This is a large and significant source of protein in world nutrition.

The critical problem with marine fisheries is their protection. Most fisheries are near land, and the life cycles of a majority of the commercial species are linked with the coastal zone, especially the estuaries. Nutrient enrichment, a problem in many freshwaters, is not known to be detrimental to marine production. At present levels, it probably stimulates production. Toxic wastes, however, have excluded many species from many areas. Dredging and filling have destroyed many environments. Food-chain accumulations of materials harmful to man have made some stocks inedible.[27]

Commerce, industry, and recreation make heavy demands upon the coastline and adjacent rivers. Conflicts between incompatible developments of the coast are as frequent as conflicts between development and protection of the marine environment. If present trends continue, marine shipping will double twice more before the end of the century.[28] Survival of the fisheries is already judged to be critical;[29] so, unless major policy changes in coastal development are implemented soon, the difference between the Series B and E projections of population growth may be academic.

Overfishing is a second threat. Catch-per-unit-effort is declining in many of the developed fisheries, and high yields are maintained by greater uses of capital and power.[30] Several fish stocks have declined greatly, probably through a combination of fishing pressure and natural events. When fish recruitment fails from natural causes, continued intense fishing prevents recovery; the next period of unfavorable conditions produces a further decline. The demand for protein is already so great that many nations compete in each of the major fisheries, making their management for sustained yield virtually impossible to implement.

Fish farming (managed production in enclosed areas) produces about three million tons of fish annually. This can be increased by the year 2000 to 30 million tons without large increases in acreage.[31] Unless more protein is produced from fish farming, or from crops such as soybeans, overfishing seems inevitable. Obviously, the problem is greater if the population grows rapidly than if it grows slowly; but, it remains insurmountable if adequate protein is planned for the present world population. Loss of the marine fisheries would be equivalent to losing about half of the world meat production.[32]

Amenities

Limitations of water supplies (Chapter 8) and crowding in recreation areas (Chapter 6) describe trade-offs between population size and amenity aspects of environmental quality. Perhaps the most serious effect is that lower-income groups will lose the most.

Projected increased costs of water resulting from population growth will reduce many uses of water: less use for lawns, gardens, swimming pools, air conditioners, fountains, etc. The combined effects of individual and municipal responses to rising water costs will be to surround inner-city people with fewer amenities that consume water. The full value of these amenities should not be underestimated. The lavish display of pools and fountains in desert cities moderates the hot dry air as well as providing visual delights. Evaporative air conditioners in the southwest add moisture to dry air; their substitutes will add heat to hot air. Urban vegetation plays a considerable role in evaporative cooling;[33] the summer coolness of trees and grass uses a lot of water. Urban trees offer sunshade and windbrake, and lawns are efficient, self-cleaning dust-traps. Vegetation that is not watered plentifully is less vigorous and more susceptible to disease. It is not only less pleasing to the eye, but less able to ameliorate the climate. Finally, dry dusty neighborhoods compare poorly with green neighborhoods at any economic level of life.

Amenity benefits from outdoor recreation areas decline as areas of high quality become more expensive, and inexpensive areas become more congested. Increasing distance to satisfying areas adds to these losses. The amenity loss from overuse is just as severe in a city park where grass, if it is to survive, must be barred from use, as it is in a national park where the natural vegetation and wildlife, if they are to survive, must be fenced against trespass. Letting the grass die, and the natural systems deteriorate, are also amenity losses.

In both of these problems, amenity losses will be greater among the lower-income groups. These will be added to other components of environmental quality that are distributed unequally. The distribution of people, pollution, and urban decay (Chapter 9) assures that urban amenity losses are concentrated among the poor. Any component of individual welfare that has an economic value will be distributed this way (it is the definition of rich versus poor), and this fact is not the focus of discussion. Rather, it is the relative magnitude of free and purchased benefits that is the issue.

Assume that income has risen at all levels of income, at similar percentage growth rates for all levels, over the last 20 years. The distribution of welfare in the population may not appear to have changed much. But income, and purchased benefits, adds to free benefits. If these have been declining, the spread of welfare in the population has been increasing. Since free benefits have been declining, it is entirely possible that the individual welfare of lower-income groups has been declining while the average of the whole population has been increasing. This study suggests that the spread will continue to increase, more rapidly under the Series B than under the Series E projection. The successive losses of free benefits can be balanced only by a correspondingly more equable distribution of income. The relationship involved between population growth and individual welfare is similar to those discussed in section two of this paper.

As stated in Chapter 1 the principal conclusions of this study are that we can find solutions to the problems generated by future population growth if we have to, but that we will not like many of the social and institutional consequences of these solutions. As an ecologist, I would go somewhat further. Before we find solutions to problems of future population growth, we must find solutions to the problems of past population growth; we will not like many of the social and institutional consequences of these solutions either.

REFERENCES

1. Study of Critical Environmental Problems (SCEP), *Man's Impact on the Global Environment* (Cambridge, Mass.: MIT Press, 1970).

2. Workshop on Global Ecological Problems, *Man in the Living Environment* (Madison, Wisc.: The Institute of Ecology, 1971).

3. *Ibid.* and SCEP, *op. cit.*

4. SCEP, *op. cit.*

5. *Ibid.*

6. Workshop on Global Ecological Problems, *op. cit.s,*

7. SCEP, *op. cit.*

8. U.S. Dept. of Agriculture, *Changes in Farm Production and Efficiency,* Statistical Bulletin 233, 1964 and 1970.

9. U.S. Dept. of Agriculture, *Consumption of Commercial Fertilizers, Primary Plant Nutrients, and Micronutrients,* Statistical Bulletin 472, 1971; and Statistical Reporting Service, Crop Reporting Board, *Commercial Fertilizers, Consumption in the United States,* 1970 and 1971.

10. American Chemical Society, *Cleaning Our Environment: The Chemical Basis for Action* (Washington, 1969).

11. "A Blueprint for Survival," *The Ecologist,* 1972, Vol. 2, No. 1, pp. 1-42.

12. G. R. Conway, "Better Methods of Pest Control," in *Environment, Resources, Pollution, and Society,* W. W. Murdoch, ed. (Stanford, Conn.: Sinauer Assoc., Inc., 1971).

13. *Ibid.*

14. *Ibid.*

15. Workshop on Global Ecological Problems, *op. cit.*

16. G. R. Conway, *op. cit.*

17. Workshop on Global Ecological Problems, *op. cit.*

18. *Ibid.*

19. United Nations, *Statistical Yearbook,* 1969.

20. Food and Agriculture Organization (FAD), *Trade Yearbook,* 1969.

21. Workshop on Global Ecological Problems, *op. cit.*

22. F. E. Smith, "Ecological Demand and Environmental Response," *Journal of Forestry,* December 1970, Vol. 68.

23. FAO, *op. cit.*

24. United Nations, *op. cit.*

25. Workshop on Global Ecological Problems, *op. cit.*

26. *Ibid.*

27. *Ibid.*

28. United Nations, *op. cit.*

29. Workshop on Global Ecological Problems, *op. cit.*

30. *Ibid.*

31. *Ibid.*

32. *Ibid.,* and United Nations, *op. cit.*

33. *Symposium on the Role of Trees in the South's Urban Environment* (Athens, Georgia: University of Georgia Center for Continuing Education, 1971.)

Chapter 11

The Model

by
H. W. Herzog, Jr. and
Ronald G. Ridker
Resources for the Future Inc.

COMMISSION ON POPULATION GROWTH AND
THE AMERICAN FUTURE, *RESEARCH
REPORTS, VOLUME III, POPULATION
RESOURCES AND THE ENVIRONMENT,*
EDITED BY RONALD G. RIDKER

CONTENTS

FIGURES

The Model

This chapter describes the model developed by Resources for the Future to project economic activity, resource requirements, and pollution loadings, nationally and regionally, out to the year 2000, and in some instances beyond. While Chapter 2 introduced this model in terms of its general framework and assumptions, here we outline the structural relationships involved and indicate the way in which they were employed for the purposes of projection and policy simulation.

The core of this model is the 185 sector University of Maryland Interindustry Forecasting Model developed and maintained by Clopper Almon and the staff of the Interindustry Forecasting Project at the University of Maryland. We are indebted to Dr. Almon and his staff for providing Resources for the Future with this model and for help in understanding its intricacies. This core was modified and added to in a number of ways to be discussed in more detail below. Suffice it to say here that these modifications involved extension of the time horizon from 1980 to the year 2020, modifications to make the model more sensitive to demographic changes, the introduction of a mechanism to permit changes in technology on a sector-by-sector basis, and the internalization of the public component of final demand, treated as an exogenous input in the original model.

In addition, a number of subsidiary models were developed. The complete package, which, for convenience, we shall refer to as the RFF model, is presented schematically in Figure 1. In contrast to the more general conceptual layout presented in Chapter 2, this figure is organized on a computational basis, the arrows representing flows of information provided by one stage or sub-model to another. The organization of this chapter, as well as Chapter 12, follows from this figure, some segments receiving more attention than others. Several important components, or sub-models, were developed for RFF by International Research and Technology Corporation and are presented in detail in Chapter 12. References are provided to Maryland Interindustry Forecasting Project documents for segments within the input-output model that have not been altered by RFF.

THE CORE MODEL

The core model may be described in static terms using standard input-output equations,

$$AX + Y = X \qquad (1)$$

where:

X = column vector (185×1) of total outputs
Y = column vector (185×1) of final demands
A = 185 order matrix of input-output coefficients $a_{ij} \geqslant 0$, where a_{ij} = million dollars of purchases by industry j from industry i required per million dollars of total output produced in industry j.

Given a forecast of final demand, Y, and the satisfaction of the usual input-output theorems such that $|\, I - A\, | \neq 0$, then

$$X = (I - A)^{-1} Y \qquad (2)$$

All outputs and final demands are forecast in constant 1967 dollars, 1967 being the base year of the model.

The model is linked to time in a number of important ways. First, it is recursive, requiring some prior year projections to obtain future year projections. For this reason, the model moves forward a year at a time, a projection to the year 2000 requiring 34 iterations. Second, technical change is handled explicitly by allowing the technical coefficients, a_{ij}, to change over time (see Chapter 12). Thus, the linear relationship that links total output to final demand is itself a function of time. Third, the equations that predict sectoral personal consumption expenditures as a function of several independent variables each contain two shift coefficients that alter the relative importance of these variables over time. The degree to which these coefficients operate at the sector level is dependent on several demographic characteristics of families.

The exogenous information required by the core model defines the scenario under consideration. In general, this information consists of projected values for future years for each of the following: disposable

FIGURE 11-1
SCHEMATIC OUTLINE OF RFF MODEL

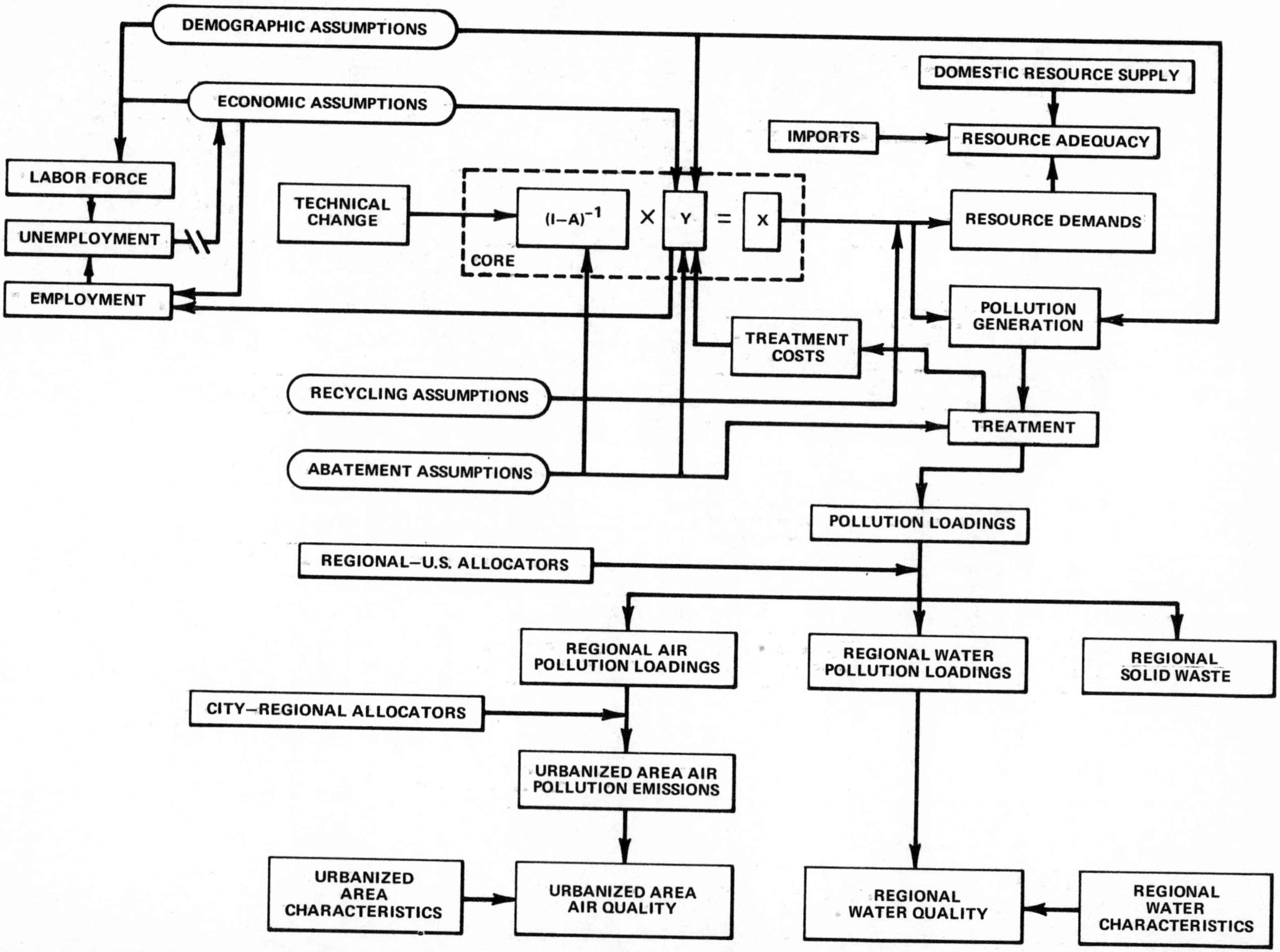

income per capita, population, school age population, labor force, and number of households and their distribution by age of head and size. All but the first of these exogenous inputs to the model are defined by the particular population series projection selected for consideration. Once such a series has been selected, various time streams of disposable income per capita may be chosen to reflect alternative levels of individual well-being to include, besides the monetary measure, preferences for leisure. The choice of an appropriate time stream for per capita income is also dependent upon assumptions about growth in labor productivity and acceptable unemployment rates. Final choice of a time stream for this variable, as well as for a number of public expenditure variables, must be made on a trial and error basis, the aim being to obtain a satisfactory unemployment rate. This will be more fully explained below under the section addressed to policy simulation.

As Figure 1 indicates, this exogenous information influences the model through its effect on sectoral final demands. For example, disposable income per capita, population size, and household characteristics determine the total level and relative distribution of personal consumption expenditures. The final demand vector, Y, in Figure 1, is the summation over a number of vectors, each representing a different category of final demand. The forecasting method for the sectoral values of these vectors is specific to each category of final demand. For this reason, the projection technique for each component of final demand will be given individual attention in the section that follows.

PROJECTION OF FINAL DEMANDS
Personal Consumption Expenditures

Personal consumption expenditures are important not only because of their magnitude—in 1970 they accounted for 63 percent of GNP—but also because they provide one of the key linkages between changes in demographic characteristics and the resource and environmental consequences of these changes.

The Maryland input-output model identifies some 126 items of personal consumption and provides an equation for each.[1] These equations take the general form,

$$c_{it} = \hat{b}_{i0} + b_{i1} Y_t + \hat{b}_{i2} p_{it} + \hat{b}_{i3} t + \hat{b}_{i4} \Delta Y_t \quad (3)$$

$$C_{it} = c_{it} P_t \quad (4)$$

where the subscripts i and t represent sector number and time respectively, and:

c = per capita consumption
C = total consumption

Y = disposable per capita income
ΔY_t = $Y_t - Y_{t-1}$
p = price index for the sector relative to the overall price index for all sectors combined
P = population
t = time in years,

$\left.\begin{array}{l}\hat{b}_0, \\ \hat{b}_2, \\ \hat{b}_3, \\ \hat{b}_4,\end{array}\right\}$ = parameters estimated by regressions, and

b_1 = parameter estimated algebraically

To minimize changes in the original model, we retained the general form of these equations but "conditioned" them to reflect changing family demographic characteristics.

All equations were re-estimated using the same personal consumption time series information as in the Maryland model but more detailed cross-section expenditure data. The parameter b_{i1}, the marginal propensity to spend on good i out of disposable income, was algebraically determined from two cross-section consumption expenditure surveys.[2] Because the classification of consumption expenditures in these surveys did not perfectly match those under the input-output sectoral definition, a method was developed to make the assignment under a strict set of correspondence rules.[3]

The consumption expenditures in the surveys were grouped into three-way distributions indexed by family size, age of head of family, and total consumption expenditure. For any two-way classification by age of head and family size, a total expenditure elasticity may be computed. For any particular consumption item, this elasticity measures the percent change in expenditures on that item as total expenditures on all items increase by one percent, family size and age of head remaining unchanged. If this procedure is repeated for all demographic groupings and the resulting elasticities weighted by the relative occurrence of families in each grouping in the base year, 1961, an average expenditure elasticity results.[4] Expenditure elasticities were computed for 90 categories of consumption items, each averaged over nine family size groupings, and seven age of head groupings.

The parameters b_{i1} in equation (3) were derived from the total expenditure elasticities, n_i^o, as follows:

$$b_{i1} = n_i^o \left(\frac{c_{it}}{Y_t}\right) \qquad t = 1961 \quad (5)$$

Thus, the cross-section consumption surveys were employed to provide information relevant to the pattern and not the levels of personal consumption expenditures. A time series regression covering the period 1958 through 1969 was then performed for each input-output consumption expenditure category. The dependent variable in each case was that portion of consumption not explained by income:

Regression:

$$z_{it} = \hat{b}_{i0} + \hat{b}_{i2}p_{it} + \hat{b}_{i3}t + \hat{b}_{i4}\Delta Y_t \qquad (6)$$

Subject to:

$$|\hat{b}_{i4}| \leqslant \hat{b}_{i1} \text{ if } \hat{b}_{i4} \leqslant 0 \qquad (7)$$

Where:

$$z_{it} = c_{it} - b_{i1}Y_t \qquad (8)$$

As the equations stand, the only demographic linkage is provided by the total population variable, P_t, a strict multiplier to per capita consumption in equation (4). A certain amount of demographic influence could possibly enter through the taste change parameters, $\hat{b}_{i3}$; however, one would suspect that the short period over which the regressions were performed would impart very little, if any, of this influence to the regression estimates. Thus, at this point, the estimated forecasting equations for per capita consumption are, for all practical purposes, "demographic-neutral."

The required demographic linkage is provided by a reweighting procedure on the cross-section expenditure survey data. For each population projection for the year 2000, a two-way distribution of families by age of family head and size was developed, and used to generate new total expenditure elasticities for the 126 consumption forecasting equations.

However, it is not these new elasticities, but the components that determine them, that will be employed as "shift parameters" in a modified version of equation (3). Graphs such as that in Figure 2 can be constructed from the cross-section expenditure data for any particular item of consumption i. The two relationships that are plotted reflect how much of good i is consumed, on a per capita basis, at different levels of total expenditure. The line marked "base" is the relationship determined from the cross-section information using the actual family characteristics existing in the base year. The other line marked "scenario K," is the relationship obtained under the reweighting technique already mentioned.

The total expenditure elasticity, n_i^o, employed in equation (5), is the ratio of the marginal to average propensities to spent on good i, computed using the base period weights. In Figure 2, this elasticity may be represented as:

$$n_i^o = \frac{c_o - c^*_o}{\bar{\epsilon}} \Big/ \frac{c_o}{\bar{\epsilon}} \qquad (9)$$

$$n_i^o = \frac{c_o - c^*_o}{c_o} \qquad (9')$$

where $\bar{\epsilon}$ is the average total expenditure on all goods. In a like manner, the total expenditure elasticity characterizing scenario K may be represented by:

$$n_i^k = \frac{c_k - c^*_k}{c_k} \qquad (10)$$

In order to capture the character of the shift portrayed in Figure 2, two adjustments, or shift parameters, have been introduced. The first involves the rotation of the base line about the fixed intercept point, c^*_o, or a change in the manner in which individuals spend on good i out of increased (or decreased) income (total expenditures). If scenario K is representative of the year 2000, and the rotation is assumed to begin in 1970 and apply equally over the 31 year period, then for any year t^*, the new income parameter is equal to:

$$b_{i1} + t^*\delta_i \qquad t^* = 0 \text{ in } 1969 \qquad (11)$$

where:

$$\delta_i = \frac{n_i^k - n_i^o}{31}\left(\frac{c_{it}}{Y_t}\right) \qquad t = 1961 \qquad (12)$$

FIGURE 11-2

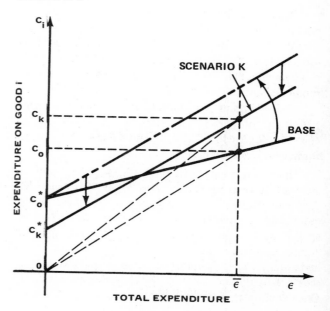

The second adjustment to equation (3) involves a shift downward (or upward) in the base line, once rotated, in Figure 2. This shift in intercept from c_o^* to c_k^* is interpreted, irrespective of the direction or magnitude of the first type of adjustment, as a change in the relative importance of non-income factors in determining the level of consumption of good i. Like the first shifter, this adjustment will be applied to equation (3) in 31 equal increments. It will be entered as a percentage change in cross-section intercept to the non-income determinants of per capita consumption. Thus, for any year t*, this second shift parameter is equal to:

$$1 + t^* \phi_i \qquad t^* = 0 \text{ in } 1969 \qquad (13)$$

where:

$$\phi_i = \frac{(c_k^* - c_o^*)/c_o^*}{31} \qquad (14)$$

Because of the length of the projection period, the private savings rate, s, was entered in an explicit manner as a control on the total personal consumption expenditures over the forecast period. Equations (3) and (4) may now be restated to include all of the above refinements.[5]

$$C_{it}^* = v_t C_{it} \qquad (15)$$

where:

$$C_{it} = \left\{ (b_{i1} + t^* \delta_i) Y_t + (1 + t^* \phi_i)[\hat{b}_{i0} + \hat{b}_{i2} p_{it} \right.$$
$$\left. + \hat{b}_{i3} t + \hat{b}_{i4} \Delta Y_t] \right\} P_t \qquad (16)$$

and:

$$v_t = \frac{(1-s)Y_t P_t}{\sum\limits_{i=1}^{126} C_{it}} \qquad (17)$$

$$t = 0 \text{ in } 1966$$
$$t^* = 0 \text{ in } 1969$$

Gross Private Domestic Investment

Equipment Investment

Ninety-three categories of producers' durable equipment are forecast within the core model. The equations that predict this particular category of final demand are quite sophisticated and, thus, will not be treated at length within this discussion.[6] In general, sectoral equipment investment is made a function of the amount and average age of equipment already on hand, change in sector output, and the cost of obtaining new capital. Once equipment demand is determined at the 93 sector

level of aggregation, a capital flow matrix is employed to distribute these purchases across the 185 element equipment final demand vector.

Construction

Twenty-eight categories of construction are forecast within the model. Of these, 17 are specific to the private sector, while 11 relate to public construction at all levels of government. The private categories of construction are projected using several techniques. Some of the independent variables employed are time, income, population, number of households, total personal consumption expenditures, and various financial variables. Several categories of private construction are forecast with a lagged stock adjustment.

The general form of the equations used to project the public construction categories is:

$$S_{it} = \left[a_{i1} \Delta P_t + a_{i2} \frac{Y_t}{Y_o} + a_{i3} t \right] \geqslant S_i^* \qquad (18)$$

where:

S_{it} = expenditures on type i public construction category in year t

ΔP_t = average yearly population change over the past five years

Y_t, Y_o = per capita disposable income in year t and the base year respectively

t = time

$\left. \begin{array}{l} a_{i1} \\ a_{i2} \\ a_{i3} \end{array} \right\}$ = parameters

S_i^* = minimum value for S_{it}

The equation for public educational structures replaces ΔP_t with a like expression for school enrollment. Similar private and public expenditures are combined and spread across the 185 element construction final demand vector to reflect the material requirements for each major type of structure.

Inventory Changes

Like investment in equipment, inventory investment depends on changes in sectoral total output. The model has an inventory change prediction equation for each of the input-output sectors, the amount of inventory change being simultaneously determined with sectoral total outputs and competitive imports.

Exports and Imports

Exports and imports are projected for each input-output sector, thus each has 185 prediction equations.

Exports, E_{it}, are determined, for any sector i and time period t, by one of the following equations:

$$E_{it} = \begin{Bmatrix} a_{i1} + a_{i2}(\text{Total Imports})_{t-1}, \text{ or} \\ |b_{i1}E_{it-1} \end{Bmatrix} \quad (19)$$

where a_{i1}, a_{i2}, and b_{i1} are parameters. Thus, exports in the model either track lagged total imports or follow an exponential growth path.

Imports into the United States economy can be divided into competitive and non-competitive goods and services. Examples of the latter are those raw materials and minerals for which there is no domestic supply. This type of import is treated as a fixed requirement per unit of sectoral output. Thus, within the A-matrix in equations (1) and (2), there exists a row of coefficients that identify sales from the "directly allocated import" sector to all other sectors. Competitive imports, I_{it}, for sector i and year t, are forecast for most of the 185 input-output sectors by equations of the form:

$$I_{it} = a_{i1} + a_{i2}(X_{it} - E_{it}) \quad (20)$$

where a_{i1} and a_{i2} are parameters, X_{it} is total output for sector i in year t, and E_{it} is the exports from this same sector as defined above in equation (19). Competitive imports, therefore, are a function of sectoral total output produced for domestic consumption.

Government Purchases of Goods and Services

Government expenditures on goods and services are, for the purpose at hand, best divided among three major categories: expenditures for wages of public employees, construction expenditures, and expenditures on goods and services exclusive of wages and construction. Only the second and third categories solicit the production of economic goods (and thus total output) and need be included in the sectoral forecast of final demand. Public construction expenditures have already been discussed above. Thus, the present section outlines the method used in the core model to project public expenditures on non-wage, non-construction related goods and services. For this purpose, it is best to discuss Federal expenditures apart from those made at the state and local government level.

Federal expenditures for non-wage, non-construction goods and services are divided between defense and non-defense functions. For the purposes of this study, the total defense portion was assumed to increase from the 1970 level at a constant two percent per year. The non-defense portion was tied to population level and per capita disposable income. Once determined in the aggregate, these two values are distributed within the core model over their separate final demand vectors using the same distribution of these expenditures over input-output categories that prevailed in 1970.

State and local non-wage, non-construction expenditures on goods and services are projected in the aggregate for four functional classifications of public outlays. Like those at the Federal level, the total of these four expenditures is related to population size and disposable per capita income, the relative shares either fixed or dependent on time. Once determined in the aggregate, these four state and local components (education; health, welfare, and sanitation; safety; and general) are distributed over individual final demand vectors using the same proportions that obtained in 1970. The 185-element government final demand vector is the summation across the six vectors just defined. Total final demand, vector Y in Figure 1, is the sum of the individual vectors for personal consumption expenditures, equipment investment, construction, inventory change, net exports, and government purchases of non-wage, non-construction goods and services.

RESOURCE REQUIREMENTS AND POLLUTION GENERATION

The sectoral total outputs obtained from the solution of the dynamic input-output equations provide a basis for the projection of both natural resource demand and pollution loadings onto the environment. Each projection will be discussed in turn.

The United States demand, D_{rt}, for a resource of type r in year t is projected in the model, but outside the core, by equations of the form:

$$D_{rt} = \begin{Bmatrix} a_r(X_{jt} + I_{jt}), \text{ or} \\ b_r(t)[X_{jt} + I_{jt}] \end{Bmatrix} \quad (21)$$

where X_{jt} and I_{jt} are total output and imports, respectively, for input-output sector j in year t, and a_r and b_r are parameters, the latter being time-dependent. In each case, the demand for a mineral resource has been related to total domestic consumption of a particular input-output activity.[7] The parameters were established for 1970 between the resource quantities consumed in the United States and the dollar values of domestic total output plus imports of the most closely related input-output sector.

The demand projections for the basic minerals, aluminum, copper, iron, lead, and zinc, were made with the first equation. The second equation, that with the time-dependent parameter, was employed to obtain companion projections for the minor minerals, chromium, manganese, molybdenum, nickel, tungsten, and vanadium. These projections of United States demand have been compared with projected domestic supply and imports in Chapter 4 for an assessment of year 2000 resource adequacy.

Future pollution loadings onto the environment originate from two basic sources in the RFF model. This can be seen in Figure 1 by the two arrows that enter the box marked "pollution generation." One type originates in the production of goods and services to satisfy the final demands of the economy. This type of pollution, hereafter termed pollution from production, is tied directly to sectoral total outputs in the model. The other type of waste generation stems from the consumption of goods and is thus termed pollution from final consumption. This type of pollution is related to the magnitude of variables best considered under the demographic assumptions of the model. These include the projections of population size and its distribution between urban and rural locations, number of automobiles and miles traveled, and number of sewered dwelling units.

Fifteen categories, or types, of pollution are estimated in the model to be discharged to three receiving media: air, water, and land. The gross (untreated) pollution of type k originating in year t from source i, G_{it}^k, is forecast in the model by equations of the form:

$$G_{it}^k = a_{it}^k B_{it}^k \qquad (22)$$

where a_{it}^k is a time-dependent parameter for source i and pollution type k, and B_{it}^k is the source, or pollution producing base, defined as:

$$B_{it}^k = \begin{cases} X_{it}, \text{ or total output, for} \\ \quad \textit{pollution from} \\ \quad \textit{production} \\ \text{Population, automobile} \\ \quad \text{mileage, etc. for } \textit{pollution} \\ \quad \textit{from final consumption} \end{cases}$$

The total gross pollution of type k generated in year t is:

$$G_t^k = \sum_i a_{it}^k B_{it}^k \qquad (23)$$

If abatement procedures for type k pollutants achieve an overall treatment efficiency of b_t^k in year t, then the net pollution loading, N_t^k, of this pollutant in year t is:

$$N_t^k = (1 - b_t^k) \sum_i a_{it}^k B_{it}^k \qquad (24)$$

Equation (24) indicates that the submodel built to forecast pollution loadings has gross generation coefficients, a_{it}^k, for each pollutant, that are not only specific

to source, but time dependent as well. The treatment efficiencies, on the other hand, although time-dependent, are not specific to the source. Chapter 12 of this volume presents more detail on the parameters of equation (24).

REGIONAL ENVIRONMENTAL QUALITY

In order to assess alternative future environmental quality under the array of basic demographic and economic scenarios established for this study, the national totals for net pollution loadings had to be given a regional dimension. This was accomplished by allocating the national water pollution loadings to water resource regions and the net air pollution emissions to urbanized areas. However, distribution of all pollutants to OBE economic areas was performed as the first step to regionalization.[8]

This allocation is performed in two steps within the model. First, national totals for net pollution from final consumption are distributed to each economic area in proportion to the United States population share forecasted for that area. Second, net pollution from production is allocated on the basis of forecasted industry-specific regional earnings shares. Since the OBE industry classifications are more aggregated than those in the model, an assignment was made on the basis of Standard Industrial Classification codes between each input-output sector and the OBE sector into which it had been aggregated. The net pollution of type k from production in OBE economic area m in year t, N_{mt}^k, may be represented as:

$$N_{mt}^k = (1 - b_t^k) \sum_i r_{j(i)t}^m a_{it}^k X_{it} \qquad (25)$$

where $r_{j(i)t}^m$ is the ratio of earnings in region m in year t for OBE industry j to total earnings in the United States for the same industry and year; and j(i) defines the assignment between the OBE and input-output industry aggregation levels. For any pollutant, the sum of the net pollution from final consumption and production represents the region's share of national pollution loadings. This regionalization procedure was carried out on the four basic scenarios for the year 2000.

Still, nothing can be said about future environmental quality. These projected regional pollution loadings are only a measure of the total demand on regional air, water, and land resources for waste assimilation. Nothing has yet been said about the characteristics of the regional receiving media, the rivers and urban air sheds that transform and transport wastes on an inter- and intra-regional basis. As Figure 1 indicates, these considerations have been made for both air and water quality in the year 2000.

Both the national and regional projections have been employed to yield regional water quality measures for the future. This was accomplished within a sub-model already developed that projects water quality by 22 water resource regions.[9] The model also yields information on water withdrawals, supply, and thus regional shortages (surpluses), and, among other things, the cost of treatment and flow augmentation.

Urbanized area mean air quality for 95 cities and five air pollutants is projected in the RFF model by way of a second allocation of national emission totals, in this instance from OBE economic areas to the urbanized areas of large United States cities. The metropolitan population growth rates developed by Jerome Pickard were used to forecast the population in the urbanized portions of these areas in the year 2000 from their measured 1970 levels.[10] Based on this population, each area was then assigned a share of the net United States total pollution from final consumption. Each urbanized area was also assigned its share of net pollution from production in its own OBE economic area. This latter proportion was computed from historical data on the ratio of employment in heavily polluting industries in the urbanized area to employment in these same industries within the OBE economic area. For each urbanized area, a relationship was established between this employment share and a similar ratio for population in the two areas. Thus, for each urbanized area, the Pickard population growth rate establishes the future population, and this is employed to allocate pollution generation to the urbanized area from both final consumption and production. Although the relationship is less direct for pollution from production, both sources of pollution in the urbanized area are completely determined in the model by population level. Therefore, net emissions, N_{mt}^k, of pollutant k in year t in urbanized area m may be represented as:

$$N_{mt}^k = f(P_{mt}) \qquad (26)$$

where P_{mt} is the population in year t in the same urbanized area.

Meteorological "potential," θ_k, may be thought of as the relationship that links average air quality to average emission per unit area. For the purposes of this study, meteorological potential is related to three characteristics of each urbanized area:[11] (1) mean air mixing height (h), (2) mean wind speed (u), and (3) city diameter (s). For any assumption, d, on future urbanized area population density, both the land area, A, and city diameter may be computed.[12] Thus:

$$A_{mt} = g(d, P_{mt}) \qquad (27)$$

$$s_{mt} = 2 \left(\frac{A_{mt}}{\pi} \right)^{\!1/2} \qquad (28)$$

$$\theta_{mt} = \theta(h_m u_m s_{mt}) \qquad (29)$$

Since the pollution potential, θ_{mt}, relates air quality to emissions per time period and unit of land area, theoretical mean air quality, $\bar{Q}_{mt}^k$, in year t for pollutant type k and urbanized area m is equal to:

$$\bar{Q}_{mt}^k = \theta(h_m u_m s_{mt}) \frac{f(P_{mt})}{g(d, P_{mt})} \qquad (30)$$

These estimates of "theoretical" mean air quality are normalized against mean "measured" air quality in 1970, $\bar{M}_{m70}^k$, in order to project the quality of urban air for the future, $\bar{M}_{mt}^k$. Thus:

$$\bar{M}_{mt}^k = \bar{M}_{m70}^k \left(\frac{\bar{Q}_{mt}^k}{\bar{Q}_{m70}^k} \right) \qquad (31)$$

POLICY SIMULATION

The RFF model outlined above has been employed to assess the differential impact on resources and the environment of various policy alternatives for the future. These alternatives are most easily considered under three main groupings, the first of which concerns the specification of the demographic and economic assumptions under which the model is run.

Parametric variations of this type enter the model in two principal ways, first through their effect on final demand vectors, especially the size and composition of personal consumption and government expenditures, and second through their effect on overall production capacity. In general, the approach followed was to initiate a particular set of runs by guessing at an appropriate time path for disposable income per capita. The first guess was chosen by applying particular assumptions about trends in manhour productivity and hours of work to labor-force projections in order to estimate GNP and, from the latter, a "guestimate" for disposable income per capita. This was then modified in subsequent runs until acceptable unemployment rates were obtained.

The second type of policy alternative explicitly handled within the model concerns the degree of which industrial materials are recycled within the economy in the future. As Figure 1 indicates, the degree of recyling is assumed to affect the resource requirements per unit of output. Chapter 4 provides more information on this procedure.

The third type of policy simulation considered within the model relates to average waste treatment practices employed within the economy. For this purpose, three new input-output industries were created, one each for air, water, and solid waste treatment, a new row and column added to the A-matrix for each. These rows and columns were made dynamic with respect to time and exhibit the logistic pattern of change described in Chapter 12. In addition, three new equipment investment and construction equations were added to reflect the final demand requirements on these industries. Personal consumption expenditures for the purchase and maintenance of abatement equipment were also added. Finally, the treatment efficiencies employed against gross pollution from both production and final consumption were made a function of the abatement assumptions. An accounting procedure was added to measure the extent and distribution of abatement expenditures over time.[13]

REFERENCES

1. The estimation procedure used is discussed in detail in Clopper Almon, Jr., *The American Economy to 1975* (New York: Harper & Row, 1966), Chapter 2.

2. Urban strata of the 1960-61 U.S. Bureau of Labor Statistics, *Survey of Consumer Expenditures* and the U.S. Department of Agriculture, *1965 Household Food Consumption Survey* (unpublished).

3. A more detailed explanation of this and other procedures involved in the personal consumption forecasts are enumerated in Henry W. Herzog, Jr., "A Method for Recognizing 'Demographic Specific' Family Expenditure Pattern Shifts in Long-Run Personal Consumption Forecasting" (Washington: Resources for the Future, Jan. 1972).

4. The "total consumption expenditure elasticity" was selected over the income elasticity because total expenditure is generally regarded as a better proxy for "permanent income" than reported cross-section income itself. In addition, since total consumption rises proportionally with "across-the-board" income increases, the two definitions of elasticity collapse to one.

5. The year 2000 projections presented in Chapter 2 all were made with s = .14. Over the forecast period, 1970 through 2020, the multiplier, v, was always greater than 1.0 and less than 1.05.

6. A detailed discussion of the method of forecasting equipment expenditures is contained in Clopper Almon and Thomas C. Reimbold, "Estimation of Capital Stock and Investment Equations," Maryland Interindustry Forecasting Project, Research Memorandum No. 28 (College Park, Md.: University of Maryland, Nov. 16, 1970).

7. A complete explanation of this procedure is found in Michael Harrell, "The U.S. Demand for Mineral Resources, Methodology for the Year 2000 Forecasts" (Washington: Resources for the Future, December 1971).

8. These economic areas, of which there are 173, have been delineated by the Regional Economics Division, Office of Business Economics (OBE), U.S. Department of Commerce. We are grateful to the Regional Economics Division for providing us with an allocation tape for these economic areas.

9. The model is a computerized version of Nathaniel Wollman and Gilbert W. Bonem, *The Outlook for Water: Quality, Quantity and National Growth* (Baltimore: The Johns Hopkins Press for Resources for the Future, 1971). We are indebted to James McFarland and Leon Hyatt for running this model for us.

10. Jerome P. Pickard, "U.S. Metropolitan Growth and Expansion, 1970-2000, With Population Projections" (paper prepared for the Commission on Population Growth and the American Future, 1972).

11. The method of computing this potential, as well as the data on mixing heights and wind speed, were taken from a paper by George C. Holzworth, "Meteorological Potential for Urban Air Pollution in the Contiguous United States," Paper No. ME-20C (presented at the Second International Clean Air Congress, Washington, D.C., December 6-11, 1970).

12. For the purpose of computing the diameter, the urbanized areas are assumed to have a circular shape in the year 2000. Therefore, their diameters are equal to

$$2\left(\frac{A}{\pi}\right)^{1/2}$$

13. This procedure is described in more detail in: L. Ayres, I. Gutmanis, A. Shapanka, "Environmental Implications of Technological and Economic Change for the United States 1967-2000: An Input-Output Analysis," IRT-229-R (Washington, D.C.: International Research and Technology Corp., Dec. 1971).

Chapter 12

Technological Change, Pollution and Treatment Cost Coefficients in Input-Output Analysis

by
Robert U. Ayres and
Ivars Gutmanis
International Research and
Technology Corporation

COMMISSION ON POPULATION GROWTH AND
THE AMERICAN FUTURE, *RESEARCH
REPORTS, VOLUME III, POPULATION
RESOURCES AND THE ENVIRONMENT,*
EDITED BY RONALD G. RIDKER

Table 1.—Types of Substitution

Type	Substitutor	Substitutee	Example	Effect on I-O matrix elements
I	Output of ith sector as input to m^{th} sector	Output of jth sector as input to m^{th} sector	Synthetic for rubber in tires, plastic for steel in auto industry	Element a_{im} increases Element a_{jm} decreases $(a_{im} + a_{jm} = constant)$
II	Output of ith sector as input to all other sectors	Output of jth sector as input to all other sectors	Use of telephone replacing use of postal service	All elements in i^{th} row increase All elements in j^{th} row decrease $(a_{im} + a_{jm} = constant$ for all)
III	Output of ith sector as input to m^{th} sector	Output of $j^{th}, k^{th}, l^{th}...$ sectors as inputs to m^{th} sector	Plastic in building industry replacing plywood, metal, tile, plaster, etc.	Element a_{im} increases Element $a_{jm}, a_{km}, a_{lm}...$ decreases $(a_{im} + a_{jm} + a_{km} + a_{lm}... = constant)$
IV	Output of ith sector as input to all other sectors	Output of $j^{th}, k^{th}, l^{th}...$ sectors as inputs to all other sectors	Air transport replacing rail, truck, ship	All elements in i^{th} row increase All elements in $j^{th}, k^{th}, l^{th}...$ rows decrease $(a_{im} + a_{jm} + a_{lm}... = constant$ for all)
V	Output of ith sector as input to m^{th} sector	Labor as input to sector m^{th}	Machinery replacing labor for agriculture	Element a_{im} increases
VI	Output of ith sector as input to all other sectors	All other inputs to all other sectors (since labor cannot be replaced for whole economy)	Computers, electric energy replace all other inputs	All elements a_{im} increase for all m All other elements a_{jm} decrease for all j and m $: \Sigma\ a_{jm} = constant$ for all m

because they are both included in the same sector (SIC 2841), at the four-digit level of disaggregation. Failure of the model to distinguish between these two industries will inevitably result in some errors as the relative outputs of soaps and detergents change with time. On the other hand, as this sector shifts from soap to detergents its purchases from other sectors will change (soap requires animal or vegetable fats from the food processing or agriculture sectors; detergents require inputs from petrochemical and mining industries.

Table 2 illustrates a number of specific possible substitutions and identifies the specific economic sectors affected. While most listed substitutions are already occurring and visible in existing trends, it is perfectly possible to postulate hypothetical future substitutions which can be treated in similar fashion. To take an obvious example, we could consider the potential impact of substituting electric for gasoline-powered automobiles. Or, in the longer term, we might examine the economic implications of large-scale use of synthetic products based on petrochemical or other nonagricultural raw materials.

Various substitution models have been proposed in the past.[2] Our model falls somewhere between the technological determinism of Fisher and Pry and the economic determinism of Mansfield or Chow. We postulate a simple exponential relationship between output ratio and price ratio. This turns out to be equivalent to assuming a logistic form of substitution function. The simplest case (type I) will suffice for an explanation of the method to be used. All other cases are generalizations.

Suppose Y_A is the (dollar) output of industrial sector A, and P_A is the "unit price" of the service provided by the product in question. (Difficulties in defining a meaningful price relationship between non-equivalent materials or products are discussed later.) Similarly Y_B and P_B are defined. We may assume A is successfully competing with B for the same market so that Y_A is gradually increasing at the expense of Y_B. Thus, A and B might be synthetic rubber and natural rubber, respectively, so that Y_A is the dollar output of the synthetic rubber industry (I-O sector 63) and Y_B is the dollar output of the forestry and fishery products industry (I-O sector 8)—or that part of it which is replaceable by synthetic rubber, viz., natural rubber.

Table 2.—Substitutions and Sectors[a] Involved

Substitutor (new material)	Substitutee (old material)	Consuming industry
Reinforced fiberglass[a] (62)	Sheet steel (83)	Truck, bus, and tractor bodies (132)
PVC pipe[a] (74)	Iron pipe (94, 100)	Construction (18, 19)
Plastic[a] (vinyl) (74)	Hardwood flooring (43)	Construction (18, 19)
Plastic (vinyl) (62, 74)	Hardwood (42, 43)	Wood furniture (45, 46)
Plastic, e.g., Melamine (62)	Steel, aluminum (83, 87)	Household appliances (123)
Plastic containers (74)	Glass bottles (78)	Household chemicals, cleaning, and toilet drugs (66, 67)
Vinyl/PVC[a] (62)	Leather (74)	Shoes (76)
Vinyl, fiberglass (74)	Textile upholstery (e.g., mohair) (37)	Motor vehicles, home furnishings (45, 46, 132, 133)
Paper from polyolefins (74)	Paper from pulp (48)	Fine paper (49) Containers (51) Newspapers (52)
Cellulosic synthetic fibers (e.g., rayon) (74)	Cotton (4)	Broad woven fabric knit goods, textiles, miscellaneous apparel (35, 37, 38, 39, 40)
Non-cellulosic[a] synthetic fibers, (e.g., acrilan) (65)	Wool (3)	Broad woven fabric, miscellaneous textiles, floor coverings, apparel, knit goods (35, 36, 37, 38, 39, 40)
Synthetic rubber (63)	Natural rubber (8)	Tires, miscellaneous rubber products (72, 73)
Artificial sweeteners (60)	Sugar (28)	Canned and frozen foods, bakery products, confectionery products, soft drinks, and flavorings (25, 27, 29, 31)
Paper products (49)	Broadwoven knit goods (35, 38)	Apparel (39)
Knits[a] (38)	Broadwoven goods (35)	Apparel (39)
Aluminum (87)	Steel (83)	Engines and turbines (102), farm machinery (103), construction machinery (104), materials handling (105), metal working machinery (108), special industrial machinery (109), motor vehicles (133), aircraft (134), truck and trailer bodies (132), ships (137), railroad equipment (138), motorcycles (139), trailer coaches (140), metal cans (92), stampings (97), plumbing and heating equipment (94)
Aluminum (87)	Zinc and steel (86, 83)	Steel industry (galvanizing); structural metal products (95)
Aluminum[a] (87)	Copper (84)	N.F. wire drawing; stampings (radiators) (90, 97)
Pharmaceuticals (biological controls) (66)	Pesticides (60)	Agricultural chemicals (60)
Photographic materials (145)	All inputs to printing	Printing and publishing (53, 54)
Nuclear fuel (13)	Fossil fuel (14, 15)	Electric power (160)

Table 2.—Continued

Substitutor (new material)	Substitutee (old material)	Consuming industry
Electric power[a] (160)	Industrial manpower	All
Telephone[a] (158)	Mail (177)	All outputs
Computer rental (185)	Manpower	All
Air freight (155)	Rail freight (151)	All
Air passenger[a] (155)	Rail passenger (151)	PCE (186)
Scrap iron (9)	Iron ore (11)	Steel (83)
Scrap aluminum (9)	Aluminum ore (13)	Aluminum (87)
Scrap copper (9)	Copper ore (12)	Copper and N.F., secondary (84)
Scrap zinc (9)	Zinc ore (13)	Zinc (86)
Waste paper (9)	Pulpwood (41)	Pulp (47)
Waste aggregate (9)	Sand and gravel (stone and clay mining) (16)	Concrete, paving (71, 81)
Cullet (9)	Sand (16)	Glass (78)
Organic wastes converted (9)	Grain, grain mill products (5, 26)	Dairy products, poultry and eggs and meat products (1, 2, 3)

[a]Maryland Interindustry model numbering scheme.

Assuming all the relevant measures exists, it is convenient to define the ratios

$$Y = \frac{Y_A}{Y_B}, \qquad P = \frac{P_A}{P_B}$$

in such a way that Y may vary from zero to infinity over a period of time as the substitution process goes to completion. It is convenient to introduce a function, f, the fractional penetration, as follows:

$$f = \left(\frac{Y_A}{Y_A + Y_B}\right) = \frac{Y}{1+Y} \qquad (1)$$

The actual replacement, of course, takes place gradually over a period of time, due to a number of "inertial" factors in the system including capital replacement scheduling, established commercial relationships and lags in the rate of diffusion of technical information.

We postulate that the relationship between output ratios and price ratios is given as follows:

$$Y = Y_o P^{-m} \qquad (2)$$

We also assume that the price ratios tend to change rather smoothly in time, following an exponential decay, so that:

$$p = p_o \exp\left(\frac{k}{m} t\right) \qquad (3)$$

where t represents elapsed time in years starting from an arbitrarily selected and initial year (for example, 1850).

It follows, then, that

$$Y = Y_o P_o^{-m} \exp(kt) \qquad (4)$$

Thus, substituting (4) into (1)

$$f = \frac{1}{1 + Y_o^{-1} P_o^m \exp(-kt)}$$

$$= \frac{1}{1 + \exp[-k(t-u)]} \qquad (5)$$

which is the so-called "logistic" growth function. Note that f is completely specified by the two parameters k and u, and that $f = 1/2$ when $t = u$ whence u is the midpoint of the substitution. This function satisfies the simple differential equation:

$$\frac{1}{f(1-f)} \frac{df}{dt} = k \qquad (6)$$

Evidently, (6) is a direct consequence of the assumptions (2) and (3); thus, an alternative form of the displacement function (6) would be inconsistent with either (2) or (3), or both.

The specific procedure we have followed to determine appropriate values of k and u consists of the following steps:

1. Compile historical time series data on Y and p (see subsequent discussion).

2. Determine best exponential fit to p using computerized "least-square" routine.

3. Prepare visually smoothed trend curve for Y (to eliminate effects of short term fluctuations).

4. Determine best exponential fit to smoothed Y.

5. Compute k and u from fitted exponential functions.

This procedure was carried out explicitly for the substitutions denoted by footnote "a" on Table 2, for which it was judged that available output and price data were sufficiently relevant to justify the effort. The results are summarized in a separate IR&T report. Graphical plots of the data and the fitted Y and p function are also displayed.[3] In the remaining cases, we have estimated the parameters k and u based on scattered data modified by heuristic judgments.

On the basis of similarities between the cases listed in Table 3, the following k and u values were assumed for other substitutions where relevant data is not readily available, or (more often) where the substitution process has not yet really begun. Thus, the items listed in Table 4 can be regarded as "technological forecast" in the purest sense.

Table 3.—Fitted Parameters for Substitution Function
(Listed in increasing order)

Substitution	k	u
Electricity for labor	.021	1971
Telephone for mail	.031	1916
Knits for woven goods	.115	1992
Vinyl for hardwood floor	.150	1966
Aluminum for copper wire	.153	1986
Air for rail travel	.164	1957
PVC for cast iron pipe	.183	1966
Nylon for wool	.188	1963
Fiberglass for steel in autos	.219	1988
Vinyl for leather goods	.227	1975
Computers for labor	.548	1971-1975

Table 4.—Made-Up Parameters for Substitution Function

Substitution	k	u
Converted waste for animal feed[a]	0.08	2000
Scrap for metal ores[a]	0.10	1990
Polyolefins for fine paper	0.10	1982
Paper products for woven fabrics	0.115	1985
Polyolefins for kraft paper	0.12	1990
Polyolefins for newsprint	0.15	2000
Nuclear fuel for fossil fuel	0.15	1991
Plastic for wood furniture	0.15	1967
Vinyl for textiles in furnishings	0.18	1966
Photographic inputs to printing		1971
Plastic for glass bottles	0.18	1961 - cosmetics
		1967 - drugs
		1979 - food & dairy
Biologicals for chemical pesticides	0.18	1979
Rayon for cotton	0.19	1958 - knits & misc. textiles
		1969 - woven fabric
Artificial sweeteners for sugar	0.2	1978 - prepared foods, soft drinks, etc.
Plastic (melamine or ABS) for steel in appliances	0.22	1969

[a]Assuming recycling becomes national policy and is encouraged by legal and institutional changes.

Technological Change, Pollution and Treatment
Cost Coefficients in Input-Output Analysis

The use of the input-output analysis framework to estimate the levels of wasteloads and the cost of abatement has been proposed before.[4] The principal difference between this study and others lies in the integrated approach of this report and the long (five decade) time horizon over which the pollution levels and abatement costs have been projected.[5]

The research effort for this portion of the study included three major tasks: identification of major polluting sectors of economy and estimation of current and future pollution loads per unit of output; determination of current and future abatement costs; and allocation of these costs to sectors of economy supplying equipment and services. Selection of the particular industries and pollutants for this study was based on two criteria. The first was the significance of the industry in terms of its size and the quantity of residuals discharged. The second criterion was the availability of data.

Table 5 indicates which industries and final demand sectors were considered to be important air and water polluters and large contributors to solid waste generation, and were therefore included in this study.

A list of significant residuals was also determined. In general, "significance" is a reflection of the degree to

Table 5.—Sectors of Economy Contributing to Air Pollution Emissions, Water Pollution Discharges and Solid Waste Generation

Sector Title	Sector No.	Air pollution emissions	Water pollution discharges	Solid waste generation
Dairy farm products	1	X	X	X
Poultry and eggs	2	X	X	X
Meat, animals and miscellaneous livestock products	3	X	X	X
Cotton	4	X	X	X
Grains	5	X	X	X
Tobacco	6	X	X	X
Fruits, vegetables and other crops	7	X	X	X
Forestry and fishery products	8	...	...	...
Agricultural, forestry and fishery services	10	...	...	...
Iron ores	11	...	...	...
Copper ore	12	...	X	X
Other non-ferrous metal ores	13	...	X	X
Coal mining	14	...	X	X
Crude petroleum and natural gas	15	...	X	X
Stone and clay mining	16	...	X	X
Chemical fertilizer mining	17	...	X	X
New construction	18	...	X	X
Maintenance and repair construction	19	...	...	...
Complete guided missiles	20	...	...	...
Ammunition	21	X	X	X
Other ordnance	22	X	X	X
Meat products	23	X	X	X
Dairy products	24	X	X	X
Canned and frozen foods	25	X	X	X
Grain mill products	26	X	X	X
Bakery products	27	X	X	X
Sugar	28	X	X	X
Confectionary products	29	X	X	X
Alcoholic beverages	30	X	X	X
Soft drinks and flavorings	31	X	X	X
Fats and oils	32	X	X	X
Miscellaneous food products	33	X	X	X
Tobacco products	34	X	...	X
Broad and narrow fabrics	35	X	X	X
Floor coverings	36	X	X	X
Miscellaneous textiles	37	X	X	X

Table 5.—Continued

Sector Title	Sector No.	Sector contributions		
		Air pollution emissions	Water pollution discharges	Solid waste generation
Knitting	38	X	X	X
Apparel	39	X	...	X
Household textiles	40	X	...	X
Lumber and wood products	41	X	...	X
Veneer and plywood	42	X	...	X
Millwork and wood products	43	X	...	X
Wooden containers	44	X	...	X
Household furniture	45	X	...	X
Other furniture	46	X	...	X
Pulp mills	47	X	...	X
Paper and paperboard mills	48	X	X	X
Paper products	49	X	X	X
Wall and building paper	50	X	X	X
Paperboard containers	51	X	X	X
Newspapers	52	X	...	X
Books, periodicals and miscellaneous publishing	53	X	...	X
Other printing and services	54	X	...	X
Industrial chemicals	55	X	X	X
Fertilizers	59	X	X	X
Pesticides and other agricultural chemicals	60	X	X	X
Miscellaneous chemical products	61	X	X	X
Plastic materials and resins	62	X	X	X
Synthetic rubber	63	X	X	X
Cellulosic fibers	64	X	X	X
Non-cellulosic fibers	65	X	X	X
Drugs	66	X	X	X
Cleaning and toilet preparations	67	X	X	X
Paints	68	X	X	X
Petroleum refining and related products	69	X	X	X
Paving and asphalt	71	X	X	X
Tires and inner tubes	72	X	X	X
Rubber products	73	X	X	X
Miscellaneous plastic products	74	X	X	X
Leather tanning and industrial leather products	75	X	X	X
Leather footwear	76	X	X	X
Other leather products	77	X	X	X
Glass	78	X	...	X
Structural clay products	79	X	...	X
Pottery	80	X	...	X
Cement, concrete and gypsum	81	X	...	X
Other stone and clay products	82	X	...	X
Steel	83	X	X	X
Copper	84	X	X	X
Lead	85	X	X	X
Zinc	86	X	X	X
Aluminum	87	X	X	X
Primary non-ferrous metals	88	X	X	X
Non-ferrous rolling and drawing	89	X	X	X
Non-ferrous wire drawing and insulation	90	X	X	X
Non-ferrous castings and forgings	91	X	X	X
Metal cans	92	X	X	X
Metal barrels, drums and pails	93	X	X	X
Plumbing and heating equipment	94	X	X	X

Technological Change, Pollution and Treatment
Cost Coefficients in Input-Output Analysis

Table 5.—Continued

Sector Title	Sector No.	Sector contributions		
		Air pollution emissions	Water pollution discharges	Solid waste generation
Structural metal products	95	X	X	X
Screw machine products	96	X	X	X
Metal stampings	97	X	X	X
Cutlery, hand tools and hardware	98	X	X	X
Miscellaneous fabricated wire products	99	X	X	X
Valves, pipe fittings and fabricated pipes	100	X	X	X
Other fabricated metal products, NEC	101	X	X	X
Engines and turbines	102	X	X	X
Farm machinery	103	X	X	X
Construction, mining and oil field machinery	104	X	X	X
Materials handling machinery	105	X	X	X
Machine tools, metal cutting	106	X	X	X
Machine tools, metal forming	107	X	X	X
Other metal working machinery	108	X	X	X
Special industrial machinery	109	X	X	X
Pumps, compressors, blowers and fans	110	X	X	X
Ball and roller bearings	111	X	X	X
Power transmission equipment	112	X	X	X
Industrial patterns	113	X	X	X
Computers and related machines	114	X	X	X
Other office machinery	115	X	X	X
Service industry machinery	116	X	X	X
Machine shop products	117	X	X	X
Electrical measuring instruments	118	X	X	X
Transformers and switchgear	119	X	X	X
Motors and generators	120	X	X	X
Industrial controls	121	X	X	X
Welding apparatus and graphite products	122	X	X	X
Household appliances	123	X	X	X
Electric lighting and wiring equipment	124	X	X	X
Radio and TV receiving	125	X	X	X
Phonograph records	126	X	X	X
Communication equipment	127	X	X	X
Electronic components	128	X	X	X
Batteries	129	X	X	X
Engine electrical equipment	130	X	X	X
X-ray equipment and electrical equipment . . . . : .	131	X	X	X
Truck, bus and trailer bodies	132	X	X	X
Motor vehicles and parts	133	X	X	X
Aircraft	134	X	X	X
Aircraft engines and parts	135	X	X	X
Aircraft equipment	136	X	X	X
Ship and boat building and repair	137	X	X	X
Railroad equipment	138	X	X	X
Cycles and parts, transportation equipment	139	X	X	X
Trailer coaches	140	X	X	X
Engineering and scientific instruments	141	X	X	X
Mechanical measuring devices	142	X	X	X
Optical and ophthalmic goods	143	X	X	X
Medical and surgical instruments	144	X	X	X
Photographic equipment	145	X	X	X
Watches, clocks and parts	146	X	X	X

Population, Resources, and the Environment

Table 5.—Continued

Sector Title	Sector No.	Sector contributions		
		Air pollution emissions	Water pollution discharges	Solid waste generation
Jewelry and silverware	147	X	X	X
Toys, sporting goods, musical instruments	148	X	X	X
Office supplies	149	X	X	X
Miscellaneous manufacturing	150	X	X	X
Railroads	151	X	...	...
Busses	152	X	...	...
Trucking	153	X	X	...
Water transportation	154	X	...	...
Airlines	155	X	...	...
Pipelines	156	...	...	...
Freight forwarding	157	...	...	...
Telephone and telegraph	158	...	...	...
Radio and TV broadcasting	159	...	...	...
Electric utilities	160	X	X	X
Natural gas	161	...	...	...
Water and sewer services	162	...	...	...
Wholesale trade	163	X	X	X
Retail trade	164	X	X	X
Credit agencies and brokers	165	...	...	...
Insurance and brokers' agents	166	...	...	...
Owner-occupied dwellings	167	X	X	X
Real estate	168	X	X	X
Hotel and lodging places	169	...	...	...
Personal and repair services	170	...	...	...
Business services	171	...	...	...
Advertising	172	...	...	...
Auto repair	173	...	...	...
Motion pictures and amusements	174	...	...	...
Medical services	175	...	...	...
Private schools and non-profit organizations	176	...	...	...
Post office	177	...	...	...
Federal government enterprises	178	...	...	...
Local government passenger transit	179	...	...	...
State and local electric utilities	180	...	...	...
Directly allocated imports	181	...	...	...
Business travel	182	...	...	...
Office supplies	183	...	...	...
Unimportant industry	184	...	...	...
Computer rental	185	...	...	...
Personal consumption expenditures	186	...	...	...
Producers' durable equipment and construction	187	...	...	...
Change in inventories	188	...	...	...
Gross experts	189	...	...	...
Defense expenditures	190	...	...	...
Non-defense federal expenditures	191	...	...	...
State and educational expenditures	192	...	...	...
Health, welfare and sanitation	193	X	X	X
Police, fire and safety	194	...	...	...
General state and local government expenditures	195	...	...	...
Gross imports	196	...	...	...
Transferred imports and second hand goods	197	...	...	...

which a pollutant can degrade the environment, and the extent to which it already constitutes an apparent danger. Solid waste was not, however, analyzed in the same terms as air and water pollution. Rather than classifying the types of solid waste—for example, by source or composition—the focus was placed on the magnitude and method of disposal, namely, sanitary landfill, dumping, or incineration.

The final list comprised five air and seven water pollutants as well as solid waste. The air pollutants were: particulates, hydrocarbons, sulfur oxides, carbon monoxide, and nitrogen oxides. Water pollutants included: chemical oxygen demand (COD), biological oxygen demand (BOD), refractory organics, suspended solids, dissolved solids, nitrogen, and phosphate compounds. Estimation of waste generation coefficients comprised the next major phase of the research effort. Waste generation coefficients are a measure of the wastes generated by economic activity per unit output.

Because air pollution, in particular is generally associated with specific activities common to many sectors, separate estimates were made for pollution from electric power production (within a sector), space heat and process heat within each sector, in addition to more sector-specific manufacturing activities.

The levels of current emissions from the use of fossil fuels (gas, oil, and coal) vary from one industry to another. The residuals output from combustion processes was calculated from data on the quantity of fossil fuels used by each industry in the year nearest to 1967 for which information was available.

With regard to the waterborne waste coefficient determination, it must be noted that, for a number of sectors, the magnitude of wastes depend not only on the level of economic activity but also on precipitation, streamflow, and other hydrological characteristics of specific regions. These local variations have been taken into account by allocating residuals by industry on a regional basis and subsequently summing nationally.[6]

Solid waste encompasses several types of residuals. Current coefficients for household solid waste were based on the total weight of refuse collected by

Table 6.—Direct Air Pollution Output Coefficients from Heat and Power Generation and Industrial Processes, United States, 1967-1979

(Thousands of pounds emitted into the atmosphere per unit of output)

I-O Sector No.	SIC No.	Sectors of economy	P	HC	SO_x	CO	NO_x
67	—	Owner occupied dwellings; residential space heating	12.132	—	50.552	—	18.199
68p	65p	Rental occupied dwellings; residential space heating	12.132	—	50.551	—	18.198
68p	65p	All other space heating	7.308	—	30.451	—	10.962
62p	4953p	Solid waste incineration	18.543	26.972	1.685	131.486	10.114
63,64	49,50	Wholesale and retail trade	—	365.199	—	—	—
60	491	Electric utilities	571.954	—	1715.862	—	408.538
51-155 68p	40-42 44-45	Transportation	—	—	—	—	—
52-153p 53-152p	41-42	Motor vehicles	—	—	—	—	—
52p	—	Passenger cars	.8	12.5	.6	165.0	8.5
53	42	Motor freight transportation	3.1	55	1.3	253	24
52	41-42	Passenger buses	9.5	4.6	3.5	172	31
55	45	Aircraft (includes fan-jets only)	7.4	29.0	—	20.6	9.2

Population, Resources, and the Environment

Table 6.—Continued

I-O Sector No.	SIC No.	Sectors of economy	P	HC	SOx	CO	NOx
55-68	28	Chemical and allied products	128.666	38.719	87.022	26.066	28.122
69-71	29	Petroleum and coal products	84.436	344.892	255.505	218.0	16.276
72-74	30	Rubber and plastics products	41.423	2.7460	23.562	.7586	6.709
75-77	31	Leather and leather products	15.649	.11777	11.171	.2990	11.313
78-82	32	Stone, clay and glass products	454.332	.96683	80.582	2.7426	29.901
83-91	33	Primary metal industries	154.729	.45926	210.212	26.783	16.122
92-101	34	Fabricated metal products	7.557	.066970	7.0619	.1537	2.537
102-117	35	Machinery, except electrical	12.267	.09078	8.525	.2331	2.636
118-131	36	Electrical machinery	8.008	.05977	5.648	.1527	1.777
132-140	37	Transportation equipment	11.268	.07554	6.551	.2071	1.937
141-146	38	Instruments and related products	15.142	.10686	9.667	.2830	2.742
147-150	19,39	Miscellaneous manufacturing, including ordnance	65.74	.11891	35.630	.2937	3.436
151	40	Railroads	.539	.809	.270	.270	1.078
154	44	Vessels	.730	.730	2.190	2.190	1.460
—	—	Non-highway use of motor fuels	1.976	5.927	1.976	35.563	5.927
1-7	01	Agriculture	64.395	5.366	8.049	222.700	8.049
23-33	20	Food and kindred products	47.368	.145	12.9545	.3869	4.251
34	21	Tobacco products	10.580	.0683	5.7247	.1921	1.546
35-38	22	Textile mill products	31.555	.232	797.710	.5982	6.123
39-40	23	Apparel and related products	1.641	.0146	1.534	.03334	.4598
41-44	24	Lumber and wood products	6.007	.0662	7.701	.1334	2.386
45-46	25	Furniture and fixtures	13.027	.0876	7.6199	.2398	2.241
47-52	26	Paper and allied products	218.451	1.021	89.796	91.969	26.093
53-54	27	Printing and publishing	1.335	.01437	1.6612	.02945	.6221
—	—	Miscellaneous					
—	—	Forest fires	—	—	—	—	—
—	—	Structural fires	—	—	—	—	—
—	—	Coal refuse	245.663	184.247	61.416	105.481	184.247

Technological Change, Pollution and Treatment
Cost Coefficients in Input-Output Analysis

Table 7.—Direct Water Pollution Coefficients from Economic Activities, United States, 1967-1969
(Thousands of pounds of pollutants and millions of gallons of wastewater into surface waters and aquifers per unit of output)

I-O Sector No.	SIC No.	Sectors of economy	Waste water	COD	BOD	RO	SS	DS	N	P
167p		Owner-occupied dwellings, sewered population	124.5	401.995	301.984	101.004	280.996	890.989	48	8.01
165p	65p	Rental-occupied dwellings, sewered population	124.5	365.991	275	91.975	254.985	810.017	44	7.98
167p 165p	65p	Non-sewered population	118.7	474.002	361.976	112.026	343.025	750.976	36.01	11.02
		Run-off from urbanized areas	187.0	189.23	38.26	—	248.171	—	6.52	1.35
160	491	Electric utilities								
1-7		Agriculture								
1	132	Dairy farms								
2	133,135	Poultry and eggs	23.273	5542.035	791.71	—	22,217.0	—	621.19	226.86
3	135-139	Meat animals & livestock								
5,6	113,114	Cropland	1931.358	—	—	—	4473.2	86.831	21.047	1.579
7,4	12,112	Irrigated acreage	2377.127	—	—	—	631.58	12.285	15.997	.298
		Manufacturing								
23-33	20	Food and kindred products	5.85	—	59.182	—	90.837	16.571	—	—
23	201	Meat products	4.831	—	34.734	—	34.734	—	—	—
24	202	Dairy products	3.096	—	38.697	—	22.251	—	—	—
25	203	Canned and frozen foods	10.301	—	16.933	—	8.467	—	—	—
26	206	Sugar refining	87.215	—	878.421	—	3137.2	—	—	—
26,27, 29-33	204-205 207-209	All other food	2.471	—	19.026	—	3.124	—	—	—
35-38	22	Textile mill products	10.488	—	49.128	—	—	56.249	—	—
47-51	26	Paper and allied products	99.661	—	332.204	—	168.92	724.94	—	—
65-68	28	Chemicals and allied products	27.055	—	267.79	—	52.454	1428.2	—	—
69-71	29	Petroleum & coal products	11.637	—	24.243	—	22.304	35.346	—	—
72-74	30	Rubber & plastic products	1.79	—	3.759	—	4.698	—	—	—
83-91	33	Primary metal industries	41.958	—	14.386	—	140.858	187.312	—	—
83	331	Blast furnaces & steel mills	51.419	—	6.88	—	184.266	—	—	—
84-88	333,334	All other primary metals	19.94	—	31.888	—	42.878	—	—	—
102-117	35	Machinery, except electrical	.763	—	1.476	—	1.23	—	—	—
118-131	36	Electrical machinery	1.203	—	2.16	—	.617	—	—	—
132-140	37	Transportation equipment	1.21	—	2.045	—	—	—	—	—
20-22 34-39 40-46 52-54 75-82 89-101 141-150	21, 23-25 27,29 31,32 34,38 39,19	All other manufacturing	1.677	—	3.012	—	6.049	—	—	—

Source: Leslie Ayres and Ivars Gutmanis, *A Model for Strategic Allocation of Water Pollution Abatement Funds*, IRT-R-43, August 1971.

municipalities.[7] Data for mining operation was obtained from the U.S. Bureau of Mines and included all operations except strip mining. Industrial solid waste includes those residuals derived from (1) industrial processes, per se,[8] (2) air and water pollution abatement activities (e.g., solid waste "captured" in an air filtration abatement process), and (3) shipping, that is, factory trash and discarded packaging material.

All current waste generation coefficients for airborne, waterborne, and solid residuals are shown in Tables 6, 7, and 8. The output base for all industrial sectors is measured in dollars of shipments.[9] For the household and transportation sectors, the output was assumed to be the number of dwelling units (households) and passenger and/or cargo miles traveled, respectively.[10]

Waste generation coefficients, as opposed to emissions, are not affected by changing abatement technology. Future variations in the factors of production, however, will affect these coefficients. Four factors were considered here in forecasting coefficients: (1) changes in *production processes*, (2) changes in *technology*, (3) changes in the type of *end-products* produced, and (4) changes in the *materials* used. Thus, these four separate factors may affect any and all waste generation processes. Furthermore, the magnitude and the direction of the affect of these factors vary from one sector of the economy to another; and, at times, several of the four factors may have opposite affects within one sector of the economy.

In order to explain all these factors and their interdependence, several illustrative examples may be of some benefit.

In the case of production process change, the example of canning of peaches is well suited for this purpose. It is a major sector and various peach products have a high consumer demand. At the same time, peach processing has undergone considerable change in the area of production process technologies as well as in the area of raw material inputs, and in the composition of the products.

With regard to changes in production process technologies, the most significant changes in this area which affect the waste generation resulting from peach processing is the re-introduction of dry peeling processes instead of using the old, and still prevailing, method of wet peeling. In summary, the dry peeling process uses abrasives as the basic mechanism by which peaches are peeled. The use of this dry peeling technology reduces BOD generation from this activity by some 75 percent. Furthermore, the introduction of new technologies which allow peeled peaches to be conveyed to the canning phase using fluming water in which equilibrium

Table 8.—Direct Solid Waste Generation Output Coefficients from Selected Economic Sectors, United States, 1967-1979

(Thousands of pounds per unit of output)

I-O Sector No.	SIC No.	Sectors of Economy	Solid waste output coefficients
167	...	Population in owner-occupied dwellings	1,059
168$_p$	65$_p$	Population in rental-occupied dwellings	913
168$_p$	65$_p$	All other real estate	1,711
193$_p$	4953$_p$	Solid waste incineration	463
193$_p$	4953$_p$	Street refuse, urban areas	92.3
160	491 4931	Electric utilities	2,284.27
11-17	10-14	Mining	106,904.12
1-7	01	Agriculture	36,886.28
...	...	Manufacturing	...
23-33	20	Food and kindred products	170.43
41-44	24	Lumber and wood products	5,781.21
45-46	25	Furniture and fixtures	585.08
47-51	26	Paper and allied products	525.67
52-54	27	Printing and publishing	891.14
55-68	28	Chemicals and allied products	163.76
72-74	30	Rubber and plastics products	462.22
78-82	32	Stone, clay and glass products	363.92
83-91	33	Primary metal industries	85.58
...	...	Miscellaneous	...
...	...	Demolition	1,786.00

Sources: American Public Works Association, *Municipal Refuse Disposal*, 1970; Combustion Engineering, Inc., *Technical-Economic Study of Solid Waste Disposal Needs and Practices*, Prepared for the U.S. Bureau of Solid Waste Management under Contract No. PH-86-66-163, 1969; R.U. Ayres, *National Goals as Related to Environmental Quality* (International Research and Technology Corporation, 1971), IRT-225-R; and U.S. Bureau of Mines, Office of Science and Technology, *Solid Waste Disposal*, May 1969.

of sugar content is reached between the peeled peach and the water further reduces BOD generation loads. The net result of the application of this technology is the reduction in all waste generation from this sector by some 80 to 85 percent as compared to the old technologies employed.

Further reduction in waste generation from this sector results from improvement in the quality of raw products (the peaches grown on the farm). Due to careful selection of peach hybrids, careful quality in harvesting, precise timing of harvesting operations, and related factors, the quality of peaches received at the cannery has been highly improved.

Finally, with regard to the end product mix, here again the new trends serve to reduce waste generation. These new trends consist of considerable increase in the variety of peach end products, whereas a decade ago, the peach product was canned as halves and slices. At the present time, several new peach end products are being produced—for example, irregular sizes, for production of pies, peach nectars, and others. The net result of these two additional factors have increased the peach case yield of 40 cases per ton to 55 cases per ton over a period of the last 15 to 20 years, with additional increases in yield projected for the future.

The above-described trends in production technologies, in raw materials, and in raw product mix, when combined, reduced waste generation existing also for numerous other food products such as carrots, apples, pears, beets, and so forth.

Furthermore, identical trends are present also in other food processing sectors such as meat-packaging plants, dairies, and so forth. It is important to note here, however, that, while the above trends exist in all other sectors of manufacturing, this does not always result in the reduction of waste generation. On the contrary, in some sectors, the change in end product mix and/or changes in raw materials result in increased volume of waste. Furthermore, these increased volumes of waste, in effect, overcome any reduction of waste load generation resulting from changes in production technologies.

Again, selected examples may be useful to illustrate these trends. In the case of the first primary metal sector, for example, the more advanced production technologies such as the use of continuous casting techniques or pelletizing (which replaces the sintering process) may reduce waste load generation.

However, other technological process changes in primary metals sectors may increase the waste generation. Prior to 1950, for example, open hearth furnaces discharged about 8 to 12 pounds of dust per ton of steel. Subsequent developments in steel-making technology, particularly the adoption of the basic oxygen furnace, have resulted in doubling the waste dust generated per ton of steel produced.

Furthermore, while the change in some production technologies in this sector may increase waste generation, the end product mix increases waste to considerable volume. To be more specific, the new demands for high strength steels, the increase in the various types of structural steel members, and similar increases, require increases in the number and type of finishing operations, each of which generate considerable additional residuals. The net result of this is an increase of approximately 30 percent of residual generation per ton of steel produced over a period of the last 15 years.

Thus, in this sector, the increase in the end product mix and more rigorous specifications may result in higher residual generation; a result opposite to that found in the food products sector.

In summary, the effect of these four factors on waste generation coefficients over time evidently varies from one industry to another. In order to determine the net result of the impact of these factors on waste generation, quantitative estimates were undertaken for each of these four factors and for each major waste generation sector.

The estimating processes consisted of a comprehensive literature search, followed by interviews with process engineers and other experts in the major waste generation sectors, which in turn was subjected to another review by a second set of outside experts.

The results of this effort were projections of future waste coefficients expressed as percent change from the current (1970) coefficient, for 1980, 1990, and the year 2000. These projections are presented in Tables 9, 10, and 11.

There are two principal types of costs related to an abatement process. The first category is capital costs, that is, the amount that would need to be expended on producers' durable equipment (PDE) such as machinery, and to be expended in construction buildings, lagoon sites, water towers, and the like. These costs were annualized roughly, based on an assumed 25-year amortization at six-percent annual interest. The second category is operating costs including labor, electricity, and expendable materials such as reagents, flocculants, and so forth.

It is important to take account of the fact that a complete treatment process may transform wastes from one form to another several times before they are finally reduced to an inert solid and "disposed of" permanently. For example, airborne residuals from power generation may be trapped by a scrubber and converted into water waste. In turn, the water used in the scrubber is then processed and the waste transformed into a sludge which ultimately dries to a solid. In this study, first- and second-round treatment costs are considered for both air and water pollution abatement. For solid wastes, however, only first round costs are assessed—although this clearly results in some over-simplification (for example, with regard to incineration).

The abatement costs for a sector are also a function of the standards of abatement required of that sector. The greater the degree of control of air and water residuals, the higher the costs.

The Clean Air Act of 1963, as amended in 1970,

Table 9.—Projected Trends in Air Pollution Loads from Heat and Power Generation and from Industrial Processes—Percentage Changes from 1967 Loads, 1980-2000

(Numbers indicate reductions unless otherwise indicated)

Sectors of economy	SIC No.	By 1980					By 1990					By 2000				
		P	HC	SO_x	CO	NO_x	P	HC	SO_x	CO	NO_x	P	HC	SO_x	CO	NO_x
Owner-occupied dwellings; residential space heating	—	50	—	25	—	25	70	—	50	—	50	70	—	50	—	50
Rental occupied dwellings; residential space heating	65p	50	—	25	—	25	70	—	50	—	50	70	—	50	—	50
All other space heating	65p	50	—	25	—	25	70	—	50	—	50	70	—	50	—	50
Solid waste incineration	4953p	15	15	15	15	15	25	25	25	25	25	25	25	25	25	25
Wholesale and retail trade	49,50	—	5	—	—	—	—	10	—	—	—	—	25	—	—	—
Electric utilities	491	25	—	25	—	25	50	—	50	—	50	50	—	50	—	—
Transportation	40-42, 44-45	—	—	—	—	—	—	—	—	—	—	—	—	—	—	—
Motor vehicles	41-42	—	—	—	—	—	—	—	—	—	—	—	—	—	—	—
Passenger cars	—	—	65	—	65	40	—	90	—	90	85	—	95	—	95	90
Passenger buses	41-42	—	65	—	65	40	—	90	—	90	85	—	95	—	95	90
Motor freight transportation	42	—	65	—	65	40	—	90	—	90	85	—	95	—	95	90
Aircraft	45	50	40	0	20	0	75	60	—	35	0	90	80	—	50	0
Railroads	40	85	85	85	85	85	85	85	85	85	85	85	85	85	85	85
Vessels	44	0	0	0	0	0	0	0	0	0	0	0	0	0	0	0
Non-highway use of motor fuels	—	0	0	0	0	0	0	0	0	0	0	0	0	0	0	0
Agriculture	01	50	50	50	50	50	70	70	70	70	70	80	80	80	80	80
Food and kindred products	20	22	25	25	25	25	55	50	50	50	50	61	50	50	50	50
Tobacco products	21	25	25	25	25	25	75	50	50	50	50	75	50	50	50	50
Textile mill products	22	25	25	25	25	25	75	50	50	50	50	75	50	50	50	50
Apparel and related products	23	25	25	25	25	25	75	50	50	50	50	75	50	50	50	50
Lumber and wood products	24	25	25	25	25	25	75	50	50	50	50	75	50	50	50	50
Furniture and fixtures	25	25	25	25	25	25	75	50	50	50	50	75	50	50	50	50
Paper and allied products	26	16	25	25	7	25	48	50	50	4	50	48	50	50	4	50
Printing and publishing	27	25	25	25	25	25	75	50	50	50	50	75	50	50	50	50
Chemical and allied products	28	23	10	20	11	21	69	11	37	13	39	68	11	37	13	39
Petroleum and coal products	29	+2	+10	+9	+10	19	13	3	12	10	43	13	3	12	10	43
Rubber and plastics products	30	25	25	25	25	25	75	50	50	50	50	75	50	50	50	50
Leather and leather products	31	25	25	25	25	25	75	50	50	50	50	75	50	50	50	50
Stone, clay and glass products	32	15	25	25	25	25	32	50	50	50	50	50	32	50	50	50
Primary metal industries	33	1	25	+7	+13	25	15	50	11	+22	50	15	50	11	+17	50
Machinery, except electrical	35	25	25	25	25	25	75	50	50	50	50	75	50	50	50	50
Electrical machinery	36	25	25	25	25	25	75	50	50	50	50	75	50	50	50	50
Transportation equipment	37	25	25	25	25	25	75	50	50	50	50	75	50	50	50	50
Instruments and related products	38	25	25	25	25	25	75	50	50	50	50	75	50	50	50	50
Miscellaneous manufacturing, including ordnance	19,39	14	25	25	25	25	29	50	26	50	50	33	50	30	50	50
Miscellaneous	—															
Forest fires	—											—	—	—	—	—
Structural fires	—											—	—	—	—	—
Coal refuse	—	35	35	35	35	35	60	60	60	60	60	80	80	80	80	80

Table 10.—Projected Trends in Unit Water Pollution Loads—Percentage Changes from 1967 Loads, 1980-2000

(Numbers indicate reductions unless otherwise indicated)

Sectors of economy and SIC No.	By 1980 COD	BOD	RO	SS	DS	N	P	H₂O	By 1990 COD	BOD	RO	SS	DS	N	P	H₂O	By 2000 COD	BOD	RO	SS	DS	N	P	H₂O
Owner-occupied dwellings, sewered population	0	0	0	0	0	+5	+10	+15	0	0	0	0	0	+5	+10	+15	0	0	0	0	0	+5	+10	+15
Rental-occupied dwellings, sewered population ... 65p	0	0	0	0	0	+5	+10	+15	0	0	0	0	0	+5	+10	+15	0	0	0	0	0	+5	+10	+15
Runoff from urbanized areas	0	0	0	0	0	0	0	0	0	0	0	0	0	0	0	0	0	0	0	0	0	0	0	0
Non-sewered population ... 65p	0	0	0	0	0	+5	+10	+15	0	0	0	0	0	+5	+10	+15	0	0	0	0	0	+5	+10	+15
Electric utilities	—	—	—	—	—	—	—	—	—	—	—	—	—	—	—	—	—	—	—	—	—	—	—	—
Agriculture																								
Diary farms ... 132	0	0	0	0	0	0	0	0	0	0	0	0	0	0	0	0	0	0	0	0	0	0	0	0
Poultry and eggs ... 133-134	0	0	0	0	0	0	0	0	0	0	0	0	0	0	0	0	0	0	0	0	0	0	0	0
Meat animals and misc. livestock production ... 135-136, 139,193	0	0	0	0	0	0	0	0	0	0	0	0	0	0	0	0	0	0	0	0	0	0	0	0
Cropland ... 113,114	—	—	—	—	—	—	—	—	—	—	—	—	—	—	—	—	—	—	—	—	—	—	—	—
Irrigated acreage ... 112,119,12	—	—	—	—	—	—	—	—	—	—	—	—	—	—	—	—	—	—	—	—	—	—	—	—
Manufacturing																								
Food and kindred products ... 20																								
Meat products ... 201	20	20	—	15	20	11	11	20	20	35	—	23	30	—	—	35	20	50	—	30	40	—	—	50
Dairy products ... 202	25	25	—	25	30	—	—	0	35	35	—	35	45	—	—	0	50	50	—	50	50	—	—	0
Canned and frozen foods ... 203	10	10	—	10	5	—	—	5	20	20	—	20	15	—	—	15	30	30	—	30	30	—	—	25
Sugar refining ... 206	20	20	—	20	20	—	—	20	20	25	—	25	25	—	—	25	40	40	—	40	40	—	—	40
All other food ... 204,205 207-209	10	10	—	20	20	—	—	20	15	15	—	25	25	—	—	25	20	20	—	30	30	—	—	30
Textile mill products ... 26	0	0	—	10	10	—	—	5	10	10	—	15	15	—	—	10	—	25	—	20	20	—	—	10
Paper and allied products ... 26	+15	+15	—	0	5	—	—	+10	+25	+25	—	+5	5	—	—	+20	+25	+25	—	+5	5	—	—	+20
Chemicals and allied products ... 28	20	20	—	15	25	—	—	+10	25	25	—	20	30	—	—	+10	25	25	—	20	30	—	—	+15
Petroleum and coal products ... 29	+15	+5	—	0	+10	—	—	+10	20	20	—	15	20	—	—	15	30	30	—	25	30	—	—	20
Primary metal industries ... 32	0	0	—	10	—	—	—	+10	0	0	—	15	0	—	—	+20	0	0	—	15	0	—	—	+25
Blast furnaces and steel mills ... 3312	0	0	—	10	0	—	—	+10	0	0	—	15	0	—	—	+20	0	0	—	15	0	—	—	+25
All other primary metals ... 333,334	0	0	—	0	0	—	—	0	0	0	—	0	0	—	—	0	0	0	—	0	0	—	—	0
Machinery, except electrical ... 35	5	5	—	20	20	—	—	20	10	10	—	25	25	—	—	20	10	10	—	30	30	—	—	20
Electrical machinery ... 36	5	5	—	20	20	—	—	20	10	10	—	25	25	—	—	20	10	10	—	30	30	—	—	20
Transportation equip. ... 37	5	5	—	20	20	—	—	20	10	10	—	25	25	—	—	20	10	10	—	30	30	—	—	20
All other manufacturing ... 21,23-25, 27,31,32,34, 38,39,19	5	5	—	20	20	—	—	20	10	10	—	25	25	—	—	20	10	10	—	30	30	—	—	20

Table 11.—Projected Trends in Unit Solid Waste Generation Loads from Selected Sectors of Economy—Percentage Changes from 1967 Loads, United States, 1980-2000

(Numbers indicate reductions unless otherwise indicated)

Sectors of economy	SIC No.	By 1980	By 1990	By 2000
Population in owner-occupied dwellings . . .	—	+30	+55	+75
Population in rental-occupied dwellings . . .	65$_p$	+30	+55	+75
All other real estate	65$_p$	+15	+30	+30
Solid waste incineration	4953$_p$	+40	+60	+70
Street refuse, urban areas	4953$_p$	+5	+10	+10
Electric utilities	491 4931	+5	+10	+10
Mining	10-14	+20	+40	+80
Agriculture	01	10	20	20
Manufacturing	—	—	—	—
Food and kindred products	20	30	40	50
Lumber and wood products	24	20	30	40
Furniture and fixtures . . .	25	20	30	40
Paper and allied products	26	+15	+20	+20
Printing and publishing . . .	27	10	15	15
Chemicals and allied products	28	+10	+15	+15
Rubber and plastics products	30	+10	+15	+15
Stone, clay and glass products	32	+10	+20	+20
Primary metal industries . .	33	+10	+20	+25
Miscellaneous	—	—	—	—
Demolition	—	0	0	0

provides a statutory basis for the air pollution standards in this cost study. In the case of water pollutants, the equivalent of secondary treatment has been assumed, since the degree of treatment necessary to achieve regional standards has never been established. It was assumed, also, that future solid waste disposal standards will not allow open dumping, and that solid wastes will be disposed of by incineration and/or sanitary landfills.

On the basis of the above assumptions, costs of waste treatment[11] per unit of waste were estimated and subsequently converted to costs of treatment per unit of output for each sector. Costs were based on the amount and type of fuel used for electric power and process heat, the volume of waste-water flow and wastes combined, and the characteristic residuals discharged from industrial processes based on various studies carried out by the Environmental Protection Agency and its predecessor agencies. Tables 12, 13, and 14 show the current cost estimates for waste treatment using the general methodology described above. Moreover, these costs have been elaborated to show the proportion of pollution cost attributed to each sector that provides inputs to the waste treatment industry. Tables 15, 16, and 17 indicate assumed allocation of the pollution abatement expenditures.

Tables 18 and 19 display, as an example, a detailed breakdown of expenditures for water pollution abatement for operating and capital costs.

The projections of abatement costs into the future were accomplished on the basis of projected waste load changes already discussed, but on the assumption of unchanging abatement costs per unit of residual. Obviously, this assumption is too simplistic and explicit technico-economic forecasts of abatement would be desirable.

REFERENCES

1. See, for instance, A. D. Little Interindustry Study, "Competition of Materials," published by *Scientific American*, 1968, and Anne P. Carter, *Structural Change in the American Economy* (Cambridge: Harvard University Press, 1970).

2. E. Mansfield, "Technical Change and the Rate of Imitation," *Econometrics*, 1961, Vol. 29, No. 4; G. Chow, "Technological Progress and the Demand for Computers," *American Economic Review*, December 1967; and J. C. Fisher and R. H. Pry, "A Simple Model of Technological Change," in *Practical Applications of Technological Forecasting in Industry*, M. Cetron and C. Ralph, eds. (New York: John Wiley and Sons, Inc., 1971).

3. R. U. Ayres, Stedman Noble, and Don Overly, "Technological Change as an Explicit Factor of Economic Growth," IRT-219-R (prepared for Resources for the Future, Inc., Washington, D.C., July 1971).

4. See for example, John H. Cumberland, "Application of Input-Output Technique to the Analysis of Environmental Problems," prepared for United Nations, Fifth International Conference on Input-Output Techniques, Geneva, Switzerland, January 11-19, 1971; see also, Wassily Leontief, "Environmental Repercussions and the Economic Structure: An Input-Output Approach," *The Review of Economics and Statistics*, August 1970.

5. The results are summarized in L. Ayres, I. Gutmanis, and A. Shapanka, "Environmental Implications of Technological and Economic Change for the United States 1967-2000: An Input-Output Analysis," IRT-229-R (prepared for Resources for the Future, Inc., December 1971).

6. L. Ayres, I. Gutmanis, "A Model for Strategic Allocation of Water Pollution Abatement Funds," IRT-R-43 (prepared for the Brookings Institution and the Urban Coalition, Washington, D.C., August 1971). Also, U.S. Water Resources Council, *The Nations Water Resources*, 1968.

7. *Municipal Refuse Disposal,* American Public Works Association, Chicago, 1970.

8. *Technical-Economic Study of Solid Waste Disposal Needs and Practices,* Combustion Engineering, Inc., Windsor, Conn., 1969.

9. Clopper Almon, Jr., *First Forecast with the 185-Sector Model* (Bureau of Business and Economic Research, University of Maryland, Feb. 1971), Vol. 1.

10. U.S. Bureau of the Census, *Statistical Abstract of the United States, 1970.*

11. As a rule, in all cases the abatement costs represented here are treatment costs. In some isolated instances, however, the cost calculations include some changes in production process modification. Such cases, however, are few.

Table 12.—Cost Coefficients for Air Pollution Abatement from Heat and Power Generation and Industrial Processes by Selected Sectors of Economy Per Unit of Output, Assuming Clean Air Act Standards, United States, 1967-1979

(All costs in 1967$)

I-O Sector No.	SIC No.	Sectors of economy	Total costs per unit of output	Total costs ($ million)	Total first round costs ($ million)	First round costs per unit of output	Total second round costs ($ million)	Second round costs per unit of output
167	—	Residential space heat; owner-occupied dwellings	0	0	0	0	0	0
168$_p$	65$_p$	Residential space heat; rental-occupied dwellings	0	0	0	0	0	0
168$_p$	65$_p$	All other space heat	376	21.6	20.52	357	1.08	19.0
193$_p$	4953$_p$	Solid waste incineration	49.1	97.18	92.32	467	4.86	24.0
180	491,4931	Electric utilities	18,709	366.36	348.04	17,773	18.32	936.0
163,164	49,50	Wholesale and retail trade	22	324	3.18	21	.06	1.0
151-155	40,42 44,45	Transportation						
155	45	Aircraft	500	—	—	—	—	—
51	40	Railroads	120	—	—	—	—	—
154	44	Vessels	80	—	—	—	—	—
152,153	41,42$_p$	Motor vehicles						
—	—	Passenger cars	6,600	—	—	—	—	—
152	41$_p$	Passenger buses	4,500	—	—	—	—	—
153	42	Motor freight transportation						
—	—	Non-highway use of motor fuels						
1-7	01	Agriculture						
		Manufacturing						
23-33	20	Food and kindred products	633.35	55.129	52.445	602	2.680	32.5
34	21	Tobacco products	193	1.4154	1.36	186	.05	7.0
35-38	22	Textile mill products	870	18.872	17.93	826	.94	44
39,40	23	Apparel and related products	93	1.8872	1.81	89	.07	4
41-44	24	Lumber and wood products	381	4.718	4.482	362	.236	19
45,46	25	Furniture and fixtures	317	2.359	2.265	305	.094	12
47-51	26	Paper and allied products	4,708	100.143	94.354	4,436	5.789	272
52-54	27	Printing and publishing	99	1.8872	1.81	95	.07	4
55-68	28	Chemicals and allied products	2,983.9	129.455	121.332	2,796.5	8.123	187.4

Table 12.—Continued

I-O Sector No.	SIC No.	Sectors of economy	Total costs per unit of output	Total costs ($ million)	Total first round costs ($ million)	First round costs per unit of output	Total second round costs ($ million)	Second round costs per unit of output
69,71	29	Petroleum and coal products	1,039	25.652	24.231	981	1.421	58
72-74	30	Rubber and miscellaneous plastic products	944.7	12.046	11.444	897.9	.602	46.8
73-77	31	Leather and leather products	599	2.831	2.689	569	.141	30
78-82	32	Stone, clay and glass products	6,486.2	90.895	85.952	6,133.2	4.943	353
82-91	33	Primary metal industries	16,838.7	676.938	630.412	13,854	46.526	2,984.7
92-101	34	Fabricated metal products	307	9.9078	9.412	291	.495	16
102-117	35	Machinery, except electrical	300	14.6258	13,895	285	.730	15
118-131	36	Electrical machinery	243	9.436	8.964	231	.472	12
132-140	37	Transportation equipment	282	19.816	18.825	268	.990	14
141-146	38	Instruments and related products	367	3.303	3.137	349	.165	18
20-22 147-150	19,39	Miscellaneous manufacturing, including ordnance	255	4.718	4.482	243	.236	12
—	—	Miscellaneous						

Table 13.—Cost Coefficients of Water Pollution Abatement by Selected Sectors of Economy per Unit of Output Assuming Secondary Treatment Efficiency, 1967-1979
(All Costs In 1967$)

I-O Sector No.	SIC No.	Sectors of economy	Total costs per unit of output	First round costs[a]	Second round costs[a]	Total costs ($ million)	Total first round costs ($ million)	First round costs per unit of output	Total second round costs ($ million)	Second round costs per unit of output
157p	—	Owner-occupied dwellings	24,079	15.2	3.8	19.0[b] 692	554	19,277	138	4,802
168p	65p	Rental-occupied dwellings, sewered population	21,817	15.2	3.8	19.0[b] 384	307	17,443	77	4,375
167p 188p	65p	Non-sewered population	58,609	45.0	4.4	49.4[b] 935	761	53,415	74	5,194
—	—	Runoff from urbanized areas	35,128	15.2	3.8	19.0[b] 971	777	28,110	194	7,019
160	491	Electric utilities								
1-7	—	Agriculture[c]								
1	132	Dairy farms								
2	134	Poultry and eggs	12,568	51.5	2.5	372	354	11,986	17	582
3	135-139	Meat animals and livestock								
5,6	113,114	Cropland	—							
7,4	12,112	Irrigated acreage	—							
—	—	Manufacturing								
23-33	20	Food and kindred products	2,295	33.0	6.3	39.3[b] 200	168	1,928	32	367
23	201	Meat products	1,863	35.0	3.9	38.9[b] 42	38	1,686	4	177

Table 13.—Continued

I-O Sector No.	SIC No.	Sectors of economy	Total costs per unit of output	First round costs[a]	Second round costs[a]	Total costs ($ million)	Total first round costs ($ million)	First round costs per unit of output	Total second round costs ($ million)	Second round costs per unit of output
24	202	Dairy products	785	24.0	2.5	26.5[b] 10	9.2	722	.8	63
25	203	Canned and frozen foods	3,951	36.0	3.9	39.6[b] 34	32	3,719	2	232
28	206	Sugar refining	48,404	33.8	3.9	47.7[b] 79	57	34,925	22	13,479
26,27 29-33	204,205 207-209	All other food	841	30.0	3.7	33.7[b] 35	32	769	3	72
35-38	22	Textile mill products	3,382	30.1	3.1	33.1 75	69	3,112	6	270
47-51	26	Paper and allied products	40,448	35.2	4.6	39.8[b] 844	747	35,800	97	4,648
55-68	28	Chemicals and allied products	8,047	24.1	5.7	29.8[b] 350	283	6,507	67	1,540
69-71	29	Petroleum and coal products	3,073	24.2	1.4	25.6[b] 73	70	2,947	3	126
83	331	Blast furnaces and steel mills	15,262	24.0	5.2	29.2[b] 490	345	12,537	75	2,779
83-91	33	Primary metal industries	12,639	24.0	5.2	29.2[b] 420	345	12,537	75	2,779
84-88	333,334	All other primary metals	6,222	24.0	5.2	29.2[b] 70	58	5,156	12	1,066
102-117	35	Machinery, except electrical	183	23.6	1.5	25.1[b] 9.3	8.8	173	.5	10
83	331	Electrical machinery	305	23.6	1.5	25.1[b] 12	11	279	1	26
132-140	37	Transportation equipment	275	23.6	1.5	25.1[b] 21	20	262	1	13
20-22, 34-39, 40-46, 52-54, 75-82, 89-101, 141-150	21, 23-25, 27,29, 31,32, 34,38, 39,19	All other manufacturing	509	28.0	2.4	30.4[b] 85	79	473	6	36

[a]Cents per thousand gallons.

[b]Combined first and second round costs (cents per gallon).

[c]Costs in Agriculture Sector are shown only for the entire sector.

Source: Leslie Ayres and Ivars Gutmanis, *A Model for Strategic Allocation of Water Pollution Abatement Funds*, IRT-R-43, August 1971.

Table 14.—Cost Coefficients of Solid Waste Disposal by Selected Sectors of Economy Per Unit of Output, United States, 1967-1979

I-O Sector No.	SIC No.	Sectors of economy	Total costs per unit of output	First round costs[a]	Second round costs[a]	Total costs ($ million)	Total first round costs ($ million)	First round costs per unit of output	Total second round costs ($ million)	Second round costs per unit of output
167	—	Population in owner-occupied dwellings	10,220	18.40	.90	1,282	19.3	9,741	60	479
168$_p$	65$_p$	Population in rental-occupied dwellings	8,824	18.40	.90	639	19.3	8,410	30	414
168$_p$	65$_p$	All other real estate	16,530	18.40	.90	950	19.3	15,747	45	783
193$_p$	4953$_p$	Solid waste incineration	692	3.00	—	137	3.0	692	—	—
160	491 4931	Electric utilities	2,860	2.50	—	56	2.50	2,860	—	—
193$_p$	4953$_p$	Street refuse, urban areas	889	18.40	.90	129	19.3	848	6	41
11-17	10-14	Mining	7,998	.15	—	177	.15	7,998	—	—
1-7	01	Agriculture	63,635	3.35	.15	3,232	3.50	61,784	94	1,951
—	—	Manufacturing								
23-33	20	Food and kindred products	425	4.80	.24	37	5.09	414	1	11
41-44	24	Lumber and wood products	13,694	4.50	.23	166	4.73	13,034	8	660
45,46	25	Furniture and fixtures	1,345	4.40	.22	10.2	4.62	1,304	.5	41
47-51	26	Paper and allied products	1,222	4.50	.23	26	4.73	1,175	1	47
52-54	27	Printing and publishing	2,095	4.50	.23	40	4.73	1,991	2	104
52-54	27	Chemicals and allied products	507	5.50	.66	22	6.16	461	2	46
72-74	30	Rubber and plastics products	1,334	5.00	.60	17	5.60	1,177	2	157
78-32	32	Stone, clay, and glass products	607	3.10	.16	8.5	3.26	578	.4	29
83-91	33	Primary metal industries	—	—	—	—	—	—	—	—
—	—	Miscellaneous								
—	—	Demolition	2,848	3.20	—	76	3.20	2,848	—	—

[a]Dollars per ton of solid waste.

Table 15.—Distribution of Annual Water Pollution Abatement Costs Among Major Expenditure Categories

Expenditure category	Proportion of expenditure
Capital expenditures	31.16%
Operating expenditures	68.84
Labor	33.87
Electricity	9.67
Utilities	3.22
Supplies	16.12
All other	5.96

Source: Leslie Ayres and Ivars Gutmanis, *A Model for Strategic Allocation of Water Pollution Abatement Funds*, RT-R-43, August 1971.

Table 16.—Distribution of Annual Air Pollution Abatement Costs Among Major Expenditure Categories

Expenditure category	Proportion of expenditure
Capital expenditures	35.32%
Operating expenditures	64.68
Labor	31.81
Electricity	9.09
Utilities	3.03
Supplies	15.15
All other	5.60

Source: Ivars Gutmanis, unpublished memorandum for Division of Air Pollution, Public Health Service, 1964; and IR&T engineering cost estimates.

Technological Change, Pollution and Treatment
Cost Coefficients in Input-Output Analysis

Table 17.—Distribution of Annual Solid Waste Disposal Costs Among Major Expenditure Categories

Expenditure category	Proportion of expenditure
Capital expenditures	40.76%
Operating expenditures	59.24
Labor	29.16
Electricity	8.33
Utilities	2.77
Supplies	13.88
All other	5.10

Source: International Research and Technology Corporation engineering cost estimates.

Table 18.—Distribution of Annual Operating Water Pollution Abatement Costs Among Sectors Supplying Required Goods and Services

Expenditure category	Supplying sectors			Proportion supplied
	I-O Sector No.	SIC No.	Sector title	
Labor				33.87%
Electricity	160	4910 4930	Electric utilities	9.67
Utilities	162	4940 4950 4960 4970	Water and sewer services	0.65
Supplies	55	2810	Industrial chemicals	8.00
	61	2861	Miscellaneous chemical products	8.60
	79	3251 3253 3255 3259	Structural clay	—
	69	2910 2990	Petroleum refining and related products	2.57
All other	39	2310-80 3670 3992	Apparel	.197
	46	2521-22 2531 2541-42 2591,99	Other furniture	.489
	67	2840-44	Cleaning & toilet preparations	.781
	73	3021 3031 3069	Rubber products	.685
	74	3079	Miscellaneous plastic products	.685
	76	3111 3121	Leather footwear	.197
	93	3491	Metal barrels, drums & pails	.095
	98	3421 3423 3425 3429	Cutlery, hand tools & hardware	.095
	149	3950	Office supplies	.584
	170	7200 7600	Personal & repair services	.781
	171	7300 7694 7699	Business services	.977
	173	7500	Automobile repair	.393

Source: Leslie Ayres and Ivars Gutmanis, *A Model for Strategic Allocation of Water Pollution Abatement Funds,* IRT-R-43, August 1971.

Table 19.—Distribution of Annual Water Pollution Capital Abatement Costs Among Supplying Sectors

I-O Sector No.	SIC No.	Sector title	Proportion supplied
4[a]		Industrial construction	14.02
19	1500	Maintenance and repair construction	1.25
95	3441-4 3446 3449	Structural metal products	.16
100	3494 3498	Valves, pipe fittings and fabricated pipes	2.49
101	3471 3479 3492-3 3496-7 3499	Other fabricated metal products	.16
102	3511 3519	Engines and turbines	.16
105	3534-7	Materials handling machinery	.93
109	3551-5 3559	Special industrial machinery	5.30
110	3561 3564	Pumps, compressors, blowers and fans	1.87
112	3566	Power transmission equipment	.47
116	3581-2 3585-6 3589	Service industry machinery	.16
118	3611	Electrical measuring instruments	.31
119	3612-3	Transformers and switchgear	.47
120	3621	Motors and generators	1.25
121	3622	Industrial controls	.93
124	3641-4	Electric lighting and wiring equipment	.16
132	3713 3715	Truck, bus and trailer bodies	.47
133	3711 3714 3717	Motor vehicles and parts	.47
142	3821-2	Mechnical measuring devices	.16
187	8200	Producers' durable equipment and construction	31.16

[a]Construction Sector 4.

Source: Leslie Ayres and Ivars Gutmanis, *A Model for Strategic Allocation of Water Pollution Abatement Funds,* IRT-R-43, August 1971.

PART II

Two
Other
Views

The Environmental Cost of Economic Growth

by
Barry Commoner
Washington University

COMMISSION ON POPULATION GROWTH AND
THE AMERICAN FUTURE, *RESEARCH
REPORTS, VOLUME III, POPULATION
RESOURCES AND THE ENVIRONMENT,*
EDITED BY RONALD G. RIDKER

CONTENTS

ABSTRACT

This paper is an evaluation of the environmental costs of economic growth. An analysis of the growth of a broad spectrum of productive activities in the United States economy since 1946 shows that many major environmental problems are primarily results neither of population growth nor of an increase in affluence, but of changing production technology. With very few exceptions, rapidly growing productive activities have intense environmental impacts, which are markedly greater than the impacts of the activities which they displace; the growth pattern is counter ecological.

For the purposes of this analysis, environmental impact (I) is defined as the amount of emission of an agent capable of degrading the ecosystem into which it is intruded, and is linked to economic and social factors by the following identity:

$$I = \text{Population} \times \frac{\text{Economic Good}}{\text{Population}} \times \frac{\text{Pollutant}}{\text{Economic Good}}$$

This relationship permits the estimation of the respective contribution to the total environmental impact of population size; production (or consumption) per capita, i.e., "affluence"; and environmental impact (i.e., amount of pollutant) generated per unit of production (or consumption), which reflects the nature of the productive technology.

It seems probable, if we are to survive economically as well as biologically, that much of the technological transformation of the United States economy since 1946 will need to be redone in order to bring the nation's productive technology much more closely into harmony with the inescapable demands of the ecosystem.

It has been pointed out often enough that environmental pollution represents a long-unpaid debt to nature. Is it possible that the United States economy has grown since 1946 by deriving much of its new wealth from enlargement of that debt? If this should turn out to be the case, what strains will develop in the economy if, for the sake of the survival of our society, that debt should now be recalled? How will these strains affect our ability to pay the debt—or to survive?

The Environmental Cost of Economic Growth

INTRODUCTION

This paper is concerned with an evaluation of the environmental costs of economic growth in the United States. This is a complex issue which has appeared rather suddenly on the horizon of public affairs; it therefore suffers somewhat from a high ratio of concern to fact. In addition, the issue is one which does not coincide with the domain of any established academic discipline. For environmental costs have been, until rather recently, so far removed from the concerns of orthodox economics as to have been nearly banished from that realm under the term "externalities." And for its part, the discipline of ecology has, also until very recently, maintained a position of lofty disdain for such mundane matters as the price of ecological purity.

It is useful to begin with a brief summary of the ecological background of the issue. This follows:

1. The environment is defined as a system comprising the earth's living things and the thin global skin of air, water and soil which is their habitat.

2. This system, the ecosphere, is the product of the joint, interdigitated evolution of living things and of the physical and chemical constituents of the earth's surface. On the time scale of human life, the evolutionary development of the ecosphere has been very slow and irreversible. Hence the ecosphere is irreplaceable; if the system should be destroyed, it could never be reconstituted or replaced either by natural processes or by human effort.

3. The basic functional element of the ecosphere is the ecological cycle, in which each separate element influences the behavior of the rest of the cycle, and is in turn itself influenced by it. For example, in surface waters fish excrete organic waste, which is converted by bacteria to inorganic products; in turn, the latter are nutrients for algal growth; the algae are eaten by the fish, and the cycle is complete. Such a cyclical process accomplishes the self-purification of the environmental system, in that wastes produced in one step in the cycle become the necessary raw materials for the next step. Such cycles are cybernetically self-governed, dynamically maintaining a steady state condition of indefinite duration. However if sufficiently stressed by an external agency, such a cycle may exceed the limits of its self-governing processes and eventually collapse. Thus, if the water cycle is overloaded with organic animal waste, the amount of oxygen needed to support waste decomposition by the bacteria of decay may be greater than the oxygen available in the water. The oxygen level is then reduced to zero; lacking the needed oxygen, the bacteria die and this phase of the cycle stops, halting the cycle as a whole. It becomes evident, then, that there is an inherent limit to the turnover rate of local ecosystems and of the global ecosystem as a whole.

4. Human beings are dependent on the ecosphere not only for their biological requirements (oxygen, water, food) but also for resources which are essential to all their productive activities. These resources, together with underground minerals, are the irreplaceable and essential foundation of all human activities.

5. If we regard economic processes as the means which govern the disposition and use of resources available to human society, then it is evident from the above that the continued availability of those resources which are derived from the ecosphere (i.e., non-mineral resources), and therefore the stability of the ecosystem, is an essential prerequisite for the success of any economic system. More bluntly, any economic system which hopes to survive must be compatible with the continued operation of the ecosystem.

6. Because the turnover rate of an ecosystem is inherently limited, there is a corresponding limit to the rate of production of any of its constituents. Different segments of the global ecosystem (for example, soil, fresh water, marine ecosystems) operate at different intrinsic turnover rates and therefore differ in the limits of their productivity. On purely theoretical grounds, it is self-evident that any economic system which is impelled, by its own requirements for stability, to grow by constantly increasing the rate at which it extracts wealth from the ecosystem must eventually drive the ecosystem to a state of collapse. Computation of the rate limits of the global ecosystem or of any major part of it are, as yet, in a rather primitive state. Apart from the foregoing theoretical and as yet unspecified limit to economic growth, such a limit may arise much more rapidly if the growth of the economic system is dependent on produc-

tive activities which are especially destructive of the stability of the ecosystem.

7. Unlike all other forms of life, human beings are capable of exerting environmental effects which extend, both quantitatively and qualitatively, far beyond their influence as biological organisms. Human activities have also introduced into the environment not only intense stresses due to natural agents (such as bodily wastes), but also wholly new substances not encountered in natural environmental processes: artificial radioisotopes, detergents, pesticides, plastics, a variety of toxic metals and gases, and a host of man-made, synthetic substances. These human intrusions on the natural environment have thrown major segments of the ecosystem out of balance. Environmental pollution is the symptom of the resultant breakdown of the environmental cycles.

THE PROBLEM

In order to evaluate the cost of economic growth in terms of the resultant environmental deterioration, it is, of course, necessary to define both terms, if possible, in quantitative dimensions that might permit a description of their relationship. The common definition of economic growth would appear to be applicable here: the increase in the goods generated by economic activity. Environmental deterioration is a more elusive concept. On the basis of the foregoing discussion it may be defined as degradative changes in the ecosystems which are the habitat of all life on the planet. The problem is, then, to describe such ecological changes in terms that can be related, quantitatively if possible, to the processes of economic growth—i.e., to increased production of economic goods.

To begin with we can take note of the self-governing nature of the ecosystem. It is this property which ensures its stability and continued activity. This basic property helps to define both the process of ecological degradation and the nature of the agencies that can induce it. We can define ecological, or environmental, degradation as a process which so stresses an ecosystem as to reduce its capability for self-adjustment, and which, therefore, if continued can impose an irreversible stress on the system and cause it to collapse.

An agency which is capable of exerting such an effect on an ecosystem must arise from *outside* that system. This is because the cyclical nature of the ecosystem causes it to automatically readjust to any *internal* change in the number or activity of any of its normal biological constituents. For what characterizes the behavior of a constituent which is part of an ecological cycle is that it both influences and is influenced by the remainder of the cycle. For example, organic waste produced by fish in a closed aquatic ecosystem, such as a balanced aquarium, cannot degrade

the system because the waste is converted to algal nutrients, and simply moves through the ecological cycle back to fish. In contrast, if organic waste intrudes upon this same ecosystem from without, it is certain to speed up the cycle's turnover rate and, if sufficiently intense, to consume all of the available oxygen, and bring the cycle to a halt.

The internal changes in an ecosystem which occur in response to an external stress are complex, non-linear processes and not readily reduced to simple quantitative indices. The aquatic ecosystem is one of the relatively few instances in which this goal can, to some degree, be approached—in that oxygen tension is a sensitive internal indicator of the system's approach to instability. However, in most cases such internal measures of the state of an ecosystem have not yet been elucidated. Hence, as a practical, but, it is to be hoped, temporary expedient we need to fall back on a measure of the *impact* on the ecosystem of an external degradative agency as an index of environmental quality. This expedient has the virtue of enabling the quantitative comparison of the effects of ecological impacts of different origins, a matter of particular importance in connection with their relation to economic processes. Such data can later be translated to the resultant internal changes, when the necessary ecological information becomes available.

In what follows, then, the environmental cost of a given economic process will be represented by its *environmental impact,* a term which has the dimensions of the amount of an agency external to the ecosystem which, by intruding upon it, tends to degrade the system's capacity for self-adjustment.

Turning now to the possible environmental impacts that may result from *human* activity, we find the situation somewhat complicated by the special role of human beings on the earth. In one sense, human beings are simply another animal in the earth's ecosystem, consuming oxygen and organic foodstuff and producing carbon dioxide, organic wastes, heat, and more people. In this role, the human being is a constituent part of an ecosystem and, therefore, in terms of the previous definition, exerts no environmental impact on it. However, a human population has a zero environmental impact only as long as it is in fact part of an ecosystem—for example, if food is acquired from soil which receives the population's organic waste. If a population is separated from this cycle, for example by settling in a city, their wastes are intruded, with or without treatment, into surface waters. Now the population is no longer a part of the soil ecosystem, and the wastes become *external* to the *aquatic* system on which they intrude. Here an environmental impact is generated, leading to water pollution.

On the basis of these considerations, then, people—viewed simply as biological organisms—generate an environmental impact only insofar as they become separated from the ecosystem to which, in nature, terrestrial animals belong. This is, of course, nearly universally true in the United States. The intensity of this environmental impact is generally proportional to the population size.

All other environmental impacts are generated not by human biological activities, but by human *productive activities,* and are therefore governed by economic processes. Such impacts may be generated in several different ways:

1. Certain economic gains can be derived from an ecosystem by exploiting its biological productivity. In these cases, a constituent of the ecosystem which has economic value—for example, an agricultural crop, timber or fish—is withdrawn from the ecosystem. Insofar as the withdrawn substance or a suitable substitute fails to return as nutrient to the ecosystem from which it was removed, it constitutes a drain on that system which cannot continue indefinitely without causing it to collapse. Destructive erosion of the soil following excessive exploitation or the incipient destruction of the whaling industry due to the extinction of whales are examples of such effects.

2. Environmental stress may also arise from an intrusion of opposite sign to that described above—that is, the amount of some component of the ecosystem is augmented from outside that system. This may be done either for the purpose of disposing of waste or in order to accelerate the system's rate of turnover and thus increase its yield. Examples of these effects are the intrusion of sewage into surface water and the intensive use of fertilizer nitrogen in agriculture. In the latter case, following a reduction in the nitrogen available from the soil's natural store of nutrient (its organic humus) due to a period of over-exploitation through uncompensated crop withdrawal (i.e. a stress of the type described in (1) above), the nitrate level is artificially raised by adding fertilizer to the soil's ecological cycle. Because of the low efficiency of nutrient uptake by the crop's roots (which is in turn a result of inadequate soil energy due to reduced porosity stemming from the decreased humus content) a considerable portion of the fertilizer leaches from the soil into surface waters—where it becomes an external stress on the aquatic ecosystem, causing algal overgrowths and the resulting breakdown of the self-purifying aquatic cycle.

3. Apart from the above stresses—which represent the impact of externally altered concentrations of natural ecosystem constituents—environmental impact may be due to the intrusion into an ecosystem of a substance wholly foreign to it. Thus, DDT has a

powerful environmental impact in part because it readily upsets the naturally balanced ecological relations among plants, insect pests, and the insects which, in turn, prey on the pests. DDT-induced outbreaks of insect pests often result. In general, there is a considerable risk of environmental pollution whenever productive activity introduces foreign substances into the natural environment.

We turn now to the practical problem of evaluating the environmental cost of economic growth. The most general theoretical aspect of this problem has already been alluded to: Given that the global ecosystem is closed and that its integrity is essential to the continued operation of any conceivable economic system, it is evident that there must be an upper limit to the growth of productive activities on the earth.

However, such a theoretical statement is hardly an effective guide to practice. The chief reason is that the theory fails to specify the time scale in which the ecological limitation on economic growth is likely to take effect. For one can readily grant the truth of such an abstract theorem—for example, that economic growth will eventually be limited by the extinction of the sun—and disregard its practical consequences because of the rather long time scale involved, in this case some billions of years.

Accordingly it would seem useful to make the problem more concrete by examining the relationship between economic growth and environmental impact in the real world. And since growth is, of course, a time-dependent process, this suggests the value of an historical approach.

THE ORIGINS OF ENVIRONMENTAL IMPACTS

In what follows, I wish to report the results of an initial effort to describe the origins of environmental impacts in the United States.[1] Most United States pollution problems are of relatively recent origin. The postwar period, 1945-46, is a convenient benchmark, for a number of pollutants—man-made radioisotopes, detergents, plastics, synthetic pesticides, and herbicides—are due to the emergence, after the war, of new productive technologies. The statistical data available for this period in the United States provide a useful opportunity to compare the changes in the levels of various pollutants with the concurrent activities of the United States productive system.

Although, unfortunately, we lack sufficient comprehensive data on the actual environmental levels of most pollutants in the United States, some estimates of historical changes can be made from intermittent observations and from computed data on emissions of pollutants from their sources. Some of the available data are summarized in Table 1, which indicates that since 1946, emissions of pollutants have increased by 200-2000 percent. In the case of phosphate, which is a pollutant of surface waters and enters mainly from municipal sewage, data on the long-term trends are available,[2] these are shown in Figure 1. In the 30-year period between 1910 and 1940, phosphorus output from municipal sewage increased gradually from about 17 million lbs./year to about 40 million lbs./year. Thereafter the rate of output rose rapidly, so that in the 30-year period 1940-1970, phosphorus output increased to about 300 million lbs./year.

tions of different sources to the overall degradation of the environment.

If we define the amount of a given pollutant introduced annually into the environment as the *environmental impact* (I), it then becomes possible to relate this value to the effects of three major factors that might influence the value of I by means of the following identity:

$$I = \text{Population} \times \frac{\text{Economic Good}}{\text{Population}} \times \frac{\text{Population}}{\text{Economic Good}}$$

Here *Population* refers to the size of the United States population in a given year; *Economic Good* refers to the

Table 1.—Post-War Increases in Pollutant Emissions

Pollutant	Annual production				Percent increase over indicated period
	Year	Amount	Year	Amount	
Inorganic fertilizer nitrogen	1949	.91 × 10⁶ tons	1968	6.8 × 10⁶ tons	648
Synthetic organic pesticides	1950	286 × 10⁶ lbs.	1967	1,050 × 10⁶ lbs.	267
Detergent phosphorus	1946	11 × 10⁶ lbs.	1968	214 × 10⁶ lbs.	1,845
Tetraethyl lead[a]	1946	.048 × 10⁶ tons	1967	.25 × 10⁶ tons	415
Nitrogen oxides[a]	1946	10.6[b]	1947	77.5[b]	630
Beer bottles	1950	6.5 × 10⁶ gross	1967	45.5 × 10⁶ gross	595

[a]Automotive emissions.

[b]Dimension = NO_x (ppm) × gasoline consumption (gals × 10^{-6}); estimated from product of passenger vehicle gasoline consumption and ppm of NO_x emitted by engines of average compression ratio 5.9 (1946) and 9.5 (1967) under running conditions, at 15 in. manifold pressure. NO_x emitted: 550 ppm in 1946; 1200 ppm in 1967 (Ref.).

It should be noted that these are data regarding the computed *emission* of pollutants, which are not necessarily descriptive of their actual concentrations in the environment or of their ultimate effects on the ecosystems or on human health. Numerous, complex and interrelated processes intervene between the entry of a pollutant into the ecosystem and the expression of its biological effect. Moreover, two or more pollutants may interact synergistically to intensify the separate effects. Most of these processes are still too poorly understood to enable us to convert the amount of a pollutant entering an ecosystem to a quantitative estimate of its degradative effects. Nevertheless it is self-evident that these effects (such as the incidence of respiratory disease due to air pollutants or of algal overgrowths due to phosphate and nitrate) have increased sharply, along with the rapid rise of pollutant levels, since 1946. Since pollutant emission is a direct measure of the activity of the source, it is a useful way to estimate the contribu-

amount of a designated good produced (or, where appropriate, consumed) during the given year; and *Pollutant* refers to the amount of a specific pollutant (defined as above) released into the environment as a result of the production (or consumption) of the designated good during the given year. This relationship enables us to estimate the contribution of three factors to the total environmental impact: (1) the size of the population; (2) the production (or consumption) per capita, i.e., "affluence"; and (3) the environmental impact (i.e., amount of pollutant) generated per unit of production (or consumption), which reflects the nature of the productive technology.

Since we are concerned with identifying the sources of the sharp increases in the environmental impacts experienced in the United States in the period from 1946 to the present, it becomes of interest to examine the concurrent changes in the nation's productive activities. The most general data relevant to these

Population, Resources, and the Environment

FIGURE 1
PHOSPHORUS EMITTED BY UNITED STATES MUNICIPAL SEWAGE

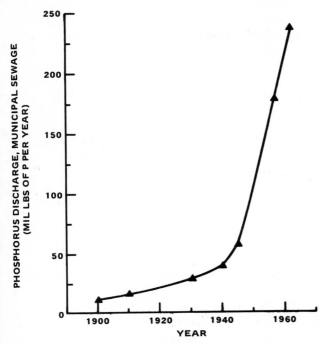

Source: U.S. Congress, House, Committee on Science and Astronautics, *The Adequacy of Technology for Pollution Abatement, Hearings* before the Subcommittee on Science, Research and Development, by L.W. Weinberger, et al., 89th Cong., 2nd Sess., 1966, Vol. II, p. 756.

changes are presented in Figure 2. In the period 1946-68, United States population has increased at an approximately constant rate by about 42 percent; GNP (adjusted to 1958 dollars) has increased exponentially by about 126 percent in that period; GNP per capita has also increased approximately exponentially by about 59 percent.

We can see at once that, as a first approximation, the contribution of population growth to the overall values of the environmental impacts generated since 1946 is on the order of 40 percent. In most cases, this represents a relatively small contribution to the total environmental impact, since these values increased by 200-2000 percent, in that period of time. (See Table 1.)

In order to evaluate the effects of the remaining factors it is useful to examine the growth rates of different sectors of the productive economy. For this purpose, a series of productive activities which are likely to contribute significantly to environmental impact and are representative of the overall pattern of the economy have been selected. From the annual production (or where appropriate, consumption) data for the United States as a whole, the annual percentage rates of increase

or decrease are calculated by computer. The results of these computations are presented in Figure 3. From these, it is possible to derive certain useful generalizations about the pattern of economic growth, which are relevant to environmental impacts:

1. Production and consumption of certain goods have increased at an annual rate about equal to that of the population, so that *per capita* production remains essentially unchanged. This group includes food, fabric and clothing, major household appliances, and certain basic metals and building materials, including steel, copper, and brick. In effect, with respect to these basic items, average "affluence"—that is, per capita production (or consumption)—has remained essentially unchanged in 1946-68.

2. The annual production of certain other goods has decreased since 1946, or has increased at an annual rate below that of the population. Horsepower produced by work animals is the extreme case; it declined at an annual rate of about 10 percent. Other items in this category are saponifiable fat, cotton fiber, wool fiber, lumber, milk, railroad horsepower, and railroad freight. These are goods which have been significantly displaced in the pattern of production during the course of the overall growth of the economy. Cultivated farm acreage also declined in this period.

FIGURE 2
CHANGES IN POPULATION, GROSS NATIONAL PRODUCT (REDUCED TO 1958 DOLLARS) AND GNP PER CAPITA FOR THE UNITED STATES SINCE 1946

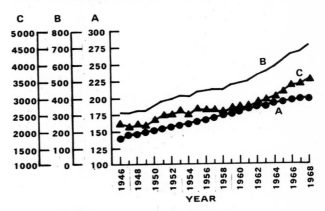

A - RESIDENT POPULATION (MILLIONS)
B - GNP (BIL 1958 $)
C - GNP/CAP. (1958 $)

Sources: U.S. Bureau of the Census, *Statistical Abstract of the United States*, 1970, p. 5 and U.S. Department of Commerce, *The National Income and Product Accounts of the United States, 1929-1965*, 1966, pp. 4-5.

3. Among the productive activities which have increased at an annual rate in excess of that exhibited by the population, the following classes can be discerned:

First, there are certain productive activities which are substitutes for activities that have declined in rate, relative to population. These generally represent technological displacement of an older process by a newer one, with the sum of goods produced remaining essentially constant, per capita, or increasing somewhat. These displacement processes include the following: natural fibers (cotton and wool) by synthetic fibers, lumber by plastics, soap by detergents, steel by aluminum and cement, railroad freight by truck freight, harvested acreage by fertilizer, and returnable by non-returnable bottles.

The second group of rapidly growing productive activities evident in Figure 3 are secondary consequences of displacement processes. Thus the displacement of natural products by synthetic ones involves the increased use of synthetic organic chemicals, so that this category has increased sharply. Moreover, since many organic syntheses require chlorine as a reagent, the rate of chlorine production has also increased rapidly. Finally, because chlorine is efficiently produced in a mercury electrolytic cell, the use of mercury for this purpose has also increased at a very considerable rate. Similarly, the rapidly rising rate of power utilization is, in part, a secondary consequence of certain displacement processes, for a number of the new technologies are more power consumptive than the technologies which they replace.

Finally, among the rapidly growing productive activities evident in Figure 3 are some which represent neither displacements of older technologies, nor sequelae to such displacements, but true increments in per capita availability of goods. An example of this category is consumer electronics (radios, television sets, sound equipment, etc.). Such items represent true increases in "affluence."

In sum, the pattern of growth in the United States economy in 1946-68 may be generalized as follows: Basic life necessities, representing perhaps one-third of the total GNP, have grown in annual production at about the pace of population growth, so that no significant overall change in *per capita* production has taken place in this period. However, within these general categories of goods—food, fiber and clothing; freight haulage; and household necessities—there has been a pronounced displacement of natural products by synthetic ones, of power-conservative products by relatively power-consumptive ones, of reusable containers by "disposable" ones.

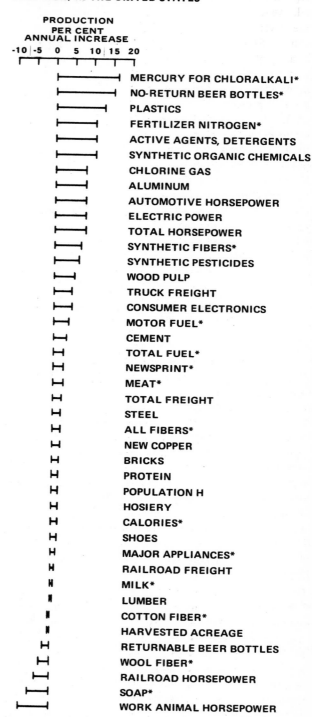

FIGURE 3

ANNUAL GROWTH RATES OF PRODUCTION (OR CONSUMPTION) IN THE UNITED STATES

PRODUCTION
PER CENT
ANNUAL INCREASE
-10 -5 0 5 10 15 20

MERCURY FOR CHLORALKALI*
NO-RETURN BEER BOTTLES*
PLASTICS
FERTILIZER NITROGEN*
ACTIVE AGENTS, DETERGENTS
SYNTHETIC ORGANIC CHEMICALS
CHLORINE GAS
ALUMINUM
AUTOMOTIVE HORSEPOWER
ELECTRIC POWER
TOTAL HORSEPOWER
SYNTHETIC FIBERS*
SYNTHETIC PESTICIDES
WOOD PULP
TRUCK FREIGHT
CONSUMER ELECTRONICS
MOTOR FUEL*
CEMENT
TOTAL FUEL*
NEWSPRINT*
MEAT*
TOTAL FREIGHT
STEEL
ALL FIBERS*
NEW COPPER
BRICKS
PROTEIN
POPULATION H
HOSIERY
CALORIES*
SHOES
MAJOR APPLIANCES*
RAILROAD FREIGHT
MILK*
LUMBER
COTTON FIBER*
HARVESTED ACREAGE
RETURNABLE BEER BOTTLES
WOOL FIBER*
RAILROAD HORSEPOWER
SOAP*
WORK ANIMAL HORSEPOWER

*CONSUMPTION

Source: U.S. Bureau of the Census, *Statistical Abstract of the United States*, 1948-1970.

Population, Resources, and the Environment

THE ENVIRONMENTAL IMPACT OF ECONOMIC GROWTH

Given the foregoing conclusions we can now rephrase the original question as follows: What are the relative costs, in intensity of environmental impact, of the several distinctive features of the growth of the United States economy from 1946 to the present? Reasonably complete quantitative answers to this question are, unfortunately, well beyond the present state of knowledge. At the present time, it is possible in most cases to provide only an informal qualitative description of the changes in environmental impact which have been induced by the postwar transformation of the United States economy. In some cases, it is also possible to produce a quantitative evaluation in the form of an Environmental Impact Index, and in a few cases a partial Environmental Impact Inventory can be constructed. As shown below, evidence leads to the general conclusion that in most of the technological displacements which have accompanied the growth of the United States economy since 1946, *the new technology has an appreciably greater environmental impact than the technology which it has displaced; and the postwar technological transformation of productive activities is the chief reason for the present environmental crisis.*

Agricultural Production

As shown in Figure 3, agricultural production in the United States, as measured by the Department of Agriculture Crop Index, has increased at about the same rate as the population since 1946. However, the technological methods for achieving agricultural production have changed significantly in that period. One important change is illustrated by Figure 4, which shows that although agricultural production per capita has increased only slightly, harvested acreage has decreased, and the use of inorganic nitrogen fertilizer has risen sharply. This displacement process—i.e., of fertilizer for land—leads to a considerably increased environmental impact.

Briefly stated, the relevant ecological situation is the following:[3] Nitrogen, an essential constituent of all living things, is available to plants in nature from organic nitrogen, stored in the soil in the form of humus. Humus is broken down by bacteria to release inorganic forms of nitrogen, eventually as nitrate. The latter is taken up by the plant roots and reconverted to organic matter, such as the plant's protein. Finally the plant may be eaten by a grazing animal, which returns the nitrogen not retained in the growth of its own body to the soil as bodily wastes.

Agriculture imposes a negative drain on this cycle; nitrogen is removed from the system in the form of the plant crop or of the livestock produced from it. In

FIGURE 4

CHANGES IN TOTAL CROP OUTPUT (AS DETERMINED BY U.S.D.A. CROP INDEX), IN CROP OUTPUT PER CAPITA, IN HARVESTED ACREAGE, AND IN ANNUAL USE OF INORGANIC NITROGEN FERTILIZER IN THE UNITED STATES SINCE 1946

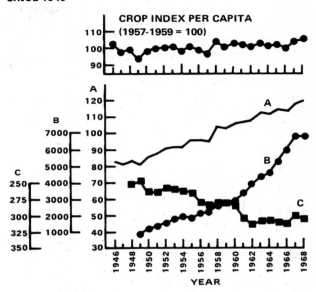

A - CROP OUTPUT INDEX (1957-1959 = 100)
B - FERTILIZER NITROGEN (1000'S OF TONS)
C - MILLIONS OF ACRES HARVESTED

Sources: U.S. Department of Agriculture, *Agricultural Statistics*, 1967, pp. 531, 544, and 583; and 1970, pp. 444, 454, and 481.

ecologically sound husbandry all of the organic nitrogen produced by the soil system, other than the food itself—plant residues, manure, garbage—is returned to the soil, where it is converted by complex microbial processes to humus and thus helps to restore the soil's organic nitrogen content. The deficit, if it is not too large, can be made up by the process of nitrogen fixation, in which bacteria, usually in close association with the roots of certain plants, take up nitrogen gas from the air and convert it into organic form. If the nitrogen cycle is not in balance, agriculture "mines" the soil nitrogen, progressively depleting it. This process does more than reduce the store of organic nitrogen available to support plant growth, for humus is not only a nutrient store. Due to its polymeric structure humus is also responsible for the porosity of the soil to air. And air is essential to the soil, not only as a source of nitrogen for fixation, but also because its oxygen is essential to the root's metabolic activity, which in turn is the driving force for the absorption of nutrients by the roots. In the United States, for example in Corn Belt soils, about one-half of the original soil organic nitrogen has been lost since 1880. Naturally, other things being equal, such soil is relatively infertile and produces relatively poor crop yields. However, beginning after World War II, a technological solution was intensively applied to this problem: Sharply increasing amounts of inorganic nitrogen were applied to the soil in the form of fertilizer. Annual nitrogen fertilizer usage in the United States increased by an order of magnitude in 1946-68.

In effect, then, nitrogen fertilizer can be regarded as a substitute for land. With the intensive use of fertilizer, it becomes possible to accelerate the turnover rate of the soil ecosystem, so that each acre of soil annually produces more food than before. The economic benefits of this new agricultural technology are appreciable and self-evident. However, this economic advantage may be counterbalanced by the increased impact on the environment. This arises because, given the reduced humus content of the soil, the plant's roots do not efficiently absorb the added fertilizer. As a result, an appreciable part leaches from the soil as nitrate and enters surface waters where it becomes a serious pollutant. Nitrate may encourage algal overgrowths, which on their inevitable death and decay tend to break down the self-purifying aquatic cycle.

Excess nitrate from fertilizer drainage leads to another environmental impact, which may affect human health. While nitrate in food and drinking water appears to be relatively innocuous, *nitrate* is not, for it combines with hemoglobin in the blood, converting it to methemoglobin—which cannot carry oxygen. Unfortunately nitrate can be converted to nitrite by the action of bacteria in the intestinal tract, especially in infants, causing asphyxiation and even death. On these grounds, the United States Public Health Service has established 10 ppm of nitrate nitrogen as the acceptable limit of nitrate in drinking water. In a number of agricultural areas in the United States, nitrate levels in water supplies obtained from wells, and in some instances from surface waters, have exceeded this limit. Our own studies in the area of Decatur, Illinois show quite directly that in the spring of 1970 when the city's water supply, which is derived from an impoundment of the Sangamon River, recorded 9 ppm of nitrate nitrogen, a minimum of 60 percent of the nitrate was derived from inorganic fertilizer applied to the surrounding farmland.[4]

The effect of this change in agricultural technology is evident from Table 2, which compares relative influence on the total environmental impact of the component factors influence in 1968. During that period, the total annual use of fertilizer nitrogen, i.e., the total environmental impact, increased 648 percent. The influence of population size increased by 34 percent; the influence of crop production per capita ("affluence") increased by 11 percent; the influence of the change in fertilizer technology increased by 405 percent. Clearly the last factor dominates the large increase in the total environmental impact of fertilizer nitrogen. Specifically, it should be noted that in 1949 about 11,000 tons of fertilizer nitrogen were used *per unit crop production,* while in 1968 about 57,000 tons of nitrogen were employed for the *same* crop yield. This means that the efficiency with which fertilizer nitrogen contributes to crop yield has *declined* five-fold. Obviously an appreciable part of the added nitrogen does not enter the crop and must appear elsewhere in the ecosystem.

The biological basis for this effect is shown in Figure 5, which compares the corn yield in the State of Illinois with the concurrent amounts of nitrogen fertilizer added to the soil.[5] This shows that as fertilizer levels increased, the yield per acre rose; but eventually the

Table 2.—Environmental Impact Index—Fertilizer Nitrogen

	(a) Population (1,000's)	Index factors (b) Crop production Population (prod. units/cap.)	(c) Fertilizer nitrogen Crop production (tons/prod. unit)	Total index Fertilizer nitrogen (1,000's of tons)
1949	149,304	5.43×10^{-7}	11,284[a]	914
1968	199,846	6.00×10^{-7}	57,008	6,841
1968:1949	1.34	1.11	5.05	7.48
Percent increase	34	11	405	648

[a]The crop output index is an indicator of agricultural productivity with the 1957-1959 average = 100.

FIGURE 5
CORN YIELD AND NITROGEN USAGE FOR THE STATE OF ILLINOIS

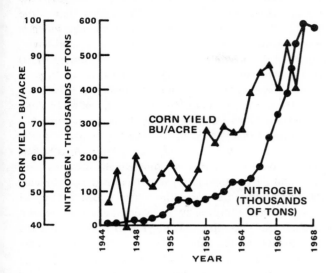

yield leveled off due to the natural limits of plant growth. Thus, between 1962 and 1968, fertilizer usage doubled; but crop yield rose only about 10-15 percent. Clearly at the higher levels of fertilizer usage an increasingly small proportion of the fertilizer contributes to the crop. As indicated earlier, the remainder leaches into surface waters where it causes serious pollution problems. Thus, this innovation in agricultural technology sharply increases the environmental stress due to agricultural production.

A similar situation exists in the case of pesticides. This is shown by the changes in the environmental impact index of pesticides between 1950 and 1967 (Table 3). In that time, there was a 168 percent increase in the amount of pesticides used *per unit crop production,* as a national average. By killing off natural insect

predators and parasites of the target pest, while the latter often becomes resistant to insecticides, the use of modern synthetic insecticides tends to exacerbate the pest problems that they were designed to control. As a result, *increasing* amounts of insecticides must be used to maintain agricultural productivity. Insecticide usage is, so to speak, self-accelerating—resulting in both a decreased efficiency and an increased environmental impact.

Another instance of technological displacement in agriculture is the increased use of feedlots for the production of livestock in preference to range feeding. Range-fed cattle are integrated into the soil ecosystem; they graze the soil's grass crop and restore nutrient to the soil as manure. When the cattle are maintained instead in huge pens, where they are fed on corn and deposit their wastes intensively in the feedlot itself, the wastes do not return to the soil. Instead the waste drains into surface waters where it adds to the stresses due to fertilizer nitrogen and detergent phosphate. The magnitude of the effect is considerable. At the present time, the organic waste produced in feedlots is more than the organic waste produced by all the cities of the United States. Again, the newer technology has a serious environmental impact, and in this case has displaced a technology with an essentially zero environmental impact.

Textiles

Figure 6 describes changes in textile production since 1946. While total fiber production per capita has remained constant, natural fibers (cotton and wool) have been significantly displaced by synthetic ones. This technological change considerably increases the environmental impact due to fiber production and use.

One reason is that the energy required for the synthesis of the final product, a linear polymer (cellulose

Table 3.—Synthetic Organic Pesticides

	Index factors			Total index
	(a)	(b)	(c)	(a × b × c)
		Crop production	Pesticide consumption	Synthetic organic pesticides (million lbs.)
	Population (1,000's)	Population (crop production units/cap.)	Crop production (1,000 lbs./ production unit)	
1950	151,868	5.66×10^{-7}	3,326	286
1967	197,859	5.96×10^{-7}	8,898	1,050
1967:1950	1.30	1.05	2.68	3.67
Percent increase, 1967:1950	30	5	168	267

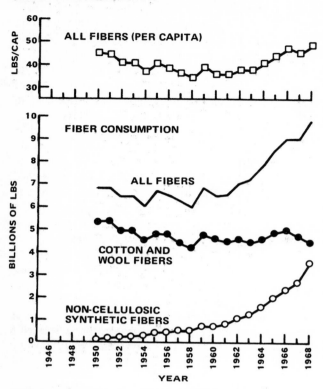

FIGURE 6

NATURAL AND SYNTHETIC FIBER PRODUCTION IN THE UNITED STATES SINCE 1946

Source: U.S. Bureau of the Census, *Statistical Abstract of the United States,* 1962, p. 198; 1966, p. 789; and 1970, p. 713.

in the case of cotton, keratin in the case of wool, and polyamides in the case of nylon), is greater for the synthetic material. Although quantitative data are not yet available, this is evident from the comparison of productive processes of cotton and nylon provided by Table 4. Nylon production involves as many as 10 steps of chemical synthesis, each requiring considerable energy in the form of heat and electric power to overcome the entropy associated with chemical mixtures and to operate the reaction apparatus. In contrast, energy required for the synthesis of cotton is derived, free, from a renewable source—sunlight—and is transferred without combustion and resultant air pollution. Moreover, the raw material for cellulose synthesis is carbon dioxide and water, both freely available renewable resources, while the raw material for nylon synthesis is petroleum or a similar hydrocarbon—nonrenewable resources. As a result it would appear that the environmental stress due to the *production* of such an artificial fiber is probably well in excess of that due to the production of an equal weight of cotton. This is only an approximation, for we need far more detailed, quantitative estimates, in the form of the appropriate environmental impact indices,

that would also take into account the fuel and other materials used in the production of cotton.

Because a synthetic fiber such as nylon is unnatural, it also has a greater impact on the environment as a waste material, than do cotton or wool. The natural polymers in cotton and wool, cellulose and keratin are important constituents of the soil ecosystem. Through the action of molds and decay bacteria they contribute to the formation of humus—a substance which is essential to the natural fertility of the soil. In this process cellulose is readily broken down in the soil ecosystem. Thus, in nature, cellulose and keratin are *not* "wastes," because they provide essential nutrients for soil micro-organisms. Hence they cannot accumulate. This results from the crucial fact that for every polymer which is produced in nature by living things, there exist in some living things enzymes which have the specific capability of degrading that polymer. In the absence of such an enzyme the natural polymers are quite resistant to degradation, as evident from the durability of fabrics which are protected from biological attack.

The contrast with synthetic fibers is striking. The structure of nylon and similar synthetic polymers is a human invention and does not occur in natural living things. Hence, unlike natural polymers, synthetic ones find no counterpart in the armamentarium of degradative enzymes in nature. Ecologically, synthetic polymers are literally indestructible. Hence, every bit of synthetic fiber or polymer that has been produced on the earth is either destroyed by burning—and thereby pollutes the air—or accumulates as rubbish. One result, according to a recent report, is that microscopic fragments of plastic fibers, often red, blue or orange, have now become common in certain marine waters.[6] For technological displacement has been at work in this area too; in recent years natural fibers such as hemp and jute have been nearly totally replaced by synthetic fibers in fishing operations. A chief reason for this use of synthetic fibers is that they resist degradation by molds, which, as already indicated, readily attack cellulosic net materials such as hemp or jute. Thus, the property which enhances the economic value of the synthetic fiber over the natural one—its resistance to biological degradation—is precisely the property which increases the environmental impact of the synthetic material.

Detergents

Figure 7 shows that synthetic detergents have largely replaced soap in the United States as domestic and industrial cleaners, with the total production of cleaners per capita remaining essentially unchanged. Soap is based on a natural organic substance, fat, which is reacted with alkali to produce the end product. Being

Table 4.—Environmental Characteristics of Cotton and Nylon

	Cotton	Nylon	Comparitive environmental impact
Raw materials	CO_2, H_2O	Petroleum	Cotton, renewable Nylon, non-renewable
Process	$CO_2 + H_2O$ light	Petroleum (distill)	Fuel combustion and resultant
	Glucose cellulose (ca 70-90° F)	Benzene (550° F)	Air pollution
	Cultivation, ginning, spinning, require power	Cyclohexane (300° F)	Nylon probably cotton
		Cyclohexanol (200-400° F)	
		Adipic acid (600-700° F)	
		Adiponitrile (200-250° F)	
		Hexamethylene diamine Nylon 610	
		Distillation and other purification at most of above steps; power required to operate process	
Product	Cellulose	Polyamide	Cellulose wholly biodegradable, polyamide not degradable

a natural product, fat is extracted from an ecosystem (for example that represented by a coconut palm plantation), and when released into an aquatic ecosystem after use, soap is readily degraded by the bacteria of decay. Since most municipal wastes in the United States are subjected to treatment which degrades organic waste to its inorganic products, in actual practice the fatty residue of soap wastes is degraded by bacterial action within the confines of a sewage treatment plant. What is then emitted to surface waters is only carbon dioxide and water. Hence, there is little or no impact on the aquatic ecosystem due to biological oxygen demand (which accompanies bacterial degradation of organic wastes) arising from soap wastes. Nor is the product of soap degradation, carbon dioxide, usually an important ecological intrusion since it is in plentiful supply from other environmental sources, and in any case is an essential nutrient for photosynthetic algae. Hence, as compared with soap the production of synthetic detergents is a more serious source of pollution.

Once used and released into the environment in waste, detergents generate a more intense environmental impact than a comparable amount of soap. Soap is wholly degradable to carbon dioxide, which is usually rather innocuous in the environment. In contrast even the newer detergents which are regarded as degradable because the paraffin chain of the molecule (being unbranched, in contrast with the earlier non-degradable detergents) is broken down by bacterial action, nevertheless leave a residue of phenol which may not be degraded and may accumulate in surface waters. Phenol is a rather toxic substance, being foreign to the aquatic ecosystem.

Unlike soap, detergents are compounded with considerable amounts of phosphate in order to enhance their cleaning and water softening abilities. Phosphate may readily induce water pollution by stimulating heavy overgrowths of algae, which on dying release organic matter into the water and thus overburden the aqueous ecosystem. Figure 8 shows that nearly all of the increase in sewage phosphorus in the United States can be accounted for by the phosphorus content of detergents. Since soap, which has been displaced by detergents, is quite free of phosphate, the environmental impact due to phosphate is clearly a consequence of the technological change in cleaner production.

The change in the environmental impact index of phosphate in cleaners between 1946 and 1968 is shown in Table 5. In this period, the overall environmental impact index increased 1845 percent. The increase in the effect of population size was 42 percent; the effect of per capita use of cleaners does not change; the technological factor, i.e., that due to the displacement of phosphate-free soap by detergents containing an average

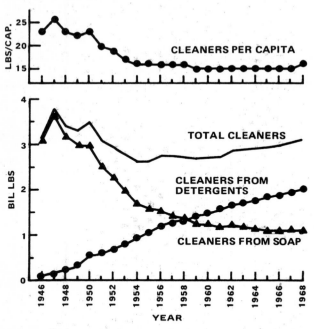

FIGURE 7
TOTAL SOAP AND DETERGENT PRODUCTION AND PER CAPITA CONSUMPTION OF TOTAL CLEANERS (SOAP PLUS DETERGENT) IN THE UNITED STATES SINCE 1946

Note: Detergent data represent actual content of surface-active agent, which is estimated at about 37.5% of the total weight of the marketed detergent.

Source: U.S. Department of Agriculture, *Agricultural Statistics*, 1970, p. 149.

of about 4 percent phosphorus, increased about 1270 percent. The relative importance of this change in cleaner technology in intensifying environmental impact is quite evident.

Secondary Environmental Effects of Technological Displacements

Increased production of synthetic organic chemicals leads to intensified environmental impacts in several different ways. This segment of industry has heavy power requirements; in contributing to increased power production the industry adds as well to the rising levels of air pollutants that are emitted by power plants. In addition, organic synthesis releases into the environment a wide variety of reagents and intermediates, which are foreign to natural ecosystems and often toxic, thus generating important, often poorly understood, environmental impacts. Common examples are massive fish kills and plant damage resulting from release of organic wastes, insecticides, and herbicides in to surface waters or the air.

Perhaps the most serious environmental impact attributable to the increased production of synthetic organic chemicals is due to the intrusion of mercury into surface waters. This effect is mediated by chlorine production. Chlorine is a vital reagent in many organic syntheses; about 80 percent of present chlorine production finds its end use in the synthetic organic chemical industry. Moreover, a considerable proportion of chlorine production is carried out in electrolytic mercury cells; until recent control measures were imposed on the industry, about .2-.5 lbs. of mercury were released to the environment per ton of chlorine manufactured in mercury electrolytic cells. This means, for example, that the substitution of nylon for cotton has generated an intensified environmental impact due to mercury; nylon production (unlike cotton production) involves the use of chlorinated intermediates, therefore of chlorine, and hence the release of mercury into the environment. The rapid, parallel rise in production of synthetic organic chemicals of chlorine production, and in the use of mercury for the latter is illustrated in Figure 9.

Similarly the displacement of steel and lumber by aluminum adds to the burden of air pollutants, for

FIGURE 8
CONCURRENT VALUES OF PHOSPHORUS OUTPUT FROM MUNICIPAL SEWAGE IN THE UNITED STATES AND PHOSPHORUS CONTENT OF DETERGENTS PRODUCED

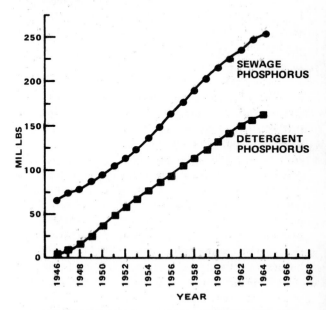

Note: Detergent data are based on detergent production (See Note, Figure 7) assuming an average of 4% P in marketed detergents.

Source: See Source, Figure 1.

Table 5.—Environmental Impact Index—Detergent Phosphorus

	(a) Population (1,000's)	(b) Cleaners[a] Population (lbs./cap.)	(c) Phosphorus Cleaners (lbs/ton of cleaner)	Total impact (a × b × c) Phosphorus from detergents[b] (10^6 lbs.)
1946	140,686	22.66	6.90	11
1968	194,846	15.99	137.34	214
1968:1946	1.42	0.69 (1.00)[c]	19.90 (13.70)	19.45
Percent increase, 1946-1968	42	(0)	(1,270)	1,845

[a]Assuming that 35% of detergent weight is active agent.

[b]Assuming average phosphorus content of detergents = 4%.

[c]Because of uncertainties regarding the content of active agent in detergents, especially soon after their introduction, the apparent reduction in per capita use of cleaners is not regarded as significant; the numbers contained in parentheses are based on the assumption that this value does not change significantly.

aluminum production is extremely power consumptive. Per pound of aluminum produced, about 29,860 BTU's of power are required to generate the necessary electricity, whereas about 4,615 BTU's are used per pound of steel produced. Cement, which tends to displace steel in construction is also extremely power consumptive. The production of chemicals, aluminum and cement account for about 28 percent of the total industrial use of electricity in the United States.

Packaging

The displacement of older forms of packaging by "disposable" containers such as non-returnable bottles is another example of the intensification of environmental impact due to the postwar pattern of economic growth. This is illustrated in Figure 10 and Table 6. Here it is evident that there has been a very striking increase in environmental impact due to beer bottles, which are not assimilated by ecological systems and are, in their manufacture, quite power consumptive. It is also evident that the major factor in this intensified environmental impact is the new technology—the use of non-returnable bottles to contain beer—rather than "affluence," with respect to per capita consumption of beer, or increased population. At the same time a recent study shows that the total expenditure of energy (for bottle manufacture, processing, shipping, etc.) required to deliver equal amounts of fluid in non-returnable bottles is 4.7 times that for returnable ones.[7]

Automotive Vehicles

Finally there is the problem of assessing the environmental impact of changes in patterns of passenger travel and freight traffic since 1946. Particularly important has been the increased use of automobiles, buses, and trucks.

The environmental impact of the internal combustion engine is due to the emission of nitrogen oxides, carbon monoxide, waste fuel, and lead. The intensities of these impacts, as measured by the levels of these pollutants in the environment, is a function, not only of the vehicle-miles traveled, but also of the nature of the engine itself—i.e., technological factors are relevant as well.

The technological changes in automotive engines since World War II have worsened environmental impact. These are illustrated in Figure 11. Thus, for passenger automobiles, overall mileage per gallon of fuel declined from 14.97 in 1949 to 14.08 in 1967, largely because average horsepower increased from 100 to 240. Another important technological change was in average compression ratio, which increased from about 5.9 to 9.5 in 1946-68. This engineering change has had two important effects on the environmental impact of the gasoline engine. First, increasing amounts of tetraethyl lead are needed as a gasoline additive in order to suppress the engine knock that occurs at high compression ratios. As shown in Figure 12, annual use of tetraethyl lead has increased significantly in 1946-68. Essentially all of this

FIGURE 9
CHANGES IN ANNUAL PRODUCTION OF SYNTHETIC ORGANIC COMPOUNDS AND OF CHLORINE GAS, AND CONSUMPTION OF MERCURY FOR CHLORINE GAS PRODUCTION IN THE UNITED STATES SINCE 1946

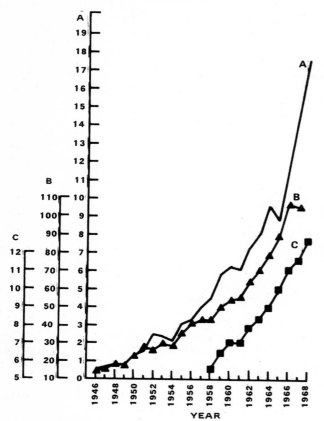

A - MERCURY CONSUMPTION FOR CHLOR-ALKAL 1
    PRODUCTION (1000'S OF 76-LB FLASKS)
B - SYNTHETIC ORGANIC CHEMICALS (BIL LBS)
C - CHLORINE PRODUCTION (MIL TONS)

Sources: U.S. Bureau of the Census, Current Industrial Reports,
Series M28A, *Inorganic Chemicals and Gases*, and *Statistical
Abstract of the United States.*

lead is emitted from the engine exhaust and is disseminated into the environment. Since lead is not a functional element in any biological organism, and is in fact toxic, it represents an external intrusion on the ecosystem and generates an appreciable environmental effect.

A second consequence of the increase in engine compression ratio has been a rise in the concentration of nitrogen oxides emitted in engine exhaust. This has occurred because the engine temperature increases with compression ratio. The combination of nitrogen and oxygen, present in the air taken into the engine cylinder, to form nitrogen oxides is enhanced at elevated tempera-

tures. Nitrogen oxide is the key ingredient in the formation of photochemical smog. Through a series of light-activated reactions involving waste fuel, nitrogen oxides induce the formation of peroxyacetyl nitrate, the noxious ingredient of photochemical smog. Smog of this type was first detected in Los Angeles in 1942-3; it was unknown in most other United States cities until the late 1950's and 1960's, but is now a nearly universal urban pollutant. Peroxyacetyl nitrate is a toxic agent to man, agricultural crops and trees. Introduction of this agent has probably increased by about an order of magnitude in 1946-68.

The Environmental Impact Indices for nitrogen oxides and lead are shown in Tables 7 and 8 respectively. The total environmental impact for nitrogen oxides increased by about 630 percent between 1946 and 1967. The technological factor (the amount of nitrogen oxides emitted per vehicle-mile) increased by 158 percent, vehicle-miles traveled per capita increased by about 100 percent, and the population factor by about 41 percent. In the case of tetraethyl lead, the largest increase in impact is in vehicle-miles travelled per capita (100 percent) followed by the technological factor (83 percent), and the population factor (41 percent). It is evident that the two major influences on automotive air pollution are increased per capita mileage (in part because of changes in work-residence distribution due to the expansion of suburbs) and the increased environmental impact per mile traveled due to technological changes in the gasoline engine.

FIGURE 10
PER CAPITA CONSUMPTION OF BEER AND PRODUCTION OF BEER BOTTLES IN THE UNITED STATES

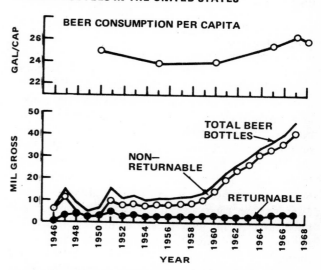

Source: U.S. Bureau of the Census, *Statistical Abstract of the
United States*, 1951, p. 792; 1955, p. 833; and 1970, p. 12.

Population, Resources, and the Environment

Table 6.—Environmental Impact Index—Beer Bottles

| | Index factors | | | Total index |
	(a)	(b)	(c)	(a X b X c)
	Population (1,000's)	Beer consumption	Beer bottles	Beer bottles (1,000 gross)
		Population (gallons/cap)	Beer consumption (bottles/gallon)	
1950	151,868	24.99	.25	6,540
1967	197,859	26.27	1.26	45,476
1967:1950	1.30	1.05	5.08	6.95
Percent increase, 1950-1967	30	5	408	595

A similar situation exists with respect to overland shipments of intercity freight. Here truck freight has tended to displace railroad freight. And again the displacing technology has a more severe environmental impact than does the displaced technology. This is evident from the energy required to transport freight by rail and truck: 624 BTU/ton-mile by rail and 3462 BTU/ton-mile by truck. It should be noted as well that the steel and cement required to produce equal lengths of railroad and expressway (suitable for heavy truck traffic) differ in the amount of power required in the ratio 1 to 3.6. This is due to the rather power consumptive nature of cement production and to the fact that four highway lanes are required to accommodate heavy truck traffic. In addition, the divided roadway requires a 400 foot right-of-way while a train roadbed needs only 100 feet. In all these ways the displacement of railroads by automotive vehicles, not only for freight, but also for passenger travel, has intensified the resultant environmental impact.

THE ENVIRONMENTAL IMPACT INVENTORY

It will be recognized that the foregoing analysis represents only small fragments of a complex whole. What is required is a full inventory of the various Environmental Impact Indices associated with the productive enterprise and the identification of the origins of these impacts within the production process and of the ecosystems on which they intrude. Such an assemblage of data, representing an *Environmental Impact Inventory* is derived as an exploratory exercise in what follows, with reference to a productive item for which a certain amount of the needed data happen to be at hand—the production of chlorine and alkali by chlor-alkali plants employing mercury electrolytic cells.

The needed data include: (1) the Environmental Impact Indices associated with the input goods, chiefly,

electric power, salt and mercury; (2) the Environmental Impact Indices representative of the process's wastes and the properties of the ecological systems which are affected by them; (3) the Environmental Impact Indices representative of the ecologically significant wastes

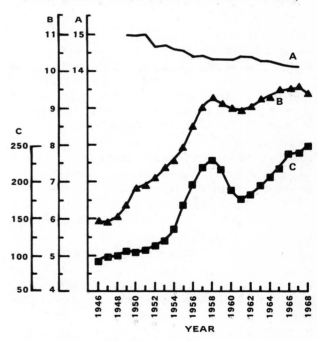

FIGURE 11

AVERAGE CHARACTERISTICS OF PASSENGER CAR ENGINES PRODUCED IN THE UNITED STATES SINCE 1946

A - AVERAGE MILES PER GALLON
B - AVERAGE COMPRESSION RATIO
C - AVERAGE BRAKE HORSEPOWER

Source: Brake horsepower and compression ratio data are from "Brief Passenger Car Data", Ethyl Corporation, Vols. for 1951 and 1970. Gasoline consumption data are from U.S. Bureau of the Census, *Statistical Abstract of the United States.*

FIGURE 12
LEAD EMISSIONS, FROM TETRAETHYL LEAD IN GASO-LINE, IN THE UNITED STATES SINCE 1946

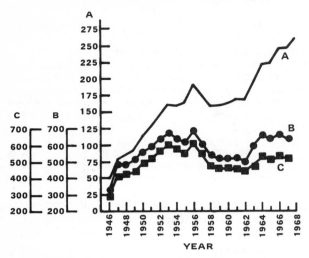

A - LEAD CONSUMPTION FOR GASOLINE ADDITIVES (1000'S OF TONS)
B - LBS OF LEAD PER 10^5 GAL. OF FUEL
C - LBS OF LEAD PER 10^6 VEHICLE-MILES

Source: U.S. Bureau of the Census, *Minerals Yearbook 1947-1968* and *Statistical Abstract of the United States* (see Sources, Figure 10).

associated with the process's output goods (chlorine and alkali) and the environmental fate of this material. Thus, the production of one megawatt of electricity by fossil-fuel burning plants results in the release of 34.20 lbs. of sulfur oxides to the atmosphere. Since 4300 kwh is consumed by a mercury cell chlor-alkali plant per ton of chlorine produced, on the average, 147 lbs. of sulfur oxides are released to the environment per ton of chlorine produced. In this way, the corresponding values for other power-plant pollutants (e.g., nitrogen oxides, dust) can be computed as well.

The major ecologically significant waste from chlor-alkali production is mercury metal. Two studies provide data on the amounts of mercury released to the air, released to surface waters, or buried in land-fill, per ton of chlorine produced.[8] For example, per ton of chlorine produced, about 17-35 gm of mercury vapor is emitted to the air as waste. Chemical engineering data indicate a total "mercury loss" of .2-.5 lbs. per ton of chlorine for the process. This agrees rather well with the total losses to the environment estimated directly bh the foregoing studies, .13-.57 lbs. of mercury per ton of chlorine.

The present data indicate that as much as 20 grams of mercury may become incorporated in the alkali produced in the course of producing a ton of chlorine; this alkali is used in some 42 separate products. From an input-output analysis of the chlor-alkali industry one could construct a comprehensive matrix for the movement of mercury contained in alkali through various manufacturing processes into the environment. Recently, economic input-output methods have been adapted to include environmental externalities.[9] For the present purposes we shall restrict the analysis to a group of products—wood pulp and paper, soap, lye, and cleansers—which use about 26 percent of the alkali output. Hence, we may estimate that of every 20 grams of mercury which goes into alkali, 26 percent or 5 grams appears in the products listed above. The environmental fates of these products are known: Waste water containing cleansers goes into waterways, as do the fluid wastes from pulp and paper production; paper is eventually burned, releasing its mercury to the air as vapor.

The ecological data relevant to an Environmental Impact Inventory for chlor-alkali production are just beginning to be investigated. When metallic mercury is dumped into surface waters it sinks into the bottom mud as droplets. There it may be acted on by certain species of bacteria which convert the mercury to an organic form, methyl mercury. While metallic mercury does not dissolve in water, methyl mercury does. Hence in this form, the mercury is readily taken up by living organisms in the water, ultimately contaminating fish that may be eaten by people. In recent months it has been found that mercury wastes from a number of chlor-alkali plants have caused mercury levels in fish in adjacent surface water to exceed acceptable public health limits. Emitted into the air, mercury may be taken up directly by human beings through absorption in the lungs, or it may be washed down into soil and water by precipitation—and thus enter into these ecosystems. Very little is known about the ecological transfer of mercury in the soil as yet. Finally, since mercury is very volatile, when heated (as in an incinerator) it is vaporized and emitted into the air. A recent study shows that St. Louis domestic incinerators emit about 2-3,000 lbs. of mercury into the air annually. Much of this originates in the incineration of paper and wood pulp products.

On the basis of such data one can now produce (here in a quite incomplete and tentative form) an Environmental Impact Inventory for chlor-alkali production. This is presented in Table 9.

SOME CONCLUSIONS

The data presented above reveal a functional connection between economic growth—at least in the United States since 1946—and environmental impact. It is significant that the range of increase in the computed environmental impacts agrees fairly well with the independent measure of the actual levels of pollutants

Population, Resources, and the Environment

Table 7.—Environmental Impact Index—Nitrogen Oxides (Passenger Vehicles)

	(a)	(b)	(c)	Total index
		Index factors		
	Population (1,000's)	Vehicle-miles	Nitrogen oxides[a]	Nitrogen oxides[a]
		Population	Vehicle-miles	
1946	140,686	1,982	33.5	10.6
1967	197,849	3,962	86.4	77.5
1967:1946	1.41	2.00	2.58	7.3
Percent increase	41	100	158	630

[a]Dimension = NO_x (ppm) × gasoline consumption (gals. × 10^{-6}). Estimated from product of passenger vehicle gasoline consumption and ppm of NO_x emitted by engines of average compression ration 5.9 (1946) and 9.5 (1967) under running conditions, at 15 in. manifold pressure: 1946, 500 ppm NO_x; 1967, 1,200 ppm.

Sources: T.A. Huls and H.A. Nickol, "Engine Variables Influence Nitric Oxide Concentration in Exhuast Gas," *Society of Automotive Engineers Journal,* August 1968, p. 40. Also General Motors research staff, unpublished paper on the effect of engine-operating variables on oxides of nitrogen—report to the variables panel of the group on composition of exhaust gases, CRC, Sept. 25, 1957.

Table 8.—Environmental Impact Index—Tetraethyl Lead

	(a)	(b)	(c)	Total index
		Index factors		
	Population (1,000's)	Vehicle-miles[a]	Tetraethyl lead[b]	Tetraethyl lead[b] (1,000's of tons)
		Population (veh. mi./cap.)	Vehicle-miles[a] (lbs/million (veh. mi.)	
1946	140,686	1,984[c]	300[c]	48[c]
1967	197,859	3,962	630	247
1967:1946	1.41	2.00	1.83	5.15
Percent increase	41	100	83	415

[a]Passenger vehicles only.
[b]Weight refers to lead content.
[c]See note for Table IX.

occurring in the environment. Thus, the increase in environmental impact index for tetraethyl lead computed from gasoline consumption data for 1946-67 is about 400 percent; a similar increase in environmental lead levels has been recorded from analyses of layered ice in glaciers.[10] Similarly, the 648 percent increase in the 19-year period 1949-68 in the environmental impact index computed for nitrogen fertilizer is in keeping with the few available large-scale field measurements. Thus, field data show that nitrate entering the Missouri River as it traversed Nebraska in the 6-year period 1956-62 increased a little over 200 percent.[11] The environmental impact indices computed for several aspects of automotive vehicle use are also in keeping with general field observations. It is widely recognized that the most striking increase among the several aspects of environmental deterioration due to automotive vehicles has occurred with respect to photochemical smog. This pollutant was detected for the first time in Los Angeles in 1942-43. Since then it has increased, nationally, by probably an order of magnitude, appearing in nearly every major city and even in smaller ones in the last 5 years. However, in the period 1946-68 total use of automotive vehicles, as measured by gasoline consumption, increased by only about 200 percent—an increment too small to account for the concurrent rise in the incidence of photochemical smog. It is significant, then, that this disparity between the observed increase in smog levels and the increase in vehicle use is accounted for by the environmental impact index computed for nitrogen oxides, the agent which initiates the smog reaction, for that index increased by 630 percent in 1946-67.

These agreements with actual field data support the conclusion that the computations represented by the environmental impact index provide a useful approximation of the changes in environmental impact associ-

ated with the relevant features of the growth of the United States economy since 1946. In particular, we can therefore place some reliance on the subdivision of the total impact index into the several factors: population size, per capita production or consumption, and the technology of production and use.

It is of interest to make a direct comparison of the relative contributions of increases in population size and in "affluence," and of changes in the technology of production, to the increases in total environmental impact which have occurred since 1946. The ratio of the most recent total index value to the value of the 1946 index (or to the value for the earliest year for which the necessary data are available) is indicative of the change in the total impact over this period of time. The relative contributions of the several factors to these total changes is then given by the ratios of their respective partial indices. Figure 13 reports such comparisons for the six productive activities evaluated. The population factor contributes only between 12 and 20 percent of the total changes in impact index. For all but the automotive pollutants, the "affluence" factor makes a

Table 9.—Environmental Impact Inventory—Chloralkali Production by Means of Mercury Electrolytic Cells

	Production process	Relevant ecological systems[b]	Environmental impact (per ton of chlorine produced)
Input goods[a]	Electric power (4300 kwh/ton Cl)	Air	SO_x: 147.1 lbs. NO_x: 29.4 lbs. Particulates: 5.9 lbs. Mercury: .004 gm. Heat: 5.51×10^6 Btu's
		Surface waters	Heat: 16.56×10^6 Btu's
	H_2 gas ventilation	Air	Mercury: 17-35 gm.
Production process step[a]	H_2 condensate, wash water	Surface waters via settling pond or drainage system	Mercury: 35-121 gm.
	Brine sludge removal	Surface waters	
	Anode sweepings removal	Soil via land fill	Mercury: 6-97 gm.
Output goods[a]	Selected alkali-using goods (soap, lye, cleansers, pulp and paper)	Air surface waters	Mercury: 1-5 gm.

Note: Total mercury = 59-258 gm./ton chlorine (.10-.57 lbs./ton chlorine).

[a]Only a few of the actual items are shown, for purposes of illustration.

[b]In an actual index reference would be made to a standardized description of each of the indicated relevant ecological systems.

ST   STAND—

Population, Resources, and the Environment

FIGURE 13

RELATIVE CONTRIBUTIONS OF SEVERAL FACTORS TO CHANGES IN ENVIRONMENTAL IMPACT INDICES. THE CONTRIBUTIONS OF POPULATION SIZE "AFFLUENCE" (PRODUCTION PER CAPITA), AND TECHNOLOGICAL CHARACTERISTICS (AMOUNT OF POLLUTANT RELEASED PER UNIT PRODUCTION) TO THE TOTAL ENVIRONMENTAL IMPACT INDICES WERE COMPUTED AS SHOWN IN THE TEXT. EACH BAR IS SUBDIVIDED TO SHOW THE RELATIVE CONTRIBUTIONS, ON A SCALE OF 1.0, OF THE SEVERAL FACTORS TO THE RATIO OF THE TOTAL IMPACT INDEX VALUE FOR THE LATER YEAR TO THE VALUE FOR THE EARLIER YEAR

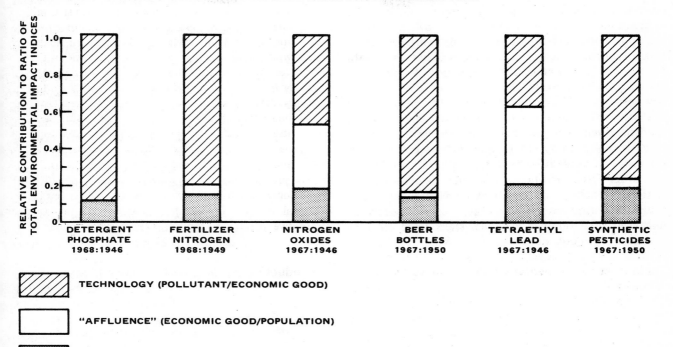

rather small contribution—no more than 5 percent—to the total changes in impact index. For nitrogen oxides and tetraethyl lead (from automotive sources), this factor accounts for about 40 percent of the total effect, reflecting a considerable increase in the number of vehicle-miles traveled per capita since 1946. The technological changes in the processes which generate the various economic goods, contribute from 40-90 percent of the total increases in impact.

In evaluating these results it should be noted that automotive travel is itself strongly affected by a kind of technological transformation: the rapid increase of suburban residences in the United States and the concomitant failure to provide adequate railroad and other mass transportation to accommodate to this change. That the overall increase in vehicle-miles traveled per capita since 1946 (about 100 percent) is related to increased residence-work travel incident upon this change is suggested by the results of a 1970 survey. It was found that 90 percent of all automobile trips,

representing 43 percent of total mileage traveled, are 10 miles or less in length.[12] The median residence-work travel distance was about 5.5 miles.[13] Thus, it is probably appropriate to regard the increase in per capita vehicle-miles traveled by automobile as not totally attributable to increased "affluence," but rather as a response to new work-residence relationships which are costly in transportation.

During the period from 1946 to the present, pollution levels in the United States have increased sharply—generally by an order of magnitude or so. It seems evident from the data presented above that most of this increase is due to one of the three factors that influence environmental impact—the technology of production—and that both population growth and increase in "affluence" exert a much smaller influence. Thus the chief reason for the sharp increase in environmental stress in the United States is the sweeping transformation in production technology in the post-war period. *Productive activities with intense environmental impacts have displaced activities with less serious environmental impacts; the growth pattern has been counter-ecological.*

The foregoing conclusion is easily misconstrued to mean that technology is therefore, per se, ecologically harmful. That this interpretation is unwarranted can be seen from the following examples.

Consider the following simple transformation of the present, ecologically faulty, relationship among soil, agricultural crops, the human population and sewage. Suppose that the sewage, instead of being introduced into surface water as it is now, whether directly or following treatment, is instead transported from urban collection systems by pipeline to agricultural areas, where—after appropriate sterilization procedures—it is incorporated into the soil. Such a pipeline would literally reincorporate the urban population into the soil's ecological cycle, restoring the integrity of that cycle, and incidentally removing the need for inorganic nitrogen fertilizer—which also stresses the aquatic cycle. Hence the urban population is then no longer external to the soil cycle and is therefore incapable either of generating a negative biological stress upon it or of exerting a positive ecological stress on the aquatic ecosystem. But note that this state of zero environmental impact is not achieved by a return to "primitive" conditions, but by an actual technological advance, the construction of a sewage pipeline system.

Or consider the example provided by the technological treatment of gold and other precious metals. Gold is, after all, subject to numerous technological manipulations, which generate a series of considerable economic values. Yet we manage to accomplish all of this without intruding more than a rather small fraction of all the gold ever acquired by human beings into the ecosphere. Because we value it so highly very little gold is "lost" to the environment. In contrast, most of the mercury which has entered commerce in the last generation has been disseminated into the environment, with very unfortunate effects on the environment. Clearly, given adequate technology—and motivation—we could be as thrifty in our handling of mercury as we are of gold, thereby preventing the entry of this toxic material into the environment. Again what is required is not necessarily the abandonment of mercury-based technology, but rather the improvement of that technology to the point of satisfactory compatibility with the ecosystem.

Generally speaking then, it would appear possible to reduce the environmental impact of human activities by developing alternatives to ecologically faulty activities. This can be accomplished, not by abandoning technology and the economic goods which it can yield, but by developing *new* technologies which incorporate not only the knowledge of the physical sciences (as most do moderately well), but ecological wisdom as well.

The foregoing considerations show that the deterioration of the environment, whatever its cost in money, social distress and personal suffering, is chiefly the result of the ecologically faulty technology which has been employed to remake productive enterprises. The resulting environmental impacts stress the basic ecosystems which support the life of human beings, destroy the "biological capital" which is essential to the operation of industry and agriculture, and may, if unchecked, lead to the catastrophic collapse of these systems. The environmental impacts already generated are sufficient to threaten the continued development of the economic system. Warnings can be seen in current difficulties in siting new power plants at a time of severe power shortage, and the recent curtailment of industrial innovation in the fields of detergents, chemical manufacturing, insecticides, herbicides, chlorine production, oil drilling, oil transport, supersonic aviation, nuclear power generation, and industrial uses of nuclear explosives, all resulting from public rejection of the concomitant environmental deterioration.

We come, then, to the matter of the actual cost of the degradation which has been the response of the environmental system to the intensified impacts upon it. This is, of course, a very difficult matter. As indicated earlier, the theory which links environmental impact to ecological effect is for the most part poorly developed. At the same time, there are formidable difficulties confronting the economist who attempts to return the "externalities" represented by ecological damage to the realm of economic evaluation. These efforts, which appear to be developing increasingly useful information, need not be reviewed here. For there is, I believe, a simpler and more direct way to express the cost to the economic system represented by environmental deterioration.

It seems to me that a meaningful way to evaluate this cost is somewhat along the following lines:

1. Given that the deterioration of the environment, whatever its cost in money, social distress and personal suffering, is chiefly the result of the ecologically faulty technology which has been employed to remake productive enterprises in the United States since 1946;

2. And given that the resulting environmental impacts stress the basic ecosystems which support the life of human beings, destroy the "biological capital" which is essential to the operation of industry and agriculture, and may in a period of a few decades lead to the catastrophic collapse of these systems;

3. And given further that the environmental impacts already generated are sufficient to threaten the continued development of the economic system—witness

the difficulties in siting new power plants at a time of severe power shortage, the recent curtailment of industrial innovation in the fields of detergents, chemical manufacturing, pesticides, herbicides, chlorine production, oil drilling, oil transport, supersonic aviation, nuclear power generation, industrial uses of nuclear explosives, all resulting from public rejection of the concomitant environmental deterioration;

4. Then, it seems probable, if we are to survive economically as well as biologically, that much of the technological transformation of the United States economy since 1946 will need to be, so to speak, redone in order to bring the nation's productive technology much more closely into harmony with the inescapable demands of the ecosystem. This will require the development of massive new technologies, including systems to return sewage and garbage directly to the soil; to replace synthetic materials by natural ones; to support the reversal of the present trend to retire soil from agriculture and to elevate the yield per acre; to develop land transport that operates with maximal fuel efficiency at low combustion temperatures; and to enable the sharp curtailment of the use of biologically active synthetic organic agents. In effect what is required is a new period of technological transformation of the economy, which reverses the counter-ecological trends developed since 1946. We might estimate the cost of the new transformation from the cost of the former one, which must represent a capital investment in the range of hundreds of billions of dollars. To this must be added, of course, the cost of repairing the ecological damage which has already been incurred, such as the eutrophication of Lake Erie, again a bill to be reckoned in the hundreds of billions of dollars.

The enormous size of these costs raises a final question: Is there some functional connection in the economy between the tendency of a given productive activity to inflict an intense impact on the environment (and the size of the resultant costs) and the role of this activity in economic growth? For it is evident from even a cursory comparison of the productive activities which have rapidly expanded in the United States economy since 1946 with the activities which they have displaced, that the displacing activities are also considerably more profitable than those which they displace. The correlation between profitability and rapid growth is one that is presumably accountable by economics. Is the additional linkage to intense environmental impact also functional, or only accidental?

It has been pointed out often enough that environmental pollution represents a long-unpaid debt to nature. Is it possible that the United States economy has grown since 1946 by deriving much of its new wealth through the enlargement of that debt? If this should turn out to be the case what strains will develop in the economy if, for the sake of the survival of our society, that debt should now be called? How will these strains affect our ability to pay the debt—to survive?

REFERENCES

1. This study has been carried out as part of the program of the American Association for the Advancement of Science Committee on Environmental Alterations in collaboration with Michael Corr and Paul J. Stamler. For a preliminary report of this work, see Barry Commoner, Michael Corr, and Paul J. Stamler, *Environment,* 1971, Vol. 13, No. 3, p. 2.

2. L. W. Weinberger, D. G. Stephan, and F. M. Middleton, *Annals New York Academy of Sciences,* 1966, Vol. 136, p. 131-154.

3. Barry Commoner, "Threats to the Integrity of the Nitrogen Cycle: Nitrogen Compounds in Soil, Water, Atmosphere and Precipitation," *Global Effects of Environmental Pollution,* S. Fred Singer ed., Symposium organized by the American Association for the Advancement of Science, Dallas, Texas, December 1968 (New York: Springer-Verlag, 1970).

4. D. H. Kohl, G. B. Shearer, and Barry Commoner, *Isotopic Analysis of the Movement of Fertilizer Nitrogen into Surface Water,* in press 1971.

5. J. H. Dawes, T. E. Larson, and R. H. Harmeson, proceedings of the 24th Annual Meeting, Soil Conservation Society of America, Ft. Collins, Colorado, 1968, pp. 94-102.

6. See note in *Marine Pollution Bulletin,* February 1971, Vol. 2, p. 23.

7. Personal communication from Bruce Hannon, University of Illinois, Urbana.

8. See Robin A. Wallace, *et al., Mercury in the Environment, The Human Element* (Oak Ridge National Laboratories, January 1971), p. 61.

9. See, for example, W. Isard, *et al., Papers of the Regional Science Association,* 1969, Vol. 21, p. 79.

10. C. C. Patterson, *Environment,* 1967, Vol. 10, p. 72.

11. Barry Commoner, *op. cit.*

12. U.S. Dept. of Transportation, preliminary results from the Nationwide Personal Transportation Survey, 1969-70.

13. U.S. Bureau of the Census, *Census of Transportation, 1963,* Vol. I, *Passenger Transportation Survey.*

Impact of
Population Growth

by
Paul R. Ehrlich
Stanford University and
John P. Holdren
University of California

COMMISSION ON POPULATION GROWTH AND
THE AMERICAN FUTURE, *RESEARCH
REPORTS, VOLUME III, POPULATION
RESOURCES AND THE ENVIRONMENT,*
EDITED BY RONALD G. RIDKER

CONTENTS

ABSTRACT

In the wealth of literature dealing with population, resources, and the environment, population growth is often presented as a minor contributor to the environmental crisis. This paper seeks to refute this and related misconceptions. We consider here (1) the negative impact of population growth on the environment; (2) the interrelatedness of population growth, resources, and the environment; (3) the dangers of redistribution as opposed to reduced growth; (4) the broadening scope of the term "environment"; and (5) the distinction between theoretical and operational solutions. Because population is the most unyielding of all environmental pressures, work on it must begin at once, in order to preclude any desperate and repressive measures which might be contemplated in the future.

Impact of Population Growth

The interlocking crises in population, resources, and environment have been the focus of countless papers, dozens of prestigious symposia, and a growing avalanche of books. In this wealth of material, several questionable assertions have been appearing with increasing frequency. Perhaps the most serious of these is the notion that the size and growth rate of the United States population are only minor contributors to this country's adverse impact on local and global environments.[1] We propose to deal with this and several related misconceptions here, before persistent and unrebutted repetition entrenches them in the public mind—if not the scientific literature. Our discussion centers around five theorems which we believe are demonstrably true and which provide a framework for realistic analysis:

1. Population growth causes a *disproportionate* negative impact on the environment.

2. Problems of population size and growth, resource utilization and depletion, and environmental deterioration must be considered jointly and on a global basis. In this context, population control is obviously not a panacea—it is necessary, but not alone sufficient to see us through the crisis.

3. Population density is a poor measure of population pressure, and redistributing population would be a dangerous pseudosolution to the population problem.

4. "Environment" must be broadly construed to include such things as the physical environment of urban ghettos, the human behavioral environment, and the epidemiological environment.

5. Theoretical solutions to our problems are often not operational and sometimes are not solutions.

We now examine these theorems in some detail.

POPULATION SIZE AND PER CAPITA IMPACT

One of the most misunderstood matters that enters into discussions of optimum population is the nature of the relationship between the size of the human population and the effect of that population on the ecology of our planet. In an agricultural or technological society (as distinguished from a hunting-gathering society), each human individual, in the course of obtaining the requisites of existence, has a net negative impact on his environment. His need for food causes some of the simplification (and resulting destabilization) of ecological systems associated with the practice of agriculture.[2] His needs for water, metals, and fibers lead to the conversion of resources into waste; and the procedures of extraction, processing, and waste disposal themselves have simplifying—and therefore adverse—effects on ecosystems. Of course, it may be judged that an individual's beneficial contribution to his culture outweighs his adverse contribution to the stability of the ecosystem. Unfortunately, society's level of culture will be of little consequence if the collective ecological impact exceeds the point of no recovery.

It is axiomatic that the total impact of a society on the ecosystem can be expressed by the relation

$$I = P \cdot F,$$

where I is the total impact, P is the population size, and F is the impact per capita. Obviously, an increase in I can come about if P alone increases, if F alone increases, if both increase simultaneously, or if one increases faster than the other declines. The particularly rapid increase in total impact over the past several decades has occurred because both P and F have, in fact, been increasing simultaneously. The rapidity with which the product of two increasing quantities grows is simply a matter of arithmetic, but this point has apparently not been understood by some writers who have disparaged the role of population growth in producing man's present predicament. To examine quantitatively the relative importance of the two components of total impact, when both are increasing simultaneously, let I, P, and F be the initial values of total impact, population size, and per capita impact; and let ΔI, ΔP, and ΔF be the observed increases in these quantities during some time period. We assume for the purposes of this purely arithmetic exercise that per capita impact is independent of population size. The initial total impact is

$$I = P \cdot F, \tag{1}$$

and the subsequent total impact is

$$I + \Delta I = (P + \Delta P) \cdot (F + \Delta F). \qquad (2)$$

The relative increase is obtained by dividing equation (2) by equation (1):

$$\frac{I + \Delta I}{I} = \left(\frac{P + \Delta P}{P}\right) \cdot \left(\frac{F + \Delta F}{F}\right), \qquad (3)$$

or

$$1 + \frac{\Delta I}{I} = \left(1 + \frac{\Delta P}{P}\right)\left(1 + \frac{\Delta F}{F}\right), \qquad (4)$$

where $\Delta I/I$, $\Delta P/P$, and $\Delta F/F$ are the fractional increases in I, P, and F, and percentage increase = fractional increase $\times$ 100.

Obviously, the fractional increases in P and F do not add up to the fractional increase in I, even though many writers have proceeded as if they do. Thus one can read statements equivalent to, "Total impact increased 300 percent; but population, which increased only 100 percent, accounted for only one-third of the increase." The implication is that the growth of per capita impact must have accounted for the other two-thirds. In reality, the multiplicative effect of population and per capita impact increasing simultaneously has produced (in this example) a 300 percent increase in I even though *both* P and F increased only 100 percent:

$$\left(1 + \frac{\Delta P}{P}\right)\left(1 + \frac{\Delta F}{F}\right) = (1 + 1)(1 + 1) = 4 = 1 + \frac{\Delta I}{I}, \frac{\Delta I}{I} = 3.$$

To take an example from the experience of the United States, assume that the measure of environmental impact is energy production (actually a very reasonable assumption). Total energy production increased 140 percent between 1940 and 1969, while population increased by 53 percent. We have

$$\frac{\Delta I}{I} = 1.40, \frac{\Delta P}{P} = .53$$

and, from equation (4), $\Delta F/F = .56$. The per capita increase in energy production was only 56 percent, yet, combined with an almost identical increase in population, this led to a 2.4 fold increase in *total* energy production:

$$\left(1 + \frac{\Delta P}{P}\right)\left(1 + \frac{\Delta I}{I}\right) = 1.53 \times 1.56 = 2.40 = \frac{I + \Delta I}{I}.$$

The temptation to say population "caused" only 38 percent of the observed increase must be resisted

(.53/1.40 = .38); by the same token, the growth in per capita production "caused" only 40 percent of the increase, and one is left with no "cause" for the remaining 22 percent. In reality, because of the multiplicative effect, the two growing factors contributed about equally to the much faster growth of the product. If one prefers energy *consumption* (incorporating imports and exports) to production as an indicator of environmental impact, the relative arithmetic importance of population declines only slightly; total energy consumption was 2.75 times as large in 1969 as in 1940, and one finds $\Delta I/I = 1.75$, $\Delta P/P = .53$, $\Delta F/F = .79$.

Of course, many variables affect population size and per capita impact on the environment, and population and per capita impact affect each other. These interactions involve more than just arithmetic; they involve biology, technology, and economics. Consider the per capita impact alone, which we have called F. This quantity is obviously related to per capita consumption—of food, water, energy, fibers, metals—but it also depends on the technology used to make the consumption possible. For example, the per capita impact associated with a given level of metals consumption is smaller if recycling is employed in place of the prevalent "once-through" conversion of resources into waste. Similarly, the per capita impact associated with a certain level of electricity consumption is smaller if power plant effluents are controlled than if they are not. Thus improvements in technology can sometimes hold the per capita impact, F, constant or even decrease it, despite increases in per capita consumption.

Some people have argued, on the basis of such examples, that *all* of our environmental impact can be traced to misuse of existing technologies and failure to develop environmentally benign ones. They imply that neither population size nor per capita consumption is important if only the proper technologies are used. The fallacy in this argument is that no technology can completely eliminate the impact of a given amount of consumption. For example, recycling is never perfect; there is always some loss of material which becomes waste and which requires further depletion to replace. Moreover, recycling anything requires energy, although usually less than the once-through method; and energy is *not* recyclable. It can only be used once, and in use it generates waste heat. These facts are sad but unavoidable consequences of the second law of thermodynamics.

Pollution control and all other means of minimizing per capita environmental impact are also imperfect: Zero release of any containment is an unattainable ideal, and attempts to approach it consume great quantities of energy. In a different vein, the ecological disruption caused by agriculture is central to the enterprise, not a peripheral side effect. We may conclude that improving technology to reduce the impact of consumption is worthwhile, but not the entire answer. Under any set of technological conditions, there will be some impact associated with each unit of consumption, and therefore some level of population size and per capita consumption at which the total impact becomes unsustainable.

Analysis of the role of population in environmental deterioration is made particularly difficult by the *causal* interactions that entangle population growth and per capita impact, and those that eventually relate population growth back to total impact. In mathematical terms, the equation connecting I, P, and F is "nonlinear" and should be written

$$I = P(I,F) \cdot F(P)$$

This is only a compact way of saying that, although I equals P times F, F also depends on P, and P depends on I and F. As we indicated, it is a tangled relationship! Although almost none of these interactions has been studied thoroughly, it is easy to give some illustrative examples.

First, consider some ways in which changes in total and per capita impact can cause changes in population growth. Suppose an increase in F occurs in the form of an increase in per capita consumption of energy. If the extra energy per person is used to provide medical services, the death rate may drop and increase the rate of population growth; but, if the extra energy powers television sets that keep people up late at night, the birth rate may drop and decrease the rate of population growth. If the total impact, I, becomes great enough, the resulting environmental disaster—whether it be loss of fisheries productivity, crop failure, epidemic, or chronic poisoning—will certainly increase the death rate and perhaps reduce the population size more or less instantaneously.

Conversely, population size and growth rate have important effects on per capita impact. A possibility well known to economists occurs when rapid population growth inhibits the growth of per capita income. This means per capita consumption grows more slowly than it would in the absence of such rapid population growth, so per capita impact grows more slowly, too. Thus, in this case, the interaction between population and per capita impact has a moderating effect on the growth of the product: Increasing the growth rate of one factor (P) tends to decrease the growth rate of the other (F). This effect is probably important in under-developed countries, but much less so elsewhere.

Effects of the opposite sort, in which increases in population size operate to increase per capita impact on the environment, occur in both developed countries and under-developed countries. These interactions serve to *accelerate* the growth in total impact, compared to what the growth would be if population and per capita impact were independent. They partly explain the very rapid rate of environmental deterioration that has been observed in the developed countries, where the disproportionate amount of consumption—and, hence, impact—makes the effects especially visible.

Perhaps the best understood of the effects that link population size and per capita impact is the law of diminishing returns. This refers to a situation in which, in the jargon of the economist, the additional output resulting from each additional unit of input is becoming less and less. Here "output" refers to a desired good such as food or metal, and "input" refers to what we must supply—say, fertilizer, energy, or raw ore—to obtain the output. Suppose that per capita consumption of outputs is to be held constant while population increases. If the law of diminishing returns prevails, the per capita consumption of inputs needed to provide the fixed per capita level of outputs will increase. Since environmental impact is generated by the inputs as well as by the outputs, the per capita impact will also increase.

To see how the law of diminishing returns looks in a specific example, consider the problem of providing nonrenewable resources such as minerals and fossil fuels to a growing population, even at fixed levels of per capita consumption. More people mean more demand, and thus more rapid depletion of resources. As the richest supplies of these resources and those nearest to centers of use are consumed, it becomes necessary to use lower-grade ores, drill deeper, and extend supply networks. All these activities increase the *per capita* use of energy and hence the *per capita* impact on the environment. In the case of partly renewable resources such as water (which is effectively nonrenewable when groundwater supplies are mined at rates far exceeding natural recharge), per capita costs and environmental impact escalate enormously when the human population demands more than is locally available. Here the loss of free-flowing rivers and other economic, aesthetic, and ecological costs of massive water-movement projects represent increased per capita diseconomies directly simulated by population growth. These effects would, of course, also eventually overtake a stable population that demands more than the environment can supply on a perpetual basis; growth simply speeds the process and allows less time to deal with the problems created.

The law of diminishing returns is also operative in increasing food production to meet the needs of growing populations. Typically, attempts are made both to overproduce on land already farmed and to extend agriculture to marginal land. The former requires disproportionate energy use in obtaining and distributing water, fertilizer, and pesticides. The use of marginal land also increases per capita energy use, since the amount of energy invested per unit yield increases as less desirable land is cultivated. Both activities "consume" the fertility built into the natural soil structure. Similarly, as the richest fisheries stocks are depleted, the yield per unit effort drops; and more and more energy per capita is required to maintain the supply.[3] Once a stock is depleted it may not recover—it may be nonrenewable.

In theory, diminishing returns may be counterbalanced by improved technology and by economies of scale. The latter term refers to savings in labor, materials, or both which may result simply from carrying on an enterprise such as farming or manufacturing on a large scale. In practice, economies of scale hold sway up to a point and then give way to diminishing returns. Improved technology can postpone the onset of diminishing returns but cannot avert it. In the United States and in most other developed countries, technological innovation and economies of scale are still holding their own in certain service and manufacturing enterprises; but in the critical matter of supplying the raw materials of existence—food, water, fibers, metals—the technologies required to cope with growing populations have been using more inputs per capita, not less.

Population size influences per capita impact in ways other than diminishing returns. One is *increasing complexity,* for the intricacy and unwieldiness of such activities as transportation, communication, and government expand disproportionately as population grows. For example, consider the over-simplified but instructive situation in which each person in the population has links with every other person—roads, telephone lines, and so forth. These links involve energy and materials in their construction and use. Since the number of links increases much more rapidly than the number of people, so does the per capita consumption associated with the links.[4]

Population growth may cause even more rapid increases in per capita impact on the environment through the mechanism we call the *threshold effect.* For example, below a certain level of pollution, trees will survive in smog. But when a small increment in population produces a small increment in smog, living trees become dead trees. Five hundred people may be able to live around a lake and dump their raw sewage into it, and the natural systems of the lake will be able to break down the sewage and keep the lake from undergoing rapid ecological change. But 505 people may overload the system and result in a "polluted" or eutrophic lake.

Synergisms comprise another class of phenomena capable of causing near-discontinuities. For instance, as cities expand into farmland, air pollution increasingly becomes a mixture of agriculture chemicals with effluents from power plants and automobiles. Sulfur dioxide from the city paralyzes the cleaning mechanisms of the lungs, thus increasing the residence time there of potential carcinogens in the agricultural chemicals. The joint effect may be synergistic; it may be much more than the sum of the individual effects. Investigation of such synergistic effects is one of the most neglected areas of environmental evaluation.

Not only is there a connection between population size and per capita damage to the environment, but the cost of maintaining environmental quality at a given level escalates disporportionately as population size increases. This effect occurs in part because costs increase very rapidly as one tries to reduce contaminants per unit volume of effluent to lower and lower levels (diminishing returns again!). Consider municipal sewage, for example. The cost of removing 80 to 90 percent of the biochemical and chemical oxygen demand, 90 percent of the suspended solids, and 60 percent of the resistant organic material by means of secondary treatment is about eight cents per 1,000 gallons in a large plant.[5] But if the volume of sewage is such that its nutrient content creates a serious eutrophication problem (as is the case in the United States today), or if supply considerations dictate the reuse of sewage water for industry, agriculture, or groundwater recharge, advanced treatment is necessary. The cost ranges from two to four times as much as for secondary treatments (17 cents per 1,000 gallons for carbon absorption, 34 cents per 1,000 gallons for disinfection to yield a potable supply). This example of diminishing returns in pollution control has its counterpart for industrial effluents, automobile exhausts, and so forth.

Now consider a situation in which the limited capacity of the environment to absorb abuse requires that we hold human impact in some sector constant as population doubles. This means that *per capita effectiveness* of pollution control in this sector must double (that is, effluent per person must be halved). In a typical situation, this would yield doubled per capita costs, or quadrupled total costs (and probably energy consumption) in this sector for a doubling of population.

Again, the possible existence of "economies of scale" does not invalidate these arguments. Such savings, if available at all, would apply in the case of our sewage example to a change in the amount of effluent to be handled at an installation of a given type. For most technologies, the United States is already more than populous enough to achieve such economies and is doing so. They are accounted for in our example by citing figures for the largest treatment plants of each type. Population growth, on the other hand, forces us into quantitative *and* qualitative changes in how we handle each unit volume of effluent—what fraction and what kinds of material we remove. Here, economies of scale do not apply at all, and diminishing returns are the rule.

The relations among population and total and per capita impact on the environment are far from being thoroughly understood, but the examples just given should be sufficient to demonstrate that the role of population cannot be lightly dismissed. Many authors who have disparaged the importance of population size and growth rates as contributors to environmental deterioration have apparently misunderstood the multiplier effect of population growth; have underestimated the role of diminishing returns, threshold effects, and synergisms; and have ignored the relation between complexity and stability in ecosystems altogether.

Two additional errors should be mentioned. One is the tendency to confuse changes in the composition of consumption with absolute increases, and thus to overestimate the role of per capita consumption relative to that of population in generating today's environmental predicament. Consider, for example, Ansley Coale's observation that, since 1940, "population has increased by 50 percent but per capita use of electricity has been multiplied several times."[6] Actually, in this case, as in many others, very rapid increases in consumption reflect a shift among alternatives within a larger and much more slowly growing category. Thus, the 760 percent increase in electricity consumption since 1940 occurred in large part because the electrical *component* of the energy budget was (and still is) increasing much faster than the total energy budget itself. Generation of electricity accounted for 12 percent of the United States energy consumption in 1940 versus 23 percent in 1969.[7] Total energy consumption, a more important figure than its electrical component in terms of demands on resources and the environment, increased much less dramatically—by a factor of 2.75 from 1940 to 1969. As noted above, population growth was an important component of this increase, even in the purely arithmetic analysis. Similar considerations reveal the imprudence of citing, say, aluminum consumption to show that population growth is an "unimportant" factor in resource use. Aluminum consumption has increased more than 15-fold since 1940, but much of this growth has been due to the substitution of aluminum for steel in many applications. Thus, a fairer measure is the combined consumption of aluminum and steel, which has risen by only a factor of 2.2 since 1940. Here, in the purely arithmetic analysis, population growth is "responsible" for more than half of

the increase. Such arguments leave little ground for the assumption, popularized by Barry Commoner and others, that a one percent rate of population growth spawns only one percent effects.[8]

GLOBAL CONTEXT

We will not deal in detail with the best example of the global nature and interconnections of population, resource, and environmental problems—namely, the problems involved in feeding a world in which 10 to 20 million people starve to death annually and in which the population is growing by some 70 million people per year.[9] The ecological problems created by high-yield agriculture are awesome and are bound to have a negative feedback on food production.[10] Indeed, the Food and Agriculture Organization of the United Nations has reported that in 1969 the world suffered its first absolute decline in fisheries yield since 1950. It seems likely that part of this decline is attributable to pollution originating in terrestrial agriculture.

A second source of the fisheries' decline is, of course, overexploitation of fisheries by the developed countries. This problem, in turn, is illustrative of the situation of many other resources, where similarly rapacious and shortsighted behavior by the developed nations is compromising the aspirations of the bulk of humanity to a decent existence. It is now becoming more widely comprehended that the United States alone accounts for perhaps 30 percent of the nonrenewable resources consumed in the world each year (for example, 37 percent of the energy, 25 percent of the steel, 28 percent of the tin, and 33 percent of the synthetic rubber).[11] This behavior is in large part inconsistent with American rhetoric about "developing" the countries of the Third World. *We* may be able to afford the technology to mine lower grade deposits when we have squandered the world's rich ores, but the underdeveloped countries, as their needs grow and their means remain meager, will not be able to do so. Some observers argue that the poor countries are today economically dependent on our use of their resources, and indeed that economists in these countries complain that world demand for their raw materials is too low.[12] This proves only that their economists are as shortsighted as ours.

It is abundantly clear that the entire context in which we view the world resource pool and the relationships between developed and underdeveloped countries must be changed if we are to have any hope of achieving a stable and prosperous existence for all human beings. It cannot be stated too forcefully that the developed countries (or, more accurately, the overdeveloped countries) are the principal culprits in the consumption and dispersion of the world's nonrenewable resources, in addition to their appropriation of much more than their share of the world's protein.[13] Because of this consumption and because of the enormous negative impact on the global environment accompanying it, the population growth in these countries must be regarded as the most serious in the world today.

In relation to theorem 2 we must emphasize that, even if population growth were halted, the present population of the world could easily destroy civilization as we know it. There is a wide choice of weapons—from unstable plant monocultures and agricultural hazes to DDT, mercury, and thermonuclear bombs. If population size were reduced and per capita consumption remained the same (or increased), we would still quickly run out of vital, high-grade resources or generate conflicts over diminishing supplies. Racism, economic exploitation, and war will not be eliminated by population control. (Of course, they are unlikely to be eliminated without it.)

POPULATION DENSITY AND DISTRIBUTION

Theorem 3 deals with a problem related to the inequitable utilization of world resources. One of the most common errors made by the uninitiated is to assume that population density (people per square mile) is the critical measure of overpopulation or underpopulation. For example, demographer Ben Wattenberg has stated that the United States is not very crowded by "international standards," because Holland has 18 times our population density.[14] We call this notion "the Netherlands fallacy." The Netherlands actually requires large chunks of the earth's resources and vast areas of land outside its borders to maintain itself. For example, it is the second largest per capita importer of protein in the world; and it imports 63 percent of its cereals, including 100 percent of its corn and rice. It also imports all of its cotton, 77 percent of its wool, and all of its iron ore, antimony, bauxite, chromium, copper, gold, lead, magnesite, manganese, mercury, molybdenum, nickel, silver, tin, tungsten, vanadium, zinc, phosphate rock (fertilizer), potash (fertilizer), asbestos, and diamonds. It produces energy equivalent to some 20 million metric tons of coal and consumes the equivalent of over 47 million metric tons.[15]

A certain preoccupation with density as a useful measure of overpopulation is apparent in the article by Coale.[16] He points to the existence of urban problems such as smog in Sydney, Australia ("even though the total population of Australia is about 12 million in an area 80 percent as big as the United States"), as evidence that environmental problems are unrelated to population size. His argument would be more persuasive if problems of population *distribution* were the only ones with environmental consequences and if population distribution were unrelated to resource distribution and population size. Actually, since the carrying capacity of the Australian continent is far below that of the United States, one would *expect* distribution problems—of which Sydney's smog is one symptom—to be encountered at a much lower total population there. Resources, such as water, are in very short supply, and people cluster where resources are available. (Evidently, it cannot be emphasized enough that carrying capacity includes the availability of a wide variety of resources in addition to space itself, and that population pressure is measured relative to the carrying capacity. Rather than land area, one would expect water, soils, or the ability of the environment to absorb wastes to be the limiting resource in most instances.)

In addition, of course, many of the most serious environmental problems are essentially independent of the way in which population is distributed. These include the global problems of weather modification by carbon dioxide and particulate pollution, and the threats to the biosphere posed by man's massive inputs of pesticides, heavy metals, and oil.[17] Similarly, the problems of resource depletion and ecosystem simplification by agriculture depend on how many people there are and their patterns of consumption, but not in any major way on how they are distributed.

Naturally, we do not dispute that smog and most other familiar urban ills are serious problems or that they are related to population distribution. Like many of the difficulties we face, these problems will not be cured simply by stopping population growth; direct and well-conceived assaults on the problems themselves will also be required. Such measures may occasionally include the redistribution of population, but the considerable difficulties and costs of this approach should not be underestimated. People live where they do, not because of a perverse intention to add to the problems of their society, but for reasons of economic necessity, convenience, and desire for agreeable surroundings. Areas that are uninhabited or sparsely populated today are presumably that way because they are deficient in some of the requisite factors. In many cases, the remedy for such deficiencies—for example, the provision of water and power to the wastelands of central Nevada—would be extraordinarily expensive in dollars, energy, and resources and would probably create environmental havoc. (Will we justify the rape of Canada's rivers to "colonize" more of our western deserts?)

Moving people to more "habitable" areas, such as the central valley of California or, indeed, most suburbs, exacerbates another serious problem—the paving-over of prime farmland. This is already so serious in California that, if current trends continue, about 50 percent of the best acreage in the nation's leading agricultural state will be destroyed by the year 2020.[18] Encouraging that trend hardly seems wise.

Whatever attempts may be made to solve distribution-related problems, they will be undermined if population growth continues, for two reasons. First, population growth and the aggravation of distribution problems are correlated—part of the increase will surely be absorbed in urban areas that can least afford the growth. Indeed, barring the unlikely prompt reversal of present trends, most of it will be absorbed there. Second, population growth puts a disproportionate drain on the very financial resources needed to combat its symptoms. Economist Joseph Spengler has estimated that four percent of national income goes to support the one percent per year rate of population growth in the United States.[19] The four percent figure now amounts to about $30 billion per year. It seems safe to conclude that the faster we grow the less likely it is that we will find the funds either to alter population distribution patterns or to deal more comprehensively and realistically with our problems.

MEANING OF ENVIRONMENT

Theorem 4 emphasizes the comprehensiveness of the environment crisis. All too many people think in terms of national parks and trout streams when they say "environment." For this reason many of the suppressed people of our nation consider ecology to be just one more "racist shuck."[20] They are apathetic or even hostile toward efforts to avert further environmental and sociological deterioration because they have no reason to believe they will share the fruits of success.[21] Slums, cockroaches, and rats are ecological problems, too. The correction of ghetto conditions in Detroit is neither more nor less important than saving the Great Lakes—both are imperative.

We must pay careful attention to sources of conflict both within the United States and between nations. Conflict within the United States blocks progress toward solving our problems; conflict among nations can easily "solve" them once and for all. Recent laboratory studies on human beings support the anecdotal evidence that crowding may increase aggressiveness in human males.[22] These results underscore long-standing suspicions that population growth, translated through the inevitable uneven distribution into physical crowding, will tend to make the solution of all of our problems more difficult.

As a final example of the need to view "environment" broadly, note that human beings live in an epidemiological environment which deteriorates with crowding and malnutrition—both of which increase with population growth. The hazard posed by the prevalence of these conditions in the world today is compounded by man's unprecedented mobility: Potential carriers of diseases of every description move routinely and in substantial numbers from continent to continent in a matter of hours. Nor is there any reason to believe that modern medicine has made widespread plague impossible.[23] The Asian influenza epidemic of 1968 killed relatively few people only because the virus *happened* to be nonfatal to people in otherwise good health, not because of public health measures. Far deadlier viruses, which easily could be scourges without precedent in the population at large, have on more than one occasion been confined to research workers largely by good luck (for example, the Marburg virus incident of 1967 and the Lassa fever incident of 1970).[24]

SOLUTIONS: THEORETICAL AND PRACTICAL

Theorem 5 states that theoretical solutions to our problems are often not operational and sometimes are not solutions. In terms of the problem of feeding the world, for example, technological fixes suffer from limitations in scale, lead time, and cost.[25] Thus, potentially attractive theoretical approaches—such as desalting seawater for agriculture, new irrigation systems, high-protein diet supplements—prove inadequate in practice. They are too little, too late, and too expensive; or they have sociological costs which hobble their effectiveness.[26] Moreover, many aspects of our technological fixes, such as synthetic organic pesticides and inorganic nitrogen fertilizers, have created vast environmental problems which seem certain to erode global productivity and ecosystem stability.[27] This is not to say that important gains have not been made through the application of technology to agriculture in the poor countries, or that further technological advances are not worth seeking. But it must be stressed that even the most enlightened technology cannot relieve the necessity of grappling forthrightly and promptly with population growth (as Norman Borlaug aptly observed on being notified of his Nobel Prize for development of the new wheats).[28]

Technological attempts to ameliorate the environmental impact of population growth and rising per capita affluence in the developed countries suffer from practical limitations similar to those just mentioned. Not only do such measures tend to be slow, costly, and insufficient in scale; but in addition they most often shift our impact rather than remove it. For example, our first generation of smog-control devices increased emissions of oxides of nitrogen while reducing those of hydrocarbons and carbon monoxide. Our unhappiness about eutrophication has led to the replacement of phosphates in detergents with compounds like NTA—nitrilotriacetic acid—which has carcinogenic breakdown products and apparently enhances teratogenic effects of heavy metals.[29] And our distaste for lung diseases apparently induced by sulfur dioxide inclines us to accept the hazards of radioactive waste disposal, fuel reprocessing, routine low-level emissions of radiation, and an apparently small but finite risk of catastrophic accidents associated with nuclear fission power plants. Similarly, electric automobiles would simply shift part of the environmental burden of personal transportation from the vicinity of highways to the vicinity of power plants.

We are not suggesting here that electric cars, or nuclear power plants, or substitutes for phosphates are inherently bad. We argue rather that they, too, pose environmental costs which must be weighed against those they eliminate. In many cases, the choice is not obvious, and in *all* cases there will be some environmental impact. The residual per capita impact, after all the best choices have been made, must then be multiplied by the population engaging in the activity. If there are too many people, even the most wisely managed technology will not keep the environment from being overstressed.

In contending that a change in the way we use technology will invalidate these arguments, Commoner claims that our important environmental problems began in the 1940's with the introduction and rapid spread of certain "synthetic" technologies: pesticides and herbicides, inorganic fertilizers, plastics, nuclear energy, and high-compression gasoline engines.[30] In so arguing, he appears to make two unfounded assumptions. The first is that man's pre-1940 environmental impact was innocuous and, without changes for the worse in technology, would have remained innocuous even at a much larger population size. The second assumption is that the advent of the new technologies was independent of the attempt to meet human needs and desires in a growing population. Actually, man's record as a simplifier of ecosystems and plunderer of resources can be traced from his probable role in the extinction of many Pleistocene mammals, through the destruction of the soils of Mesopotamia by salination and erosion, to the deforestation of Europe in the Middle Ages, and the American dustbowls of the 1930's, to cite only some highlights.[31]

Man's contemporary arsenal of synthetic technological bludgeons indisputably magnifies the potential for disaster, but these were evolved in some measure to *cope* with population pressures, not independently of them.

In many cases, traditional technologies and sources of raw materials would have been unable to cope with the demand created by population growth combined with increasing affluence. In the past 50 years, plastics have replaced wood in many applications. How many acres of timberland would it take to provide wood to replace those plastics today? How many acres of cotton fields or grazing land for sheep would be required to reverse the substitutions of synthetic fibers for cotton and wool? Finally, it is worth noting that, of the four global environmental threats emphasized by the prestigious Williamstown study,[32] three are associated with pre-1940 technologies which have simply increased in scale (heavy metals, oil in the seas, and carbon dioxide and particulates in the atmosphere, the latter probably due in considerable part to agriculture).[33] Surely, then, we can anticipate that supplying food, fiber, and metals for a population even larger than today's will have a profound (and destabilizing) effect on the global ecosystem under *any* set of technological assumptions.

CONCLUSION

John Platt has aptly described man's present predicament as "a storm of crisis problems."[34] Complacency concerning any component of these problems—sociological, technological, economic, ecological—is unjustified and counterproductive. It is time to admit that there are no monolithic solutions to the problems we face. Indeed, population control, the redirection of technology, the transition from open to closed resource cycles, and the equitable distribution of opportunity and the ingredients of prosperity must *all* be accomplished if there is to be a future worth having. Failure in any of these areas will surely sabotage the entire enterprise.

In connection with the five theorems elaborated here, we have dealt at length with the notion that population growth in industrial nations such as the United States is a minor factor, safely ignored. Those who so argue often add that, anyway, population control would be the slowest to take effect of all possible attacks on our various problems, since the inertia in attitudes and in the age structure of the population is so considerable. To conclude that this means population control should be assigned low priority strikes us as curious logic. Precisely because population is the most difficult and slowest to yield among the components of environmental deterioration, we must start on it at once. To ignore population today because the problem is a tough one is to commit ourselves to even gloomier prospects 20 years hence, when most of the "easy" means to reduce per capita impact on the environment will have been exhausted. The desperate and repressive measures for population control which might be contemplated in the future are reason in themselves to proceed with foresight, alacrity, and compassion today.

REFERENCES

1. A.J. Coale, *Science,* 1970, Vol. 170, p. 132; and B. Commoner, *Saturday Review,* 1970, Vol. 53, p. 50, and *Humanist,* 1970, Vol. 30, p. 10.

2. For a general discussion, see P.R. Ehrlich and A.H. Ehrlich, *Population, Resources, Environment* (San Francisco: Freeman, 1970), chap. 7. More technical treatments of the relationship between complexity and stability may be found in R.H. MacArthur, *Ecology,* 1955, Vol. 36, p. 533; D.R. Margalef, *General Systems,* 1958, Vol. 3, p. 3671; E.G. Leigh, Jr., *Proceedings of the National Academy of Sciences of the United States,* 1965, Vol. 53, p. 777; and O.T. Loucks, "Evolution of Diversity, Efficiency and Stability of a Community" (paper delivered at meeting of the American Association for the Advancement of Science, Dallas, Texas, Dec. 30, 1968).

3. A dramatic example of this effect is given in R. Payne's analysis of whale fisheries in *New York Zoological Society Newsletter,* Nov. 1968. The graphs in Payne's paper are reproduced in Ehrlich and Ehrlich, *op. cit.*

4. If N is the number of people, then the number of links is $N(N - 1)/2$, and the number of links per capita is $(N - 1)/2$.

5. These figures and the others in this paragraph are from *Cleaning Our Environment: The Chemical Basis for Action* (Washington: American Chemical Society, 1969), pp. 95-162.

6. Coale, *op. cit.*

7. The figures in this paragraph are based on data in U.S. Bureau of the Census, *Statistical Abstract of the United States, 1970.* The energy figures take into account the average efficiency of energy conversion from fuel to electricity. Because the efficiency rose considerably between 1940 and 1969, electricity's 8.6-fold increase in kilowatt-hours was achieved with a much smaller increase in fuel burned.

8. B. Commoner, *Saturday Review, op. cit.* and *Humanist, op. cit.* In his unpublished testimony before the President's Commission on Population Growth and the American Future (Nov. 17, 1970), Commoner acknowledged the operation of diminishing returns, threshold effects, and so on. Since such factors apparently do not account for *all* of the increase in per capita impact on the environment in recent decades, however, Commoner drew the unwarranted conclusion that they are negligible. He has since published a similar view in *Environment,* April 1971.

9. R. Dumont and B. Rosier, *The Hungry Future* (New York: Praeger, 1969), pp. 34-35.

10. See Ehrlich and Ehrlich, *op. cit.;* MacArthur, *op. cit.;* Margalef, *op. cit.;* Leigh, Jr., *op. cit.;* and Loucks, *op. cit.* See also, L. Brown, *Scientific American,* 1970, Vol. 223, p. 160; and P. R. Ehrlich, *War on Hunger,* 1970, Vol. 4, p. 1.

11. Based on data from U.N., *United Nations Statistical Yearbook 1969* (New York, 1969), with estimates added for consumption by Mainland China when none were included.

12. Coale, *op. cit.*

13. The notion that dispersed resources, because they have not left the planet, are still available to us, and the hope that mineral supplies can be extended indefinitely by the application of vast amounts of energy to common rock have been the subject of lively debate elsewhere. See, for example, the articles by P. Cloud, T. Lovering, and A. Weinberg, *Texas Quarterly,* Summer 1968, Vol. 11, pp. 103, 127, and 90; and National Academy of Sciences, *Resources and Man* (San Francisco: Freeman, 1969).

While the pessimists seem to have had the better of this argument, the entire matter is academic in the context of the rate problem we face in the next 30 years. Over that time period, at least, cost, lead time, and logistics will see to it that industrial economies and dreams of development stand or fall with the availability of high-grade resources.

14. B. Wattenberg, *New Republic,* April 4, 1970, p. 162 and April 11, 1970, p. 18.

15. The figures are from U.N., *op. cit.;* U.N., *Food and Agriculture Organization (FAO) Trade Yearbook,* (New York, 1968), and *FAO Production Yearbook* (New York, 1968); and from G. Borgstrom, *Too Many* (Toronto, Ont.: Collier-Macmillan, 1969).

16. Coale, *op. cit.*

17. *Man's Impact on the Global Environment, Report of the Study of Critical Environmental Problems* (Cambridge, Mass.: M.I.T. Press, 1970).

18. *A Model of Society, Progress Report of the Environmental Systems Group* (Davis, Calif.: Univ. of Calif. Institute of Ecology, April 1969).

19. J.J. Spengler in *Population: The Vital Revolution,* R. Freedman, ed. (New York: Doubleday, 1964), p. 67.

20. R. Chrisman, *Scanlan's,* Aug. 1970, Vol. 1, p. 46.

21. A more extensive discussion of this point is given in an article by P.R. Ehrlich and A.H. Ehrlich in *Global Ecology: Readings Toward a Rational Strategy for Man,* J.P. Holdren and P.R. Ehrlich, eds. (New York: Harcourt, Brace, Jovanovich, 1971).

22. J.L. Freedman, A. Levy, J. Price, R. Welte, M. Katz, and P.R. Ehrlich (in preparation).

23. J. Lederberg, *Washington Post,* March 15 and 22, 1970.

24. Lederberg, *op. cit.;* C. Smith *et al., Lancet,* 1967, Vol. II, pp. 1119 and 1128; and Associated Press wire service, Feb. 2, 1970.

25. P.R. Ehrlich and J.P. Holdren, *BioScience,* 1969, Vol. 19, p. 1065.

26. See L. Brown, *Seeds of Change* (New York: Praeger, 1970) for a discussion of unemployment problems exacerbated by the "Green Revolution."

27. G. Woodwell, *Science,* 1970, Vol. 168, p. 429.

28. *New York Times,* Oct. 22, 1970, p. 18; and *Newsweek,* Nov. 2, 1970, Vol. 76, p. 50.

29. S.S. Epstein, *Environment,* Sept. 1970, Vol. 12, No. 7, p. 2; and *New York Times,* News Service, Nov. 17, 1970.

30. B. Commoner, *Saturday Review, op. cit.,* and *Humanist, op. cit.;* and *supra,* note 8.

31. G.S. Krantz, *American Scientist,* Mar.-Apr. 1970, Vol. 58, p. 164.

32. *Man's Impact on the Global Environment, op. cit.*

33. R.A. Bryson and W.M. Wendland, in *Global Effects of Environmental Pollution,* S.F. Singer ed. (New York: Springer-Verlag, 1970).

34. J. Platt, *Science,* 1969, Vol. 166, p. 1115.